1968

College Algebra and Plane Trigonometry

This book is in the

ADDISON-WESLEY SERIES IN MATHEMATICS

SECOND EDITION

College Algebra and Plane Trigonometry

ABRAHAM SPITZBART AND ROSS H. BARDELL

University of Wisconsin-Milwaukee

ADDISON-WESLEY PUBLISHING COMPANY, INC.
READING, MASSACHUSETTS · PALO ALTO · LONDON

Library of Congress Catalog Card No. 64-17384

Preface

Since the appearance of the first edition of this book, the principle of presenting an integrated treatment of algebra and trigonometry to the student preparing for the calculus has become very widely accepted. The authors should like to feel that, in some part, this first edition had some influence in establishing that principle.

The second edition of this book has been designed to maintain the essential features of the first edition, with some notable changes. Perhaps the most significant is the axiomatic development, in Chapter 1, of the real number system. It was felt that the use of the Peano axioms for this purpose was too advanced for the level for which the book was written. Rather, a set of axioms was chosen for the natural numbers which permitted definitions and proofs that are understandable to the students concerned. These axioms permit, in later chapters, showing the axiomatic basis of various topics, such as inequalities in Chapter 6 and mathematical induction in Chapter 11.

A concentrated review of the material of elementary algebra, including work in factoring, fractions, and exponents and radicals, then appears in Appendix A. This review material was organized with the idea that topics requiring special review could be readily referred to, whether for the explanations given there, the illustrative examples, or the abundance of exercises.

The emphasis in the book is still on the study of the elementary functions of mathematics, their properties and applications, based on the principles of algebra, leaving the subsequent study of these functions based on the idea of limit as the province of the calculus.

The important function concept is defined, in Chapter 2, in terms of sets of ordered pairs, and this idea is carried forward as new functions are introduced, including the trigonometric and inverse trigonometric functions. In Chapter 13 a brief presentation of sequences is given as an introduction to progressions; sequences are there related to functions whose domain is the set of natural numbers.

The distance formula is presented in Chapter 2 and is then used in the proof of the addition formulas for the values of the trigonometric ratios and the derivation of the Law of Cosines for triangles.

Chapter 17 on "Permutations, Combinations, and Probability" has been expanded, with the introduction of sections on conditional probability, permutations as functions, mathematical expectation, and others.

The authors feel that a book such as the present one can also serve the purpose of the student who requires a terminal course in mathematics. In particular, the axiomatic development of the real number system in the first chapter and the relation of later topics to the developments of this chapter emphasize the idea of logical development which can persist even when special skills may be forgotten.

The book is perhaps ideally suited to the student with a minimum of one and one-half years of high school algebra, with the review material of Appendix A available to fill any gaps that may exist in preparation or memory. For such students there is ample material for a five-semester hour course, with some leeway permitted the instructor in the selection of topics. A four-semester hour course can also be served with, of course, a broader omission of some topics. For a course with similar motivation, for students with only one year of high school algebra, the authors' *Introductory Algebra and Trigonometry* is available.

As in the first edition of the book, no attempt was made to force an integration of algebra and trigonometry where it does not naturally occur. In many cases the exercises to be worked by the student have been designed so as to use principles and methods of both of these subjects. Answers to the odd-numbered exercises are provided at the back of the book. Answers to even-numbered exercises are available to the teacher in a separate booklet.

Milwaukee, Wisconsin A.S.
February, 1964 R.H.B.

Contents

USEFUL ITEMS FROM PLANE GEOMETRY

1. Two angles are complementary if their sum is 90°.
2. Two angles are supplementary if their sum is 180°.
3. The sum of the angles of any triangle is 180°.
4. *Theorem of Pythagoras.* In a right triangle the square of the hypotenuse is equal to the sum of the squares of the legs.
5. If a right triangle has a 30° angle, the side opposite that angle is equal to one-half of the hypotenuse.
6. If two angles of a triangle are equal, the opposite sides are equal, and conversely.
7. Two triangles are similar if the angles of one are equal, respectively, to the angles of the other.
8. If two triangles are similar, corresponding sides of the triangles are proportional.
9. If the sides of an angle are perpendicular, respectively, to the sides of another angle, the angles are either equal or supplementary.
10. The area of any triangle is equal to one-half the product of any side and the altitude drawn to that side.
11. The angle bisectors of a triangle intersect in a point, which is the center of the inscribed circle.
12. The perpendicular bisectors of the sides of a triangle meet in a point, which is the center of the circumscribed circle.

GREEK ALPHABET

α alpha	β beta	γ gamma	δ delta	ϵ epsilon	ζ zeta
η eta	θ theta	ι iota	κ kappa	λ lambda	μ mu
ν nu	ξ xi	o omicron	π pi	ρ rho	σ sigma
τ tau	υ upsilon	ϕ phi	χ chi	ψ psi	ω omega

CHAPTER 1

The Real Number System

1–1 INTRODUCTION

Any mathematical system deals with certain entities, called the *elements* of the system, and rules for working with them, the "rules of the game." In abstract systems very little is required of these rules except that they be consistent; it would be fruitless if some rules were contradictory, or if, by applying the rules in different sequences, contradictory conclusions could be reached. Of course, we should like the system to have some "use," to have some bearing on something concrete, but this is not a requisite of a mathematical development. It would have been difficult to find a use for non-Euclidean geometry at the time it was developed. The later discovery of uses was fortunate, if only because it demonstrated that utility alone should not motivate the study of mathematical systems.

The "rules of the game" are stated in the form of *axioms* or *postulates*—the fewer the better—from which, by the use of definitions and logical deductions (theorems) the structure is extended higher and higher. The entities on which the structure is built may be very general, and are usually assumed to be undefined. The type of structure, then, is determined by the axioms. The use of such a system derives from the identification of a familiar set of rules with the assumed axioms. Many such abstract systems are studied in mathematics, and many uses have been found for them. Surprisingly, perhaps, to the reader at this stage of his study, the entities in such applications need not be ordinary numbers as he knows them.

The study of algebra, however, is based on ordinary numbers, and the development of the number system should be our first concern. The number system to be considered is, of course, the number system with which the reader is familiar. It is, in a sense, precisely this familiarity which makes a logical development important. It is, perhaps, easy to show that $3 \times 7 = 7 \times 3$, assuming that multiplication has been defined. It is less easy to show that $2153 \times 749 = 749 \times 2153$. We "know" that it is so, but with some reflection we could very well decide that much of our knowledge of arithmetic is based merely on our having been told that it was so.

After this introduction it may appear surprising that we make no effort here to give a complete, systematic development of the real number system. Such developments are rather sophisticated, and can better await a greater mathematical maturity of the student. Rather, we present a brief outline of one possible manner in which this development may take place, and use the opportunity thus afforded to highlight some important properties of these numbers. The study of algebra is a natural outcome, or even concomitant, of this development.

1–2 THE POSITIVE INTEGERS OR NATURAL NUMBERS

We shall start with the positive integers, or *natural numbers* as they are also called. All properties of the system of natural numbers may be developed from a basic set of postulates or axioms, together with appropriate definitions and logical deductions therefrom. The following set of axioms may be considered a set of assumptions concerning the natural numbers upon which all the properties of the natural numbers, and in fact the entire real number system, may be based. In other words, the natural numbers may be considered an undefined collection, or set, of objects merely satisfying the following axioms. We assume that the student is familiar with the use of letters and symbols to denote numbers. In the following axioms letters denote natural numbers, the undefined elements or objects of the system. The two operations of addition and multiplication which appear in the axioms are also taken as undefined.

Axioms for the Natural Numbers

1. The *sum* $a + b$ and *product* $a \times b$ or $a \cdot b$ or ab of two natural numbers are uniquely defined natural numbers.
2. The *commutative laws of addition and multiplication*, respectively, hold:
$$a + b = b + a, \qquad ab = ba.$$
3. The *associative laws of addition and multiplication*, respectively, hold:
$$a + (b + c) = (a + b) + c = a + b + c,$$
$$a(bc) = (ab)c = abc.$$
4. The *distributive law of multiplication with respect to addition* holds:
$$a(b + c) = ab + ac.$$
5. There is a natural number 1 such that, for any natural number a, the following holds:
$$a \cdot 1 = a.$$
6. The following *cancellation laws* hold for natural numbers:
   (a) If $a + x = b + x$, then $a = b$. (b) If $ax = bx$, then $a = b$.
7. If a and b are two natural numbers, then one and only one of the following holds:
   (a) $a = b$.
   (b) There is a natural number x such that $a = b + x$.
   (c) There is a natural number y such that $b = a + y$.

8. Let M be a set of natural numbers with the following properties:
   (a) 1 belongs to M.
   (b) If a belongs to M then $a + 1$ belongs to M.

Then the set M consists of all the natural numbers.

The requirement in Axiom 1 that the sum and product of natural numbers be natural numbers is often stated as, "the natural numbers are *closed* under the operations of addition and multiplication." The uniqueness of addition and multiplication includes the *substitution principle*, which is that *in any sum or product any element may be replaced by an equal element.*

Axiom 2 states that two natural numbers may be added or multiplied in either order, with the same result. Axiom 3 states that when three natural numbers are added the grouping of the numbers is immaterial, and the same result is obtained in each instance; there is a similar implication with respect to multiplication. Axiom 4 states that the product of a natural number by the sum of two natural numbers is equal to the sum of the products of the first number by each of the other two.

Axiom 5 ensures the existence of the number 1, the *multiplicative identity*, or *unity*. The cancellation laws of addition and multiplication in Axiom 6 are self-explanatory. Axiom 7 permits us to define positiveness of numbers; it also leads to the definitions of inequality, which will be amplified in Chapter 6. Finally, concerning Axiom 8, we merely state here that it is the *Principle of Finite Induction*, which will be treated in Chapter 11 and is not used prior to that.

The rules of logic which will be applied include the three following properties of the relation of equality.

Reflexive property: $a = a$.
Symmetric property: If $a = b$ then $b = a$.
Transitive property: If $a = b$ and $b = c$ then $a = c$.

These properties state, in brief, that *any element is equal to itself*, and *things equal to the same thing are equal to each other.* It is necessary to state these properties, since the fact that two things are equal does not always mean that they are identical.

Examples.

AXIOM 2: $3 + 7 = 7 + 3 = 10, \quad 4 \cdot 9 = 9 \cdot 4 = 36.$

AXIOM 3:
Addition, $7 + (4 + 13) = 7 + 17 = 24, \quad (7 + 4) + 13 = 11 + 13 = 24.$
Multiplication, $2 \cdot (7 \cdot 9) = 2 \cdot 63 = 126, \quad (2 \cdot 7) \cdot 9 = 14 \cdot 9 = 126.$

AXIOM 4: $7(8 + 11) = 7 \cdot 19 = 133, \quad 7 \cdot 8 + 7 \cdot 11 = 56 + 77 = 133.$

AXIOM 7: If $a = 7$ and $b = 15$, then the relation $b = a + y$ holds with $y = 8$.

It should be noted that the associative properties in Axiom 3 make the use of parentheses or other grouping symbols unnecessary for a sum or product of natural numbers. We assume that the reader is familiar with the use of grouping symbols.

The natural numbers are also known as the positive integers, but this name has been avoided; we shall use it later, when we come to the definition of positivity of numbers.

EXERCISE GROUP 1–1

In each of Exercises 1–18, by a sequence of steps using the axioms of Section 1–2, reduce the left member to the right member.

1. $(2 + 3) + 5 = (2 + 5) + 3$
2. $3 + (5 + 7) = 5 + (3 + 7)$
3. $(2 + 5) + (3 + 7) = (2 + 3) + (5 + 7)$
4. $2(3 + 5) = 2 \cdot 3 + 2 \cdot 5$
5. $6 \cdot 2 + 6 \cdot 7 = 6(2 + 7)$
6. $(4 + 5) \cdot 3 = 4 \cdot 3 + 5 \cdot 3$
7. $4(2 + 3 \cdot 5) = 4 \cdot 2 + (4 \cdot 3) \cdot 5$
8. $3(5 \cdot 7 + 4 \cdot 9) = (3 \cdot 5) \cdot 7 + (3 \cdot 4) \cdot 9$
9. $2(3 \cdot 5 + 7 \cdot 11) = 5(3 \cdot 2) + (2 \cdot 7) \cdot 11$
10. $2 \cdot 3 \cdot 7 + 5 \cdot 9 \cdot 11 = 3(2 \cdot 7 + 11 \cdot 15)$
11. $ab + ac = a(b + c)$
12. $c(a + b) = ac + bc$
13. $(ab)c = b(ac)$
14. $(a + b) + c = b + (a + c)$
15. $a(b + cd) = ab + c(ad)$
16. $a(bc + cd) = c(ab) + c(da)$
17. $a(b + c) + d(b + c) = b(a + d) + c(a + d) = (a + d)(b + c)$
18. $b(a + e) + c(a + e) + d(a + e) = a(b + c + d) + e(b + c + d) = (a + e)(b + c + d)$

In each of Exercises 19–26, insert grouping symbols so as to make the value of the first expression equal to the number which follows.

19. $2 \cdot 3 + 5$; 16
20. $2 \cdot 3 + 5$; 11
21. $2 \cdot 4 + 5 \cdot 6$; 38
22. $2 \cdot 4 + 5 \cdot 6$; 68
23. $2 \cdot 4 + 5 \cdot 6$; 78
24. $2 \cdot 4 + 5 \cdot 6$; 108
25. $2 + 3 \cdot 4 + 2 \cdot 3$; 66
26. $2 + 3 \cdot 4 + 2 \cdot 3$; 90
27. Insert grouping symbols in the expression $a + b + c + d$ so that each operation requires the addition of only two numbers.
28. Insert grouping symbols in the expression $a \cdot b \cdot c \cdot d$ so that each operation requires the multiplication of only two numbers.
29. Prove that there is only one natural number with the property expressed in Axiom 5. [*Hint:* Show that if U is a natural number with the same property, then $U = 1$.]

For each of the following, state which part of Axiom 7 holds.

30. $a = 7, b = 3$
31. $a = 9, b = 14$
32. $a = 9 + 3, b = 5 + 7$
33. $a = 2 + 5, b = 5 + 2$
34. $a = 3 \cdot 7 + 4, b = 4 \cdot 6$
35. $a = 5 \cdot 7, b = 4(4 + 5)$
36. $a = 24 + 5 \cdot 9, b = (17 + 7) \cdot 3$
37. $a = (18 + 4) \cdot 4, b = 5(7 + 18)$

1–3 THE SET OF ALL INTEGERS

The axioms for natural numbers, as presented in Section 1–2, involve only the two operations of addition and multiplication. Any such operation with natural numbers results again in a natural number; this property was expressed in the statement that *the natural numbers are closed under addition and multiplication.* Other operations with natural numbers may be defined.

The next operation to be considered is that of *subtraction*, which is the process of finding the *difference* between two numbers. The difference between two natural numbers a and b is defined as the number, if it exists, which must be added to b to give a. For example, the difference between 9 and 2 is 7 since $2 + 7 = 9$.

It is convenient at this point to introduce the minus sign $(-)$ and to indicate the difference between a and b as $a - b$. Thus we have $9 - 2 = 7$. By Axiom 7, if a and b are unequal, written as $a \neq b$, we may find either $a - b$ or $b - a$ as a natural number, but *not both.* Accordingly, the difference $a - b$ of two natural numbers need not exist in the system of natural numbers; however, such a difference, when it does exist, is unique (see Exercise 1 in Exercise Group 1–2).

In order to have a system of numbers in which subtraction is always possible, it is necessary to define a larger system of numbers, to be known as *the system of all integers*, which will, in effect, turn out to consist of the natural numbers, zero, and the negative integers.

To do this we define a *set of natural number pairs*, such as (2, 1), (1, 2), (a, b), and so on, with the following properties:

***Definition* 1–1.** $(a, b) = (c, d)$ *if and only if* $a + d = b + c$.

***Definition* 1–2.** $(a, b) + (c, d) = (a + c, b + d)$.

***Definition* 1–3.** $(a, b) \cdot (c, d) = (ac + bd, ad + bc)$.

***Definition* 1–4.** (a, b) *is positive if and only if* $a = b + x$ *for some natural number* x.

Examples.

$$(2, 4) = (7, 9) \text{ since } 2 + 9 = 4 + 7.$$
$$(3, 8) + (4, 1) = (3 + 4, 8 + 1) = (7, 9).$$
$$(5, 2) \cdot (3, 6) = (5 \cdot 3 + 2 \cdot 6, 2 \cdot 3 + 5 \cdot 6) = (27, 36).$$
$$(5, 2) \text{ is positive, since } 5 = 2 + x \text{ holds with the natural number } x = 3.$$

If these natural number pairs are themselves considered to be the elements of a new system, it can be shown that, with certain modifications, the first seven axioms of Section 1–2 hold for this system. For example, Axiom 2 becomes, for addition

$$(a, b) + (c, d) = (c, d) + (a, b).$$

The property of Axiom 5 is taken care of by the following result.

Theorem 1–1. *The unity of Axiom* 5 *may be taken as* (2, 1).

Proof. We must show that

$$(a, b) \cdot (2, 1) = (a, b).$$

By Definition 1–3 and the commutative laws for natural numbers, we have

$$(a, b) \cdot (2, 1) = (2a + b, 2b + a),$$

and, by Definition 1–1,

$$(2a + b, 2b + a) = (a, b), \quad \text{since} \quad (2a + b) + b = (2b + a) + a.$$

This completes the proof.

In Axiom 7 the number pairs which replace x and y must be stated as being positive.

The properties contained in Axioms 1 to 7 are no longer axioms for the system of all integers. They are now provable, and not merely assumed.

The three properties of equality described in Section 1–2 hold for equality as defined in Definition 1–1, since they depend only on these properties for the natural numbers. We illustrate one of these.

Symmetric property. If $(a, b) = (c, d)$ then $(c, d) = (a, b)$.

Proof. If $(a, b) = (c, d)$, then by Definition 1–2 we have $a + d = b + c$. Then $b + c = a + d$ by the symmetric property for natural numbers, and $c + b = d + a$ by the commutative property of addition for natural numbers. Hence, by Definition 1–2 again, $(c, d) = (a, b)$.

We may now define a number pair to play the role of *zero.*

***Definition* 1–5.** *Zero, denoted by* 0, *is* (1, 1).

We are now in a position to prove some of the familiar properties associated with zero.

Theorem 1–2. *For any pair* (a, b), *we have*

$$(a, b) + 0 = (a, b).$$

Proof. The student should supply the reason for each of the following equalities:

$$(a, b) + 0 = (a, b) + (1, 1) = (a + 1, b + 1) = (a, b).$$

Theorem 1–3. *For any pair* (a, b), *the equation*

$$(a, b) + (x, y) = 0$$

has a unique solution (x, y).

Proof. For a proof of existence it is necessary merely to exhibit a solution. The pair (b, a) suffices, since

$$(a, b) + (b, a) = (a + b, b + a) = (1, 1) = 0.$$

The uniqueness follows from the cancellation law for addition.

The following theorem is the required modification of Axiom 6b of Section 1–2.

Theorem 1–4. *If* $(a, b)\cdot(c, d) = (a, b)\cdot(e, f)$, *and* $(a, b) \neq 0$, *then*

$$(c, d) = (e, f).$$

Proof. By Definition 1–3, we have

$$(ac + bd, ad + bc) = (ae + bf, af + be),$$

and by Definition 1–1,

$$ac + bd + af + be = ad + bc + ae + bf. \tag{1}$$

Now $(a, b) \neq 0$; hence $a \neq b$ (why?). Then by Axiom 6 of the natural numbers either

$$a = b + x \qquad \text{or} \qquad b = a + y.$$

If $a = b + x$, substitution in (1) gives

$$\begin{aligned}(b + x)c + bd + (b + x)f + be \\ = (b + x)d + bc + (b + x)e + bf.\end{aligned} \tag{2}$$

By the axioms of natural numbers we may expand (2) and by Axiom 6a we may cancel

$$bc + bd + bf + be,$$

to leave

$$xc + xf = xd + xe,$$

which may be written as

$$x(c + f) = x(d + e).$$

(Why?) By the cancellation law of natural numbers we get

$$c + f = d + e,$$

so that by Definition 1–1,

$$(c, d) = (e, f).$$

This completes the proof in the case $a = b + x$. The proof is entirely similar if $b = a + y$.

Zero was defined as $0 = (1, 1)$. Since $(a, a) = (1, 1)$ for any natural number a, we may write

$$0 = (a, a).$$

EXERCISE GROUP 1–2

1. Show that the difference of two natural numbers is unique; that is, if $a - b = c$ and $a - b = c'$, then $c = c'$.
2. Verify each of the following for integers as pairs of natural numbers.
   (a) $(6, 3) = (11, 8)$
   (b) $(5, 19) = (2 + 3 \cdot 4, 4 \cdot 7)$
   (c) $(9, 3) + (2, 5) = (6, 3)$
   (d) $(2, 7) + (1, 3) = (1, 8)$
   (e) $(3, 2) \cdot (1, 4) = (3, 6)$
   (f) $(5, 1) \cdot (3, 15) = (1, 49)$
3. Determine which of the following are positive integers:
$$(2, 1), (3, 4), (8, 17), (4, 7).$$
4. State and prove, for integers as pairs of natural numbers, each of the following:
   (a) The commutative law of multiplication.
   (b) The associative law of addition.
   (c) The associative law of multiplication.
   (d) The distributive law of multiplication with respect to addition.
   (e) The cancellation law for addition.
5. Carry out the proof of Theorem 1–4, given that $b = a + y$.
6. Show that the unit (2, 1) is positive.
7. Show that the zero integer is not positive.
8. Show that the sum of two positive integers is positive.
9. Show that the product of two positive integers is positive.
10. Prove the transitive property of equality for the set of all integers.
11. Show that Axiom 7 holds for the set of all integers. (See the statement following Theorem 1–1.)

1–4 DISCUSSION OF THE SET OF ALL INTEGERS

What has been accomplished by the development of Section 1–3? We now have a larger set of elements, called the *set of integers*, which contains elements "like" the natural numbers. We may identify the natural number a with the pair $(a + 1, 1)$. Then addition and multiplication of such number pairs behave exactly like addition and multiplication of the natural numbers with which they are identified. Thus

$$(a + 1, 1) + (b + 1, 1) = (a + b + 2, 2) = [(a + b) + 1, 1],$$

so that the sum of the number pairs corresponding to a and b is the number pair corresponding to $a + b$, and we may say that addition behaves correspondingly. Moreover

$$\begin{aligned}(a + 1, 1) \cdot (b + 1, 1) &= [(a + 1)(b + 1) + 1, (a + 1) + (b + 1)] \\ &= (ab + a + b + 2, a + b + 2) = (ab + 1, 1),\end{aligned}$$

and multiplication behaves correspondingly. In fact, *all the axioms* of the natural numbers can be shown to hold for the particular number pairs $(a + 1, 1)$, so that these may be identified with the natural numbers, and we may now use single letters for all integers, with the understanding that they satisfy the axioms of Section 1–2 and the theorems of Section 1–3.

It follows from Definition 1–4 that *every natural number is identified with a positive integer.*

For example, the natural number 2 is identified with the number pair $(2 + 1, 1)$ or $(3, 1)$, but is not strictly equal to it. However, as a convenience we may use the symbol "2" as a natural number when we discuss natural numbers, and we may also use it as a symbol for the natural number pair, or integer, $(3, 1)$ when discussing such numbers, without fear of ambiguity.

1–5 SUBTRACTION OF INTEGERS

By Theorem 1–3 there is, corresponding to any integer A, a unique integer B such that

$$A + B = 0.$$

This integer B is called the *negative* of A, and is written as $-A$, so that we may write

$$A + (-A) = 0 \qquad \text{for any integer } A. \tag{3}$$

We have seen that the natural numbers correspond to positive integers. We now define a *negative integer* as the negative of a positive integer.

We are now in a position to define the *difference* of any two integers A and B.

***Definition* 1–6.** $A - B = A + (-B)$.

The difference of two integers always exists, so that *the set of all integers is closed under subtraction*, as well as under addition and multiplication.

The following theorem relates the definition of subtraction of integers to the definition of subtraction of natural numbers.

Theorem 1–5. *If $A - B = X$, then $A = B + X$, and conversely.*

Proof.

$$\begin{aligned} B + X &= B + (A - B) = B + A + (-B) \\ &= B + (-B) + A = 0 + A = A. \end{aligned}$$

Proof of the converse.

$$\begin{aligned} A - B &= B + X + (-B) \\ &= X + B + (-B) = X + 0 = X. \end{aligned}$$

By use of the properties of integers given above we can derive all the familiar properties of integers, including all the rules of signs. We present several properties here; others will appear in the exercises.

I. $(-A) + (-B) = -(A + B)$.

Proof. By (3) we have $A + (-A) = 0$, $B + (-B) = 0$. By adding the two quantities which are zero, we again obtain zero (by Theorem 1-2); hence

$$[A + (-A)] + [B + (-B)] = 0,$$

which we may rearrange as

$$(A + B) + [(-A) + (-B)] = 0.$$

The definition of the negative of $A + B$ then gives

$$(-A) + (-B) = -(A + B).$$

II. $A \cdot 0 = 0$ for any integer A.

Proof. $A \cdot 0 + A = A \cdot 0 + A \cdot 1 = A(0 + 1) = A = 0 + A$.

By the cancellation law for addition of integers, it follows that $A \cdot 0 = 0$.

III. $$A(-B) = -AB.$$

Proof. $$AB + A(-B) = A[B + (-B)] = A \cdot 0 = 0.$$

From this it follows, by the definition of the negative of AB, that $A(-B) = -AB$.

IV. $(-A)(-B) = AB$.

Proof. We have the following two relations:

$$0 = [A + (-A)](-B) = A(-B) + (-A)(-B),$$
$$0 = A[B + (-B)] = AB + A(-B).$$

The first states that $(-A)(-B)$ is the negative of $A(-B)$, and the second states that AB is the negative of $A(-B)$. Since an integer can have only one negative, the result follows.

V. If $AB = 0$, then $A = 0$ or $B = 0$ (or both).

Proof. If $A = 0$, the result is valid immediately. If $A \neq 0$, we have, since $A \cdot 0 = 0$,

$$0 = AB = A \cdot 0, \qquad A \neq 0,$$

and by the cancellation law for multiplication of integers, we have $B = 0$.

The effect of the preceding developments in this chapter is that we have merely obtained the familiar properties of the set of all integers—positive, negative, and zero—based ultimately on the original axioms for the natural numbers. We have derived no new properties, but the familiar properties have now been placed on a logical basis.

EXERCISE GROUP 1-3

In Exercises 1–8, the number pairs represent integers. Identify each by an equivalent single symbol.

1. (4, 2)
2. (5, 4)
3. (13, 12)
4. (7, 9)
5. (3, 3)
6. (8, 19)
7. (2, 5)
8. (41, 17)

In Exercises 9–32, evaluate the given expression.

9. $(-3)(-5)$
10. $(-5)(7)$
11. $(-9)(-7)$
12. $(17)(-13)$
13. $(-2)(-6)(7)$
14. $(-5)(-7)(-9)$
15. $(-4)(6)(-7)$
16. $(2)(-4)(-6)(8)$
17. $(-4)(-7)(3)(-9)$
18. $(3)(5)(7)(-9)$
19. $(-3)(-6)(-9)(-12)$
20. $(31)(-27)(-19)(-11)$
21. $(23)(-15)(-17)(33)$
22. $3 - 7(2 - 5)$
23. $-4 + 3(2 - 7)$
24. $(3 - 7)(2 - 5)$
25. $(-4 + 3)(2 - 7)$
26. $5 - 2[4 - 3(1 - 3)]$
27. $-5 - 3[(4 - 3)(1 - 3)]$
28. $7 - 3[2(7 - 4) - 3(8 - 2)]$
29. $5 - 2[-3(-2 - 7) - 5(-3 + 7)]$
30. $(-7 + 3)(-13 + 5) + (5 - 8)(26 - 11)$
31. $3 - (13 - 5) - 14(11 - 7)$
32. $8 - 3(5 + 9) + 9(3 - 5)$
33. Prove that $-(-B) = B$, for any integer B.
34. Prove that $A - (-B) = A + B$ for any integers A and B.
35. Prove that the integer 0 is not negative.
36. Prove that if A is an integer, then one and only one of the following holds:
    (a) A is positive, (b) $A = 0$, (c) A is negative.

1-6 DIVISION OF INTEGERS

Further investigation of operations with integers leads to the following problem: given two integers a and b, with $b \neq 0$, find an integer Q such that $a = bQ$. The integer Q, if it exists, is called the *quotient* in the division of a by b, and is unique.

Theorem 1-6. *If $a = bQ$ and $a = bQ'$, where $b \neq 0$, then $Q = Q'$.*

Proof. From the hypothesis we obtain $bQ = bQ'$; since $b \neq 0$, the cancellation law of multiplication for integers gives $Q = Q'$.

Why is division by zero excluded from the definition? Since the product of zero by any integer is equal to zero, we cannot have $0 \cdot Q = a$ unless $a = 0$. On the other hand, if $a = 0$, any integer would suffice for Q, and we should lose the desired uniqueness for quotients.

A simple problem such as the division of 3 by 2 shows that division is not always possible if the quotient is to be an integer, and we must again expand the number system if we are to have a system in which division is always possible (except, of course, by zero). More formally, we wish to define a new system in which division (except by zero) is possible, and such that part of this new system behaves in all respects like the set of integers. This will be accomplished by defining the system of *rational numbers.*

1–7 THE RATIONAL NUMBER SYSTEM

We shall again use number pairs, this time of integers, to define rational numbers. Let us define the system of *integer pairs*, which we shall write this time as

$$\frac{a}{b} \qquad \text{or} \qquad a/b, \qquad \text{with } b \neq 0,$$

and subject to the following definitions:

***Definition* 1–7.** $\dfrac{a}{b} = \dfrac{c}{d}$ *if and only if* $ad = bc$.

***Definition* 1–8.** $\dfrac{a}{b} + \dfrac{c}{d} = \dfrac{ad + bc}{bd}$.

***Definition* 1–9.** $\dfrac{a}{b} \cdot \dfrac{c}{d} = \dfrac{ac}{bd}$.

Such integer pairs are called *rational numbers.* We note that if $b \neq 0$ and $d \neq 0$ then $bd \neq 0$, so that by Definitions 1–8 and 1–9 the sum and product of two rational numbers are again rational numbers. It is fairly straightforward to show that equality as given in Definition 1–7 has the reflexive, symmetric, and transitive properties.

It can be shown that all the properties of integers are preserved for rational numbers. In addition, the system of rational numbers is closed under division (see Theorem 1–8). The *zero element* may be taken as $0/1$, and the *unit element* as $1/1$. The *negative* of a/b may be defined as

$$-\frac{a}{b} = \frac{-a}{b}.$$

See Exercises 10–19 for some specific statements of these properties.

We shall illustrate the methods that are used by establishing the associative property for addition of rational numbers. We must then show that

$$\frac{a}{b} + \left(\frac{c}{d} + \frac{e}{f}\right) = \left(\frac{a}{b} + \frac{c}{d}\right) + \frac{e}{f}, \qquad b \neq 0, d \neq 0, f \neq 0.$$

By Definition 1–8,

$$\frac{a}{b} + \left(\frac{c}{d} + \frac{e}{f}\right) = \frac{a}{b} + \frac{cf + de}{df} = \frac{a(df) + b(cf + de)}{b(df)}$$

$$= \frac{adf + bcf + bde}{bdf} \text{ (by the properties of integers).}$$

Similarly, we have

$$\left(\frac{a}{b}+\frac{c}{d}\right)+\frac{e}{f}=\frac{ad+bc}{bd}+\frac{e}{f}=\frac{(ad+bc)f+(bd)e}{(bd)f}$$
$$=\frac{adf+bcf+bde}{bdf},$$

and the two sums are equal.

We define the rational number a/b to be *positive* if a and b are both positive integers, or are both negative integers. We then define a *negative rational number* as the negative of a positive rational number.

The following theorem applies to any rational number.

Theorem 1–7.

$$\frac{a}{-b}=\frac{-a}{b}=-\frac{a}{b}.$$

Proof. The first equality follows from Definition 1–7, since $(-a)(-b) = ab$. The second equality is merely a statement of the definition of the negative of a rational number.

We must still prove the theorem which establishes the closure of the rational number system under division.

Theorem 1–8. *The relation*

$$\frac{a}{b}=\frac{c}{d}\cdot\frac{x}{y}$$

always has a unique solution if $c/d \neq 0/1$. (As always, $b \neq 0$, $d \neq 0$.)

Proof. The requirement $c/d \neq 0/1$ implies that $c \neq 0$. Since $b \neq 0$ and $c \neq 0$, it follows that $bc \neq 0$. We shall now show that the rational number $x/y = ad/bc$ is a solution, that is, that it satisfies the given equation; thus

$$\frac{c}{d}\cdot\frac{x}{y}=\frac{c}{d}\cdot\frac{ad}{bc}=\frac{acd}{bcd}=\frac{a}{b},$$

the last equality by Definition 1–7.

The proof of uniqueness now follows. If

$$\frac{c}{d}\cdot\frac{x}{y}=\frac{c}{d}\cdot\frac{x'}{y'},$$

then

$$\frac{cx}{dy}=\frac{cx'}{dy'},\qquad cxdy'=cx'dy,\qquad xy'=x'y,\qquad \text{and}\quad \frac{x}{y}=\frac{x'}{y'},$$

so that any two solutions must be equal rational numbers.

One matter that remains is to show that part of the rational number system behaves like the set of integers. This is done by identifying the integer a with the rational number $a/1$. It can then be shown that this subset of the rational number system does, in fact, behave in all respects like the set of integers. To illustrate the correspondence between addition of the integers a and b and the addition of the rational numbers $a/1$ and $b/1$ with which they are identified, it is merely necessary to show that

$$\frac{a}{1} + \frac{b}{1} = \frac{a+b}{1},$$

which follows from previous properties [see Exercise 13(a) in Exercise Group 1–4].

Moreover, positiveness carries over from integers to rational numbers, for, if a is a positive integer, then $a/1$ is, by definition, a positive rational number.

What has, in effect, been accomplished in this section may be stated as follows: we have defined the set of rational numbers, such that a subset of this set retains all the properties of integers. Additionally, in the set of rational numbers division is always possible, except by zero. In practice, with no chance of ambiguity, we may write the zero rational number as 0, and the unit rational number as 1, and we may say that the rational numbers contain the integers as a subset.

EXERCISE GROUP 1–4

In each of Exercises 1–9, determine whether the two given rational numbers are equal.

1. $\frac{2}{3}, \frac{57}{85}$
2. $\frac{18}{19}, \frac{126}{133}$
3. $\frac{425}{-80}, \frac{-85}{16}$
4. $\frac{2}{56}, \frac{9}{252}$
5. $\frac{270}{6}, \frac{225}{5}$
6. $\frac{8801}{5932}, \frac{756}{509}$
7. $\frac{3}{84}, \frac{14}{392}$
8. $\frac{-67}{2}, \frac{2915}{-87}$
9. $\frac{293}{814}, \frac{576}{1601}$
10. Show that the sum of two positive rational numbers is positive.
11. Show that the product of two positive rational numbers is positive.
12. Show that the product of two negative rational numbers is positive.
13. If a and b are integers, show that

$$\text{(a)}\quad \frac{a}{1} + \frac{b}{1} = \frac{a+b}{1}, \qquad \text{(b)}\quad \frac{a}{1}\cdot\frac{b}{1} = \frac{ab}{1}.$$

14. Prove that equality for rational numbers possesses the reflexive, symmetric, and transitive properties as defined in Section 1–2.
15. Prove the commutative property of addition for rational numbers.
16. Prove the commutative property of multiplication for rational numbers.
17. Show that a/b is a negative rational number if
    (a) a is a positive integer and b is a negative integer;
    (b) a is a negative integer and b is a positive integer.
18. Show that if a is a rational number, then one and only one of the following can hold:
    (a) a is positive, (b) $a = 0$, (c) $-a$ is positive.
19. Show that Axiom 7 of Section 1–2 holds for the set of all rational numbers.

1–8 THE REAL NUMBER SYSTEM

It has been shown that *the rational number system is closed under the four arithmetic operations of addition, subtraction, multiplication, and division by nonzero rational numbers.*

It is more difficult to define the real number system, and not feasible at this stage of our work. We shall present a brief account of this system, relying on intuitive concepts.

The rational number system is still inadequate for our needs. There are entire classes of numbers which cannot be expressed as the quotient of two integers. For example, in a square of which the length of each side is unity, the length of a diagonal is not a rational number, for the theorem of Pythagoras states: *In a right triangle the square of the length of the hypotenuse is equal to the sum of the squares of the lengths of the other sides.* Hence, if x is the length of the diagonal (Fig. 1–1), it follows by the theorem of Pythagoras that $x^2 = 1 + 1 = 2$, and it can be proved that such a value of x is not rational. (Recall that x^2 means $x \cdot x$. A review of exponents appears in Appendix A.)

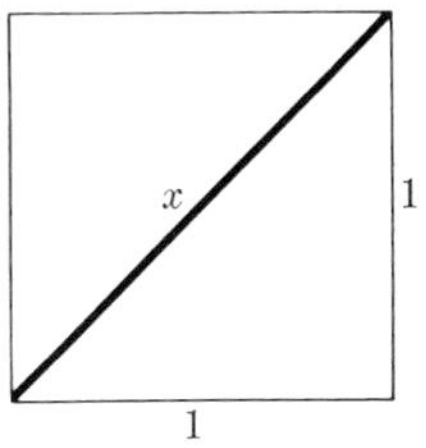

FIGURE 1–1

As defined in more advanced presentations, the real number system is a system of numbers which may be said to contain the rational number system as a subset, satisfies all the properties of rational numbers, and, very importantly, possesses a *completeness property.*

Intuitively, a completeness property, in whatever form it may be given, implies that there are no gaps in the real number system. It has been stated that there is no rational number x for which $x^2 = 2$. However, there are rational numbers whose squares are close to 2, as close as we wish to 2, in fact. The familiar decimal approximations 1.4, 1.41, 1.414, 1.4142, . . . , are such rational numbers. Furthermore, 1.5, 1.42, 1.415, 1.4143, . . . are also such rational numbers. Between these two sets of rational numbers a gap exists which cannot be filled by any rational number. Among the real numbers, however, there is one to fill the gap. It is written as $\sqrt{2}$, and has the property that $(\sqrt{2})^2 = 2$. A real number which is not rational is called *irrational;* hence $\sqrt{2}$ is an irrational number.

It can be shown that in a reasonable sense there are, indeed, more irrational numbers than rational numbers. Additional ones are $\sqrt{3}$, $\sqrt{5}$, but not $\sqrt{4}$ since $\sqrt{4} = 2$. Another example of a familiar number which is irrational is π, the ratio of the circumference of any circle to its diameter.

Intuitively, then, we may say that the irrational numbers fill in the gaps that exist in the rational number system, and that the real number system consists of the rational and irrational numbers.

We may now summarize briefly the properties of the set of real numbers:

1. Addition and multiplication are always possible, unique, associative, and commutative, with a distributive law for multiplication with respect to addition.

2. Division, except by zero, and subtraction are always possible.
3. There are a zero element and a unit element.
4. There is a completeness property.
5. The real numbers consist of positive numbers, negative numbers, and zero, with the familiar rules of signs for the arithmetic operations. For any real number a, exactly one of the following is true: a is positive, or a is negative, or a is zero.
6. The real numbers contain as a subset the positive integers, which satisfy the axioms of Section 1–2 for the natural numbers.
7. The real numbers also contain as a subset the rational numbers, each of which may be expressed as a quotient of two integers a/b, with $b \neq 0$.
8. Finally, all operations with rational numbers, as described in Section 1–7, are also valid for real numbers.

1–9 THE COMPLEX NUMBER SYSTEM

For some algebraic purposes, in particular the solution of certain equations, the real number system is still inadequate. There is no real number x to satisfy the equation

$$x^2 + 1 = 0; \tag{4}$$

the reason for this is that (1) $x = 0$ will not suffice, (2) if x is positive or negative, x^2 will be positive and the addition of two positive numbers cannot give zero.

This inadequacy can be removed by enlarging the real number system, by defining a new system whose elements are *pairs of real numbers*, (a, b), with the following properties:

***Definition* 1–10.** $(a, b) = (c, d)$ *if and only if* $a = c$ *and* $b = d$.

***Definition* 1–11.** $(a, b) + (c, d) = (a + c, b + d)$.

***Definition* 1–12.** $(a, b) \cdot (c, d) = (ac - bd, ad + bc)$.

This new system, called the *system of complex numbers*, has all the properties of the real number system except for the property that nonzero numbers are either positive or negative. The property of positiveness or negativeness is not attributed to complex numbers in general.

The *zero element* may be taken as $(0, 0)$, and the *unit element* as $(1,0)$.

The equation for complex numbers analogous to (4) is then

$$(x, y)^2 + (1, 0) = (0, 0). \tag{5}$$

It is this equation for which we should like a solution to exist in the new number system. The following theorem provides precisely such a solution.

Theorem 1–9. *The equation* (5) *has a solution in the complex number system.*

Proof. The complex number (0, 1) is such a solution since, by Definitions 1–12 and 1–11,

$$\begin{aligned}(0, 1)^2 + (1, 0) &= (0 \cdot 0 - 1 \cdot 1, 0 \cdot 1 + 0 \cdot 1) + (1, 0)\\ &= (-1, 0) + (1, 0) = (-1 + 1, 0 + 0) = (0, 0).\end{aligned}$$

We may consider the complex number system as containing the real number system as a subset if we identify the real number a with the complex number $(a, 0)$. Then all operations with real numbers correspond exactly to the same operations with the complex numbers with which they are identified.

It is permissible to use single letters to denote complex numbers. It is customary to use the letter i for the number (0, 1) of Theorem 1–9,

$$i = (0, 1),$$

for which we have

$$i^2 = (0, 1) \cdot (0, 1) = (-1, 0).$$

Thus i is a complex number whose square corresponds to the real number -1. Now the complex number (a, b) may be written as

$$(a, b) = (a, 0) + (0, b),$$

and, since by Definition 1–11 we get $(0, b) = (b, 0) \cdot (0, 1)$, we may write

$$(a, b) = (a, 0) + (b, 0) \cdot (0, 1).$$

Since the complex numbers $(a, 0)$ and $(b, 0)$ are associated with the real numbers a and b, respectively, we may associate the complex number (a, b) in a purely formal manner with the expression $a + bi$, where a and b are real. In either form a is called the *real part* of the complex number, and b is the *imaginary part*. In a number of ways complex numbers behave like real expressions containing square roots. In particular, the parts containing i are similar terms and may be combined; moreover, we may write $i^2 = -1$. Thus

$$\begin{aligned}(2 + 3i) - (4 + 2i) &= (2 - 4) + (3 - 2)i = -2 + i;\\ (2 + 3i)(4 + 2i) &= 2 \cdot 4 + (2 \cdot 2 + 3 \cdot 4)i + 3 \cdot 2i^2\\ &= 8 + 16i - 6 \qquad (\text{since } i^2 = -1)\\ &= 2 + 16i.\end{aligned}$$

Example. Evaluate $x^2 - 2x + 6$ for $x = 3 + 2i$.

Solution. Substituting the given value, we get

$$\begin{aligned}x^2 - 2x + 6 &= (3 + 2i)^2 - 2(3 + 2i) + 6\\ &= 9 + 12i + (2i)^2 - 6 - 4i + 6\\ &= 9 + 12i - 4 - 6 - 4i + 6 \qquad [\text{since } (2i)^2 = 4i^2 = -4]\\ &= 5 + 8i.\end{aligned}$$

The arithmetic operations on complex numbers, including that of division, will be considered in greater detail in Chapter 15.

It is emphasized here that in our development of number systems we have started with the natural numbers and by successive enlargements have arrived at the set of integers, followed by the set of rational numbers, then the set of real numbers, and finally, the set of complex numbers. Each set thus obtained contains the previous set as part of it, that is, as a *subset*.

EXERCISE GROUP 1-5

By use of operations on complex numbers in the form $a + bi$, perform the indicated operations in Exercises 1–12, and in each instance reduce the final result to the form $a + bi$.

1. $(5 + 3i) + (7 - 2i)$
2. $(3 - 7i) - (3 + 2i)$
3. $(7 - 2i) + (5 + 3i) - (4 - 9i)$
4. $(3 + 11i) - (9 - 6i) + (15 - 8i)$
5. $(a + ci) + (b + di) + e$
6. $(a - di) - (c + ei) + (bi - f)$
7. $(2 + 3i)(5 - 4i)$
8. $(5 + 7i)(6 - 13i)$
9. $(3 + 4i - 5i^2)(6i^3 + 7i^2)$
10. $(2i^3 - 3i^2 + 1)(7 - 5i)$
11. $(a + bi)(c + di)i$
12. $(c + ai)(d - bi)$

13. Determine the value of $4x^2 - 8x + 5$ when $x = 1 + \frac{1}{2}i$.
14. Determine the value of $2x^2 + 6x + 5$ when $x = \frac{1}{2}(-3 - i)$.
15. Show that the equation $(c + di)z = a + bi$ is satisfied by the complex number

$$z = \frac{(ac + bd) + (bc - ad)i}{c^2 + d^2}.$$

16. Use the result of Exercise 15 to find the *reciprocal* of the complex number (a, b). (The *reciprocal* of a number is the quotient of 1 divided by that number.)

In the following exercises each number pair represents a complex number.

17. Find the negative of the complex number (a, b).
18. Show that $(a, b) + (0, 0) = (a, b)$, and $(a, b)(0, 0) = (0, 0)$.
19. Show that $(a, b)(1, 0) = (a, b)$, and $(a, b)(0, 1) = (-b, a)$.
20. Show that $(0, 1)^3 = (0, -1)$, and $(0, 1)^4 = (1, 0)$, so that $i^3 = -i$ and $i^4 = i$.

CHAPTER 2

Coordinate Geometry and Functions

2–1 INTRODUCTION

A better understanding of many problems in algebra can often be obtained by a geometrical interpretation, and many geometrical problems are facilitated when algebraic methods can be applied to their solution. The means by which this interplay of algebra and geometry can be accomplished will be introduced in the following sections.

2–2 GEOMETRICAL REPRESENTATION OF REAL NUMBERS. DIRECTED DISTANCES

If use is made of the familiar concept of length on a straight line, together with direction on the line, a very useful geometrical representation of the real numbers may be given. On a straight line which extends indefinitely in both directions, a point O is chosen as *origin* (Fig. 2–1). One of the two possible directions on the line is chosen as the *positive* direction, and the opposite direction as *negative.* In the figure the direction to the right was chosen as positive. Further, a unit of length is chosen on the line. A positive number a is then represented by a point on the line to the right of O at a distance of a units from O; a negative number $(-a)$ is represented by a point to the left of O, the same distance from O. Several illustrations are indicated in Fig. 2–1.

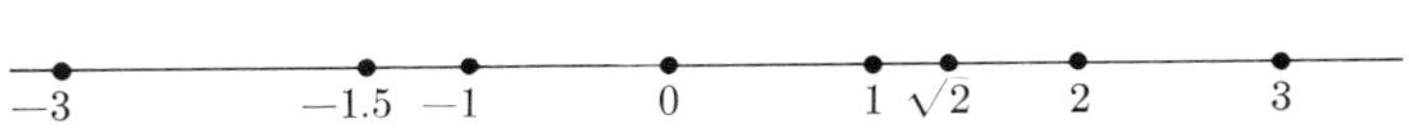

FIGURE 2–1

The line as set up in this manner is called a *coordinate line* or *axis*, and the number associated with a point on this line is the *linear coordinate* or simply *coordinate* of the point.

The important property should be noted that *to any real number there corresponds precisely one point on the line, and to any point on the line there corresponds precisely one real number.*

Let P_1 and P_2 be two points on a coordinate line. The *directed line segment* P_1P_2 is defined as the line segment in the direction from P_1 to P_2. The *directed distance* $\overline{P_1P_2}$ is defined as the length of P_1P_2 if the direction from P_1 to P_2 is the positive direction along the coordinate line, and as the negative of the length of P_1P_2 if the direction from P_1 to P_2 is the negative direction along the line. It follows that

$$\overline{P_1P_2} = -\overline{P_2P_1}.$$

If O is the origin on a coordinate line, and P is a point on this line with coordinate x, then $\overline{OP} = x$.

If A, B, C are any three points on a coordinate line, it can be shown that

$$\overline{AB} + \overline{BC} = \overline{AC} \tag{1}$$

regardless of the relative positions of the points.

Let P_1 and P_2 be points on a line with coordinates x_1 and x_2. Then by (1) we have

$$\overline{P_1P_2} = \overline{P_1O} + \overline{OP_2} = \overline{OP_2} - \overline{OP_1} = x_2 - x_1.$$

Thus the directed distance $\overline{P_1P_2}$ is the coordinate of the second point minus the coordinate of the first point.

Example. Verify (1) if A, B, C have the coordinates -3, 4, -7, respectively.

Solution. $\overline{AB} = 4 - (-3) = 7$, $\overline{BC} = -7 - 4 = -11$, $\overline{AC} = -7 - (-3) = -4$, and $7 + (-11) = -4$.

2–3 RECTANGULAR COORDINATES

We may extend the idea of a coordinate line, by which the real numbers were represented graphically, to a *coordinate plane*, by which pairs of real numbers are represented graphically. This is accomplished by constructing a line perpendicular to the line in Fig. 2–1 at the origin O. These lines are called *axes*, and are generally drawn in such a way that one may be designated as horizontal, the other as vertical. The horizontal axis is commonly called the x-axis, and the vertical axis the y-axis. A unit of measurement, and a positive direction, usually upward, are chosen on the y-axis. Generally the same unit of measure is applied to the x-axis, and the positive direction is to the right. Negative numbers are assigned to the points on the x-axis to the left of the origin and on the y-axis below the origin.

A point P in the plane is designated by the number pair (x, y), where x indicates the perpendicular distance of the point P from the y-axis, and y the perpendicular distance of P from the x-axis. The number x is called the *abscissa*, or *x-coordinate*, of the point P, and y is the *ordinate*, or *y-coordinate*, of P, while x and y together are the *coordinates* of P.

This representation of points in a plane by pairs of numbers is called *the rectangular Cartesian coordinate system*, the name Cartesian being used in recognition of René Descartes (1596–1650), who is usually credited with the discovery of the method.

Example. The location of the points A, B, C, D, whose coordinates are the number pairs (3, 1), (−8, 2), (5, −3), and (−8, −3) respectively, is given in Fig. 2–2.

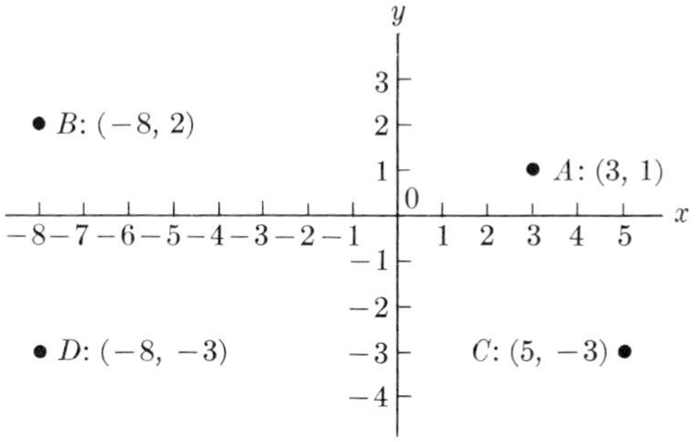

FIGURE 2–2

Note that the correspondence between points in the plane and pairs of numbers is reciprocal, in the sense that for each point there is one and only one pair of numbers, and for each pair of numbers there is exactly one point.

The idea of directed distance between two points on a line parallel to the x-axis or on a line parallel to the y-axis is now defined as in Section 2–2. For example, if P_1 is (2, 3) and P_2 is (2, −7), then

$$\overline{P_1P_2} = -7 - 3 = -10.$$

In general, for $P_1(x_1, y_1)$ and $P_2(x_1, y_2)$ we have

$$\overline{P_1P_2} = y_2 - y_1,$$

and similarly for a line segment parallel to the x-axis.

In general we do not use direction on a line not parallel to one of the coordinate axes.

EXERCISE GROUP 2–1

1. Plot the points $A(-2, 3)$; $B(-\frac{3}{2}, -\frac{2}{3})$; $C(7, -\frac{5}{2})$.
2. Plot the points $A(2, -3)$; $B(5, -\frac{3}{2})$; $C(-\frac{3}{5}, -\frac{10}{9})$.
3. Plot the points (−5, 3); (−4, 4); (−3, 2); (−2, 0); (−1, −1); (0, 0); (1, 2); (3, −2); and (5, 1). Join consecutive points with straight line segments.
4. Plot the points (−3, −5); (−2, −2); (−1, 5); (0, −3); (1, 2); (2, 4); (3, −2); (4, −7); and (5, 3). Join consecutive points with straight line segments.

5. Where are all the points whose abscissas are -3? whose ordinates are 2?
6. Where are all the points whose abscissas are a? whose ordinates are b?
7. What is the directed distance from $(2, -3)$ to $(2, 6)$?
8. What is the directed distance from $(-1, 4)$ to $(5, 4)$?
9. What is the directed distance from $(5, -3)$ to $(-8, -3)$?
10. What is the directed distance from $(-8, 2)$ to $(-8, -3)$?
11. Where are all the points which are equidistant from $(2, -3)$ and $(2, 6)$?
12. Where are all the points which are equidistant from $(-1, 4)$ and $(5, 4)$?
13. The ends of the base of an isosceles triangle are at $(3, 0)$, $(8, 0)$, and the altitude to the base is of length 4. Find the coordinates of the third vertex.
14. Three vertices of a parallelogram are $(-3, 2)$; $(1, 0)$; and $(0, 3)$. Locate the fourth vertex. Is there more than one solution?
15. Three vertices of a rectangle are $(-8, -3)$; $(5, -3)$; and $(-8, 2)$. Locate the fourth vertex. Is there more than one solution?
16. The legs of a right triangle are on the coordinate axes, and the hypotenuse is of length a. If (x, y) are the coordinates of the midpoint of the hypotenuse, show that $4x^2 + 4y^2 = a^2$.
17. Two vertices of an isosceles right triangle are at $(1, 3)$ and $(6, 3)$, and the line segment joining these points is one of the equal sides. Find the coordinates of a third vertex.
18. Verify Eq. (1) if the points have coordinates, respectively, of
   (a) $-5, -7, 2$; (b) $1.5, -2, 3.5$; (c) $-4, 0, -2$.

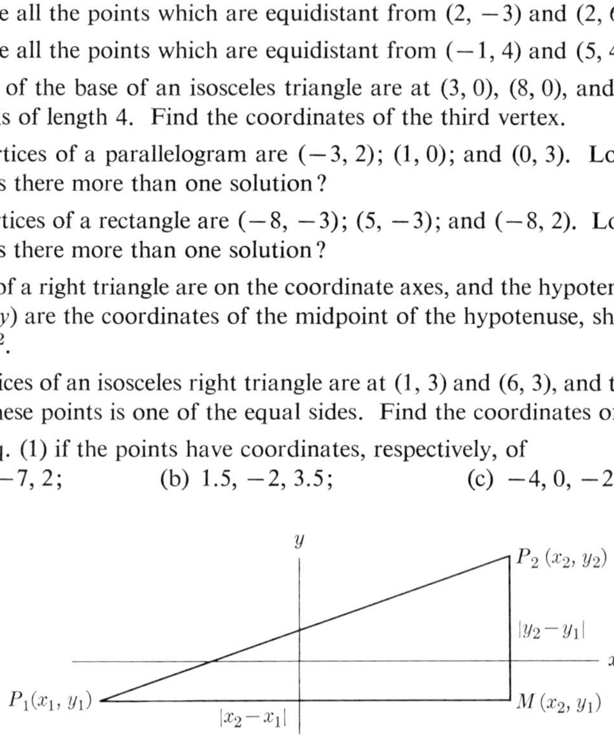

FIGURE 2–3

2–4 THE DISTANCE FORMULA AND MIDPOINT FORMULA

We shall now obtain a formula for the (undirected) distance between two points. Let the points be $P_1(x_1, y_1)$ and $P_2(x_2, y_2)$ as in Fig. 2–3. If $y_1 = y_2$, then, as in Section 2–3, we have $\overline{P_1P_2} = x_2 - x_1$. The actual length of the line segment, which we designate by $|P_1P_2|$, is either $x_2 - x_1$, or $x_1 - x_2$, whichever is nonnegative, and we may write

$$|P_1P_2| = \pm(x_2 - x_1), \qquad \text{or} \qquad |P_1P_2| = |x_2 - x_1|, \tag{2}$$

where the symbol $|a|$, for any real number a, means the *numerical value* of the number, apart from its sign. (Hence $|a|$ is never negative.)

Similarly, if $x_1 = x_2$, we have

$$|P_1P_2| = \pm(y_2 - y_1), \quad \text{or} \quad |P_1P_2| = |y_2 - y_1|.$$

We now assume that $x_1 \neq x_2$ and $y_1 \neq y_2$. Draw a line through P_1 parallel to the x-axis, and a line through P_2 parallel to the y-axis. These lines are perpendicular and their intersection may be taken as $M(x_2, y_1)$. By the above we have

$$|P_1M| = |x_2 - x_1|, \qquad |MP_2| = |y_2 - y_1|,$$

and hence, by the Theorem of Pythagoras applied to triangle P_1MP_2,

$$\boxed{d = |P_1P_2| = \sqrt{(x_2 - x_1)^2 + (y_2 - y_1)^2},} \tag{3}$$

since $(x_2 - x_1)^2 = |x_2 - x_1|^2$ and $(y_2 - y_1)^2 = |y_2 - y_1|^2$. Equation (3) is known as the *distance formula.*

It should be noted that formula (3) still holds if $x_1 = x_2$ or if $y_1 = y_2$. For example, if $y_1 = y_2$, (3) becomes

$$d = \sqrt{(x_1 - x_2)^2} = |x_2 - x_1|,$$

which is consistent with (2), and similarly if $x_1 = x_2$. Moreover, since $(x_2 - x_1)^2 = (x_1 - x_2)^2$ and $(y_2 - y_1)^2 = (y_1 - y_2)^2$, it is immaterial, when two points are given, which is designated as P_1 and which as P_2.

Example 1. Find the distance between the points $(-2, 5)$ and $(3, -7)$.

Solution. By formula (3) we have

$$d = \sqrt{[-2 - 3]^2 + [5 - (-7)]^2} = \sqrt{25 + 144} = \sqrt{169} = 13.$$

Example 2. Show that the triangle with $(-3, 2)$, $(1, 1)$, and $(-4, -2)$ as vertices is an isosceles triangle.

Solution. Let the points be designated as A, B, and C respectively. Then

$$|AB| = \sqrt{(1 + 3)^2 + (1 - 2)^2} = \sqrt{17},$$

$$|AC| = \sqrt{(-4 + 3)^2 + (-2 - 2)^2} = \sqrt{17}.$$

Hence $|AB| = |AC|$, and the triangle is isosceles. Furthermore,

$$|BC| = \sqrt{(-4 - 1)^2 + (-2 - 1)^2} = \sqrt{34}.$$

Since $|BC|^2 = |AB|^2 + |AC|^2$, the Theorem of Pythagoras holds, and ABC is a right triangle, with the right angle at A.

Let $P(x, y)$ be the midpoint of the line segment joining $P_1(x_1, y_1)$ and $P_2(x_2, y_2)$. Through P_1, P, and P_2 draw lines perpendicular to the x-axis. These lines intersect

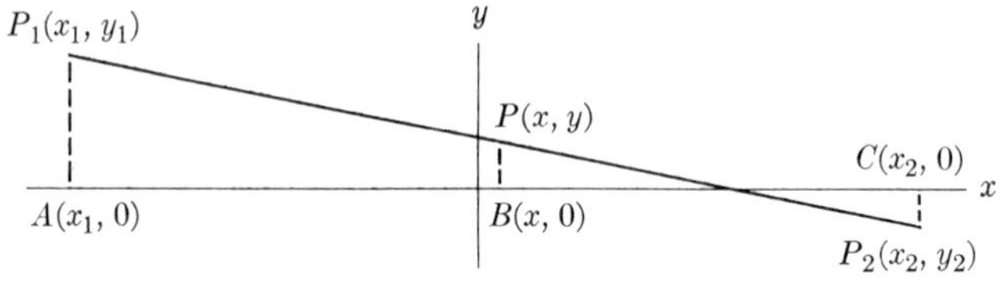

FIGURE 2–4

the x-axis in the points shown in Fig. 2–4. We must have $\overline{AB} = \overline{BC}$; hence $x - x_1 = x_2 - x$, and it then follows that

$$x = \tfrac{1}{2}(x_1 + x_2).$$

In a similar manner, by drawing lines perpendicular to the y-axis we get

$$y = \tfrac{1}{2}(y_1 + y_2).$$

We combine these in the statement: *The midpoint of the line segment joining $P_1(x_1, y_1)$ and $P_2(x_2, y_2)$ is given by*

$$\boxed{P[\tfrac{1}{2}(x_1 + x_2), \tfrac{1}{2}(y_1 + y_2)].} \tag{4}$$

This formula expresses the coordinates of the midpoint of a line segment in terms of the coordinates of its endpoints.

Example 3. Determine the coordinates of the midpoint of the line segment joining the points $(3, -8)$ and $(-7, 5)$.

Solution. The coordinates of the desired midpoint are given by formula (4) as

$$x = \tfrac{1}{2}[3 + (-7)] = -2, \qquad y = \tfrac{1}{2}(-8 + 5) = -\tfrac{3}{2}.$$

EXERCISE GROUP 2–2

In Exercises 1–9, determine the coordinates of the point midway between the two given points and also the distance between them.

1. $(-5, 2)$, $(3, -7)$
2. $(-6, -2)$, $(5, 7)$
3. $(-3, 5)$, $(7, 10)$
4. $(5, -3)$, $(8, 11)$
5. $(-3, -8)$, $(-8, 9)$
6. $(-7, -5)$, $(6, -9)$
7. (a, b), (c, d)
8. $(a, -a)$, (c, c)
9. $(a, -c)$, $(-c, a)$
10. Find the distance from the point $(3, 5)$ to the midpoint of the line segment joining the points $(5, -3)$ and $(-3, -7)$.
11. Show that the points $(0, 0)$, (a, c), (b, d), and $(a + b, c + d)$ are the vertices of a parallelogram. [*Hint:* Show that opposite sides are equal.]
12. Find the coordinates of the midpoint of the diagonals of the rectangle with vertices at the points $(0, 0)$, $(a, 0)$, $(0, b)$, (a, b).

13. Show that the triangle with vertices at $(6, -2)$, $(-2, 2)$, and $(1, -2)$ is isosceles.
14. Show that the triangle with vertices at $(5, -1)$, $(1, -3)$, and $(8, -7)$ is a right triangle.
15. Show that the quadrilateral with vertices at $(5, -1)$, $(1, -3)$, $(-2, 3)$, and $(2, 5)$ is a rectangle.
16. Given the points $A(2, 1)$, $B(6, 2)$, $C(7, 6)$, $D(3, 5)$. (a) Show that the quadrilateral $ABCD$ is a rhombus; that is, that it has four equal sides. (b) Show that the diagonals AC and BD bisect each other.

In Exercises 17–22, show that the midpoints of AB, BC, CD, and AD are the vertices of a parallelogram.

17. $A(1, 2)$, $B(4, 7)$, $C(5, 1)$, $D(1, 0)$
18. $A(2, -1)$, $B(1, -2)$, $C(-2, 4)$, $D(1, 1)$
19. $A(0, 2)$, $B(2, 4)$, $C(6, -1)$, $D(0, -2)$
20. $A(-1, -1)$, $B(3, -2)$, $C(-2, 2)$, $D(5, 3)$
21. $A(0, 0)$, $B(a, 0)$, $C(2a, 2b)$, $D(0, b)$
22. $A(a, b)$, $B(c, d)$, $C(d, e)$, $D(f, g)$

2–5 FUNCTIONS

Many mathematical concepts that play an important role in modern mathematics have developed slowly over periods of many years. Among these is the mathematical idea of correspondence between objects, or, more specifically, the mathematical concept of *function*, which we shall now discuss.

Many familiar experiences of everyday living reflect the idea of correspondence, or relationship, as we wish to use it. In a given day the temperature bears a definite relation to the time. The yield of an acre of wheat clearly depends on the amount of rainfall. The speed of an airplane certainly depends on the amount of fuel fed to the engines. The strength of a wooden beam corresponds to the thickness of the beam. Such examples can be multiplied indefinitely—each of them exhibits the correspondence between two specific quantities.

The concept can be extended to include a correspondence among three or more quantities. Thus, the yield of an acre of wheat depends on temperature as well as rainfall. The speed of an airplane depends on altitude as well as fuel consumed. In large part, however, we shall be concerned with relations or correspondences between two quantities.

We have previously introduced the idea of *set* as a collection of objects, called the *elements* of the set. A set may have numbers as its elements, or it may have other objects, such as pairs of numbers. For example, the objects

$$(1, 2),\ (1, 3),\ (1, 4),\ (1, 5)$$

form a *set of pairs of numbers*, consisting of four elements.

Let A and B be two sets of numbers, shown symbolically in Fig. 2–5, such that exactly one number in B corresponds to each number in A, and each number in B corresponds to at least one number in A. This correspondence determines *pairs* of numbers (a, b) where a is in A and b is in B. The collection of all such pairs of numbers defines a *function* whose *domain* is the set of numbers in A, and whose *range* is the set of numbers in B.

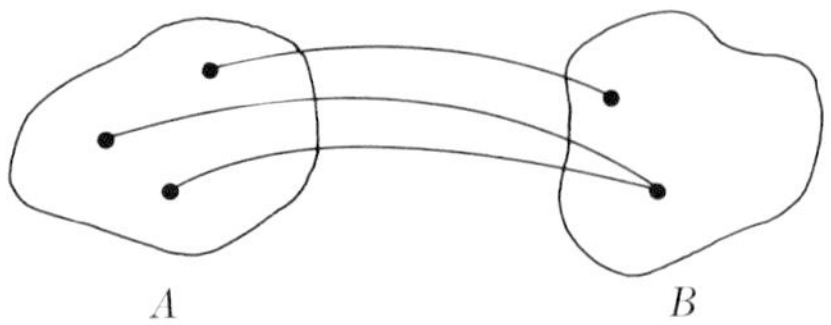

FIGURE 2-5

Example 1. The number pairs

$$(2, 3), \quad (-1, 4), \quad (3, -5), \quad (4, 3)$$

define a function with the numbers 2, -1, 3, 4 as the domain, and the numbers 3, 4, -5 as the range. Note that a number in the range may correspond to more than one number in the domain.

The set of number pairs

$$(1, 3), (2, 4), \ (1,7), (-2, 0)$$

does not constitute a function, since both 3 and 7 correspond to the same number, 1.

The second number of any pair in a function is called the *value of the function* corresponding to the first number of the pair. If the function is denoted by f, the value of the function corresponding to any number x in the domain is written as $f(x)$.

If f denotes the function in Example 1, we have

$$f(2) = 3, \qquad f(-1) = 4, \qquad f(3) = -5, \qquad f(4) = 3.$$

The value of a function may be given by an algebraic expression. If we write

$$f(x) = 2x - 3,$$

then for any value of x, the value of the function is $2x - 3$. In particular,

$$f(3) = 2 \cdot 3 - 3 = 3, \qquad f(-4) = 2(-4) - 3 = -11,$$

and so on. The function may be defined as the set of number pairs $(x, 2x - 3)$, where the domain in which x lies is the set of real numbers. We may also say, a bit more loosely, that $2x - 3$ is a function of x.

In general, if $f(x)$ is the value of a function corresponding to x, we also say that $f(x)$ is a function of x, for x in some stated or implied domain. In the latter case the domain is usually taken to consist of all real numbers for which the values $f(x)$ exist.

Many familiar equations define functions, as in the following examples.

Example 2. The perimeter P of a square is given by the formula $P = 4s$, where s is the length of a side. This relation defines the function $(s, 4s)$, with a domain, in this case, consisting of all positive numbers. We also say that P is a function of s.

Example 3. In the relation $A = lw$, where A is the area of a rectangle and l and w are the lengths of the sides, A is a function of w if l is held fixed in value, and A is a function of l if w is held fixed in value.

Letters other than f are also used to designate a function. If a function is defined by a mathematical expression and no domain is specified, it is assumed that the domain consists of all numbers for which the expression has a value.

Example 4. Let $f(x) = 3x^3 + 7x - 5$; then

$$f(2) = 3(2)^3 + 7(2) - 5 = 33, \quad f(0) = -5, \quad f(-1) = -15, \quad f(1) = 5.$$

The student should verify these values for $f(0)$, $f(-1)$, and $f(1)$.

EXERCISE GROUP 2-3

1. The following number pairs define a function g: (1, 2), (2, 3), (3, 4), (4, 5). (a) Find $g(1)$ and $g(3)$. (b) Find x if $g(x) = 3$.
2. The following number pairs define a function f: (1, 3), (2, 2), (3, −1), (5, 2). (a) Find $f(2)$ and $f(5)$. (b) Find x if $f(x) = 2$. (c) How many distinct numbers are in the domain of f? (d) How many distinct numbers are in the range of f?
3. The following number pairs define a function f: $(0, \frac{1}{2})$, $(2, -\frac{1}{2})$, (7, −3), (10, 0). (a) Find $f(0)$ and $f(10)$. (b) Find u if $f(u) = -\frac{1}{2}$. (c) Does $f(1)$ exist?
4. Define the functions f and g as follows: f: (0, 2), (1, 3), (2, 4), (3, 5); g: (0, −1), (1, 1), (2, −5), (3, 6). (a) Give the function whose values are $2f(x)$. (b) Give the function whose values are $f(x) + g(x)$.
5. The functions f and g are as defined in Exercise 4. (a) Give the function whose values are $f(x) - g(x)$. (b) Give the function whose values are $[f(x)]^2$.

In Exercises 6–13, the given number pairs define a function f with domain consisting of all real numbers for which the second expression is defined. In each case find $f(2)$, $f(0)$, and $f(-3)$.

6. $(x, 2x)$
7. $(x, 3x^2)$
8. $\left(x, \dfrac{x}{x^2 + 1}\right)$
9. $(x, x^2 - x)$
10. $(x, x^2 - 3x + 6)$
11. $\left(x, \dfrac{x + 2}{3 - x}\right)$
12. $\left(x, \dfrac{2x - 3}{3x - 2}\right)$
13. $\left(x, \dfrac{3x^2 + 2}{x - 1}\right)$

In Exercises 14–19, the number pairs $(x, x^2 + x)$ define a function f, and the number pairs $(x, x - 1)$ define a function g, the domain of each function consisting of all real numbers. Find the indicated values.

14. $f[g(1)]$
15. $g[f(2)]$
16. $f[g(a)]$
17. $g[f(a)]$
18. (a) $g(-x)$ (b) $g(x + h)$ (c) $\dfrac{1}{h}[g(x + h) - g(x)]$
19. (a) $f(-x)$ (b) $f(x + h)$ (c) $\dfrac{1}{h}[f(x + h) - f(x)]$

In Exercises 20–24, express each of the functional relations as an explicit algebraic equation.

20. The area A of a square in terms of the length of a side s.
21. The circumference C of a circle in terms of the radius r of the circle.
22. The area A of a circle in terms of the diameter d of the circle.
23. The area A of a rectangle in terms of the width w when the length of the rectangle is twice the width.
24. The hypotenuse y of a right triangle in terms of the shorter leg x when the longer leg of the triangle is twice the shorter leg.
25. Express the number of degrees F on the fahrenheit scale as a function of the number of degrees C on the centigrade scale, if the freezing point of water is given by 0°C and 32°F, while the boiling point is 100°C and 212°F.
26. A window is in the form of a semicircle mounted on a rectangle. If the height of the rectangle is twice the width, express the total area of the window as a function of the width w.
27. A ball thrown into the air with a velocity of 32 ft/sec will be above the ground s ft at any time t (measured in seconds from the instant when it is thrown), where s is given by the function $s = -16t^2 + 32t$. Compute the values of s for every quarter-second from $t = 0$ to $t = 2$. Explain the results.
28. Express the area A of an equilateral triangle as a function of the length of one side s.
29. If city property is worth $300 a front foot, express the value of a lot as a function of its width, x ft.
30. Express the altitude H of an equilateral triangle as a function of the base x.
31. The volume of a cube is given by the formula $V = x^3$, where x is the length of a side. If the length of each side is taken as a and then increased by the amount h, express the corresponding increase in the volume as a function of h.

2–6 GRAPHICAL REPRESENTATION OF FUNCTIONS

With a means for representing pairs of real numbers geometrically now at hand, we can devise an effective way of representing graphically a function f whose values are $y = f(x)$. To each value of x there corresponds a value y as determined by the function. The pair of numbers (x, y) may be represented graphically as a point in a rectangular coordinate system. We then say that the aggregate of all points (x, y) as determined by the function $f(x)$ constitutes the *graph of the function*, or the graph of the equation $y = f(x)$.

When a function is given by means of an algebraic expression in x, for example, the simplest method of graphing the function is to assign values to x, compute the corresponding values of y, plot the pairs of numbers thus obtained, and join them with a smooth curve.

Example 1. Graph the function $3x - 5$.

Solution. Let $y = 3x - 5$; then assign values to x and compute the corresponding values of y, the results being conveniently arranged in a table.

x:	0	1	2	3
y:	−5	−2	1	4

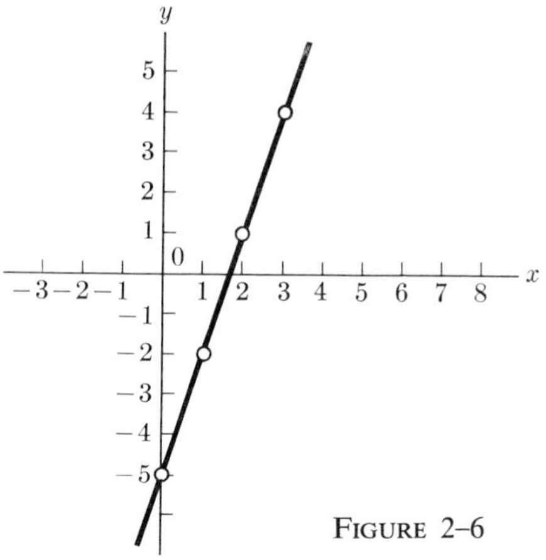

FIGURE 2–6

The various points (x, y) are then plotted and joined by a smooth curve, which turns out to be a straight line (Fig. 2–6).

Example 2. The surface S of a cube is given by the formula $S = 6x^2$, where x represents the length of an edge. Graph S as a function of x.

Solution. In the formula $S = 6x^2$, negative values of x may be used as well as positive ones. The points determined by these negative values of x belong to the graph of $S = 6x^2$, although they have no meaning in relation to the cube. The table of values from which the graph in Fig. 2–7 was constructed follows:

x:	-2	$-\frac{3}{2}$	-1	0	1	$\frac{3}{2}$	2
S:	24	$\frac{27}{2}$	6	0	6	$\frac{27}{2}$	24

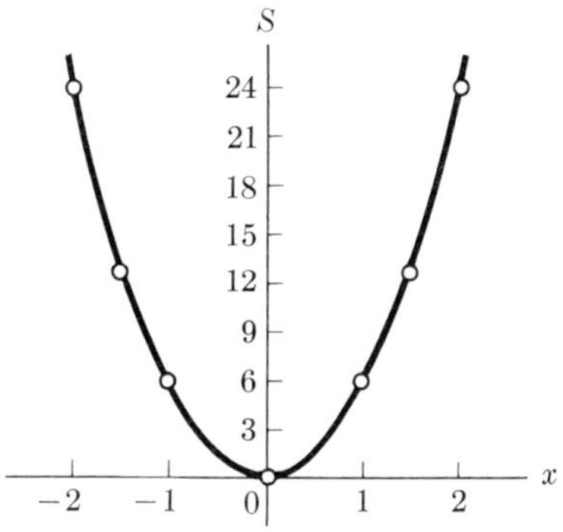

FIGURE 2–7

Note that the axis of ordinates is labeled S. Moreover, units of different size are used on the two axes; this may be done if convenient, but should be avoided where possible.

EXERCISE GROUP 2–4

In Exercises 1–14, draw the graph of the given function, the domain in each case being the set of real numbers.

1. $(x, x - 3)$
2. $(x, 2x + 5)$
3. $(x, -3x + 7)$
4. $(x, -2x - 5)$
5. $\left(x, \dfrac{-4x + 3}{5}\right)$
6. (x, x^2)
7. $(x, -x^2)$
8. $(x, 4x^2)$
9. $(x, 4x^2 - 4x)$
10. $(x, -4x^2 + 4x)$
11. $(x, 2x^2 - 3x + 1)$
12. (x, x^3)
13. $(x, -x^3 + 2x + 1)$
14. $(x, 2x^3 - x)$

In Exercises 15–20, draw the graph of the function whose values are given. The domain in each case is the set of numbers for which the values exist.

15. $\dfrac{1}{x}$ 16. $x + \dfrac{1}{x}$ 17. $\dfrac{2x + 9}{3x}$

18. $\dfrac{x}{x + 1}$ 19. $\dfrac{x}{x^2 + 1}$ 20. $-x^3$

21. If $f(x) = 2x - 3$, draw on the same coordinate system the functions whose values are, respectively, $f(2x)$, $f(\frac{1}{2}x)$, $f(x + 2)$, $f(x^2)$.

22. If $f(x) = x^2 - 3x$, draw on the same coordinate system the functions whose values are, respectively, $f(x - 3)$, $f(3x)$, $f(x/3)$.

2-7 GRAPHICAL REPRESENTATION OF EMPIRICAL DATA

The values of functions considered thus far have been largely defined by means of formulas. It is possible, however, for the quantities in two sets to be related functionally, although it may not be possible to determine a simple formula relation between the quantities of the two sets. For example, let us agree that when x is positive, y is equal to -5; when $x = 0$, $y = 2$; when x is negative, $y = -1$. A value of y is determined for each value of x; it follows from the definition of function that the pairs of numbers (x, y) define a function. The graph of this function, shown in Fig. 2-8, consists of the line $y = -1$ for negative x, the point $(0, 2)$, and the line $y = -5$ for positive x. It should be noted carefully that there is no formula expressing y in terms of x.

Experimental data, as well as such statistical data as vital statistics, populations, etc., in general cannot be expressed by means of mathematical formulas. It is often desirable, however, to have a graphical representation of such data for the use of scientists, businessmen, and engineers. The graph in Fig. 2-9 shows the mean monthly temperature for New York City, displayed as a function of time.

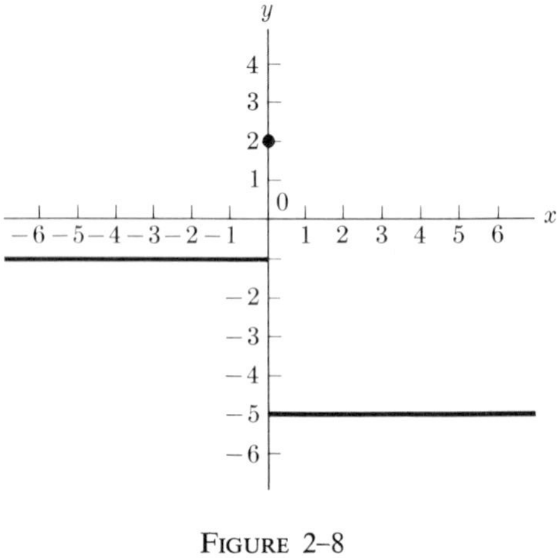

FIGURE 2-8

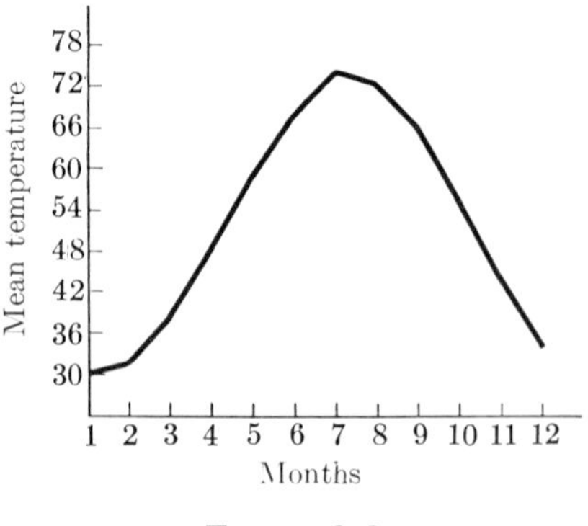

FIGURE 2-9

Month:	Jan.	Feb.	Mar.	Apr.	May	June	July	Aug.	Sept.	Oct.	Nov.	Dec.
Mean temp:	30°	31°	38°	48°	59°	68°	74°	72°	66°	56°	44°	34°

The construction of a graph representing empirical data differs in some ways from the construction of a graph of a function defined by a mathematical formula. We must decide how large the graph should be and then choose the units accordingly. We must also decide which is to be the independent variable, that is, the first quantity of the number pairs (usually this is plotted on the horizontal axis). In situations where time is one variable, this is usually taken as the independent variable, so that the graph expresses the other variable as a function of the time. Moreover, the points obtained from plotting the given data represent all the actual points of the graph. Hence, in general, no curve connecting the points exists, unlike the case of functions defined by formula. However, since the graph is more meaningful if the points are joined, it is customary to connect them, either by straight line segments as in Fig. 2–9, or by a smooth curve.

EXERCISE GROUP 2–5

In Exercises 1–3, draw the graph of the function consisting of the number pairs (x, y) as defined.

1. $(x, 2)$ for x negative, $(x, 0)$ for $x = 0$, and $(x, -1)$ for x positive.
2. $(x, -x)$ for x negative, $(x, 2)$ for $x = 0$, and (x, x) for x positive.
3. $(x, 0)$ for x less than -10, $(x, 1)$ for x greater than or equal to -10 and less than -5, $(x, 2)$ for x greater than or equal to -5 and less than 0, $(x, 3)$ for x greater than or equal to 0 and less than 5, $(x, 2)$ for x greater than or equal to 5 and less than 10, and $(x, 1)$ for x greater than or equal to 10.
4. The table gives the per capita public debt of the United States to the nearest dollar. Graph the debt as a function of the time.

Year:	1870	1880	1890	1900	1910	1920	1930	1940	1950	1960
Debt:	$61	$42	$18	$17	$12	$228	$132	$326	$1697	$1586

5. The table gives the total private debt (individual, corporate, and noncorporate) in the U. S., in billions of dollars. Graph the debt as a function of the time.

Year:	1919	1925	1931	1937	1943	1950	1953	1956	1959	1960
Debt:	$97.3	$132.7	$149.2	$128.1	$145.5	$250.9	$329.8	$439.4	$547.5	$581.9

6. The table gives the monthly average temperature for Milwaukee. Graph temperature as a function of the time.

Month:	Jan.	Feb.	Mar.	Apr.	May	June	July	Aug.	Sept.	Oct.	Nov.	Dec.
Temp:	21°	23°	33°	44°	54°	64°	71°	70°	63°	51°	37°	26°

7. The table gives the national income in the U. S., in billions of dollars. Graph the income as a function of the time.

Year:	1937	1939	1941	1943	1946	1953	1955	1957	1959	1960
Income:	$74	$73	$104	$168	$178	$306	$330	$367	$400	$417

8. The table gives the average rent paid for housing in the U. S., with the 1947–1949 average taken as 100. Graph the rent as a function of the time.

Year:	1947	1949	1950	1955	1956	1957	1958	1959	1960	1961
Rent:	94	105	109	130	133	135	138	140	142	143

9. The table gives the yearly transactions on the New York Stock Exchange, in millions of shares. Graph the transactions as a function of the time.

Year:	1900	1910	1920	1929	1930	1940	1950	1955	1958	1960
Trans:	139	164	228	1125	811	208	525	650	747	767

10. The table gives the production of meat in the U. S., in billions of pounds. Graph the production as a function of the time.

Year:	1935	1938	1941	1944	1950	1955	1958	1960
Prod:	14.4	16.5	19.5	24.7	22.1	26.9	25.7	28.2

11. The table gives the number of motor vehicles registered in the U. S., in millions (starting with 1959, Hawaii and Alaska are included). Graph the number as a function of the time.

Year:	1940	1945	1948	1949	1950	1953	1956	1959	1960
Number:	32.5	31.0	41.1	44.6	49.2	56.2	65.2	71.5	73.9

12. The table gives the production of lumber in the U. S., in billions of board-feet. Graph the production as a function of the time.

Year:	1869	1879	1889	1899	1909	1919	1929	1941	1949	1959
Prod:	12.8	18.7	27.0	35.0	44.5	35.6	36.9	33.6	32.2	37.1

13. The table gives the production of electrical energy for public use in the U. S., in millions of kilowatt-hours. Graph the production as a function of the time.

Year:	1925	1930	1935	1940	1945	1950	1955	1960
Prod:	61,145	91,112	95,287	141,837	222,486	328,998	547,038	752,861

14. The table gives the average hourly earnings (including overtime) in dollars, in manufacturing industries in the U. S. Graph earnings as a function of the time. (Draw separate graphs for durable and nondurable goods on the same axes.)

Year:	1941	1943	1945	1947	1949	1951	1953	1955	1957	1959
Av hourly earn durable goods:	0.81	1.06	1.11	1.29	1.46	1.67	1.87	2.01	2.20	2.38
Av hourly earn nondurable goods:	0.60	0.80	0.90	1.17	1.32	1.48	1.61	1.71	1.88	2.01

2-8 DIRECT VARIATION; INVERSE VARIATION

Statements of functional dependence are frequently expressed, particularly in the natural sciences, in the language of variation, and in order to treat these statements quantitatively it is desirable to express them in mathematical notation. For example, in the study of physics one encounters Hooke's Law, which states that the force applied to stretch an elastic spring varies directly as the amount of elongation. In algebraic notation the statement becomes

$$F = k \cdot s,$$

where F is the force applied, s is the amount of elongation, and k is a constant. The constant k, called a *constant of proportionality*, is an essential part of any algebraic statement of variation. In a given situation k does not depend on the values of the variables. Thus, in the example, if a pair of corresponding values of F and s is known, the value of k can be found, and it remains the same for that spring whatever values of s (within the elastic limits of the spring) may be involved. Indeed the value of k in Hooke's Law is an attribute of the spring itself and is known as the *modulus of elasticity*.

Example 1. In a spring to which Hooke's Law applies, a force of 18.6 lb stretches the spring by 1.27 in. Find k.

Solution. It is necessary merely to substitute the given values in the equation $F = ks$, obtaining

$$18.6 = k(1.27),$$

from which $k = 18.6/1.27 = 14.65$ lb/in.

A second kind of variation is involved in the statement "y varies inversely as x." Algebraically this becomes

$$y = \frac{k}{x},$$

for some constant of proportionality k.

Example 2. If y varies inversely as the cube of x, and $y = 7$ when $x = 2$, express y as a function of x.

Solution. The inverse variation is now with respect to x^3, and we have

$$y = \frac{k}{x^3}.$$

Since $y = 7$ and $x = 2$ must satisfy this relation, we obtain

$$7 = \frac{k}{2^3} = \frac{k}{8},$$

and we find $k = 7 \cdot 8 = 56$. Substitution of this value of k in the general relation gives

$$y = \frac{56}{x^3},$$

which expresses y as a function of x.

We may now, in addition, find the value of y corresponding to any value of x. If Example 2 had the added requirement to find the value of y when $x = 1.2$, the method of Example 2 would be carried out completely, and $x = 1.2$ would be substituted in the function, so that for $x = 1.2$, we have

$$y = \frac{56}{(1.2)^3} = \frac{56}{1.728} = 32.41.$$

Other expressions in use are "is proportional to" for "varies directly," and "is inversely proportional to" for "varies inversely."

EXERCISE GROUP 2–6

1. If y varies directly as x, and $y = 2$ when $x = 5$, write y as a function of x and determine the value of y when $x = 7$.
2. If y varies directly as x^2, and $y = 4$ when $x = 3$, write y as a function of x and determine the value of y when $x = -2$.
3. If u varies inversely as v, and $u = 4$ when $v = 2$, write u as a function of v and determine the value of u when $v = 3$.
4. If w varies inversely as z^3, and $w = 3$ when $z = 2$, write w as a function of z and then determine the value of w when $z = 3$.
5. If v varies directly as u where $u = xy$, and $v = 10$ when $x = 2$ and $y = 4$, write v as a function of u and find the value of v when $x = 3$ and $y = 6$.
6. If v varies inversely as u where $u = y/x$, and $v = 5$ when $x = 10$ and $y = 3$, write v as a function of u and find the value of v when $x = 7$ and $y = -1$.
7. The surface area of a sphere varies as the square of the radius. The area is 16π square units when the radius is 2. Determine a formula expressing the surface area as a function of the radius.
8. The distance a falling body travels (neglecting air resistance) varies as the square of the time of fall. If the body falls 64 ft in 2 sec (starting from rest), how far did it fall the first second? How far will it fall in t seconds?
9. The surface area of a cube varies directly as the square of the length of an edge. The surface area is 24 square units when the length of an edge is 2 units. Determine a formula expressing the surface area as a function of the length of an edge.
10. The intensity of light on a plane surface varies inversely as the square of the distance of the surface from the source of light. What is the change in the intensity when the distance is cut in half?
11. The volume of a pyramid of fixed altitude varies directly as the area of the base. The volume is 35 cubic units when the rectangular base is 5 units wide and 9 units long. Determine a formula expressing the volume as a function of the area of the base.
12. The volume of a prism of fixed altitude varies as the area of the base. The volume is 80 cubic units when the base, which is a right triangle, has edges of 3, 4, and 5 units each. Determine a formula expressing the volume of the prism as a function of the area of the base.
13. According to Newton's Law of Gravitation the force of attraction between two objects varies inversely as the square of the distance between the centers of the objects.

What is the change in the attracting force between two bodies when the distance between their centers is reduced by 50%?

14. Boyle's Law states that the pressure p of a gas at constant temperature varies inversely as the volume v. If $v = 500 \text{ in}^3$ when $p = 30 \text{ lb/in}^2$, express p as a function of v and determine the value of p when $v = 200 \text{ in}^3$.

2-9 COMBINED VARIATIONS

The laws of nature are such that functional dependence often involves more than two variables. In such cases we speak of *joint variation*, if direct variation on more than one variable is involved. We may also have inverse variation on more than one variable, or a combination of both direct and inverse variation.

In physics it is shown that the intensity of light falling on an object varies directly as the intensity of the source of illumination, and inversely as the square of the distance of the object from the source. In algebraic notation this becomes

$$I = k \cdot \frac{w}{d^2},$$

where I is used to designate the intensity of light on the object, w is the intensity of the source, d is the distance of the object from the source, and k is the constant of proportionality. The direct variation is indicated by the multiplication by w, and the inverse variation by the division by d^2.

Example. The strength S of a rectangular beam varies directly as the width w and the square of the depth d. If a beam 2 in. wide and 4 in. deep will support 1200 lb, what weight will a beam 4 in. wide and 2 in. deep support?

Solution. The relation is $S = kwd^2$, and with $S = 1200$, $w = 2$, $d = 4$, we have $1200 = k \cdot 2 \cdot 4^2$, so that $k = \frac{75}{2}$, and the formula becomes

$$S = \tfrac{75}{2} wd^2.$$

Now we set $w = 4$, $d = 2$, and we find

$$S = \tfrac{75}{2} \cdot 4 \cdot 2^2 = 600 \text{ lb}.$$

We see that a 2×4 on edge as a "beam" will support twice as much as the same 2×4 lying flat as a "plank."

EXERCISE GROUP 2-7

1. If y varies jointly as x^2 and z, and $y = 3$ when $x = 2$ and $z = 6$, write y as a function of x and z, and determine the value of y when $x = -3$ and $z = 10$.
2. If s varies jointly as r^2 and t, and $s = 3$ when $r = 2$ and $t = 5$, write s as a function of r and t, and determine the value of s when $r = -5$ and $t = 3$.
3. If u varies directly as v^2 and inversely as w^3, and $u = 5$ when $v = 3$ and $w = 2$, write u as a function of v and w, and then determine the value of u when $v = -5$ and $w = 2$.

4. If y varies directly as x^3 and inversely as z^2, and $y = 7$ when $x = -5$ and $z = 3$, write y as a function of x and z, and determine the value of y when $x = 2$ and $z = -3$.

5. W varies jointly as u and v^2 and inversely as t^3, and $W = 27$ when $u = 3$, $v = 2$, and $t = 2$. Write W as a function of u, v, and t and then determine the value of W when $u = 5$, $v = 3$, and $t = 4$.

6. S varies directly as r^2 and inversely as the product v^3t, and $S = 36$ when $r = 3$, $v = 2$, and $t = 5$. Write S as a function of r, v, and t and then determine the value of S when $r = 5$, $v = 4$, and $t = 3$.

7. Y varies jointly as x and z^2 and inversely as u^3 and v, and $Y = 90$ when $x = 5$, $z = 3$, $u = 2$, and $v = -4$. Write Y as a function of x, z, u, and v, and then determine the value of Y when $x = 3$, $z = -7$, $u = 4$, and $v = 5$.

8. The lumber required to build a closet in the corner of a room varies directly as the sum of the width and length of the closet. Which would require less lumber, a closet 4×4 ft or one 3.5×5 ft?

9. Labor costs vary jointly as the number of workers and the average number of hours of work per worker per week. If the labor costs are \$105,307 per week when there are 1200 workers with an average work week of 36.4 hours per worker, what will the labor costs be (to the nearest dollar) with an average work week of 38 hours per worker and a working force of 1100 men?

10. The gravitational attraction between two objects varies as the product of their masses and inversely as the square of the distance between their centers of mass. What will be the change in the attraction between the two objects if their masses are cut in half and the distance between their centers is also cut in half?

11. Under certain conditions the thrust T of a propeller varies jointly as the fourth power of its diameter and the square of the number of revolutions per minute that it is turning. What is the change in T when the diameter is decreased 50% and the revolutions are increased 25%?

12. The lift of an airplane wing varies as the area of the wing and the square of the velocity of the plane. Compute the change in the lift (a) if the wing area is reduced 50% and the velocity increased 50%, (b) if the wing area is increased 50% and the velocity reduced 50%.

13. The crushing load of a pillar varies as the fourth power of its diameter and inversely as the square of its length. If a load of 56 tons will crush a 6-in. pillar which is 30 ft high, what diameter must a 20-ft pillar (20 ft high) have if it is to support a load of 8 tons?

14. The safe load for a uniformly distributed load on a horizontal beam supported at both ends varies jointly as the breadth and the square of the depth and inversely as the distance between the supports. If a beam 8 ft long, 2 in. wide, and 6 in. deep can safely support 1800 lb, how much can a beam 16 ft long, 2 in. wide, and 8 in. deep safely support?

15. The time required for an elevator to lift a weight varies jointly as the weight and the distance through which the weight is lifted and inversely as the power of the motor. If 30 sec are required for a 4-hp motor to lift 600 lb through 50 ft, what power is necessary to lift 1000 lb 150 ft in 40 sec?

SUPPLEMENTARY EXERCISES FOR CHAPTER 2

In Exercises 1–4, the given number pairs define a function f with domain consisting of all real numbers for which the second expression is defined. In each case find $f(-3)$ and $f(5)$.

1. $(x, 2x^2)$
2. $\left(x, \dfrac{3x}{5 - 2x}\right)$
3. $(x, 5 + 2x - 3x^2)$
4. $(x, x - x^{-2})$
5. Given $f(x) = 15 - 2x - x^2$, find $f(-1)$, $f(0)$, $f(3)$, $f(-a)$.
6. Given $G(y) = (5 - y)/(y - 4)$, find $G(-2)$, $G(0)$, $G(-\frac{3}{2})$, $G(-x)$.
7. If $f(x) = (3x - 5)/2x$ and $G(x) = x^2/(2x + 3)$, compute $G[f(-1)]$.

Draw the graph of each of the functions in Exercises 8–11.

8. $\dfrac{x - 1}{x^2}$
9. $2 - 3x - x^2$
10. $3x - \dfrac{5}{x}$
11. $3x^2 - x^3$

In each of Exercises 12–15, find the directed distance from the first point to the second point.

12. $(7, -3)$, $(-5, -3)$
13. $(2, -7)$, $(2, 6)$
14. $(3, 5)$, $(3, -12)$
15. $(-13, 7)$, $(3, 7)$

In each of Exercises 16–19, determine the coordinates of the point midway between the two given points and also the distance between them.

16. $(-3, 5)$, $(8, -17)$
17. $(15, -9)$, $(-2, 17)$
18. (p, q), (r, s)
19. (a, d), (b, c)
20. The following table gives the population in thousands for the years indicated. Graph the population as a function of the time.

Year:	1880	1890	1900	1910	1920	1930	1940	1950
Pop:	503	1,100	1,699	2,185	2,702	3,376	3,397	3,621

21. The following table gives the petroleum production in thousands of barrels in the United States for the years indicated. Graph the production as a function of the time.

Year:	1925	1930	1935	1940	1945	1950	1955
Prod:	763,743	898,011	996,596	1,353,214	1,713,655	1,973,574	2,484,521

22. The cube of the diameter of a solid steel shaft varies directly as the hp (horsepower) transmitted and inversely as the number of revolutions per minute that it turns. If a $\frac{1}{2}$-in. shaft turning at 3000 rpm will transmit 50 hp, determine the cube of the diameter of the shaft needed to transmit 200 hp when turning at 2500 rpm.
23. The thickness of a pipe of d in. in internal diameter required to withstand a pressure of p lb/in.^{2} varies jointly as the diameter and the pressure. If a given pipe $\frac{1}{8}$ in. thick and 6 in. in diameter will withstand 50 lb/in.^{2} pressure, how thick must a 1-in. pipe of the same material be to withstand 150 lb/in.^{2} pressure?

24. The mass in grams of a metal deposited through electrolytic conduction varies jointly as the time, the current passing through the solution, and the atomic weight of the element being used, and inversely as the valence of the element. A mass of 1.22 gm of nickel (atomic weight 56.68, valence 2) is deposited in one hour by a current of one ampere. How much zinc (atomic weight 65.37, valence 2) would be deposited in $\frac{1}{2}$ hour by a current of 1.5 amp?

25. The kinetic energy of a body varies jointly as the mass of the body and the square of its velocity. If the kinetic energy is 2420 ft-lb when the mass is 10 lb and the velocity is 22 ft/sec, determine the kinetic energy of a 3000-lb automobile traveling 60 mi/hr.

26. A cylindrical tin can is to be constructed with a given fixed volume V, but with variable dimensions. Express the amount A of tin required as a function of the radius r of the base (neglect the thickness of the tin).

27. An open box (no top) is to be made from a sheet of tin 12×16 in. by cutting equal squares from each of the four corners and bending up the edges. Let x be the length of a side of the squares cut out and then express the volume V of the box as a function of x.

28. A right circular cone is inscribed in a sphere of radius 16 in. Express the volume of the cone as a function of its altitude.

29. A trough of rectangular cross section is to be made from a long rectangular sheet of metal 20 in. wide, by bending up the edges. Express the cross-sectional area of the trough as a function of its depth.

30. Show that the diagonals of a rectangle bisect each other. [*Hint*: Determine the midpoint of each diagonal.]

CHAPTER 3

The Trigonometric Ratios

3–1 INTRODUCTION TO THE TRIGONOMETRIC FUNCTIONS

Historically, the origins of the study of trigonometry lie in the determination of distances, areas, and directions on the earth by the use of triangles, for purposes of what we know as surveying. For mathematics, however, the measurement aspect of the study has assumed minor importance, although it is still significant. *The mathematics of trigonometry involves the study of the trigonometric functions, the mode of variation of these functions, and the relations among them.* The applications of trigonometry from this point of view are many, both in science and in engineering.

In algebra several classes of function, that is, certain algebraic, exponential, and logarithmic functions, are studied from various points of view. The content of the subject of trigonometry may then be described, in a very real sense, as merely the extension of algebra to the class of trigonometric functions or, briefly, as the algebra of the trigonometric functions. It is then implicit in this statement that the definitions, properties, and theorems of algebra carry over without change. Furthermore, the concepts and results of plane geometry have their use in the development of certain properties of the functions, and also in the applications involving measurement.

3–2 GENERAL ANGLES

Familiarity with the general angle and its measurement is prerequisite to the study of the trigonometric functions. Let us consider two *half-lines*, that is, two straight lines meeting at the point O, terminating at O, but extending indefinitely in the direction away from O. If A and B are two points, one on each of these lines, we shall designate the lines as OA and OB, as in Fig. 3–1, and shall define what is meant by angle as follows.

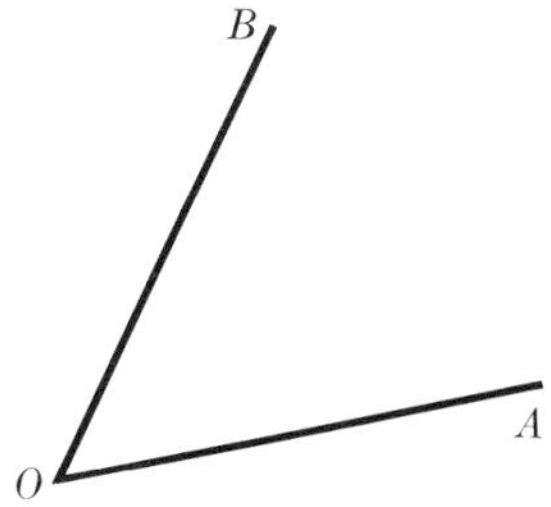

FIGURE 3–1

***Definition* 3–1.** *An angle that OB makes with OA shall mean an amount of rotation about O, in the plane of OA and OB, which is required to make OA coincide with OB.*

The designation of an angle thus requires an *initial line*, such as OA, a *terminal line*, such as OB, and an *amount of rotation.* (A discussion of the measurement of the amount of rotation in an angle appears in Section 3–3.) The intersection O of OA and OB is called the *vertex* of the angle.

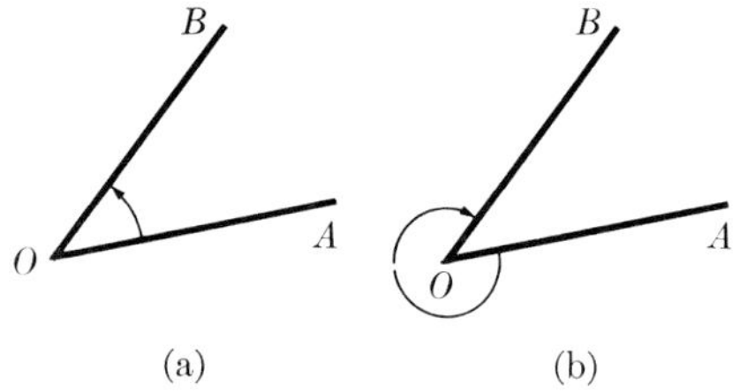

FIGURE 3–2

The student should note that the definition mentions *an* angle, rather than *the* angle. For one thing, a line may rotate in a plane about a point in either of two directions, designated as *clockwise* and *counterclockwise*, the clockwise direction being that of the motion of the hands of a clock, and the counterclockwise direction being opposite to that of the motion of the hands of a clock. The direction of rotation of an angle is not specified in the definition. Thus, Fig. 3–2(a) shows an angle that OB makes with OA, measured in a counterclockwise direction, while (b) shows an angle with the initial and terminal lines in the same position, measured in a clockwise direction.

The counterclockwise direction of rotation will be taken as the positive direction, and a clockwise rotation will be taken as negative.

Furthermore, the definition of angle does not specify that the rotation is to cease the first time the terminal side is reached. It is thus clear that the angle that OB makes with OA is not uniquely determined. In fact, the totality of all angles that OB makes with OA in Fig. 3–2(a) is obtained by adding any number of complete rotations, positive or negative, to the angle shown.

3–3 DEGREE MEASURE OF AN ANGLE

The two units of angular measure to be considered for our purposes are the *degree* and the *radian*. The angle indicated in Fig. 3–3(a) is a complete positive rotation, that in (b) is a positive straight angle, or half of a complete positive rotation, and that in (c) is a positive right angle, or half of a positive straight angle. A *degree* (°) is *defined* as $\frac{1}{360}$ of a complete rotation, or equivalently, as $\frac{1}{180}$ of a straight angle, or $\frac{1}{90}$ of a right angle, all positive; a *minute* (′) is defined as $\frac{1}{60}$ of a degree, and a *second* (″) is $\frac{1}{60}$ of a minute. The degree measures of the angles indicated in Fig. 3–3 are then given as 360°, 180°, and 90°, respectively.

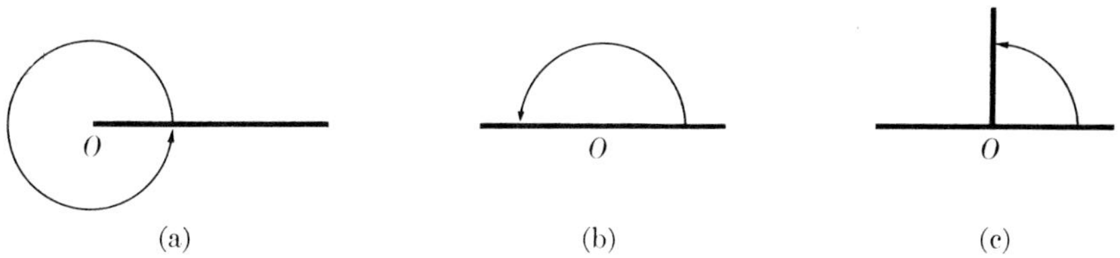

FIGURE 3–3

Examples. $\frac{1}{4}(90°) = 22°\,30'$; $\frac{1}{16}(90°) = 5°\,37'\,30''$;

$$\tfrac{1}{8}° = \tfrac{1}{8}(60') = 7.5' = 7'\,30'';$$

$$11'' = \tfrac{11}{60}' = 0.183'; \qquad 43'' = \tfrac{43}{60}' = 0.717'.$$

3–4 RADIAN MEASURE OF AN ANGLE

The second unit of angular measure to be considered will now be introduced. Consider a circle of radius r, as shown in Fig. 3–4, and lay off on the circumference, in the positive direction, an arc AB of length r, starting at any point A. *The positive angle AOB at the center of the circle, subtended by this arc of length r, will be taken as a unit of angular measure, and will be designated as* 1 *radian* (abbreviated as *rad*).

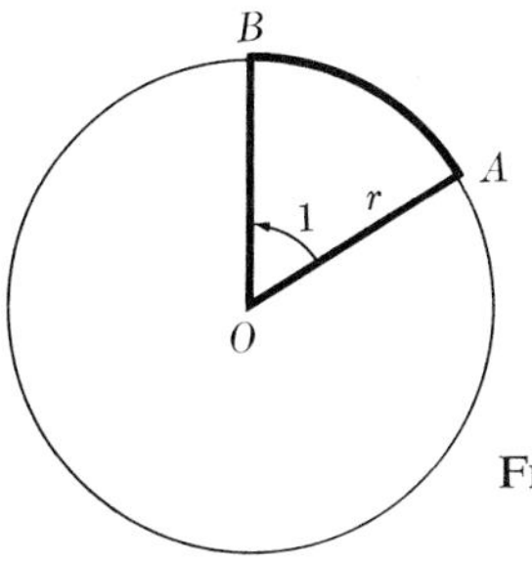

FIGURE 3–4

The student should convince himself, in the course of the following discussion, that *this unit is independent of the length of the radius of the circle.*

It is clear that the radian is large in relation to the degree, something less than 60°; the precise relation between the two units will now be determined. Since for the length C of the circumference of a circle we have the formula $C = 2\pi r$, it follows that an arc of length r can be laid off in the positive direction exactly 2π times in order to cover the complete circumference. Hence a complete rotation requires 2π rad in radian measure, and 360° in degree measure, so that the desired relation between the two measures is

$$\boxed{2\pi \text{ rad} = 360°.}$$

To convert from one type of measure to the other we usually use the following relations, which are easily obtained from the preceding one:

$$1 \text{ rad} = \frac{180^\circ}{\pi} = 57.296^\circ = 57^\circ 17' 45'' \text{ (approx.)}$$

and

$$1^\circ = \frac{\pi}{180} \text{ rad} = 0.017453 \text{ rad (approx.).}$$

When no unit of measurement is indicated for an angle, it will be understood that radian measure is implied.

Example 1.

$$180^\circ = \pi \text{ rad}; \qquad 90^\circ = \pi/2 \text{ rad};$$

$$-315^\circ = -315 \times \frac{\pi}{180} \text{ rad} = -\frac{7\pi}{4} \text{ rad};$$

$$116^\circ = 116(0.017453) \text{ rad} = 2.025 \text{ rad (approx.).}$$

Example 2.

$$\frac{5\pi}{6} \text{ rad} = \frac{5\pi}{6} \cdot \frac{180^\circ}{\pi} = 150^\circ;$$

$$-\frac{9\pi}{4} \text{ rad} = -\frac{9\pi}{4} \cdot \frac{180^\circ}{\pi} = -405^\circ;$$

$$1.67 \text{ rad} = 1.67 \times 57.296^\circ = 95.684^\circ = 95^\circ\, 41'\, 2.4'' \text{ (approx.).}$$

It must be understood, in any radian measure involving π, that π is the familiar number $\pi = 3.14159\ldots$. Thus, a straight angle of π rad is also, to two decimals, 3.14 rad.

EXERCISE GROUP 3–1

Express each of the angles in Exercises 1–16 in degrees.

1. $3\pi/4$	2. $2\pi/3$	3. $5\pi/6$	4. $2\pi/9$
5. $-5\pi/9$	6. $11\pi/10$	7. $2\pi/15$	8. $\pi/30$
9. $7\pi/15$	10. $-7\pi/30$	11. $\pi/24$	12. $3\pi/8$
13. $-5\pi/3$	14. $3\pi/5$	15. $-13\pi/45$	16. $7\pi/20$

Express each of the angles in Exercises 17–28 in degrees, minutes, and seconds.

17. 1.2 rad	18. 2.3 rad	19. 0.57 rad	20. 1.07 rad
21. 0.03 rad	22. 0.17 rad	23. 5 rad	24. 1.45 rad
25. −2.73 rad	26. −6.31 rad	27. 3.61 rad	28. −31.7 rad

Express each of the angles in Exercises 29–40 in radians, in terms of π.

29. 330°	30. 108°	31. 252°	32. 510°
33. 810°	34. 12°	35. 468°	36. 85°
37. 48°	38. 115°	39. 130°	40. 65°

Express each of the angles in Exercises 41–52 as a decimal number of radians.

41. 34° 17′	42. 56° 32′ 12″	43. 143° 19′	44. 194°
45. 210° 46′ 27″	46. −217° 56′	47. 119° 43′	48. 113°
49. −437° 37′	50. 513° 23′ 37″	51. 76° 45′	52. 473°

3–5 STANDARD POSITION OF AN ANGLE. THE REFERENCE ANGLE

The axes (also called the coordinate axes) divide the plane into four parts, or *quadrants*, each of which may be characterized by the signs of the coordinates of a point in it. The quadrant in which x and y are both positive is designated as Q_1; then Q_2, Q_3, and Q_4 are the quadrants met successively in a counterclockwise rotation about the origin. We may tabulate this information as follows:

	Q_1	Q_2	Q_3	Q_4
x:	+	−	−	+
y:	+	+	−	−

Points on the coordinate axes are not in any quadrant; the axes actually separate the quadrants.

An angle θ is said to be in *standard position* if its vertex is at the origin of a rectangular coordinate system, and the initial line of θ lies along the positive x-axis. When an angle is in standard position, the terminal line will lie either in some quadrant, or on one of the axes. *If the terminal side of an angle in standard position lies in a certain quadrant, we say also that the angle lies in that quadrant.* Thus, the negative angle θ shown in Fig. 3–5 is in standard position, and is said to lie in Q_3.

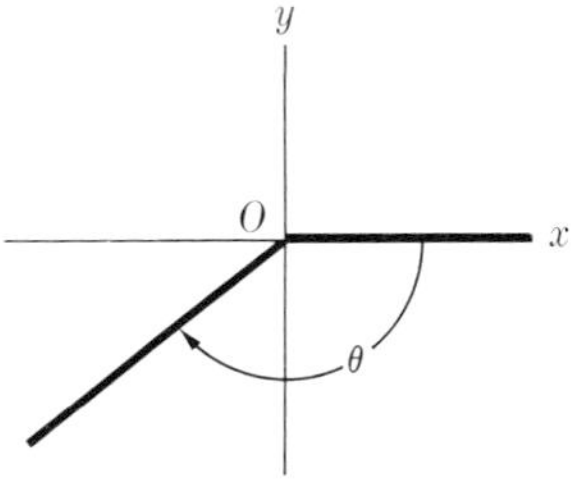

FIGURE 3–5

Example 1. Consider the angles $45° + n \cdot 90°$, where n may be any integer. If $n = 0$, the angle is 45° and is in Q_1; if $n = 1$, the angle is 135° and is in Q_2; if $n = 2$, the angle is in Q_3, and so on.

Angles which, when placed in standard position, have the same terminal side, are said to be *coterminal.* As an illustration, it is easy to see that 135°, −225°, and 495° are coterminal angles.

When an angle is placed in standard position, one of the angles between its terminal line and the x-axis will be either a positive acute angle, or a right angle, or zero. The angle thus described is known as the *reference angle* for θ. The reference angle, unless it is a right angle or zero, can always be said to lie in Q_1. For example, if the angle shown in Fig. 3–5 is −140°, the reference angle is made with the negative x-axis and is 40°. We may define the reference angle formally as follows:

***Definition* 3–2.** *The reference angle for an angle θ is the smallest non-negative angle between the terminal line of θ and the x-axis, when θ is in standard position.*

In general, the reference angle for θ is some multiple of 180°, or of π, plus or minus θ. To find the reference angle one should draw θ in standard position, or think of it as so drawn. Thus, the reference angle for 313° is 47°, that for 847° is 53°, and the one for $8\pi/3$ is $\pi/3$.

Example 2. Draw the angle −135° in standard position, and find the point on the terminal side for which $r = 2$.

Solution. The angle −135° is shown in Fig. 3–6. If $OP = 2$, we have

$$x^2 + y^2 = 4. \qquad (1)$$

Since angle $MOP = 45°$, and x and y are both negative, we have $y = x$. Then (1) gives

$$2x^2 = 4, \qquad x = -\sqrt{2}.$$

Hence the point is $P(-\sqrt{2}, -\sqrt{2})$.

Example 3. Draw the angle $2\pi/3$ in standard position, and find the point (x', y') on its terminal side for which $x' = -2$.

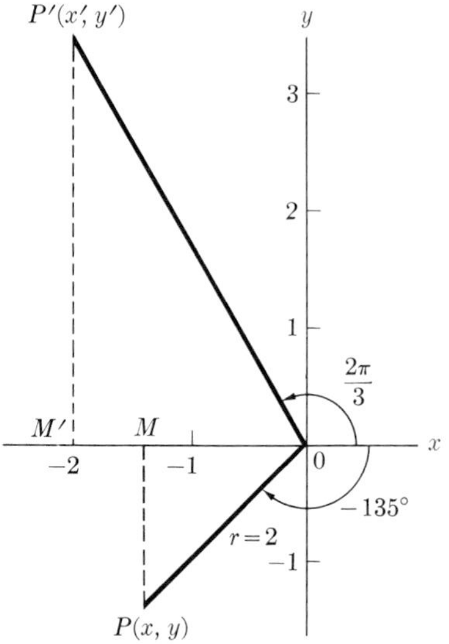

FIGURE 3–6

Solution. The angle $2\pi/3$ is also shown in Fig. 3–6 in standard position. The angle $P'OM'$ is $\pi/3$ or 60°. Hence, by a theorem of plane geometry the length of OP' is twice that of OM', and $OP' = 4$. Then, by the distance formula, we have

$$x'^2 + y'^2 = 4^2, \qquad \text{and} \qquad y'^2 = 4^2 - (-2)^2 = 12;$$

since y' is positive in Q_2, we obtain

$$y' = \sqrt{12} = 2\sqrt{3}.$$

The desired point is then $(-2, 2\sqrt{3})$.

EXERCISE GROUP 3–2

In Exercises 1–8, draw the given angle in standard position, and find the point on the terminal side of the angle for which $r = 1$.

1. $60°$ 2. $150°$ 3. $-135°$ 4. $-120°$
5. $\pi/6$ 6. $3\pi/4$ 7. $-5\pi/3$ 8. $-9\pi/4$

In Exercises 9–16, determine the quadrant in which the angle lies, and also determine the reference angle.

9. $213°$ 10. $-69°$ 11. $-227°$ 12. $437°$
13. $281° 30'$ 14. $-139° 17'$ 15. $115° 07'$ 16. $193° 58'$

In Exercises 17–26, determine whichever of the quantities x, y, r are not given, and plot the corresponding point P.

17. $x = 4$, $r = 5$, P in Q_4
18. $x = 12$, $y = -9$
19. $y = 8$, $r = 9$, P in Q_2
20. $r = 15$, $y = 10$
21. $r = \sqrt{13}$, $y = \sqrt{10}$
22. $r = 10$, $x = 6\sqrt{2}$
23. $r = 2\sqrt{17}$, $y = 4x$
24. $r = 5$, $y = 3x$
25. $r = 2 + y$, $x = -2$
26. $r = x + 1$, $y = -4$

In Exercises 27–35, find the quadrant in which the angle lies if θ is a positive acute angle.

27. $\theta + 270°$ 28. $\theta - 450°$ 29. $\theta + 180°$
30. $450° - \theta$ 31. $540° + \theta$ 32. $-630° - \theta$
33. $\theta - 3\pi/2$ 34. $7\pi/2 - \theta$ 35. $5\pi/2 + \theta$

36. If θ is between $360°$ and $450°$, (a) in what range must 2θ be? (b) in what range must $\theta/2$ be?
37. If θ is between $0°$ and $90°$, (a) in what range must 2θ be? (b) in what range must $\theta/2$ be?
38. If θ is to lie between $360°$ and $720°$, (a) in what range must $\theta/2$ be? (b) in what range must $3\theta/4$ be?
39. If θ is to lie between $0°$ and $360°$, (a) in what range must $\theta/2$ be? (b) in what range must $2\theta/3$ be?
40. In what range must $A - B$ lie, (a) if A and B are angles in the range between $0°$ and $90°$? (b) if A is between $0°$ and $90°$ and B is between $270°$ and $450°$?
41. In what range must $A + B$ lie for the angles in Exercise 40?

In each of the following problems, determine how many consecutive integral values of n, starting with zero, must be used in order that the terminal lines of these angles start repeating. Draw, in standard position, the different angles obtained.

42. $60° + n \cdot 180°$ 43. $45° + n \cdot 360°$ 44. $n \cdot 45°$
45. $30° + n \cdot 90°$ 46. $\dfrac{180° + n \cdot 360°}{5}$ 47. $\frac{2}{3}(2n\pi)$
48. $\frac{3}{2}(\pi/2 + 2n\pi)$ 49. $\dfrac{90° + n \cdot 360°}{4}$ 50. $5\pi/3 - 3n\pi/2$
51. $-\frac{3}{4}(\pi/3 + 2n\pi)$ 52. $-4\pi/3 + 2n\pi/5$ 53. $-2\pi/5 - 5n\pi/7$

3–6 DEFINITIONS OF THE TRIGONOMETRIC RATIOS

The necessary groundwork for defining the trigonometric ratios has now been laid. We shall designate the *radius vector* of a point P in a coordinate system as the line OP drawn from the origin to the point; the *length* of OP, always taken as positive or zero, will be called the *polar distance* of P. If x, y, r are the coordinates and polar distance of a point not on the coordinate axes, six ratios can be formed with these quantities; these ratios will be, *once the manner in which an angle determines these ratios is known*, the six trigonometric ratios of the angle. The trigonometric ratios to be defined are the *sine*, *cosine*, *tangent*, *cotangent*, *secant*, and *cosecant*.

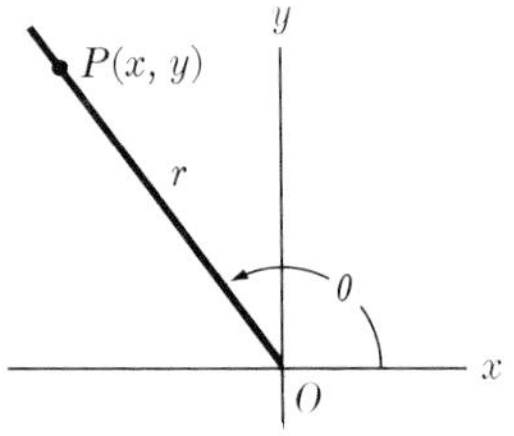

FIGURE 3–7

***Definition* 3–3.** *If θ is any angle other than an integral multiple of* 90°, *place θ in standard position. Let $P(x, y)$, with polar distance r, be a point* (*not the origin*) *on the terminal line of θ when so placed.* (See Fig. 3–7.) *The trigonometric ratios of θ are then defined as follows* (*with the abbreviation of each name given*)*:*

$$\sin\theta = \frac{y}{r} = \frac{\text{ordinate of } P}{\text{polar distance of } P},$$

$$\cos\theta = \frac{x}{r} = \frac{\text{abscissa of } P}{\text{polar distance of } P},$$

$$\tan\theta = \frac{y}{x} = \frac{\text{ordinate of } P}{\text{abscissa of } P},$$

$$\cot\theta = \frac{x}{y} = \frac{\text{abscissa of } P}{\text{ordinate of } P},$$

$$\sec\theta = \frac{r}{x} = \frac{\text{polar distance of } P}{\text{abscissa of } P},$$

$$\csc\theta = \frac{r}{y} = \frac{\text{polar distance of } P}{\text{ordinate of } P}.$$

It is apparent, on careful study of this definition, that the values of the trigonometric ratios of any angle can be found immediately, once the coordinates of a point on the terminal line of the angle in standard position are known.

Example 1. Determine the values of the trigonometric ratios of θ, if the point $(2, -5)$ lies on the terminal line of θ when θ is in standard position.

Solution. The polar distance of the given point can be found directly from the distance formula and is

$$r = \sqrt{2^2 + (-5)^2} = \sqrt{4 + 25} = \sqrt{29}.$$

The above definitions then give

$$\sin\theta = \frac{y}{r} = -\frac{5}{\sqrt{29}}, \qquad \cos\theta = \frac{x}{r} = \frac{2}{\sqrt{29}},$$

$$\tan\theta = \frac{y}{x} = -\frac{5}{2}, \qquad \cot\theta = \frac{x}{y} = -\frac{2}{5},$$

$$\sec\theta = \frac{r}{x} = \frac{\sqrt{29}}{2}, \qquad \csc\theta = \frac{r}{y} = -\frac{\sqrt{29}}{5}.$$

Note that these results do not depend on the kind of measure used for θ.

The trigonometric ratios as defined above depend only on the angle; when a value, other than a multiple of 90° or of $\pi/2$, is assigned to θ, the values of the respective ratios of θ are determined. The proof of this important fact requires merely the proof that the value of any of the above ratios depends only on the angle and is independent of the choice of the point P on the terminal side of θ, and this is a simple matter when we use similar triangles. For angles which are multiples of 90° or of $\pi/2$, and hence not included in the above definition, the definitions will appear in Section 3–8.

All properties of the trigonometric ratios are based ultimately on these definitions. A number of these properties will be treated in what follows. Two simple, but important, properties are mentioned here. The first one involves coterminal angles, which were defined in Section 3–5. Since the values of the trigonometric ratios of any angle depend only on x, y, r of a point on its terminal line, and the terminal line is the same for coterminal angles, we have at once the following result.

Theorem 3–1. *The same-named trigonometric ratios of coterminal angles are equal.*

Accordingly, statements such as the following can be made immediately:

$$\cos 395° = \cos 35°,$$

$$\tan 315° = \tan(-45°),$$

$$\csc(-753°) = \csc 327°,$$

$$\sin 4\pi/3 = \sin(-2\pi/3) = \sin(-8\pi/3).$$

The second property concerns the signs of the trigonometric ratios in the various quadrants. For example, in the second quadrant x is negative and y and r are positive. Hence, the sine of any angle in Q_2 is the quotient of two positive numbers and must be positive, while the cosine is the quotient of numbers of opposite sign, and must be negative. In this manner the following chart for the signs of the trigonometric ratios is obtained.

+	+
−	−

$\sin\theta$, $\csc\theta$

−	+
−	+

$\cos\theta$, $\sec\theta$

−	+
+	−

$\tan\theta$, $\cot\theta$

Example 2. Find the remaining trigonometric ratios of θ if $\sin\theta = -\frac{3}{4}$, with θ in Q_3.

Solution. Let $P(x, y)$ with polar distance r be a point on the terminal line of θ in standard position (Fig. 3–8). Then, by the definition of $\sin\theta$, we must have

$$\frac{y}{r} = -\frac{3}{4}.$$

We may choose any positive value for r, and then choose y such that $y = -\frac{3}{4}r$. For example, $r = 1$, $y = -\frac{3}{4}$, or $r = 2$, $y = -\frac{3}{2}$ may be used. However, we seek convenient values, and choose for this purpose $r = 4$, so that $y = -3$. Then by the distance formula we obtain $x = -\sqrt{4^2 - (-3)^2} = -\sqrt{7}$ (since x must be negative in Q_3). The definitions of the other ratios immediately give

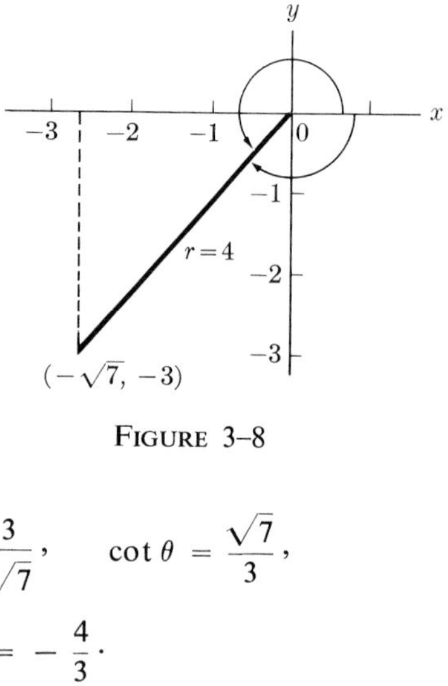

FIGURE 3–8

$$\cos\theta = -\frac{\sqrt{7}}{4}, \qquad \tan\theta = \frac{-3}{-\sqrt{7}} = \frac{3}{\sqrt{7}}, \qquad \cot\theta = \frac{\sqrt{7}}{3},$$

$$\sec\theta = -\frac{4}{\sqrt{7}}, \qquad \csc\theta = -\frac{4}{3}.$$

In Fig. 3–8 two of the possible angles θ are shown. The values of the ratios which have been obtained apply also to any angle coterminal with the angles shown.

If the restriction that θ lie in Q_3 is removed, θ may also be in Q_4, in which case $x = \sqrt{7}$, and the corresponding values of the remaining ratios would be

$$\cos\theta = \frac{\sqrt{7}}{4}, \qquad \tan\theta = -\frac{3}{\sqrt{7}}, \qquad \cot\theta = -\frac{\sqrt{7}}{3},$$

$$\sec\theta = \frac{4}{\sqrt{7}}, \qquad \csc\theta = -\frac{4}{3}.$$

EXERCISE GROUP 3–3

In Exercises 1–12, find the values of the six trigonometric ratios of the angle θ, which is in standard position, if:

1. $(-4, 3)$ is on the terminal line of θ,
2. $(20, 3)$ is on the terminal line of θ,
3. $(-3, -5)$ is on the terminal line of θ,
4. $(-7, -24)$ is on the terminal line of θ,
5. $(-8, 6)$ is on the terminal line of θ,
6. $(5, -12)$ is on the terminal line of θ,
7. for some point on the terminal line of θ, $r = 9$, $y = -2$,
8. for some point on the terminal line of θ, $r = 13$, $x = 5$,
9. for some point on the terminal line of θ, $x = 5$, $r = 3y$,
10. for every point on the terminal line of θ, $y = -x$,
11. for every point on the terminal line of θ, $y = -2x$,
12. for every point on the terminal line of θ, $3y = 4x$.

In Exercises 13–36, find the values of the remaining trigonometric ratios of θ.

13. $\sin\theta = 4/5$, $\cos\theta$ positive
14. $\tan\theta = 3/2$, $\cos\theta$ negative
15. $\sec\theta = 2$, $\sin\theta$ positive
16. $\cos\theta = 7/25$, $\sin\theta$ negative
17. $\cot\theta = -4/3$, $\sec\theta$ negative
18. $\csc\theta = -5/3$, $\cot\theta$ negative
19. $\csc\theta = 13/5$, $\tan\theta$ positive
20. $\sec\theta = -3$, $\csc\theta$ negative
21. $\tan\theta = -2/3$
22. $\sin\theta = 24/25$
23. $\sin\theta = 3/4$
24. $\cot\theta = 5/2$
25. $\sin\theta = 1/2$, θ in Q_2
26. $\cos\theta = -5/13$, θ in Q_3
27. $\cot\theta = -15/2$, θ in Q_4
28. $\sec\theta = 25/7$, θ in Q_4
29. $\csc\theta = -25/24$, θ in Q_3
30. $\tan\theta = -\sqrt{3}$, θ in Q_2
31. $\cos\theta = 2/3$
32. $\tan\theta = 5$
33. $\sec\theta = -3$
34. $\cos\theta = -2/5$
35. $\cot\theta = -7$
36. $\csc\theta = 9$

3–7 TRIGONOMETRIC RATIOS OF SPECIAL ANGLES

The values of the trigonometric ratios of any angle can be approximated as closely as desired; a table of values will be discussed later. However, for certain simple angles the *exact* values of the trigonometric ratios can be found geometrically. Specifically, the angles 30°, 45°, and 60° are shown in Fig. 3–9 in stand-

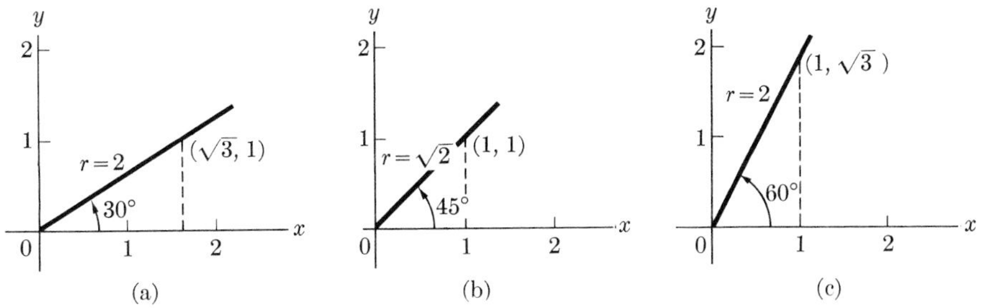

FIGURE 3–9

ard position, with a convenient point chosen on the terminal line of each by use of results from plane geometry. Thus, in (a) and (c) the length of the side of the right triangle opposite the 30° angle must be one-half that of the hypotenuse; in (b) the two legs of the 45° right triangle must be equal. It is then clear that in Fig. 3-9(a) we may choose $y = 1$, $r = 2$, and then compute the value of x as $\sqrt{3}$; in (c) we choose $x = 1$, $r = 2$, and compute $y = \sqrt{3}$; in (b) we choose $x = y = 1$ and compute $r = \sqrt{2}$.

The definitions of Section 3-6 may now be applied directly, and the following table of values is obtained.

θ	$\sin\theta$	$\cos\theta$	$\tan\theta$	$\cot\theta$	$\sec\theta$	$\csc\theta$
30°	$\frac{1}{2}$	$\frac{\sqrt{3}}{2}$	$\frac{1}{\sqrt{3}} = \frac{\sqrt{3}}{3}$	$\sqrt{3}$	$\frac{2}{\sqrt{3}} = \frac{2\sqrt{3}}{3}$	2
45°	$\frac{1}{\sqrt{2}} = \frac{\sqrt{2}}{2}$	$\frac{1}{\sqrt{2}} = \frac{\sqrt{2}}{2}$	1	1	$\sqrt{2}$	$\sqrt{2}$
60°	$\frac{\sqrt{3}}{2}$	$\frac{1}{2}$	$\sqrt{3}$	$\frac{1}{\sqrt{3}} = \frac{\sqrt{3}}{3}$	2	$\frac{2}{\sqrt{3}} = \frac{2\sqrt{3}}{3}$

The same procedure can be used to find the trigonometric ratios of any angle for which 30°, 45°, or 60° is the reference angle, upon taking into consideration the appropriate signs of x and y in the various quadrants. For, any such angle will lead to an auxiliary right triangle in which a 30°, 45°, or 60° angle appears.

Example 1. Find the values of the six trigonometric ratios of 210°.

Solution. With the angle drawn in standard position, as in Fig. 3-10, the point $(-\sqrt{3}, -1)$, with $r = 2$, is chosen on the terminal line. The ratios of 210° are then

$$\sin 210^\circ = \frac{y}{r} = -\frac{1}{2},$$

$$\cos 210^\circ = \frac{x}{r} = -\frac{\sqrt{3}}{2},$$

$$\tan 210^\circ = \frac{y}{x} = \frac{-1}{-\sqrt{3}} = \frac{\sqrt{3}}{3},$$

$$\cot 210^\circ = \frac{-\sqrt{3}}{-1} = \sqrt{3},$$

$$\sec 210^\circ = \frac{2}{-\sqrt{3}} = \frac{-2\sqrt{3}}{3},$$

$$\csc 210^\circ = -2.$$

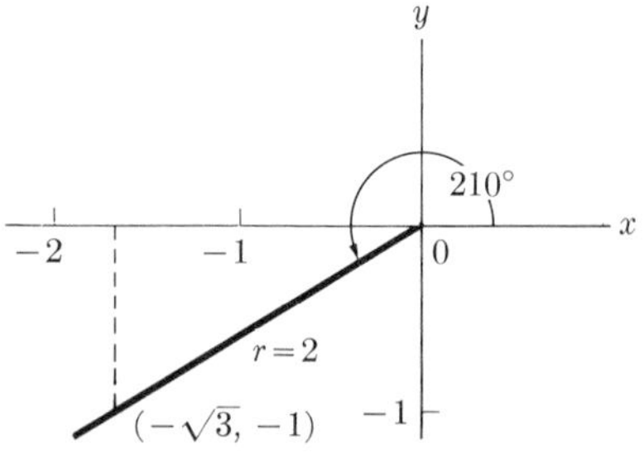

FIGURE 3-10

Example 2. Show that $\sin^2(-\pi/6) + \cos^2(-\pi/6) = 1$.

Solution. In Fig. 3–11 the angle $-\pi/6$ is shown in standard position. We may choose the point P on the terminal line with $x = \sqrt{3}$, $y = -1$, $r = 2$. The notation $\sin^2\theta$ is understood to mean the square of $\sin\theta$, so that $\sin^2\theta = (\sin\theta)^2$. Since $\sin(-\pi/6) = -\frac{1}{2}$ and $\cos(-\pi/6) = \sqrt{3}/2$, we have

$$\sin^2\left(-\frac{\pi}{6}\right) + \cos^2\left(-\frac{\pi}{6}\right) = \left(-\frac{1}{2}\right)^2 + \left(\frac{\sqrt{3}}{2}\right)^2 = \frac{1}{4} + \frac{3}{4} = 1,$$

and the desired relation is proved.

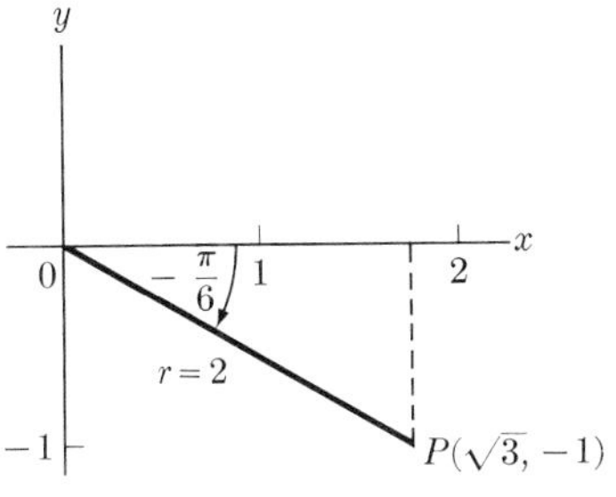

FIGURE 3–11

3–8 TRIGONOMETRIC RATIOS OF QUADRANTAL ANGLES

The definitions in Section 3–6 were so stated as to avoid those angles which are multiples of 90°, since for such angles either $x = 0$ or $y = 0$, and certain of the ratios are undefined. Angles which are multiples of 90° are called *quadrantal angles*. When these angles are in standard position, their terminal lines do not actually lie in any quadrant, but rather separate the quadrants. Accordingly, we say that the quadrantal angles lie in no quadrant.

For any quadrantal angle in standard position a point on the terminal line can always be chosen with $r = 1$. Then either x or y will be zero, and the other one will be ± 1. *We now define the trigonometric ratios of the quadrantal angles in the same manner as for other angles, but with the necessary restriction that when a denominator is zero, the corresponding ratio is undefined for that angle.*

Example. Find the values of those trigonometric ratios of 180° which are defined.

Solution. The terminal line of 180° in standard position is the negative x-axis. We choose the point on this line for which $r = 1$, $x = -1$, $y = 0$. The definitions which involve y in the denominator do not apply, and we have

$$\sin 180^\circ = \frac{0}{1} = 0, \qquad \cos 180^\circ = \frac{-1}{1} = -1,$$

$$\tan 180^\circ = \frac{0}{-1} = 0, \qquad \cot 180^\circ \text{ is undefined},$$

$$\sec 180^\circ = \frac{1}{-1} = -1, \qquad \csc 180^\circ \text{ is undefined}.$$

In this manner we may obtain the following table, in which a dash indicates that the corresponding value is undefined:

θ		$\sin\theta$	$\cos\theta$	$\tan\theta$	$\cot\theta$	$\sec\theta$	$\csc\theta$
0°	0	0	1	0	—	1	—
90°	$\frac{\pi}{2}$	1	0	—	0	—	1
180°	π	0	-1	0	—	-1	—
270°	$\frac{3\pi}{2}$	-1	0	—	0	—	-1

The values of the trigonometric ratios of the special angles, together with the quadrantal angles, are not only important in themselves, but also serve as landmarks in studying the variation of the trigonometric functions which will be defined in Section 7–1. In fact, these values can be used by themselves to give rough graphs of the functions.

EXERCISE GROUP 3–4

Draw the angles in Exercises 1–20 in standard position, and determine the values of their trigonometric ratios.

1. 60°
2. 45°
3. 135°
4. 240°
5. $-210°$
6. $2\pi/3$
7. $5\pi/6$
8. $5\pi/4$
9. 90°
10. $3\pi/2$
11. 5π
12. $-300°$
13. 2π
14. -4π
15. 315°
16. 480°
17. 540°
18. 450°
19. $7\pi/3$
20. $11\pi/6$

Use the values of the trigonometric ratios of the indicated angles to verify the statements in Exercises 21–36.

21. $\sin^2 210° + \cos^2 210° = 1$
22. $\cos 120° = \cos^2 60° - \sin^2 60°$
23. $\sin 600° = 2 \sin 300° \cos 300°$
24. $\cos 150° = -\sqrt{\frac{1}{2}(1 + \cos 300°)}$
25. $\sin \pi/4 \cos \pi/6 + \cos \pi/4 \sin \pi/6 = \sin 5\pi/12$
26. $\sin 2\pi/3 \cos 5\pi/6 - \cos 2\pi/3 \sin 5\pi/6 = -\frac{1}{2}$
27. $2 \sin 4\pi/3 \cos 4\pi\sqrt{3} = \frac{1}{2}\sqrt{3}$
28. $\sec^2 135° = 1 + \tan^2 135°$
29. $\sin (180° + 45°) = -\sin 45°$
30. $\sin 120° = \sqrt{\frac{1}{2}(1 - \cos 240°)}$
31. $\sin 300° \csc 300° = 1$
32. $\csc^2 5\pi/2 = 1 + \cot^2 5\pi/2$
33. $\tan 5\pi/6 = \dfrac{\sin 5\pi/3}{1 + \cos 5\pi/3}$
34. $\cos (\pi - \pi/3) = -\cos \pi/3$
35. $\tan (360° - 60°) = -\tan 60°$
36. $\sin (90° - 30°) = \cos 30°$

In each of Exercises 37–44, determine whether the symbol $\sim$ should be $<$ (less than), $=$, or $>$ (greater than).

37. $\cos 60° \sim 2 \cos 30°$
38. $\sin 240° \sim 2 \sin 120°$
39. $\sin 30° + \sin 60° \sim \sin 90°$
40. $\cos 60° + \cos 120° \sim \cos 180°$
41. $\cos 60° \cos 120° - \sin 60° \sin 120° \sim \cos 180°$
42. $\sin 2\pi/3 \cos \pi/6 + \cos 2\pi/3 \sin \pi/6 \sim \sin 5\pi/6$
43. $2 \sin \pi/3 \cos \pi/3 \sim \sin 2\pi/3$
44. $2 \cos^2 5\pi/6 - 1 \sim \cos 5\pi/3$

3–9 THE USE OF A TABLE OF TRIGONOMETRIC RATIOS

Except for certain ratios of the quadrantal angles, the trigonometric ratios, as we have seen, exist for all angles. In a preceding section it was also seen that, for certain special angles, these values can be found exactly, perhaps in terms of radicals. However, the method of finding the values of these ratios for an arbitrary angle must be left for more advanced mathematics courses. Suffice it to say that these values have been computed and tabulated. In Table 2 of the Appendix appears a 4-place table of values of the trigonometric ratios, for angles between 0° and 90°.

It should be understood that in this table the values of the ratios, which are, in general, infinite decimals, are given correct to four figures, that is, are *rounded off* to four figures. This means that if the part of the number after the last figure amounts to less than $\frac{1}{2}$ unit in the fourth figure, that part is dropped; if it is more than $\frac{1}{2}$ unit in that place, one is added to the digit in that place; if it is exactly $\frac{1}{2}$ unit in that place, then one is added or not, whichever makes the resulting last digit even.

The arrangement of the table must be clearly understood. It is based on an important property of the trigonometric ratios now to be presented. Let θ and θ' be *complementary angles*, that is, angles between 0° and 90° for which $\theta + \theta' = 90°$. In Fig. 3–12 two such angles are shown in standard position, with the points P and P' chosen so that $OP = OP'$. It is easy to show, by use of congruent triangles, that $x' = y$ and $y' = x$; hence, by definition, we have

$$\sin \theta = \frac{y}{r} = \frac{x'}{r} = \cos \theta',$$

and in a similar fashion it follows that

$$\cos \theta = \sin \theta', \qquad \tan \theta = \cot \theta',$$
$$\cot \theta = \tan \theta', \qquad \sec \theta = \csc \theta',$$
$$\csc \theta = \sec \theta'.$$

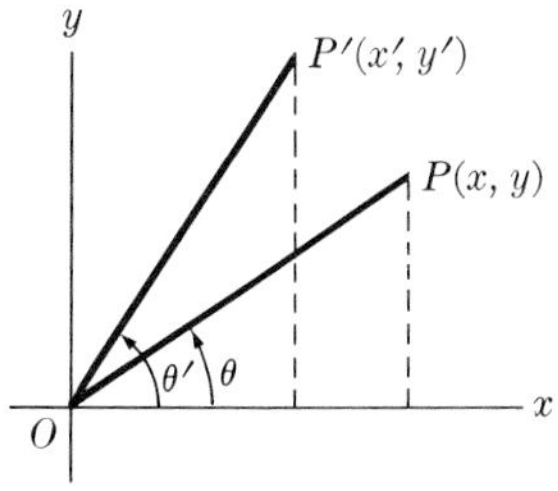

FIGURE 3–12

The six trigonometric ratios fall into three *pairs of coratios*, the sine and cosine, the tangent and cotangent, and the secant and cosecant. The result that has been proved may be stated as follows.

Theorem 3–2. *Any trigonometric ratio of a positive acute angle is equal to the coratio of the complementary angle.*

We may now examine the arrangement of the table. In the left-hand column the angles increase, as one reads downward, in steps of 10′, from 0° to 45°. The values of the ratios appear in the columns to the right, with the names of the ratios for these angles appearing at the head of each column. It is not necessary, however, to continue the table from 45° to 90°. By the above theorem we may use the values already tabulated if the columns are renamed. Thus, the angles which are between 45° and 90° appear in the extreme right-hand column, increasing as one reads upward, and the corresponding names of the ratios appear at the bottom of each column. For example, from the table we find tan 29°20′ = 0.5619. The same value, of course, appears as cot 60°40′. Similarly,

$$\sin 68^\circ\, 10' = 0.9283 = \cos 21^\circ\, 50'.$$

Example 1. Find the angle θ between 0° and 90° if $\tan 2\theta = 0.4950$.

Solution. It is clear that the value found directly from the table will be that of 2θ. From the table we find tan 26° 20′ = 0.4950, so that

$$2\theta = 26^\circ\, 20', \qquad \text{and} \qquad \theta = 13^\circ\, 10'.$$

The use of the table can be extended to angles of any magnitude. We know that the reference angle is always between 0° and 90°. Furthermore, whenever x, y, r are known for a point on the terminal line of an angle, the point on the terminal line of the reference angle, when in standard position, with the same r, will have coordinates which are positive and differ from x and y, respectively, at most in sign. Hence, corresponding ratios of an angle and its reference angle differ at most in sign. Accordingly, it is sufficient to find the same-named ratio of the reference angle, and then to assign the proper sign as determined by the quadrant in which the given angle lies.

Example 2. Use Table 2 to find cos 239° 10′.

Solution. The reference angle for 239° 10′ is 59° 10′, and from the table we find that

$$\cos 59^\circ\, 10' = 0.5125.$$

Since 239° 10′ is in Q_3, the value of the cosine is negative. Hence,

$$\cos 239^\circ\, 10' = -\cos 59^\circ\, 10' = -0.5125.$$

Example 3. Use Table 2 to find cot (−434°).

Solution. The reference angle is 74°, and we find cot 74° = 0.2867. Since the cotangent ratio is negative in Q_4, we have

$$\cot(-434^\circ) = -\cot 74^\circ = -0.2867.$$

EXERCISE GROUP 3–5

In Exercises 1–36, use Table 2 to find the value of the indicated trigonometric ratio.

1. tan 18° 50′	2. cos 74° 20′	3. sin 44° 50′
4. cot 4° 40′	5. sec 37° 20′	6. csc 64° 10′
7. cot 23°	8. sin 48° 10′	9. cos 87° 20′
10. tan 47° 30′	11. csc 36° 20′	12. sec 83° 30′
13. sin 83° 20′	14. cos 14° 50′	15. tan 72° 40′
16. cot 58° 10′	17. sec 123°	18. csc 132°
19. tan 117°	20. cot 95°	21. cos 216°
22. sin (−231°)	23. csc (−243°)	24. sec 234°
25. tan (−317°)	26. cot (−293°)	27. sin 329°
28. cos 334°	29. csc (−346°)	30. sec (−216° 10′)
31. cot (−351°)	32. tan (−126°)	33. cos (−173° 10′)
34. sin 212° 20′	35. csc 258°	36. sec (−313° 10′)

In Exercises 37–72, use Table 2 to find the smallest positive angle θ in each case.

37. $\tan\theta = 2.989$	38. $\cot\theta = 0.5022$	39. $\sin\theta = 0.9730$
40. $\cos\theta = 0.1334$	41. $\sec\theta = 1.062$	42. $\csc\theta = 1.081$
43. $\cot\theta = 2.455$	44. $\sin\theta = 0.4120$	45. $\cos\theta = 0.4462$
46. $\tan\theta = 0.4279$	47. $\csc\theta = 5.016$	48. $\sec\theta = 6.277$
49. $\sin\theta = 0.1822$	50. $\cos\theta = 0.6884$	51. $\tan\theta = 0.1644$
52. $\cot\theta = 0.9545$	53. $\sec\theta = 171.9$	54. $\csc\theta = 1.402$
55. $\cos\theta = 0.9858$	56. $\tan\theta = 1.024$	57. $\cot\theta = 17.17$
58. $\sec\theta = 1.379$	59. $\csc\theta = 57.30$	60. $\sin\theta = 0.6988$
61. $\sin\theta = -0.9945$	62. $\cos\theta = -0.0640$	63. $\tan\theta = -10.39$
64. $\cot\theta = -0.2186$	65. $\sec\theta = -4.560$	66. $\csc\theta = -1.038$
67. $\cos\theta = -0.7470$	68. $\tan\theta = -0.8491$	69. $\cot\theta = -1.664$
70. $\sec\theta = -1.167$	71. $\csc\theta = -1.540$	72. $\sin\theta = -0.6041$

Express each of the following as a ratio of the angle complementary to the given angle.

73. sin 18° 32′	74. cos 43° 17′	75. tan 73° 29′
76. cot 84° 36′	77. sec 67° 58′	78. csc 53° 42′
79. cos 38° 47′	80. tan 5° 53′	81. cot 13° 48′
82. sec 49° 28′	83. csc 68° 22′	84. sin 56° 26′

SUPPLEMENTARY EXERCISES FOR CHAPTER 3

Express each of the angles in Exercises 1–4 in radians.

1. $225°$ 2. $96°$ 3. $336°$ 4. $213° 17'$

Express each of the angles in Exercises 5–8 in degrees, minutes, and seconds.

5. $\frac{11\pi}{12}$ 6. $-\frac{19\pi}{15}$ 7. 2.06 rad 8. -1.36 rad

In Exercises 9–14, determine the values of the other five trigonometric ratios in each case. In Exercises 12–14, a, b, and c are positive.

9. $\cos\theta = -\frac{2}{3}$ 10. $\tan\theta = 5$ 11. $\csc\theta = 3$
12. $\sin\theta = a$ 13. $\cot\theta = b$ 14. $\sec\theta = c$

In Exercises 15–26, write the values of the six trigonometric ratios for the angles indicated.

15. $315°$ 16. $\frac{3\pi}{2}$ 17. $\frac{3\pi}{4}$ 18. $120°$
19. $210°$ 20. π 21. -5π 22. $-135°$
23. $510°$ 24. $\frac{11\pi}{4}$ 25. $420°$ 26. $-2025°$

Prove the statements in Exercises 27–30, if n is any integer (positive, negative, or zero).

27. $\cos n\pi = (-1)^n$ 28. $\cos (2n + 1)\frac{\pi}{2} = 0$
29. $\sin n\pi = 0$ 30. $\sin (2n + 1)\frac{\pi}{2} = (-1)^n$

Evaluate each of the expressions in Exercises 31–39 for $n = 1, 2, 3, 4, 5$.

31. $\frac{1}{n}\cos\frac{n\pi}{2}$ 32. $\frac{1}{n}\cos (n - 1)\pi$
33. $\frac{1}{n^2}\sin\frac{n\pi}{2}$ 34. $\frac{1}{n}\cos n\pi + \frac{1}{n + 2}\cos (n + 2)\pi$
35. $\frac{1}{n}\left(\cos n\pi - \cos\frac{n\pi}{2}\right)$ 36. $\frac{1}{n^2}\left(2\cos\frac{n\pi}{2} - \cos n\pi - 1\right)$
37. $f(\pi) - f(-\pi)$ if $f(x) = \frac{x^2 \sin nx}{n} + \frac{2x\cos nx}{n^2} - \frac{2\sin nx}{n^3}$
38. $f(0) - f(-\pi)$ if $f(x) = \frac{x\sin nx}{n} + \frac{\cos nx}{n^2}$
39. $f(\pi/2) - f(0) + g(\pi) - g(\pi/2)$ if $f(x) = \frac{x\sin nx}{n} + \frac{\cos nx}{n^2}$,
$$g(x) = \frac{(\pi - x)\sin nx}{n} - \frac{\cos nx}{n^2}$$
40. The area of a triangle varies directly as the square of a side and the sine of each adjacent angle, and inversely as the sine of the opposite angle. If the area $K = 4$ when the side $a = 4$, the adjacent angles $B = 45°$ and $C = 45°$, and the opposite angle $A = 90°$, write a formula expressing the area as a function of the side a and the angles A, B, C.

41. The area of a parallelogram varies as the product of two adjacent sides and the sine of the angle included between them. If the area $A = 20\sqrt{3}$ when the two sides are $b = 5$ and $c = 8$, and the angle $\theta = 60°$, write a formula expressing A as a function of b, c, and θ.

42. When a plane surface, with inclination θ (with the horizontal), is driven horizontally through the air at a fixed speed, the lifting power of the air resistance varies as $\sin^2 \theta \cos \theta$. If the lifting power is $1000\sqrt{3}$ lb when $\theta = 30°$, express the lifting power as a function of θ and compute its value when $\theta = 10°$.

43. The percentage error in the electric current due to a small error in reading a galvanometer is proportional to $\tan \theta + \cot \theta$, where θ is the angular deflection of the galvanometer. If the percentage error in the current is 2% when $\theta = 5°$, express the percentage error in the electric current as a function of θ and compute its value when $\theta = 3° 10'$.

CHAPTER 4

Linear and Quadratic Functions

4–1 INTRODUCTION

The equals sign (=) has been used frequently in the preceding pages to indicate that two numbers were equal. We now wish to use the equals sign to express the equality of two quantities one or both of which may contain a letter such as x, whose value is initially unknown. A statement of equality, in which such an unknown appears, between two quantities is called an *equation* if the equality holds for at least one value of the letter involved. Any value of the letter for which the equality holds is called a *solution of the equation*, and the procedure by which solutions are found is called *solving the equation*.

Example. The equation $3x - 5 = 2x + 4$ imposes the condition that the value of x must be 9, so that $x = 9$ is a solution of the equation.

Equations of the type illustrated in the above example, which hold for only a limited number of values of the letters which appear, are called *conditional equations*, as contrasted with equations which are true for all permissible values of the unknowns involved. Equations of the latter type are called *identities* and at times the symbol ($\equiv$) is used instead of the equals sign to emphasize that the equation is an identity. An example of an identity would be $3x + y \equiv 3(x + y) - 2y$; this equality holds for all values of x and y.

Since a conditional equation holds true for only a limited number of values of the unknown, it may be possible to find those values of the unknown for which the equation is true.

4–2 THE LINEAR FUNCTION. LINEAR EQUATIONS IN ONE UNKNOWN

Among the functions we shall study, the simplest, apart from the function $f(x) = c$, where c is a constant, is the function $f(x) = mx + b$, where m and b are constants. It is called a *linear* function, and the graph of the function

$y = mx + b$ is always a *straight line*. This line intersects the y-axis at the point $(0, b)$; b is called the *y-intercept* of the line. In the notation introduced in Chapter 2 we have $b = f(0)$. The constant m is called the *slope of the line*. It is a measure of *the rate at which the function changes as x changes*. Thus when the value of x increases by one unit, the value of the linear function changes by m units; if m is positive the function increases as x increases, while if m is negative the function decreases as x increases. If $m = 0$ the straight line is parallel to the x-axis.

The only straight line which cannot be represented by a function of the type $mx + b$ is one which is parallel to the y-axis. The equation of such a line is $x = c$ (constant). For example, the equation $x = -2$ represents a straight line parallel to the y-axis and two units to the left of it.

Example 1. The income of a business is at the rate of \$1000 a week and the expenses are at the rate of \$900 a week. If the business was worth \$8000 at the start, obtain the function showing the value of the business at the end of t weeks, assuming that the profits are retained in the business.

Solution. Since income exceeds expenses by \$100 a week, *the rate of increase of the function* is $m = 100$; the value of the function at $t = 0$ is 8000, that is, $b = f(0) = 8000$, since the original value was 8000. If t represents the number of weeks, the desired function is $f(t) = 100t + 8000$.

The time at which the business is worth a specified amount is of particular interest. For example, the time at which the business is worth \$10,000 is seen to be $t = 20$ weeks, for, with $t = 20$, we have

$$100 \cdot 20 + 8000 = 10{,}000.$$

This value of t may also be thought of as the value of t for which the function

$$(100t + 8000) - 10{,}000, \qquad \text{or} \qquad 100t - 2000$$

vanishes.

More generally, if we set the function $mx + b$ equal to c, we get

$$mx + b = c, \qquad \text{or} \qquad mx + b - c = 0.$$

The value of x which satisfies the equation in either of the two forms is then $x = (c - b)/m$. From the second form of the equation it is seen that for this value of x the value of the function $mx + b - c$ is zero.

***Definition* 4–1.** *A number a is a zero of a function $f(x)$ if $f(a) = 0$.*

In the above example, $(c - b)/m$ is a zero of the function

$$mx + b - c.$$

It is clear that there is a close connection between *zeros* of functions and *solutions* or *roots* of equations. In fact, a zero of $f(x)$ is a solution of the equation $f(x) = 0$. The finding of the zeros of a function involves the solving of an equation.

Example 2. Find the zeros of the function

$$\frac{2x + 7}{5} + \frac{3x - 5}{4} + \frac{33}{10}.$$

Solution. The zeros of the function are the roots of the equation

$$\frac{2x + 7}{5} + \frac{3x - 5}{4} + \frac{33}{10} = 0.$$

Multiplying each member of the equation by 20, which is the least common multiple of the denominators, we have

$$4(2x + 7) + 5(3x - 5) + 2 \cdot 33 = 0,$$

or

$$8x + 28 + 15x - 25 + 66 = 0, \qquad \text{and} \qquad 23x = -69.$$

Hence $x = -3$ is the zero of the given function.

Example 3. Solve the equation $a^2x + 4c^2x - 10c = 5a - 4acx$ for x.

Solution.

$$a^2x + 4acx + 4c^2x = 5a + 10c,$$
$$(a^2 + 4ac + 4c^2)x = 5(a + 2c),$$
$$(a + 2c)^2x = 5(a + 2c),$$
$$x = \frac{5(a + 2c)}{(a + 2c)^2} = \frac{5}{a + 2c}.$$

The solution just obtained is also the zero of the function

$$a^2x + 4c^2x - 10c - (5a - 4acx).$$

On solving equations. Methods of solving or working with equations are based on the *assumption that a solution exists*, that is, that there are one or more values of the unknown for which the given equation is satisfied. On this basis the permissible steps, based on properties of real numbers, are:

1. *Equal quantities may be added to or subtracted from both sides of an equation.*
2. *Both sides of an equation may be multiplied by equal, nonzero quantities, or divided by equal, nonzero quantities.*

The implication is that any value which satisfies the original equation will also satisfy any equation obtained by applying the above steps. But care is required in applying Step 2; if the multipliers or divisors contain the unknown, it is possible that the new equation may contain more or fewer solutions than the original equation. The safeguards that should be applied in this case are:

Whenever both members of an equation are multiplied or divided by equal quantities involving the unknown, check in the original equation all tentative solutions obtained, in order to determine whether they actually are solutions. If both members are divided by a quantity containing the unknown, and this quantity vanishes for a value of the unknown, consider the possibility that this value may also be a solution of the original equation.

The *ultimate criterion or test* as to whether a quantity is a solution of an equation is: *Does that quantity satisfy the equation?*

Examples. The equation $2x = 4$ has the solution $x = 2$, but the equation $2x(x - 1) = 4(x - 1)$ obtained by multiplying both members of the original equation by $x - 1$ has an additional solution $x = 1$. If $x = 1$ is tested in the original equation, it fails the test.

The equation $x - 1 = 4$ has the solution $x = 5$, but squaring both members, which is an application of Step 2 above, gives $(x - 1)^2 = 16$, which has the additional solution $x = -3$. This value fails the test.

The equation $x^2 - x = 0$ has the two solutions $x = 0$, $x = 1$. But if both members are divided by x, the new equation $x - 1 = 0$ is satisfied only by $x = 1$. A root has been "lost" by the division.

If both members of the equation $x/(x - 1) - 1/(x^2 - x) = 1$ are multiplied by $x^2 - x$, the LCD, we obtain $x^2 - 1 = x^2 - x$, whose solution is $x = 1$. However, $x = 1$ is not a solution of the original equation, the fractions being undefined when $x = 1$ (the denominators vanish).

Fractional equations. We shall understand by a *fractional equation* an equation containing fractions in which the unknown appears in one or more denominators. The usual method of solution is to remove the fractions by multiplying both members of the equation by the LCD of the fractions which appear. If the resulting equation is linear we are in a position to solve it. In view of the preceding discussion, there then remains the matter of checking in the original equation all values obtained in this manner.

Example 4. Solve the equation

$$\frac{2x}{3 + x} + \frac{3 + x}{3} = 2 + \frac{x^2}{3(x - 3)}.$$

Solution. The LCD of the fractions is $3(x - 3)(3 + x)$. Multiplying both members of the equation by the LCD we have

$$2x \cdot 3(x - 3) + (3 + x)^2(x - 3) = 2 \cdot 3(x - 3)(3 + x) + x^2(3 + x),$$

which expanded becomes

$$6x^2 - 18x + x^3 + 3x^2 - 9x - 27 = 6x^2 - 54 + x^3 + 3x^2.$$

This equation reduces to $-27x - 27 = -54$, which has the solution $x = 1$. Substituting $x = 1$ in the original equation, we have

$$\frac{2}{4} + \frac{4}{3} = 2 + \frac{1}{(-6)}, \quad \text{or} \quad \frac{11}{6} = \frac{11}{6}.$$

Hence $x = 1$ is the only solution.

When an equation contains only one trigonometric ratio of a variable, we may use the same procedure to solve for that ratio as we use to solve an equation containing just the variable. If the resulting equation is linear in that ratio, the value of that ratio which satisfies the equation may be easily obtained.

Example 5. Solve the following equation for $\tan x$:

$$\frac{\tan x}{1 + \tan x} + 2 = \frac{3 \tan x}{2 + \tan x}.$$

Solution. Multiplying both members of the equation by the LCD, which is $(1 + \tan x)(2 + \tan x)$, we have

$$\tan x(2 + \tan x) + 2(1 + \tan x)(2 + \tan x) = 3 \tan x(1 + \tan x).$$

Upon expanding and collecting terms, we obtain

$$3 \tan^2 x + 8 \tan x + 4 = 3 \tan^2 x + 3 \tan x.$$

Subtraction of $3 \tan^2 x + 3 \tan x + 4$ from both members gives $5 \tan x = -4$, from which we obtain

$$\tan x = -\tfrac{4}{5}.$$

Since neither denominator vanishes for this value, it is the solution.

EXERCISE GROUP 4-1

In Exercises 1–5, graph the function (the domain being the set of real numbers), and for each give the value of the function at $x = 0$, and also the value of x for which the function is zero.

1. $(x, 2x + 5)$
2. $(x, 3x - 2)$
3. $(x, -3x + 7)$
4. $(x, -2x + 7)$
5. $(x, 3x + 5)$

In Exercises 6–41, solve for x, y, or z, whichever appears.

6. $5x - 3 = x + 2$
7. $5x - 2 = 3 - x$
8. $\frac{3}{2}y - \frac{2}{3} = \frac{1}{3}y + \frac{5}{2}$
9. $\frac{3}{5}(z - \frac{1}{3}) = \frac{2}{3}(\frac{1}{2} - 2z)$
10. $\frac{2}{3}x - \frac{3}{5} = -\frac{1}{3} - \frac{2}{5}x$
11. $\frac{2}{5} - \frac{1}{7}x = \frac{3}{7} - \frac{2}{5}x$
12. $0.27x - 0.39 = 0.17 + 0.19x$
13. $0.25 - 0.32x = 0.37 + 1.9x$
14. $\dfrac{5 - 3x}{4} + \dfrac{7 - 4x}{5} = 2 + \dfrac{3 - x}{5}$
15. $\dfrac{2x - 3}{3} + \dfrac{5 - 3x}{7} = 4 - x$
16. $2x - \dfrac{3x - 5}{4} = 3 - \dfrac{3 - 5x}{6}$
17. $5 + \dfrac{2 - x}{3} = \dfrac{2}{5} - \dfrac{3 - 2x}{3}$
18. $5y - a = 2by + 7$
19. $by - cy = ab$
20. $a^2x + 4abx = 5a - 4b^2x$
21. $by + c^2 = b^2 + cy$
22. $acx - adx + d^2 = c^2 + bdx - bcx$
23. $\dfrac{x - 6}{3x} = \dfrac{3x - 8}{4x}$
24. $\dfrac{1 - x}{x + 7} = \dfrac{3}{5}$
25. $\dfrac{1}{x} + \dfrac{3}{x + 1} = \dfrac{-3}{x^2 + x}$
26. $\dfrac{x - 0.5}{x + 0.25} = \dfrac{x + 0.5}{x - 0.25}$
27. $\dfrac{0.6 - 0.4x}{0.06x - 0.07} + \dfrac{1.5 - 2x}{0.4 - 0.3x} = 0$

28. $\dfrac{3}{x+2} - \dfrac{2}{x-1} = \dfrac{2}{x^2+x-2}$

29. $\dfrac{1}{x+1} - \dfrac{3}{x} = \dfrac{3}{x^2+x}$

30. $\dfrac{x-1}{x-2} - \dfrac{x-3}{x-4} = \dfrac{x-2}{x-3} - \dfrac{x-4}{x-5}$

31. $\dfrac{3-x}{1-x} + \dfrac{x-5}{7-x} = 1 + \dfrac{2-x^2}{x^2-8x+7}$

32. $\dfrac{cz}{a^2-b^2} + a - b = z + \dfrac{c}{a+b}$

33. $a^2(x-b)^2 = (ax-b)(ax+b)$

34. $\dfrac{11}{12y+11} + \dfrac{5}{6y+5} = \dfrac{7}{4y+7}$

35. $\dfrac{1}{y+1} - \dfrac{2}{y+2} = \dfrac{3}{y+3} - \dfrac{4}{y+4}$

36. $5 + \dfrac{2}{3 - \dfrac{1}{4-x}} = \dfrac{45}{8}$

37. $\dfrac{1 - \dfrac{1 + \dfrac{1-x}{2}}{3}}{4} = 1$

38. $\dfrac{\dfrac{x}{x-1} - 1}{\dfrac{x}{x-1} + 1} = \dfrac{\dfrac{x}{x+1} - 1}{\dfrac{x}{x+1} + 1}$

39. $\dfrac{x+2b}{x-4b} + \dfrac{x-b}{x+b} = \dfrac{x+3b}{x-3b} + \dfrac{x+2b}{x+4b}$

In Exercises 40–49, solve for the trigonometric ratio which appears.

40. $\dfrac{7-2\sin x}{2-\sin x} = 4$

41. $\dfrac{\cos x}{1+\cos x} + 3 = \dfrac{4\cos x}{2+\cos x}$

42. $\dfrac{\tan x - 1}{2} = \dfrac{2\tan x}{3} - \dfrac{5}{3}$

43. $\dfrac{\cot x}{\cot x - 1} - \dfrac{3}{\cot x + 1} = 1$

44. $\dfrac{1}{\sec x} - \dfrac{\sec x + 5}{2\sec x + 8} + \dfrac{1}{2} = 0$

45. $\dfrac{\csc x}{1+\csc x} + 6 = \dfrac{7\csc x}{2+\csc x}$

46. $\dfrac{3\sin x + 1}{3\sin x - 1} - \dfrac{3\sin x - 1}{1 + 3\sin x} + \dfrac{8}{1 - 9\sin^2 x} = 0$

47. $\dfrac{\tan x - 1}{\tan x + 1} - \dfrac{1}{3} = \dfrac{2\tan x + 3}{\tan x + 1} - \dfrac{5}{4}$

48. $\dfrac{5\cot x}{\cot x - 3} - \dfrac{\cot x}{2 + \cot x} = 4$

49. $\dfrac{-2+\sec x}{2\sec x - 3} = \dfrac{-4+\sec x}{5+2\sec x}$

50. A train traveled 60 mi the first hour and 50 mi each hour thereafter. Find a function which gives the distance covered in t hr.

51. The monthly residential rates of a gas company are a fixed charge of \$0.60 and \$0.14 per 100 ft^3 for the first 2000 ft^3, \$0.125 per 100 ft^3 for the next 3000 ft^3, and \$0.00105 per ft^3 for all gas used in excess of 5000 ft^3. If x represents the number of cubic feet of gas used, express the cost C (in dollars) as a function of x, assuming x greater than 5000.

52. Assuming that a house depreciates 2% of its original value each year, and that the original cost was \$25,000, find a function which expresses the value of the house at the end of t yr. What would be the significance of the zero of this function?

53. If P dollars are invested for t yr at simple interest at the rate r, the amount, which equals principal plus interest, is $P + Prt$ or $P(1 + rt)$. Using this function, determine (a) the rate at which \$1 must be invested to amount to \$2 in 10 yr, (b) the time it would take \$1 to become \$5 if invested at simple interest at the rate of 3%.

54. A man left $\frac{1}{3}$ of his property to his son, $\frac{1}{4}$ to his daughter, and the remainder, which was \$25,000, to his wife. How much money did the man leave?

55. The numerator of a fraction is 5 less than the denominator. If the numerator is increased by 1 and the denominator by 6, the value of the fraction is unchanged. Find the fraction.

56. The numerator of a fraction is $\frac{1}{4}$ of the denominator. If the numerator is increased by 5 and the denominator by 3, the value of the resulting fraction is $\frac{1}{3}$. Find the fraction.

57. Find a number such that 11 less than 3 times the number equals 3 more than 5 times the number.

58. The difference between two positive numbers is 5. If 3 is added to each, the quotient of the larger by the smaller is 1.5. Find the numbers.

59. A train traveling 60 mph starts 25 min before a second train that travels 75 mph. How many hours will be required for the second train to overtake the first?

60. In a one-mile race the times of the first- and second-place runners are 4 min and 4 min 1.1 sec, respectively. How far behind the winner is the second-place runner at the finish?

61. The earth and Venus revolve around the sun in approximately 365 and 225 days, respectively. Find, to the nearest day, the time it takes Venus to gain on the earth by one revolution.

62. Find the length of the side of a square if an increase of 1 in. on each side increases the area by 15 in^2.

63. How many cubic centimeters of a 40% solution of sulfuric acid must be added to 100 cc of a 20% solution to obtain a 30% solution of the acid?

64. In an alloy of copper and tin weighing 28 lb, 40% is copper. How many pounds of copper must be added so that the new alloy is 45% copper?

65. Find the amount of money that must be invested at 4% simple interest in order to have \$5000 at the end of 7 yr.

66. One side of a rectangle is 7 more than the other side. Find the side of a square whose area equals that of the rectangle, if the side of the square is 3 more than the shorter side of the rectangle.

4–3 THE QUADRATIC FUNCTION

We turn next to functions in which the highest degree of the independent variable is two. If x is the independent variable, the most general form of such a function is $ax^2 + bx + c$, where a, b, and c are constants, and $a \neq 0$. Functions of this type are called *quadratic functions*.

We shall draw the graph of the quadratic function, and from the graph and the analysis leading to the graph we shall learn many properties of the function. Let us write

$$y = ax^2 + bx + c.$$

In determining pairs of values (x, y) which satisfy this equation, we can be guided in our choice of values of x *by expressing the quadratic function in terms of the square of a linear function of* x, as follows. The first step is to subtract c from both members and then factor out a from the right member:

$$y - c = a\left(x^2 + \frac{b}{a}x\right).$$

We then *complete the square* within the parentheses on the right by adding $b^2/4a^2$. This means that we are adding $a \cdot (b^2/4a^2) = b^2/4a$ to the right member, and we add the same quantity to the left member, so that we have

$$y - c + \frac{b^2}{4a} = a\left(x^2 + \frac{b}{a}x + \frac{b^2}{4a^2}\right) = a\left(x + \frac{b}{2a}\right)^2,$$

or

$$y - \frac{4ac - b^2}{4a} = a\left(x + \frac{b}{2a}\right)^2.$$

Since the square of any real number is either positive or zero, we see that the smallest value of $[x + (b/2a)]^2$ will occur when $x = -b/2a$, and is zero. If a is positive, the left member must be positive or zero and the smallest value that y can have is $(4ac - b^2)/4a$, which will occur when $x = -b/2a$, so that $[-b/2a, (4ac - b^2)/4a]$ is the lowest point on the graph. If a is negative, the point with these coordinates is the highest point on the graph. In either case the curve is called a *parabola* and the point $[-b/2a, (4ac - b^2)/4a]$ is called the *vertex* of the parabola. By taking values of x on each side of $-b/2a$ and computing the corresponding values of y, we obtain a set of points which, when plotted and joined by a smooth curve, give the graph of the function.

The abscissa of the vertex can also be found by using the formula $x = -b/2a$, and the ordinate can then be found by substituting this value of x in the function.

Example 1. Graph the function $3x^2 + 5x - 7$.

Solution. Let $y = 3x^2 + 5x - 7$, and apply the method described above. Then

$$y + 7 + \tfrac{25}{12} = 3(x^2 + \tfrac{5}{3}x + \tfrac{25}{36})$$

or

$$y + \tfrac{109}{12} = 3(x + \tfrac{5}{6})^2.$$

The vertex of the graph is thus at $(-\frac{5}{6}, -\frac{109}{12})$. We now take values of x on each side of $x = -\frac{5}{6}$, compute the corresponding values of y, and obtain the table of values

x:	-4	-3	-2	-1	$-\frac{5}{6}$	0	1	2
y:	21	5	-5	-9	$-\frac{109}{12}$	-7	1	15

from which the graph can be constructed (Fig. 4–1).

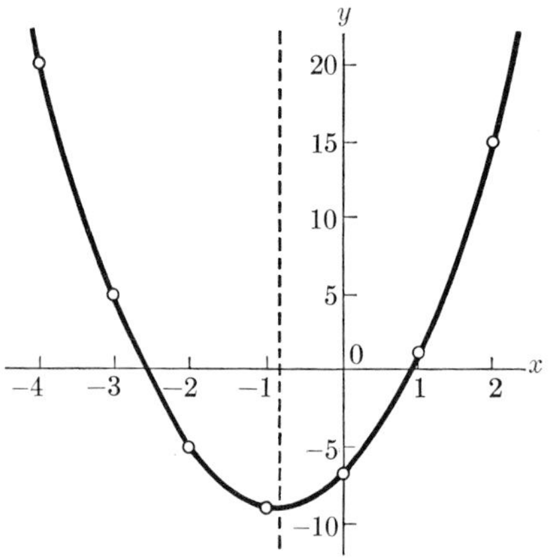

FIGURE 4–1

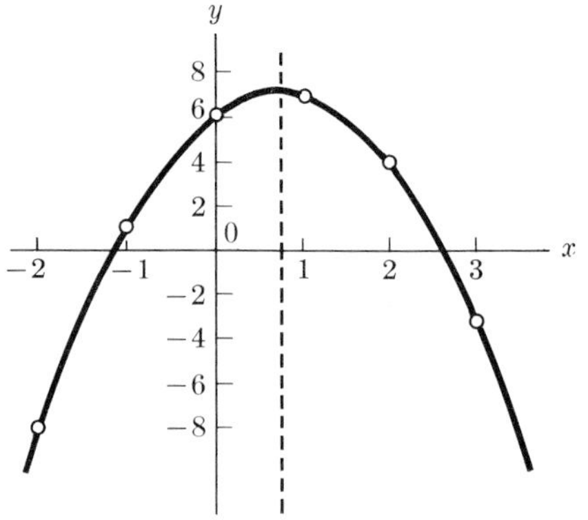

FIGURE 4–2

Example 2. Graph the function $-2x^2 + 3x + 6$.

Solution. Let $y = -2x^2 + 3x + 6$, and proceed as above. Then

$$y - 6 - \tfrac{9}{8} = -2(x^2 - \tfrac{3}{2}x + \tfrac{9}{16}) \qquad \text{or} \qquad y - \tfrac{57}{8} = -2(x - \tfrac{3}{4})^2.$$

The vertex of the graph is at $(\frac{3}{4}, \frac{57}{8})$. Using values of x on each side of $x = \frac{3}{4}$, we obtain the table

x:	-2	-1	0	$\frac{3}{4}$	1	2	3
y:	-8	1	6	$\frac{57}{8}$	7	4	-3

and the resulting graph (Fig. 4–2).

The following summarizes the preceding analysis:

1. *The graph of the function* $ax^2 + bx + c$ *is a* U-*shaped or inverted* U-*shaped curve with its vertex at*

$$\boxed{\left[-\frac{b}{2a}, \frac{4ac - b^2}{4a}\right].}$$

This curve is called a parabola.

2. *The graph is symmetrical with respect to the line* $x = -b/2a$. *(If the graph is drawn on a sheet of paper and the paper is then folded along the line* $x = -b/2a$, *the two halves of the curve will coincide.)*

3. *If* a *is positive the curve opens upward and the vertex is the lowest point on the graph (minimum); if* a *is negative the curve opens downward and the vertex is the highest point on the graph (maximum).*

4. *The graph must either cross the x-axis in two distinct points, or be tangent to it, or not touch it at all.*

EXERCISE GROUP 4–2

1. Draw on the same coordinate axes the graphs of the functions $(x, 2x^2)$, $(x, 2x^2 - 1)$, and $(x, 2x^2 + 3)$.
2. Draw on the same coordinate axes the graphs of the functions $(x, x^2 + 3x)$, $(x, x^2 + 3x + 1)$, and $(x, x^2 + 3x - 2)$.

In each of Exercises 3–26, $f(x)$ is given for the function $(x, f(x))$. Find the coordinates of the vertex and draw the graph of the function.

3. $2x^2 - 3x - 4$
4. $x^2 - \frac{3}{2}x + 2$
5. $2x^2 - 7x + 3$
6. $-3x^2 + 6x - 2$
7. $-x^2 + x - 2$
8. $-2x^2 + 3x + 5$
9. $2x^2 + x$
10. $3x^2 + 6x - 5$
11. $-x^2 + 2x - 4$
12. $2x^2 - 0.75x$
13. $x^2 - 5x + 6$
14. $5x^2 - 6$
15. $0.2x^2 + 2.2x$
16. $\frac{1}{3}x^2 - \frac{3}{2}x + 2$
17. $3x^2 - 5x + 8$
18. $-2x^2 - 3x + 4$
19. $5x^2 + 4x + 3$
20. $-6x^2 + 3x$
21. $2x - x^2$
22. $-3x^2 + 2$
23. $-2x^2 + x$
24. $(x - 1)^2 + 3(x - 1) + 1$
25. $(x + 3)^2 - 2(x + 3)$
26. $(2x + 1)^2 - 3x + 7$
27. If an object is projected vertically upward from the ground with an initial velocity of v_0 ft/sec, its distance S above the ground at the end of t sec is given by the formula
$$S = v_0t - \tfrac{1}{2}gt^2,$$
where g is the acceleration of the object due to gravity ($=32$ ft/sec^2 approx.). Draw the graph of S as a function of t if $v_0 = 56$. How high will the object rise above the ground? How long will it take to fall to the ground again? How high will it be at the end of 2 sec?
28. A man operates a rooming house with 30 rooms. He finds that he can keep all rooms rented at \$25 a month each, but will have one vacancy for each \$2 per month added to this price. Express his gross income in terms of the number x of dollars charged in excess of \$25. Graph the function and determine what rental will provide a maximum gross income.
29. Find the value of k so that the vertex of the graph of the function $2x^2 - kx + 2$ lies on the line $y = 2$.
30. Find the maximum value of the product of two numbers if their sum is 6.

31. Find the minimum value of the product of two numbers if their difference is 8.
32. It is necessary to form a rectangular field with one side lying along a stream. If 100 yd of wire fence are available to fence in the three exposed sides, find the maximum area that can be enclosed.
33. Find the dimensions of the largest rectangle that can be inscribed in an isosceles triangle with altitude 8 in. and base 4 in., if one side of the rectangle is along the base of the triangle.

4-4 THE ZEROS OF THE QUADRATIC FUNCTION. THE QUADRATIC FORMULA.

We shall now develop a method for finding the zeros of the quadratic function $ax^2 + bx + c$ or, equivalently, for solving the equation

$$ax^2 + bx + c = 0 \quad (a \neq 0). \tag{1}$$

Divide each member of Eq. (1) by a, obtaining

$$x^2 + \frac{b}{a}x + \frac{c}{a} = 0. \tag{2}$$

Now subtract c/a from both members of the equation, getting

$$x^2 + \frac{b}{a}x = -\frac{c}{a}. \tag{3}$$

The left member of this equation will become the square of a linear function if $(b/2a)^2$ is added, which is permissible if the same quantity is also added to the right member. This gives

$$x^2 + \frac{b}{a}x + \frac{b^2}{4a^2} = \frac{b^2}{4a^2} - \frac{c}{a}, \tag{4}$$

which may in turn be written as

$$\left(x + \frac{b}{2a}\right)^2 = \frac{b^2 - 4ac}{4a^2}. \tag{5}$$

If now the square root of each side is taken, we have

$$x + \frac{b}{2a} = \pm\sqrt{\frac{b^2 - 4ac}{4a^2}}, \tag{6}$$

or

$$\boxed{x = \frac{-b \pm \sqrt{b^2 - 4ac}}{2a}.} \tag{7}$$

Equation (7) is known as the *quadratic formula.*

The method used here for obtaining x is called *solving a quadratic equation by completing the square.* The fact that the values of x in (7) actually are solutions of (1) can be verified by direct substitution.

Example 1. Solve the equation $3x^2 + 5x - 7 = 0$.

Solution. (a) Add 7 to both members, and then divide both members by 3, getting

$$x^2 + \tfrac{5}{3}x = \tfrac{7}{3}.$$

(b) We now add $(\frac{5}{6})^2 = \frac{25}{36}$ to the left member to obtain a perfect square there, and add the same number to the right member, obtaining

$$x^2 + \tfrac{5}{3}x + \tfrac{25}{36} = \tfrac{7}{3} + \tfrac{25}{36}.$$

This can be written as

$$(x + \tfrac{5}{6})^2 = \tfrac{109}{36}.$$

(c) We now extract the square root of both members, which gives

$$x + \frac{5}{6} = \pm\frac{\sqrt{109}}{6}, \qquad \text{or} \qquad x = \frac{-5 \pm \sqrt{109}}{6}.$$

The two solutions are

$$x = \frac{-5 + \sqrt{109}}{6} \qquad \text{and} \qquad x = \frac{-5 - \sqrt{109}}{6},$$

which can be verified by direct substitution.

Example 2. Solve by completing the square: $-2x^2 + 3x + 5 = 0$.

Solution.

$$x^2 - \tfrac{3}{2}x - \tfrac{5}{2} = 0,$$

$$x^2 - \tfrac{3}{2}x + \tfrac{9}{16} = \tfrac{5}{2} + \tfrac{9}{16} = \tfrac{49}{16},$$

$$(x - \tfrac{3}{4})^2 = \tfrac{49}{16}, \qquad x - \tfrac{3}{4} = \pm\tfrac{7}{4},$$

Therefore

$$x = \tfrac{3}{4} \pm \tfrac{7}{4},$$

and the two solutions are

$$x = \tfrac{10}{4} = \tfrac{5}{2} \qquad \text{and} \qquad x = -\tfrac{4}{4} = -1.$$

Whereas the method of completing the square can always be used to solve a quadratic equation, it almost never is used for this purpose in practice. Its importance here revolves around its use in the derivation of the quadratic formula. The use of equation (7), that is, *the quadratic formula,* in solving a quadratic equation (1) consists in identifying the values of a, b, and c and then substituting these values in (7). After the substitution of the values it will frequently be necessary to simplify the result, as illustrated in the following examples.

Example 3. Use the quadratic formula to solve the equation

$$3x^2 + 4x - 5 = 0.$$

Solution. A comparison of the given equation $3x^2 + 4x - 5 = 0$ with the equation $ax^2 + bx + c = 0$ shows that $a = 3$, $b = 4$, and $c = -5$. Hence, by Eq. (7), we have

$$x = \frac{-4 \pm \sqrt{16 - 4 \cdot 3(-5)}}{2 \cdot 3}$$

$$= \frac{-4 \pm \sqrt{16 + 60}}{6} = \frac{-4 \pm \sqrt{4 \cdot 19}}{6}$$

$$= \frac{-4 \pm 2\sqrt{19}}{6} = \frac{-2 \pm \sqrt{19}}{3}.$$

Example 4. Use the quadratic formula to solve $2x^2 - 5x + 8 = 0$.

Solution. Proceeding as in Example 3 we see that $a = 2$, $b = -5$, and $c = 8$. We get

$$x = \frac{5 \pm \sqrt{25 - 4 \cdot 2 \cdot 8}}{2 \cdot 2} = \frac{5 \pm \sqrt{-39}}{4} = \frac{5 \pm i\sqrt{39}}{4}.$$

4–5 SOLVING A QUADRATIC EQUATION BY FACTORING

The quadratic formula may always be used to solve a quadratic equation. However, it often happens that the quadratic function $ax^2 + bx + c$ is factorable, in which case the corresponding quadratic equation can be solved by factoring. Consider the equation

$$-2x^2 + 3x + 5 = 0,$$

which can be written as

$$(-2x + 5)(x + 1) = 0.$$

For a product of quantities to be zero, it is necessary for at least one of the quantities to be zero (see Chapter 1), so that to obtain all possible values of x satisfying the equation, each factor must be set equal to zero, whenever possible. Hence

$$-2x + 5 = 0 \quad \text{and} \quad x = \tfrac{5}{2},$$

or

$$x + 1 = 0 \quad \text{and} \quad x = -1.$$

There are *two* solutions of the equation, $x = \frac{5}{2}$ and $x = -1$.

Example. Solve the equation $3x^2 + 5x = 0$.

Solution. It was pointed out in Section 1–6 that division by zero is impossible. Thus we must not divide by x since x might be equal to zero. Instead of dividing by x we factor the left member of the equation to obtain

$$x(3x + 5) = 0.$$

Therefore $x = 0$; or $3x + 5 = 0$ and $x = -\frac{5}{3}$. The two solutions of the given equation are $x = 0$ and $x = -\frac{5}{3}$.

In view of the available methods for solving a quadratic equation, the following procedure is suggested:

1. *Try to solve the equation by factoring.*
2. *If a factorization is not possible or is not readily apparent, use the quadratic formula.*

EXERCISE GROUP 4-3

In each of Exercises 1–24, solve the equation by factoring.

1. $x^2 - 8x + 15 = 0$
2. $2x^2 - x - 3 = 0$
3. $2x^2 + x - 6 = 0$
4. $3x^2 + 5x - 2 = 0$
5. $7x - 5 = -6x^2$
6. $5x^2 + 2x = 0$
7. $3x^2 = 15x$
8. $15x^2 - 6 = x$
9. $x + 2 = 15x^2$
10. $2x^2 + 7x = 15$
11. $5x^2 - 7 = 2x$
12. $16x^2 - 9 = 0$
13. $25x^2 - 36 = 0$
14. $10x^2 = 21 - x$
15. $7x + 2 = 15x^2$
16. $41x = 21x^2 + 10$
17. $10x^2 - x - 21 = 0$
18. $21x^2 - 40x - 21 = 0$
19. $35x^2 = 7x$
20. $5x^2 - 13x - 6 = 0$
21. $ax^2 + (b - ac)x - bc = 0$
22. $bx^2 + (b + ac)x + ac = 0$
23. $ax^2 + (ac - 2b)x - 2bc = 0$
24. $cx^2 + (bc - a)x - ab = 0$

In each of Exercises 25–44, solve the equation by using the quadratic formula.

25. $2x^2 + x - 3 = 0$
26. $2x^2 + 3x = 2$
27. $5x^2 - 2x - 1 = 0$
28. $5x^2 + 9 = 0$
29. $3x^2 + 5x = 0$
30. $3x^2 + 4 = 5x$
31. $3x^2 - 5x + 4 = 0$
32. $x^2 - bx = 6$
33. $2x^2 + ax + b = 0$
34. $px^2 + qx + r = 0$
35. $cx^2 + bx + a = 0$
36. $5x^2 = 2x - 7$
37. $b = 2cx - x^2$
38. $a = bx^2 - dx$
39. $cx^2 = 7x - x^2 - 5$
40. $3x + 5 = ax^2 + a$
41. $2x^2 + 3ax + bx + cd = 0$
42. $cx^2 - 2x = x^2 + a$
43. $\dfrac{3x}{x - 2} + \dfrac{1}{4 - x^2} = 2$
44. $\dfrac{1 - 2x}{x + 2} + \dfrac{x + 1}{x^2 - 4} = \dfrac{2}{3(x - 2)}$

Solve the equations in Exercises 45–60 by any appropriate method.

45. $2x^2 - 37x + 156 = 0$
46. $5x(x - 2) = \frac{3}{4} - 3x$
47. $x^2 + 8\sqrt{5}x + 72 = 0$
48. $14 + 5x = 3x(x + 2)$
49. $13x^2 - 38 = 6(1 + x)^2 + 71$
50. $\dfrac{7}{x + 5} - \dfrac{8}{x - 6} = \dfrac{3}{x - 1}$
51. $\dfrac{x - 5}{x + 3} - \dfrac{80}{x^2 - 9} = \dfrac{1}{2} + \dfrac{x - 8}{3 - x}$
52. $\dfrac{a + x}{b + x} + \dfrac{b + x}{a + x} = \dfrac{5}{2}$
53. $a + x = \dfrac{1}{a} + \dfrac{1}{x}$
54. $\dfrac{x - 1}{x + 1} = \dfrac{x + 1}{x - 1} - 1$
55. $\dfrac{1}{5(2 - x)} = \dfrac{1 - 2x}{2 + x} + \dfrac{x + 1}{x^2 - 4}$
56. $(x - 4)^2 = (3 - x)(1 + 2x)$

57. $a^2x^2 - b^2x^2 - 4abx = a^2 - b^2$

58. $abx^2 - (a^2 + b^2)x + ab = 0$

59. $a^2x^2 - x^2 + 2a^2x + a^2 = 0$

60. $px^2 - p^2x - x = -p$

Solve each of the equations in Exercises 61–66 for y in terms of x.

61. $x^2 - 4xy + 4y^2 - 16 = 0$

62. $2x^2 + xy - y^2 = 4$

63. $4x^2 - 2xy + y^2 = 7$

64. $x^2 + xy + y^2 + x + y = 1$

65. $4x^2 - 4xy + y^2 - 2x + y - 1 = 0$

66. $ax^2 + bxy + cy^2 + dx + ey + f = 0$

Solve each of the equations in Exercises 67–72 for the trigonometric ratio which appears; if x can be found without tables, find those values for which $0 \leqq x < 2\pi$, that is, x is between 0 and 2π with zero included.

67. $2 \sin^2 x + 3 \sin x - 2 = 0$

68. $6 \cos^2 x - 13 \cos x + 6 = 0$

69. $15 \tan^2 x - \tan x - 2 = 0$

70. $5 \sec x = 11 - 2 \sec^2 x$

71. $2 \cot^2 x + \sqrt{3} = (1 + 2\sqrt{3}) \cot x$

72. $\sqrt{6} \csc^2 x + 2\sqrt{3} \csc x = 4 + 2\sqrt{2} \csc x$

73. Find the value of k if the vertex of the graph of the function $2x^2 - kx + 1$ lies on the line $y = x$.

74. An object is sold for \$11, which includes a profit of as many percent as the number of dollars of original cost. Find the original cost.

75. The dimensions of a picture are 11×14 in. The area of the frame is approximately one-third the area of the picture. What is the width of the frame?

76. If a uniform border is added to a rug which is 9 ft. by 12 ft, the area is increased by 72 ft^2. Find the width of the border.

77. If each side of a square were increased by 18 in., the area would be increased by $21\frac{3}{4}$ yd^2. Find the side of the square.

78. The sum of a number and its reciprocal is 1. Find the number.

79. Find the area of a square whose diagonal is 10 in. longer than a side.

80. Find three consecutive odd integers the sum of whose squares is 251.

81. The length of a rectangle is 6 more than twice the width, and the diagonal is 39. Find the dimensions.

82. A pilot whose air speed was 250 mph found that it took him 24 min longer to fly 495 mi against the wind than to fly the same distance with the wind. Find the wind velocity.

4-6 CHARACTER OF THE ROOTS OF A QUADRATIC EQUATION

The roots of the general quadratic equation $ax^2 + bx + c = 0$ $(a \neq 0)$ are given in terms of the coefficients a, b, and c by the quadratic formula. Let the roots be designated by r_1 and r_2, where

$$r_1 = \frac{-b + \sqrt{b^2 - 4ac}}{2a}, \qquad r_2 = \frac{-b - \sqrt{b^2 - 4ac}}{2a}.$$

It is obvious from the above relations that if $b^2 - 4ac = 0$, then $r_1 = r_2 = -b/2a$. Conversely, if $r_1 = r_2$, then $r_1 - r_2 = 0$, from which it follows that

$$r_1 - r_2 = \frac{2\sqrt{b^2 - 4ac}}{2a} = 0, \qquad \text{so that} \qquad b^2 - 4ac = 0.$$

The quantity $b^2 - 4ac$ is called the *discriminant* of both the equation $ax^2 + bx + c = 0$, and of the function $ax^2 + bx + c$.

We introduce here symbols to represent the relations "greater than" and "less than." The following notation is commonly employed:

$a > b$ means that "a is greater than b,"
$a < b$ means that "a is less than b."

If the discriminant is not zero, then of course $r_1 \neq r_2$ (read: r_1 is not equal to r_2), but additional information can be obtained. For if a, b, c are real, then whether r_1 and r_2 are real or imaginary depends on the sign of $b^2 - 4ac$. If $b^2 - 4ac > 0$, then r_1 and r_2 will be real; if $b^2 - 4ac < 0$, then r_1 and r_2 will be imaginary.

These results can be immediately related also to the corresponding function $ax^2 + bx + c$ with zeros r_1 and r_2, and to the graph of the function $ax^2 + bx + c$.

Summarizing, we have the following results, if a, b, c are real:

(1) $r_1 = r_2$ *if and only if* $b^2 - 4ac = 0$, *in which case the vertex of the graph of the function* $ax^2 + bx + c$ *is on the x-axis;*

(2) r_1 *and* r_2 *are real and* $r_1 \neq r_2$ *if* $b^2 - 4ac > 0$, *in which case the graph of the function* $ax^2 + bx + c$ *crosses the x-axis in two distinct points;*

(3) r_1 *and* r_2 *are imaginary and* $r_1 \neq r_2$ *if* $b^2 - 4ac < 0$, *in which case the graph of the function* $ax^2 + bx + c$ *does not cross or touch the x-axis.*

(4) *Let* a, b, c *be rational numbers. Then* r_1 *and* r_2 *are also rational and the function* $ax^2 + bx + c$ *can be factored if and only if* $b^2 - 4ac$ *is the square of a rational number.*

If a, b, c are not necessarily real, then we also have $r_1 = r_2$ if and only if $b^2 - 4ac = 0$.

Example 1. Without solving the equation

$$2x^2 - 3x + 5 = 0,$$

determine the nature of its roots.

Solution. $a = 2$, $b = -3$, $c = 5$. The discriminant is

$$b^2 - 4ac = 9 - 4(2)(5) = -31 < 0.$$

Hence the roots are unequal and are imaginary.

Example 2. Determine h so that the graph of the function $3x^2 - 4x - 2h$ does not cross or touch the x-axis.

Solution. Since the graph does not cross or touch the x-axis, the zeros of the function must be imaginary and by (3) above we must have $b^2 - 4ac < 0$. Hence,

$$b^2 - 4ac = 16 + 24h < 0,$$

and the values of h are: $h < -\frac{2}{3}$.

Example 3. Can the expression $16x^2 - 76x + 21$ be factored?

Solution. The discriminant is

$$b^2 - 4ac = (76)^2 - 4 \cdot 16 \cdot 21 = 5776 - 1344 = 4432,$$

which is not a perfect square. Hence by (4) the expression cannot be factored into rational factors.

4-7 RELATIONS BETWEEN THE ROOTS AND COEFFICIENTS OF THE QUADRATIC EQUATION

For convenience we shall rewrite the formulas for the roots of a quadratic equation. They are

$$r_1 = \frac{-b + \sqrt{b^2 - 4ac}}{2a}, \qquad r_2 = \frac{-b - \sqrt{b^2 - 4ac}}{2a}.$$

By adding these values, we find

$$r_1 + r_2 = -\frac{2b}{2a} = -\frac{b}{a}, \tag{8}$$

and by multiplying r_1 and r_2 and simplifying the result, we obtain

$$r_1 \cdot r_2 = \frac{b^2 - (b^2 - 4ac)}{4a^2} = \frac{4ac}{4a^2} = \frac{c}{a}. \tag{9}$$

If we designate the sum of the roots by S and the product by P, *the formulas are*

$$\boxed{S = -\frac{b}{a}, \qquad P = \frac{c}{a}.} \tag{10}$$

Formula (10) permits us to write any quadratic equation in the form

$$ax^2 + bx + c = a(x^2 - Sx + P) = 0,$$

and, since $a \neq 0$, we have another form for a quadratic equation:

$$\boxed{x^2 - Sx + P = 0.} \tag{11}$$

Substituting $r_1 + r_2$ for S and $r_1 r_2$ for P in (11), we have

$$x^2 - (r_1 + r_2)x + r_1 r_2 = 0;$$

on factoring the left member, we obtain

$$\boxed{(x - r_1)(x - r_2) = 0.} \qquad (12)$$

Both (11) and (12) are very useful when we wish to obtain a quadratic equation for which the roots are known.

Example 1. Without finding the roots of the equation $3x^2 + 7x - 9 = 0$, determine the sum and product of these roots.

Solution. From Eqs. (8) and (9) above, we have, since $a = 3$, $b = 7$, $c = -9$,

$$r_1 + r_2 = -\frac{b}{a} = -\frac{7}{3}, \qquad r_1 \cdot r_2 = \frac{c}{a} = \frac{-9}{3} = -3.$$

Example 2. Determine the value of the constant h so that the zeros of the function $3hx^2 + 5x + 7hx + 9$ are numerically equal but opposite in sign.

Solution. The stated condition becomes $r_1 = -r_2$; then $r_1 + r_2 = 0$, and since $a = 3h$ and $b = 5 + 7h$, we have

$$0 = -\frac{b}{a} = -\frac{5 + 7h}{3h}, \qquad \text{so that} \qquad h = -\frac{5}{7}.$$

Example 3. Find a quadratic equation whose roots are $3 + 2\sqrt{3}$ and $3 - 2\sqrt{3}$.

Solution. From the given values of r_1 and r_2 we find that $S = 6$ and that $P = -3$. The desired equation is $x^2 - Sx + P = 0$, which takes the form $x^2 - 6x - 3 = 0$.

Example 4. Find the value of k if in the equation $2x^2 - kx^2 + 4x + 5k = 0$ one root is the reciprocal of the other.

Solution. From the given equation we see that $a = 2 - k$, $b = 4$, and $c = 5k$. If one root is the reciprocal of the other, then $r_1 = 1/r_2$, which reduces to $r_1 \cdot r_2 = 1$. Thus we have

$$P = 5k/(2 - k) = 1 \qquad \text{or} \qquad 5k = 2 - k.$$

This reduces to

$$6k = 2 \qquad \text{or} \qquad k = \tfrac{1}{3}.$$

Example 5. Find the value of the constant k in the equation

$$2x^2 - kx + 3k = 0,$$

if the difference of the roots is $\frac{5}{2}$.

Solution. If the roots are r_1 and r_2, by first adding them and then subtracting them, we have

$$r_1 - r_2 = \frac{5}{2}, \qquad r_1 + r_2 = \frac{k}{2}.$$

Solving these equations simultaneously, by first adding them and then subtracting them, we find

$$r_1 = \frac{k+5}{4}, \qquad r_2 = \frac{k-5}{4}, \qquad \text{hence} \qquad r_1r_2 = \frac{k^2-25}{16}.$$

But $r_1r_2 = 3k/2$. Hence $(k^2 - 25)/16 = 3k/2$, which becomes

$$k^2 - 24k - 25 = 0;$$

this yields the two solutions $k = -1$ and $k = 25$.

EXERCISE GROUP 4-4

In each of Exercises 1–18, compute the discriminant, and from its value determine the nature of the roots of the given equation.

1. $x^2 - 8x + 7 = 0$
2. $2x^2 + 9x + 7 = 0$
3. $3x^2 - 2x + 3 = 0$
4. $2x^2 + 12x = -18$
5. $2x^2 = 17$
6. $5x - 3 = 4x^2$
7. $5x^2 + 7x = 0$
8. $x^2 - 8x + 16 = 0$
9. $x^2 - x + 1 = 0$
10. $7x = 2x^2 + 3$
11. $8x + 1 = -16x^2$
12. $13x^2 = 6x - 1$
13. $3x^2 + 7x = 5$
14. $5x - 9 = 3x^2$
15. $9x^2 + 16 = 24x$
16. $\frac{1}{2}x^2 + \frac{4}{3} = x$
17. $3.2x^2 + 0.1 = 1.6x$
18. $\sqrt{3}x^2 - 8x + \frac{16\sqrt{3}}{3} = 0$

In each of Exercises 19–24, use the value of the discriminant to determine the values of k for which the equation will have equal roots.

19. $2x^2 - 2kx + 3 = 0$
20. $3kx^2 - 7x + 1 = 0$
21. $3x^2 - 5x - k = 0$
22. $4x^2 - 4kx + 5k = 0$
23. $kx^2 - x^2 + 4kx = 8$
24. $2kx^2 + 5x - 2k = 0$

In Exercises 25–33, determine the sum and product of the roots of each equation.

25. $3x^2 + 5x - 6 = 0$
26. $-2x^2 + 3x - 7 = 0$
27. $11 - 3x = 5x^2$
28. $5x^2 = 9$
29. $cx + d = ax^2$
30. $ax + 7 = cx^2$
31. $ax + c = bx^2$
32. $dx^2 - fx = 0$
33. $2x^2 - ix + 2 = 0$

In each of Exercises 34–45, find a quadratic equation whose roots are the given numbers.

34. $5, -3$
35. $\frac{2}{3}, -\frac{5}{4}$
36. $2 + \sqrt{3}, 2 - \sqrt{3}$
37. $-3, 2/5$
38. $2 + 3i, 2 - 3i$
39. $\frac{1 + i\sqrt{2}}{3}, \frac{1 - i\sqrt{2}}{3}$
40. $a, -2a$
41. $-3i, 1 + 3i$
42. $-3 + 5i, -3 - 5i$
43. $2 + \sqrt{7}, 2 - \sqrt{7}$
44. $\frac{1}{6}(2 \pm i\sqrt{3})$
45. $\frac{\sqrt{a} \pm \sqrt{c - a}}{a}$

In each of Exercises 46–55, find the value of the constant h for which:

46. One root is zero: $5x^2 + hx - 2h + 6 = 0$

47. One root is zero: $4hx^2 - 3x + h = 3h^2$
48. One root is the negative of the other: $5hx^2 - hx + 7 = x$
49. One root is the negative of the other: $3x^2 + 5hx + 2h^2 = 6 - 5x$
50. One root is 5: $2hx^2 - 4x - 15h = 2x^2$
51. One root is 7: $3x^2 + 10hx - h = 0$
52. One root is the reciprocal of the other: $3hx^2 + hx - 5 = 7x$
53. One root is three times the other: $hx^2 + 6x + 18 = 0$
54. The roots are equal: $(h - 13)x^2 + 5hx - 36(h + 13) = 0$
55. The roots are equal: $5(3x + h)^2 + c^2x^2 = 5c^2$
56. Prove that the roots of the equation $x^2 + 2px + p^2 - q^2 - 2qr - r^2 = 0$ are rational expressions in p, q, and r.
57. If r_1 and r_2 are the roots of the equation $ax^2 + bx + c = 0$, find the equation:
    (a) Whose roots are r_1/r_2 and r_2/r_1. [*Hint*: Find the sum and product of the new roots, and use the relation $r_1^2 + r_2^2 = (r_1 + r_2)^2 - 2r_1r_2$.]
    (b) Whose roots are $(r_1 + r_2)^2$ and $(r_1 - r_2)^2$. [*Hint*: $(r_1 - r_2)^2 = (r_1 + r_2)^2 - 4r_1r_2$.]
58. In what range of values must the sum of a real number and its reciprocal lie?
59. For the equation $ax^2 + bx + c = 0$, show that:
    (a) if one root is the negative of the other, then $b = 0$;
    (b) if the sum of the roots is equal to their product, then $b + c = 0$;
    (c) if the difference of the roots is equal to their product, then $b^2 - c^2 = 4ac$;
    (d) if the roots are reciprocals, then $a = c$;
    (e) if one root is twice the other, then $2b^2 = 9ac$;
    (f) if one root is three times the other, then $3b^2 = 16ac$.

4–8 EQUATIONS IN QUADRATIC FORM

The methods developed in Sections 4–4 and 4–5 for determining the roots of a quadratic equation apply equally well to any equation which can be reduced to a quadratic equation by means of a substitution, that is, to *an equation which is quadratic in a function of x.*

Example 1. Solve for x: $3x^4 - 4x^2 - 7 = 0$.

Solution. Let $v = x^2$, then $3v^2 - 4v - 7 = 0$, which is quadratic in v, so that the original equation is quadratic in x^2. By factoring, we have $(3v - 7)(v + 1) = 0$, and the values of v are $v = \frac{7}{3}, -1$. But $x = \pm\sqrt{v}$, therefore

$$x = \pm\sqrt{\frac{7}{3}} = \pm\frac{\sqrt{21}}{3},$$

and

$$x = \pm\sqrt{-1} = \pm i.$$

The four roots are

$$x = \pm\frac{\sqrt{21}}{3}, \quad \pm i.$$

Example 2. Solve for x: $x^4 + 6x^3 + 2x^2 - 21x - 18 = 0$.

Solution. Completing the square on the first two terms leads to

$$(x^4 + 6x^3 + 9x^2) - 9x^2 + 2x^2 - 21x - 18 = 0,$$

or

$$(x^2 + 3x)^2 - 7(x^2 + 3x) - 18 = 0. \tag{13}$$

Let $v = x^2 + 3x$; then

$$v^2 - 7v - 18 = 0,$$

or

$$(v - 9)(v + 2) = 0;$$

therefore

$$v - 9 = 0, \qquad x^2 + 3x - 9 = 0 \quad \text{and} \quad x = \frac{-3 \pm 3\sqrt{5}}{2},$$

or

$$v + 2 = 0, \qquad x^2 + 3x + 2 = 0 \quad \text{and} \quad x = -1, -2.$$

The four solutions are

$$x = -1, \quad -2, \quad \frac{-3 \pm 3\sqrt{5}}{2}.$$

Equation (13) is quadratic in $x^2 + 3x$.

EXERCISE GROUP 4-5

Determine all values of x satisfying each of the equations in Exercises 1–32.

1. $x^4 - 17x^2 + 16 = 0$
2. $x^4 - 13x^2 + 36 = 0$
3. $x^6 + 28x^3 + 27 = 0$
4. $x^6 - 56x^3 - 512 = 0$
5. $x^6 - 35x^3 + 216 = 0$
6. $x^8 - 17x^4 + 16 = 0$
7. $2x^4 - 19x^2 + 45 = 0$
8. $6x^4 - 59x^2 + 144 = 0$
9. $x^{-2} + x^{-1} - 6 = 0$
10. $x^{-2} - 8x^{-1} + 15 = 0$
11. $x^{-4} - 25x^{-2} + 144 = 0$
12. $8x^{-6} + 19x^{-3} - 27 = 0$
13. $81x^{-8} - 97x^{-4} + 16 = 0$
14. $16x^{-4} - 17x^{-2} + 1 = 0$
15. $x^{1/2} - 5x^{1/4} + 6 = 0$
16. $x^{2/3} - 6x^{1/3} + 8 = 0$
17. $5x^{1/2} - 5x^{-1/2} = 24$
18. $2x^{2/5} - x^{1/5} - 6 = 0$
19. $10x^{3/4} = 11x^{1/4} - 3x^{-1/4}$
20. $(x - 3) + 3(x - 3)^{1/2} = 10$
21. $x^3 + 19x^{3/2} = 216$
22. $(x^2 + 1)^2 + 11(x^2 + 1) + 24 = 0$
23. $(x^2 + 1)^2 - 15(x^2 + 1) + 50 = 0$
24. $(x^2 + x)^2 - 18(x^2 + x) + 72 = 0$
25. $(x^2 + x)^2 + 3(x^2 + x) - 10 = 0$
26. $2(x^2 - 3x)^2 + (x^2 - 3x) - 15 = 0$
27. $120(x^2 - 2x)^{-2} - 23(x^2 - 2x)^{-1} + 1 = 0$
28. $(x^2 - x - 12)(x^2 - x - 14) = 48$
29. $(x^2 + 2x - 5)(x^2 + 2x - 3) = 15$
30. $x^2 + 3x - \dfrac{20}{x^2 + 3x} = 8$
31. $3\left(\dfrac{1}{x} + 1\right)^2 + 5\left(\dfrac{1}{x} + 1\right) = 2$
32. $\dfrac{6x^2}{x + 1} + \dfrac{x + 1}{x^2} = 5$

Solve each of the following equations for the trigonometric ratio which appears, and if x can be found without tables, find those values in the range $0 \leqq x < 2\pi$.

33. $2\cos^{1/2} x - 1 = \cos^{1/4} x$

34. $3\sin^4 x - 2\sin^2 x = 1$

35. $3\tan^4 x + 3 = 10\tan^2 x$

36. $\sqrt{3}\cot x + 2\cot^{1/2} x = \sqrt{3}$

37. $16\sin^4 x - 16\sin^2 x + 3 = 0$

38. $4\cos^4 x + 3 = 7\cos^2 x$

39. $(1 + \sqrt{2})\sin^{1/2} x = 1 + \sqrt{2}\sin x$

40. $\cot^6 x - 8 = 7\cot^3 x$

41. $\sqrt[6]{3}\cot^{2/3} x = \cot^{1/3} x$

42. $1 + \sqrt[3]{2}\cos^{2/3} x = (1 + \sqrt[3]{2})\cos^{1/3} x$

4–9 IRRATIONAL EQUATIONS

Irrational equations are equations in which the unknown appears in one or more radicals. In general, the process of solving such an equation will involve the raising of quantities to certain powers. Since the even power of either a positive or negative quantity is positive, it follows that the process of raising to even powers may lead to an equation which has solutions which are not roots of the given equation. In other words, the method of solution may yield some values which are not roots, as well as those which are roots. The only certain way to determine which of the values found are roots is to *check in the original equation* all values obtained. Some examples will make this clear. Recall that if $x > 0$ there are two square roots of x, one of which is positive and the other negative. We agree that in this case the symbol $\sqrt{x}$ is to mean the *positive* square root of x.

Example 1. Solve the equation $\sqrt{x + 7} + x = 13$.

Solution. Subtract x from both members, which gives $\sqrt{x + 7} = 13 - x$. Then square both members, obtaining

$$x + 7 = (13 - x)^2 = 169 - 26x + x^2,$$
$$x^2 - 27x + 162 = 0,$$
$$(x - 9)(x - 18) = 0 \quad \text{and} \quad x = 9, 18.$$

Checking the value $x = 9$ in the original equation, we find

$$\sqrt{9 + 7} + 9 = 13,$$

and $x = 9$ is seen to be a root. However, if we try to check $x = 18$, we find

$$\sqrt{18 + 7} + 18 \neq 13,$$

so that $x = 18$ is *not* a root of the original equation. Hence there is only one solution of the problem: $x = 9$.

Example 2. Solve $\sqrt{3x - 5} + \sqrt{2x + 3} + 1 = 0$.

Solution. As in the solution of Example 1, we isolate one of the radicals, obtaining

$$\sqrt{3x - 5} = -1 - \sqrt{2x + 3}.$$

Squaring both members gives

$$3x - 5 = 1 + 2\sqrt{2x + 3} + 2x + 3,$$

which can be simplified to

$$2\sqrt{2x + 3} = x - 9.$$

Squaring both members of this equation gives

$$4(2x + 3) = x^2 - 18x + 81,$$

and this can be reduced to

$$x^2 - 26x + 69 = 0,$$

whose roots are $x = 3, 23$.

Checking these results in the original equation gives

$$\sqrt{9 - 5} + \sqrt{6 + 3} + 1 \neq 0 \quad \text{and} \quad x = 3 \text{ is not a root;}$$

$$\sqrt{69 - 5} + \sqrt{46 + 3} + 1 \neq 0 \quad \text{and} \quad x = 23 \text{ is not a root.}$$

Thus we see that *the given equation has no solution.*

Example 3. Solve $3\sqrt{2x + 1} - 3\sqrt{x + 4} = \sqrt{x - 3}$.

Solution. Squaring both sides, we get

$$9(2x + 1) - 18\sqrt{2x + 1}\sqrt{x + 4} + 9(x + 4) = x - 3.$$

We now simplify this equation and rewrite it so that the radical term appears by itself on one side of the equation. Thus,

$$-18\sqrt{2x + 1}\sqrt{x + 4} = -26x - 48.$$

Dividing both sides by -2 gives

$$9\sqrt{2x + 1}\sqrt{x + 4} = 13x + 24,$$

and now squaring both sides, we get

$$81(2x^2 + 9x + 4) = 169x^2 + 624x + 576,$$

which reduces to

$$x^2 - 15x + 36 = 0,$$

so that $x = 3, 12$.

Substituting these values in the original equation, we find

$$3\sqrt{25} - 3\sqrt{16} = \sqrt{9} \quad \text{and} \quad x = 12 \text{ is a root;}$$

$$3\sqrt{7} - 3\sqrt{7} = 0 \quad \text{and} \quad x = 3 \text{ is a root.}$$

EXERCISE GROUP 4-6

In each of Exercises 1–31, determine all values of x which satisfy the equation.

1. $\sqrt{x + 3} = 4$
2. $\sqrt{x - 2} = b$
3. $\sqrt{x + 2} = 3 + \sqrt{x}$
4. $\sqrt{x} + \sqrt{x + 1} = 3$
5. $\sqrt{3x + 10} - \sqrt{2x + 6} = 1$
6. $-\sqrt{2x - 9} + \sqrt{3x - 11} = 1$

7. $\sqrt{2x - 1} - \sqrt{x - 4} = 2$

8. $1 + \sqrt{2x - 5} - \sqrt{3x - 5} = 0$

9. $\sqrt{3x - 2} + \sqrt{2x - 2} = 1$

10. $\sqrt{3x - 6} + \sqrt{2x - 6} = 1$

11. $\sqrt{3x - 11} - \sqrt{6 - x} = \sqrt{2x - 9}$

12. $\sqrt{3x - 6} + \sqrt{x - 4} = \sqrt{10 - x}$

13. $\sqrt{3x + 10} - \sqrt{2x + 6} - \sqrt{15x + 6} = 0$

14. $\sqrt{5x - 4} = \sqrt{2x - 2} + \sqrt{2 - x}$

15. $2\sqrt{x + 3} - \sqrt{x + 8} - \sqrt{x} = 0$

16. $2\sqrt{x} - 2\sqrt{x + 3} = -2\sqrt{2 - x}$

17. $\sqrt{9 + x} - 2\sqrt{x + 5} = \sqrt{3 + x}$

18. $\sqrt{2x + 3} + \sqrt{x - 2} = 2$

19. $\sqrt{3x - 6} - \sqrt{6 - x} = \sqrt{2x - 6}$

20. $\sqrt{2x + 3} - \sqrt{x - 2} - \sqrt{7 - x} = 0$

21. $\sqrt{2x - 5} - \sqrt{x - 3} - \sqrt{7 - 2x} = 0$

22. $2\sqrt{x + 4} + \sqrt{x + 1} = \sqrt{9 - x}$

23. $\sqrt{4x - 1} - \sqrt{x + 3} = \sqrt{x - 2}$

24. $\sqrt{2x + 3} - \sqrt{4x - 1} = \sqrt{2 - 2x}$

25. $\sqrt{2x - 4} + \sqrt{3x + 4} + \sqrt{10x - 4} = 0$

26. $\sqrt{5 - 2x} - \sqrt{5x - 6} + \sqrt{3 - x} = 0$

27. $\sqrt{9 - x^2} - \sqrt{4x^2 + 15} = \sqrt{3}$

28. $\sqrt{4x^2 + 15} - \sqrt{9 - x^2} = \sqrt{3}$

29. $\sqrt{13 + 3\sqrt{x + 5 - 4\sqrt{x + 1}}} - 5 = 0$

30. $\dfrac{\sqrt{x + 3}}{\sqrt{x - 3}} - 2 = \dfrac{\sqrt{x - 3}}{\sqrt{x + 3}}$

31. $\dfrac{\sqrt{3x^2 + 4} + \sqrt{x^2 + 5}}{\sqrt{3x^2 + 4} - \sqrt{x^2 + 5}} = 7$

32. If a number is increased by 72, its positive square root is increased by 4. Find the number.

33. The positive square root of a number is increased by 1 when the number is increased by 19. Find the number.

34. Find the dimensions of a rectangle if the diagonal is 2 more than the longer side, which in turn is 2 more than the shorter side.

35. The square root of 3 less than twice a given number is 1 more than the square root of 2 more than the number. Find the number.

In each of the following exercises, find the value of the trigonometric ratio which satisfies the given equation, and if x can be found without tables, find those values of x in the range $0 \leqq x < 2\pi$.

36. $\sqrt{3 + 2\cos x} - \sqrt{-2 + 6\cos x} = \sqrt{-1 + 4\cos x}$

37. $\sqrt{15 - 2\sin x} - \sqrt{1 + 2\sin x} = \sqrt{19 + 6\sin x}$

38. $\sqrt{2 + \tan x} + \sqrt{10 + 3\tan x} = \sqrt{2(5\tan x + 8)}$

39. $\sqrt{1 - 2\cot x} + \sqrt{2 - \cot x} = \sqrt{1 + \cot x}$

SUPPLEMENTARY EXERCISES FOR CHAPTER 4

In each of Exercises 1–6, solve for x.

1. $\dfrac{3x+7}{5} - \dfrac{2x-3}{3} = \dfrac{7}{15} - 3$

2. $2x - 1 - \dfrac{3x-1}{x+1} = 2(x-1)$

3. $3 - \dfrac{2x+3}{3x-2} + \dfrac{x-1}{2-3x} = 0$

4. $1 - \dfrac{2x^2+3x+5}{2x^2+x-1} + \dfrac{3}{1-2x} = 0$

5. $1 - \dfrac{2x^2+5x+7}{2x^2-x-3} = \dfrac{1}{2x-3}$

6. $\dfrac{5}{x+5} - \dfrac{2}{x-3} = \dfrac{6(x+1)}{15-2x-x^2}$

In each of Exercises 7–18, use the quadratic formula in solving for x.

7. $3ax^2 - 2bx + 3a = 0$
8. $rx^2 + qx + p = 0$
9. $2ax^2 - cx + a = 0$
10. $ax^2 + cx + b = x$
11. $bx^2 + cx + a = x$
12. $x^2 + ax + b = c$
13. $2x^2 + 3x + 5 = 0$
14. $3x^2 + 2x = 17$
15. $5x^2 = 13 - 3x$
16. $2x^2 + 7 = 5x$
17. $5x^2 - 3x + 7 = 0$
18. $17 = 5x - x^2$

In each of Exercises 19–30, solve for x by the most appropriate method.

19. $2x^2 + bx + 6 = cx^2 + 3x$
20. $x^2 + ax + b = cx - dx^2$
21. $bx + c = ax^2 + d$
22. $x^2 + cx + d = ax^2 + bx$
23. $2x + 13 = ax^2 + bx - c$
24. $(x - b)^2 = a(x - c)$
25. $6x^2 + x = 35$
26. $6x^2 = 31x - 35$
27. $3x^2 = 2(x + 4)$
28. $ax^2 + bc = (b + ac)x$
29. $bx(x - a) = c(a - x)$
30. $(ax + b)^2 = x^2$

In each of Exercises 31–36, determine the values of k for which the given equation will have equal roots.

31. $x^2 + kx - 3k = 0$
32. $x^2 + 2kx + 5 = k$
33. $kx^2 = 2x^2 - 5kx + 7$
34. $(x - 2k)^2 = k(x - 2)$
35. $3x^2 + 5x + k = kx^2$
36. $(x + 2k)^2 = k(x + 2)$

In each of Exercises 37–42, determine the character of the roots and also the sum and product of the roots (without finding the roots).

37. $3x^2 + 5x - 7 = 0$
38. $2x^2 + 3x = 5x - 7$
39. $(3x + 1)^2 = 3(x - 3)$
40. $(3 - x)^2 = 5(x + 1)$
41. $x(x - 2) = 3(x - 3)$
42. $(x - 1)(x - 2) = 2x(x - 3)$

In each of Exercises 43–52, find all values of x which satisfy the given equation.

43. $x^6 + 9x^3 + 8 = 0$
44. $x^4 + 12x^2 - 64 = 0$
45. $x^4 + 16x^2 = 225$
46. $(4x^2 - 5)^2 - 3(4x^2 - 5) = 4$
47. $3(x^2 + 1)^2 = 2(x^2 + 5)$
48. $\sqrt{2 - x} + \sqrt{x - 1} = \sqrt{2x - 3}$
49. $\sqrt{x - 5} + \sqrt{x + 7} = 2\sqrt{x - 1}$
50. $2\sqrt{2x + 1} - \sqrt{x + 3} = \sqrt{3x - 1}$
51. $\sqrt{9x + 3} = \sqrt{1 - 3x} + \sqrt{3 - 6x}$
52. $\sqrt{25x - 15} + \sqrt{x + 9} = 2\sqrt{3x + 7}$

53. How many cubic centimeters of a 60% solution of sulfuric acid must be added to 200 cc of a 30% solution to obtain a 40% solution of the acid?

54. If the radius of a sphere is increased by 10%, what is the % change in the surface of the sphere? in the volume of the sphere?

55. If the interest for one year on an investment of \$3174 is \$142.83, what is the rate of interest on the investment?

56. An airplane with a 15 mph head wind takes 50% longer to fly 540 mi than it takes to fly 440 mi with a 15 mph tail wind. What is the air speed of the plane?

57. An open gutter is to be made by turning up the sides of a rectangular piece of metal w inches wide. If the cross-sectional area of the gutter is $w^2/8$ in^2, find the dimensions of the gutter.

58. A rectangular field is L yards long and W yards wide. Determine the width of rectangular strips of equal width that would need to be added to one side and to one end in order to double the area.

CHAPTER 5

Circle Relations. Right Triangles

5–1 RELATIONS IN A CIRCLE

Radian measure of angles was introduced in Section 3–4. We consider here an application that is not specifically related to trigonometric ratios. Let AB, of length s, be an arc on a circle of radius r (Fig. 5–1), and let θ be the angle subtended at the center of the circle by AB. Since the length of arc on a circle is proportional to the subtended angle, we have, for some constant k,

$$s = k\theta.$$

To find the value of the constant of proportionality k, we note that if θ is measured in radians, then $s = 2\pi r$ when $\theta = 2\pi$, since the complete circumference of a circle subtends an angle about the center O which is a complete rotation. Hence $k = r$ and, on substituting this value in the above equation, we have the desired *relation for the length of arc s on a circle in terms of the central angle θ*,

$$\boxed{s = r\theta, \qquad \theta \text{ in radians.}} \tag{1}$$

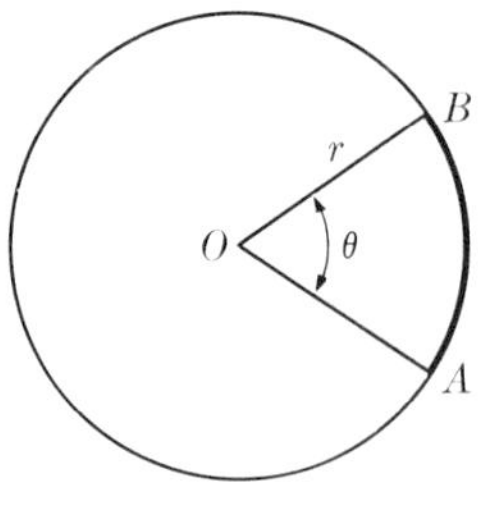

FIGURE 5–1

The area of the sector AOB, that is, of the part of the circle bounded by radii OA and OB, and arc AB, and with central angle θ, is also proportional to θ. Hence, for some constant K, we have

$$A = K\theta.$$

To determine the value of K, we use the fact that if θ is in radians, then $A = \pi r^2$ when $\theta = 2\pi$, since a complete rotation at O corresponds to a sector which is the entire circle. Hence $K = \frac{1}{2}r^2$, and *the formula for the area of AOB in terms of the central angle* θ *is*

$$A = \tfrac{1}{2}r^2\theta, \qquad \theta \text{ in radians.} \tag{2}$$

The appropriate formulas for converting back and forth from radian measure to degree measure appear in Section 3–4.

Example 1. Find the length of arc on a circle of radius 16 in. corresponding to a central angle of 112°, and find also the area of the sector formed by the angle.

Solution. For both quantities the radian measure of the angle is required; thus, we obtain

$$112^\circ = 112 \times \frac{\pi}{180} \text{ rad} = 1.955 \text{ rad}.$$

By (1) the length of arc s is then $s = r\theta = 16 \times 1.955 = 31.280$ in., and by (2) the area A of the sector is $A = \frac{1}{2}r^2\theta = \frac{1}{2}(256)(1.955) = 250.240 \text{ in}^2$.

Suppose that OA revolves about the center of the above circle in such a way that in equal intervals of time equal angles are traversed. *The angular speed of OA is then defined as the angle traversed per unit time.* Let OA revolve through an angle θ in the time t. If ω denotes the angular speed of OA, we have the formula

$$\omega = \frac{\theta}{t}. \tag{3}$$

As OA revolves at a *constant* angular speed about O, the point A moves along the circle with a constant linear speed, that is, in such a way that *the same length of arc is traversed in any unit time.* If v denotes the linear speed of A on the circle, then the corresponding formula is

$$v = \frac{s}{t}. \tag{4}$$

Dividing both members of Eq. (1) by t, we have

$$\frac{s}{t} = r\,\frac{\theta}{t};$$

by (3) and (4) this equation gives the important *relation between the angular speed ω of OA, and the linear speed v of A, as*

$$v = r\omega, \qquad \omega \text{ in radians per unit time.} \tag{5}$$

Example 2. The outer radius of the wheels of an automobile is 14 in. If the vehicle is traveling 30 mph, at how many revolutions per second are the wheels turning about their centers?

Solution. As a wheel rotates through any angle θ, the distance s which the vehicle moves is given by the length of arc on the circumference subtended by θ, so that $s = r\theta$. If both members of this equation are divided by t, it is then clear that the linear speed v of the vehicle and the angular speed ω of the wheels are related by Eq. (5). We have v = 30 mph = 528 in/sec; hence, since $r = 14$, we have by (5),

$$\omega = \frac{v}{r} = \frac{528}{14} \text{ rad/sec} = 37.7 \text{ rad/sec.}$$

Since a complete revolution corresponds to a central angle of 2π, we divide by 2π to convert ω to revolutions per second, and find that

$$\frac{\omega}{2\pi} = \frac{37.7}{2\pi} \text{ rev/sec} = 6.00 \text{ rev/sec.}$$

EXERCISE GROUP 5-1

In each of Exercises 1-18, the central angle and radius of the circle involved have the values given. Find the length of the intercepted arc, and the area of the sector.

1. 3 rad, 2 ft
2. 0.6 rad, 3 ft
3. 3.2 rad, 2.5 in.
4. 1.7 rad, 6 in.
5. 135°, 7 ft
6. 240°, 250 ft
7. 23°, 130 cm
8. 115°, 25 cm
9. 270°, 175 cm
10. 315°, 210 cm
11. 7° 20′, 65 yd
12. 19° 40′, 50 yd
13. 214° 12′, 0.6 in.
14. 313° 16′, 0.05 in.
15. 63°, 312 ft
16. 37°, 213 ft
17. 37°, 0.04 ft
18. 193°, 0.03 ft

Find the measure of the central angle in both radians and degrees, and the area of the sector, if the values of the intercepted arc and radius are those given in Exercises 19-30. The first quantity in each case is the arc length.

19. 18 in., 6 in.
20. 15 ft, 5.3 ft
21. 312 cm, 501 cm
22. 94 cm, 21.3 cm
23. 5.03 ft, 13.8 ft
24. 4.23 in., 16.5 in.
25. 127 in., 3.4 ft
26. 3.4 ft, 127 in.
27. 215 cm, 3 m
28. 52.3 in., 2.3 ft
29. 8.2 ft, 32.5 in.
30. 512 cm, 5 m

31. The wheels of an automobile are 28 in. in diameter and the automobile is traveling at a speed of 65 mph (286/3 ft/sec). Find the angular speed of the wheels in rad/sec.
32. A rotary lawn mower has a blade 20 in. in diameter and the motor runs at a speed of 3600 rpm. What is the linear speed in ft/sec of the tip of the blade?
33. In driving around a circular curve on a highway, the driver notes that the length of the curve is 0.3 mi and that the car turns through an angle of 25°. What is the radius of the curve in feet?
34. The propeller of a small airplane is 74 in. from tip to tip and it makes 2500 rpm at cruising speed. Find the linear speed in ft/sec of the tip of the propeller.

35. A curve on a highway, in the form of an arc of a circle, is 660 ft long. If the radius of the circle is 2612 ft, find the angle in degrees through which a car turns in going around the curve.
36. A curve on a highway is laid out as the arc of a circle with a radius of 1800 ft, and it subtends a central angle of 18°. A car with tires 28 in. in diameter rounds the curve, so that the inner wheels are on the center line (which has the given radius), and have angular speeds of 52.8 rad/sec. Find the speed of the car in mph, and the time required for the car to round the curve.
37. What is the angular speed, in rad/sec, of the minute hand of a clock?
38. Let us assume that the moon travels around the earth at a uniform linear speed in a circular orbit. If the orbit is 239,000 miles in radius and if it takes the moon $27\frac{1}{3}$ days to make one complete revolution, what is the linear speed in mi/sec of the moon in its orbit?
39. The moon subtends an angle of approximately 31′ to an observer on the earth. Find the approximate diameter of the moon if it is assumed to be 239,000 mi distant from the observer. [*Hint*: Consider the diameter of the moon as a circular arc.]
40. Two observation stations A and B are established, with A being 207.4 mi directly north of B. At the instant that the sun is directly over the north and south line running through A and B it is observed that the angle of elevation of the sun at B is 3° greater than it is at A. What is the radius of the earth? [*Hint*: The sun's rays are parallel.]
41. An electric motor which runs at 3000 rpm has a 6 in. (6 in. in diameter) pulley which drives a belt. Find the linear speed (in ft/sec) of the belt. If the belt drives another pulley which is 8 in. in diameter, find the angular speed in rad/sec of this second pulley.

5–2 INTERPOLATION IN THE TRIGONOMETRIC TABLE

In the applications of trigonometry the values of the trigonometric ratios are often required for angles given more accurately than to the nearest 10′. Table 2 may be used to find the values of the ratios for angles which are given to any number of minutes. *The method to be used is that of linear interpolation.* By the process of *direct interpolation* the table may be used to find the values of the ratios of such angles, and by *inverse interpolation* the table may be used to find an angle to the nearest minute when the value of a trigonometric ratio of the angle is known.

The principle of linear interpolation, as applied here, is that a sufficiently small arc of the graph representing a trigonometric ratio may be replaced by a straight line.

We may interpret this principle to mean that the difference between angles sufficiently close in value is proportional to the difference between the corresponding values of any trigonometric ratio.

In applying interpolation to a table of trigonometric ratios, it is important to keep in mind that as the angle increases from 0° to 90°, the sine, tangent, and secant also increase, while the cosine, cotangent, and cosecant decrease.

Example 1. Find tan 53° 18′.

Solution. The given angle lies between 53° 10′ and 53° 20′. Hence, by the above principle, we have

$$\frac{\tan 53^\circ 18' - \tan 53^\circ 10'}{\tan 53^\circ 20' - \tan 53^\circ 10'} = \frac{53^\circ 18' - 53^\circ 10'}{53^\circ 20' - 53^\circ 10'},$$

which becomes

$$\frac{\tan 53^\circ 18' - 1.335}{1.343 - 1.335} = \frac{8}{10}.$$

This equation can be solved for tan 53° 18′ as

$$\begin{aligned} \tan 53^\circ 18' &= 1.335 + 0.8 \times (1.343 - 1.335) \\ &= 1.335 + 0.8 \times 0.008 \\ &= 1.335 + 0.006 \\ &= 1.341. \end{aligned}$$

Note that this value is rounded off to four figures. The entire process can be abbreviated in the following schematic manner:

$$10\left[\begin{array}{l} 8\left[\begin{array}{ll} 53^\circ 10' & 1335 \\ 53^\circ 18' & x \end{array}\right] h \\ \quad 53^\circ 20' \quad 1343 \end{array}\right] 8 \qquad \begin{array}{l} \dfrac{h}{8} = \dfrac{8}{10}, \quad h = 0.8 \times 8, \\ h = 6 \text{ (to nearest integer)}, \end{array}$$

where the differences in the values of the ratio are understood to be in the last decimal places. Hence,

$$x = \tan 53^\circ 18' = 1.335 + 0.006 = 1.341.$$

Example 2. Find cos 18° 27′.

Solution. Schematically, we have

$$10\left[\begin{array}{l} 7\left[\begin{array}{ll} 18^\circ 20' & 9492 \\ 18^\circ 27' & x \end{array}\right] h \\ \quad 18^\circ 30' \quad 9483 \end{array}\right] 9 \qquad \begin{array}{l} \dfrac{h}{9} = \dfrac{7}{10}, \quad h = \dfrac{63}{10}, \\ h = 6 \text{ (to nearest integer)}. \end{array}$$

Hence, since the cosine is a decreasing ratio in the first quadrant,

$$x = 0.9492 - 0.0006 = 0.9486.$$

A similar procedure, and corresponding schematic arrangement, can be used for inverse interpolation.

Example 3. Find θ if $\sin\theta = 0.7423$.

Solution. From the table we see that $\sin\theta$ is between sin 47° 50′ and sin 48°. The schematic arrangement becomes

$$19\left[\begin{array}{l} 11\left[\begin{array}{ll} 7412 & 47^\circ 50' \\ 7423 & \theta \end{array}\right] h \\ \quad 7431 \quad 48^\circ \end{array}\right] 10, \qquad \begin{array}{l} \dfrac{h}{10} = \dfrac{11}{19}, \quad h = \dfrac{110}{19}, \\ h = 6 \text{ (to nearest integer)}. \end{array}$$

Hence we obtain

$$\theta = 47° \, 50' + 6' = 47° \, 56'.$$

Example 4. Find θ if $\cot\theta = 2.172$.

Solution. Schematically, we have

$$16\left[5\left[\begin{matrix}2177 & 24° \, 40' \\ 2172 & \theta\end{matrix}\right]h \atop \begin{matrix}2161 & 24° \, 50'\end{matrix}\right]10, \qquad \frac{h}{10} = \frac{5}{16}, \quad h = \frac{50}{16}, \quad h = 3 \text{ (to nearest integer)}.$$

Hence,

$$\theta = 24° \, 40' + 3' = 24° \, 43'.$$

EXERCISE GROUP 5-2

Use Table 2 to find the values of the trigonometric ratios in each of Exercises 1–24.

1. $\sin 13° \, 17'$	2. $\cos 24° \, 12'$	3. $\tan 57° \, 46'$
4. $\cot 63° \, 46'$	5. $\cos 74° \, 13'$	6. $\sin 84° \, 15'$
7. $\cot 59° \, 28'$	8. $\tan 17° \, 59'$	9. $\sin 22° \, 11'$
10. $\cos 7° \, 52'$	11. $\cot 53° \, 23'$	12. $\tan 46° \, 45'$
13. $\sin 15° \, 55'$	14. $\cos 213° \, 17'$	15. $\tan 312° \, 42'$
16. $\sec 173° \, 13'$	17. $\csc 47° \, 18'$	18. $\sec 132° \, 12'$
19. $\csc 217° \, 15'$	20. $\cot 313° \, 13'$	21. $\csc 284° \, 17'$
22. $\sec 42° \, 18'$	23. $\csc 147° \, 14'$	24. $\sec 413° \, 16'$

Use Table 2 to find the values of the angle θ, such that $0 < \theta < 180°$, to the nearest minute, in each of Exercises 25–48.

25. $\cos\theta = 0.0099$	26. $\sin\theta = 0.7703$	27. $\cot\theta = 0.6275$
28. $\tan\theta = 4.536$	29. $\cos\theta = 0.5116$	30. $\sin\theta = 0.1059$
31. $\cot\theta = -9.372$	32. $\tan\theta = 0.2365$	33. $\tan\theta = -0.8713$
34. $\cos\theta = 0.9162$	35. $\sin\theta = 0.5385$	36. $\cot\theta = -1.147$
37. $\cos\theta = 0.3537$	38. $\sin\theta = 0.6300$	39. $\cot\theta = 9.800$
40. $\csc\theta = 1.132$	41. $\sec\theta = 1.968$	42. $\tan\theta = -1.121$
43. $\csc\theta = 5.294$	44. $\sec\theta = 8.039$	45. $\csc\theta = 16.98$
46. $\sec\theta = 5.296$	47. $\sec\theta = 10.53$	48. $\csc\theta = 2.658$

5-3 SOLUTION OF RIGHT TRIANGLES

We mentioned, in Section 3-1, that the origins of the study of trigonometry lie in the determination of distances on the earth by the use of triangles. This process involves the solution of triangles. We shall now consider the methods which apply to the solution of right triangles; oblique triangles will be treated in Chapter 14.

In addition to the right angle, a right triangle contains two acute angles, and the three sides, which are the *hypotenuse* and the two *arms* or *legs*. Let the sides and

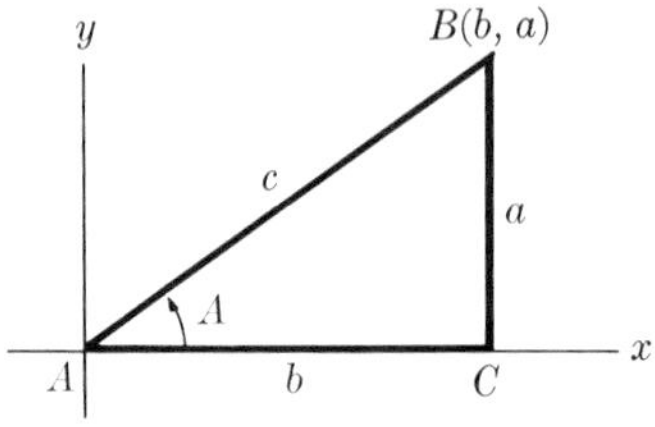

FIGURE 5–2

angles of the triangle be called the *parts of the triangle.* By theorems of plane geometry it is known that a right triangle is determined when, in addition to the right angle, any two parts, of which at least one is a side, are known. *To solve a right triangle shall mean to find all unknown parts.*

It will facilitate the solution of a right triangle to have formulas for the trigonometric ratios of the acute angles in terms of the sides. We shall use a *standard lettering ABC* for a right triangle, with C as the vertex of the right angle, and with the side opposite any vertex designated by the corresponding lower-case letter.

Let right triangle ABC be placed in a coordinate system so that angle A is in standard position and side CB is perpendicular to the x-axis (Fig. 5–2). Then B is a point on the terminal side of angle A, and b, a, c are the coordinates and polar distance, respectively, of B. By the definitions of the trigonometric ratios given in Section 3–6, we have

$$\sin A = \frac{a}{c} = \frac{\text{opposite side}}{\text{hypotenuse}},$$

$$\cos A = \frac{b}{c} = \frac{\text{adjacent side}}{\text{hypotenuse}},$$

$$\tan A = \frac{a}{b} = \frac{\text{opposite side}}{\text{adjacent side}},$$

$$\cot A = \frac{b}{a} = \frac{\text{adjacent side}}{\text{opposite side}},$$

$$\sec A = \frac{c}{b} = \frac{\text{hypotenuse}}{\text{adjacent side}},$$

$$\csc A = \frac{c}{a} = \frac{\text{hypotenuse}}{\text{opposite side}}.$$

In these equations the designations "opposite side" and "adjacent side" always refer to the angle involved. Once obtained, the formulas are, of course, independent of any coordinate system, and in particular, the verbal expressions apply to either acute angle of the triangle. Thus, if sec B is desired, the term "adjacent side" must be taken in relation to angle B, and we find that $\sec B = c/a$.

If an unknown angle of a right triangle is to be found, use is made of a trigonometric ratio of that angle which involves two known sides; to find an unknown side, a trigonometric ratio of a known angle is used which contains a known side and the unknown side. As a general rule it is desirable, where possible, to make use of given parts of a triangle in preference to parts which have been computed.

Example 1. Solve the right triangle with $A = 57° 20'$, $c = 0.0286$.

Solution. To find side a we use the relation $\sin A = a/c$, which involves the known side c, and side a. This relation can be solved for a to give

$$\begin{aligned} a &= c \sin A = 0.0286 \sin 57° 20' \\ &= 0.0286 \times 0.8418 = 0.0241. \end{aligned}$$

To find side b, we have similarly, using a relation which involves the given side c, and side b,

$$\begin{aligned} b &= c \cos A = 0.0286 \cos 57° 20' \\ &= 0.0286 \times 0.5398 = 0.0154. \end{aligned}$$

Finally, we have $B = 90° - 57° 20' = 32° 40'$ (see Fig. 5-3).

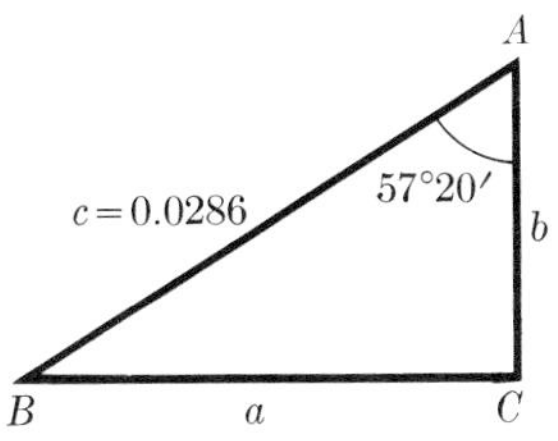

FIGURE 5-3

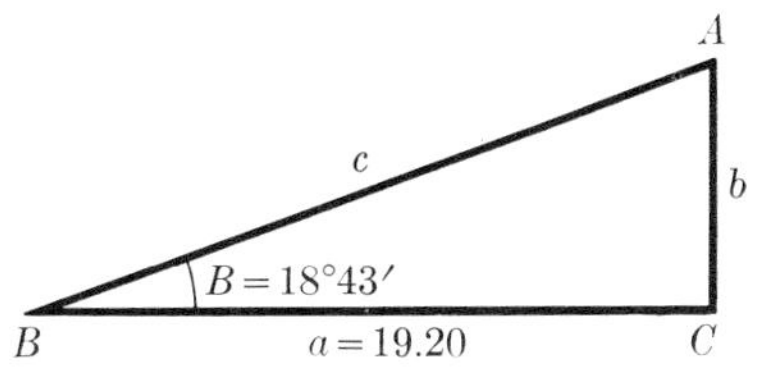

FIGURE 5-4

Example 2. Solve the right triangle with $B = 18° 43'$, $a = 19.20$.

Solution. To find side c we solve the equation $\cos B = a/c$ for c; thus,

$$c = \frac{a}{\cos B} = \frac{19.20}{\cos 18° 43'} = \frac{19.20}{0.9471} = 20.27.$$

Side b is then found from the equation $\tan B = b/a$, as follows:

$$b = a \tan B = 19.20 \tan 18° 43' = 19.20 \times 0.3388 = 6.505.$$

Again, $A = 90° - 18° 43' = 71° 17'$ (see Fig. 5-4).

Example 3. Solve the right triangle with $a = 1124$, $b = 1876$.

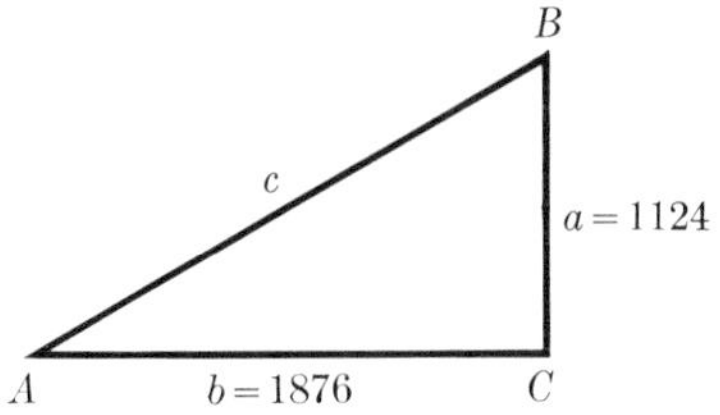

FIGURE 5–5

Solution. We may find angle A as follows, using a ratio of A which involves a and b (see Fig. 5–5):

$$\tan A = \frac{a}{b} = \frac{1124}{1876} = 0.5991; \qquad A = 30^\circ\, 56'.$$

Then the equation $\sin A = a/c$ may be solved for c, and we have

$$c = \frac{a}{\sin A} = \frac{1124}{\sin 30^\circ\, 56'} = \frac{1124}{0.5140} = 2187.$$

The remaining angle is $B = 90^\circ - 30^\circ\, 56' = 59^\circ\, 04'$.

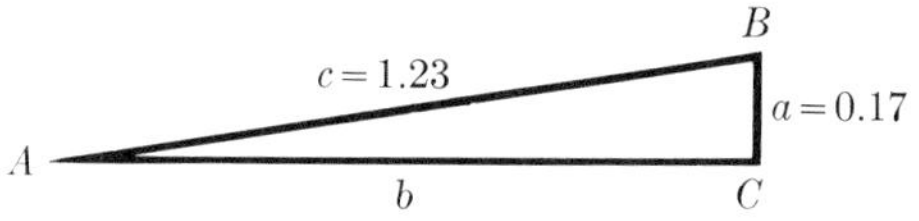

FIGURE 5–6

Example 4. Solve the right triangle with $a = 0.17$, $c = 1.23$.

Solution. We may find angle A as follows (see Fig. 5–6):

$$\sin A = \frac{a}{c} = \frac{0.17}{1.23} = 0.1382; \qquad A = 7^\circ\, 57'.$$

Then the equation $\cos A = b/c$ may be solved for b, and we have

$$b = c \cos A = 1.23 \times 0.9904 = 1.22.$$

Angle B is found to be $82^\circ\, 03'$.

EXERCISE GROUP 5–3

Solve the right triangles in Exercises 1–30. (It is assumed that $C = 90^\circ$.)

1. $c = 75.16$, $B = 37^\circ\, 14'$
2. $a = 23.20$, $B = 73^\circ\, 41'$
3. $b = 28.30$, $A = 68^\circ\, 39'$
4. $c = 63.07$, $A = 57^\circ\, 13'$
5. $a = 3.201$, $A = 36^\circ\, 22'$
6. $b = 0.0613$, $B = 28^\circ\, 34'$
7. $a = 902.3$, $B = 43^\circ\, 27'$
8. $b = 716.2$, $A = 44^\circ\, 57'$
9. $c = 86.39$, $A = 55^\circ\, 18'$
10. $c = 232.1$, $B = 19^\circ\, 26'$
11. $a = 2.135$, $b = 3.423$
12. $b = 0.2138$, $c = 1.207$
13. $a = 0.0612$, $c = 0.3818$
14. $c = 2317$, $a = 2137$
15. $c = 398.0$, $b = 153.4$
16. $a = 0.07013$, $b = 0.0071$

17. $b = 51.37$, $B = 31^\circ\ 23'$
18. $b = 32.75$, $A = 68^\circ\ 04'$
19. $a = 649.2$, $b = 496.2$
20. $a = 97.45$, $A = 39^\circ\ 34'$
21. $b = 29.64$, $A = 43^\circ\ 31'$
22. $b = 269.3$, $c = 352.4$
23. $a = 0.9426$, $A = 75^\circ\ 18'$
24. $a = 1.729$, $c = 3.376$
25. $b = 0.2514$, $a = 0.2769$
26. $a = 6.317$, $b = 4.372$
27. $c = 9.438$, $B = 56^\circ\ 03'$
28. $c = 64.19$, $A = 24^\circ\ 21'$
29. $c = 0.8364$, $b = 0.5209$
30. $c = 7.484$, $a = 3.121$

31. Compare the lengths AB, CD, and the arc length CB for $\theta = 4^\circ, 2^\circ, 0^\circ\ 30'$ in Fig. 5–7.

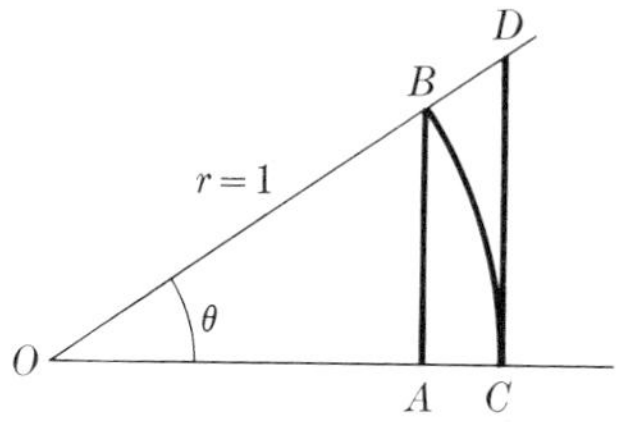

FIGURE 5–7

32. A sector of angle θ is cut from a circle of radius a, and the remaining portion is used to form the curved surface of a right circular cone. Express the altitude of the cone as a function of θ.

33. Let A, B, C be the vertices of an oblique triangle, and let $BC = a$, $AC = b$, and $AB = c$. Draw altitude BD to side AC. Justify the following equations, if angle A is acute:

$$a^2 = (BD)^2 + (CD)^2 = c^2 - (AD)^2 + (CD)^2$$
$$= c^2 - (AD)^2 + (b - AD)^2.$$

Expand the right member and obtain the result

$$a^2 = b^2 + c^2 - 2bc \cos A.$$

Show that the derivation holds in essentially the same form if A is obtuse.

5–4 APPROXIMATE NUMBERS

Almost all of the numbers which arise in applications of trigonometry as results of observation or measurement are approximate, or rather, approximations to exact numbers. Measurements of physical quantities are governed by the accuracy of the measuring devices used. If a length L is measured as 4.34 in., the implication is that the exact length in inches is closer to 4.34 than to any other two-decimal number and, in fact,

$$4.335 \leqq L \leqq 4.345.$$

Approximations are also used for numbers with many decimal places, or for numbers which cannot be represented by a finite decimal. The number π, which is an infinite decimal, is given to four decimal places as 3.1416; this means that

3.1416 is the number with four decimal places closest to the exact value of π, so that

$$3.14155 \leqq \pi \leqq 3.14165.$$

In the discussion of the accuracy of approximate numbers, the idea of *significant figures* plays an important part. In a number in decimal form any digit other than zero is always a significant figure. Zeros may or may not be significant. Zeros between nonzero digits are significant, while initial zeros are never significant. Whether final zeros in a number are significant or not depends on what is intended. For example, if 2030 is an approximate number, the first three digits are certainly significant. If the final zero is not meant to be significant, the exact number is merely known to be in the range

$$2025 \leqq x \leqq 2035.$$

However, if the final zero is meant to be significant, the exact number lies in the smaller range

$$2029.5 \leqq x \leqq 2030.5.$$

We shall agree that *final zeros which appear after the decimal point are significant.* It is then possible to express any number N in the form

$$N = m \cdot 10^c,$$

where $1 \leqq m < 10$, all digits of m are significant, and c is some integer. A number in this form is said to be in *scientific notation.* Thus, if 2030 has three significant figures it is written as 2.03×10^3, while with four significant figures the number is written as 2.030×10^3.

A number is said to be *correct to n significant figures* if the error in the $(n + 1)$st figure is at most 5; a number is *correct to n decimal places* if the error is at most 5 in the $(n + 1)$st decimal place.

Rounding off a number was explained in Section 3–9 in relation to the trigonometric table. A similar procedure applies in rounding off a number in any place, before or after the decimal point. In the former case, enough zeros are added to give the correct number of places before the decimal point. In any case, the rounded-off number has its last significant figure in the place in question.

Examples. 4.146 rounded off in the second decimal place is 4.15.

4.146 rounded off in the first decimal place is 4.1.

4146 rounded off in the tens place is 4150, with the zero not significant, or in scientific notation, 4.15×10^3.

20.75 rounded off in the first decimal place is 20.8, in accordance with our agreement to make the last figure even.

In general, the accuracy of a number is governed by the number of significant figures, and not by the size of the number. The numbers 4.146 and 4146 are thus equally accurate, if they are correct in the figures given.

5–5 OPERATIONS WITH APPROXIMATE NUMBERS

The results of arithmetic operations with approximate numbers are themselves of course subject to error, and it becomes necessary to know how such errors are propagated.

If the exact numbers $x = 20.4$ and $y = 8.709$ are added, the sum is 29.109. However, if x and y are merely known to be correct in the figures given, we have

$$20.35 \leqq x \leqq 20.45$$
$$8.7085 \leqq y \leqq 8.7095.$$

It can be shown that

$$29.0585 \leqq x + y \leqq 29.1595$$

where $29.0585 = 20.35 + 8.7085$, and $29.1595 = 20.45 + 8.7095$. It follows that the sum, which lies between 29.0585 and 29.1595, can certainly not be given to more than one decimal. Even correct to one decimal, the sum may be either 29.1 or 29.2. There is then nothing gained by carrying to more than two decimals any of the numbers to be added. If we round off 8.709 in the second decimal place as 8.71, and add 20.4, we get 29.11. This is then rounded off in the first decimal place, and the result is 29.1, of which the last figure may still be in error.

The product of the exact numbers 14.326 and 8.93 is 127.93118. However, if the numbers are merely known to be correct in the figures given, the product of the corresponding exact numbers must lie between

$$14.3255 \times 8.925 = 127.8550875$$

and

$$14.3265 \times 8.935 = 128.0072775.$$

Thus there is no justification in giving the product more accurately than to three significant figures, as 128, which is also the product to three significant figures of 14.33 and 8.93.

Similar considerations will show that in the division of two approximate numbers, the quotient cannot be given more accurately than the less accurate number.

We shall not give proofs here, but the preceding discussion should indicate the reasonableness of the following rule.

Rule. *Before adding (or subtracting) approximate numbers, round off each number in the place to the right of the last significant figure of the numbers which is farthest to the left with respect to the decimal point; the sum is then rounded off in the place of the last significant figure.* (See example below.)

Before multiplying or dividing numbers, round off the more accurate numbers to one more significant figure than in the least accurate number; the result is then rounded off to the number of significant figures of the least accurate number.

Example. Use the above rule to compute the sum of 23.79, 0.3246, 23450, and 34.278 to the accuracy permissible.

Solution. Write the numbers to be added in a column as displayed:

$$\begin{array}{r} 23.79 \\ 0.3246 \\ 23450. \\ 34.278 \end{array}$$

The last significant figures of these numbers are 9, 6, 5, and 8. We note that of these last significant numbers the 5 is the "farthest to the left with respect to the decimal point." This last significant figure 5 is in the ten's place and so in accordance with the rule we round off each number in the unit's place (which is the place to the right of the ten's place). After rounding off in the unit's place we obtained the numbers illustrated. Then according to the rule we round the sum off in the ten's place, obtaining 23510 as the desired sum.

$$\begin{array}{r} 24. \\ 0. \\ 23450. \\ 34. \\ \hline 23508. \end{array}$$

It should be understood that the last figure of any result obtained by applying the stated rule may still be in error. Furthermore, in the application of this rule, the position of the decimal point is relevant only in addition or subtraction.

A convenient working rule concerning significant figures in the solution of a triangle will now be given.

Rule. *Accuracy to two significant figures in the sides of a triangle corresponds to accuracy in the angles to the nearest degree; accuracy to three significant figures corresponds to accuracy in the angles to the nearest* 10 *minutes; accuracy to four significant figures corresponds to accuracy in the angles to the nearest minute.*

As a final comment it may be stated that in applications the possible error in a measurement may be different from that represented by rounding off. For example, a length may be measured as 2.3 with a maximum error of 0.1, whereas if 2.3 is known to be correct to one decimal place, the maximum error is only 0.05. Perhaps the length may be 2.3 with a possible error of only 0.02. With more information about possible errors the accuracy of computed results can often be established more closely. The methods required, however, involve more advanced techniques than are presently available to us.

EXERCISE GROUP 5–4

Round off the numbers in Exercises 1–12 to (1) four significant figures; (2) to three significant figures.

1. 23.4567	2. 0.03421507	3. 0.003452356	4. 2.173421
5. 2178563	6. 7132.475	7. 0.96154	8. 0.089755
9. 2.32509	10. 304780.1	11. 0.012345	12. 0.013245

Express the maximum possible error in the approximate quantities given in Exercises 13–21.

13. 31.2 cm
14. 0.023 in.
15. 4350 ft (last 0 significant)
16. 6.3127 mi
17. 71.826 ft^3
18. 20300 $in.^2$ (last 0 not significant)
19. 0.0013 yd
20. 21789 cm^2
21. 354100 $in.^3$ (last 0 significant)

Perform the indicated operations in Exercises 22–34, and round off the results to the correct number of significant figures.

22. $0.39678 - 2.34 + 8.2$
23. $3.2756 + 2.436 - 3.26$
24. $8.96 + 1.317 - 5.23479$
25. $76.93 - 23.5 + 3.1697$
26. (54.960)(35.2)
27. (317.5)(3.12)
28. (0.235)(2.3)
29. $43.1 \div 0.00034$
30. $0.00041 \div 2.167$
31. $2.3176 \div 0.003402$
32. $0.003192 \div 0.23078$
33. $(3.1416)^2$
34. $(0.0028183)^2$

In each of Exercises 35–46, find the value of $\theta(0 < \theta < 90°)$ as accurately as is justified by the given data.

35. $\sin \theta = 0.512$
36. $\cos \theta = 0.76$
37. $\tan \theta = 3.1$
38. $\cot \theta = 0.73$
39. $\sec \theta = 35.9$
40. $\csc \theta = 2.345$
41. $\tan \theta = \dfrac{3.128}{2.16}$
42. $\sin \theta = \dfrac{3.27}{40.75}$
43. $\cos \theta = \dfrac{63.7}{93.74}$
44. $\sec \theta = \dfrac{83.3}{73}$
45. $\csc \theta = \dfrac{0.8627}{0.31}$
46. $\cot \theta = \dfrac{8.637}{7.5}$

Solve the right triangles in each of Exercises 47–56, and round off the results to the correct number of significant figures.

47. $b = 43.27$, $A = 29°$
48. $b = 2.936$, $c = 3.9$
49. $a = 0.4962$, $A = 57°$
50. $a = 2.3$, $c = 3.637$
51. $a = 0.7926$, $b = 0.063$
52. $b = 7.136$, $a = 23.7$
53. $c = 9.438$, $B = 67° 08'$
54. $c = 64.19$, $A = 66°$
55. $c = 0.364$, $a = 0.12$
56. $c = 8.474$, $b = 4.8$

5-6 APPLICATIONS OF RIGHT TRIANGLES

In the applications of trigonometry important situations arise in which the determination of an angle or of a distance can be made to depend on the solution of one or more right triangles, or perhaps a partial solution in the sense that not all of the unknown parts are called for. In each problem a figure should be drawn, and analyzed for a method of solution.

One type of application involves problems stated in terms of *angle of elevation*, or *angle of depression*. If a point B is above the level of a point A, the *angle of elevation* of B from A is the angle that the line AB makes with a horizontal line through A in the same vertical plane as AB, that is, angle α in Fig. 5–8. On the other hand, angle β, the angle that AB makes with a horizontal line through B

in the same vertical plane as AB, is called the *angle of depression* of A from B. It is clear from the figure that $\alpha = \beta$. However, it should be understood that the angle of elevation and angle of depression are different concepts. The term "angle of elevation" applies when the observed object is above the observer, while the term "angle of depression" applies when the observed object is below the observer.

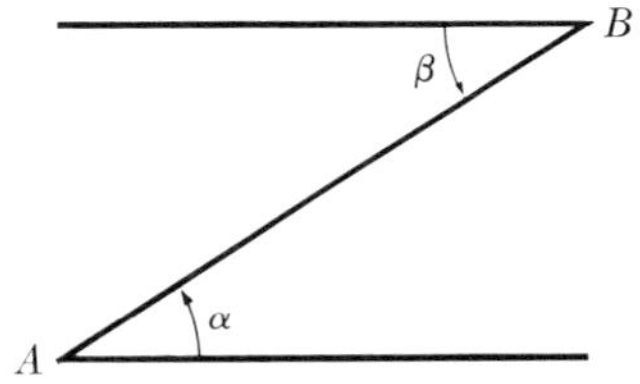

FIGURE 5-8

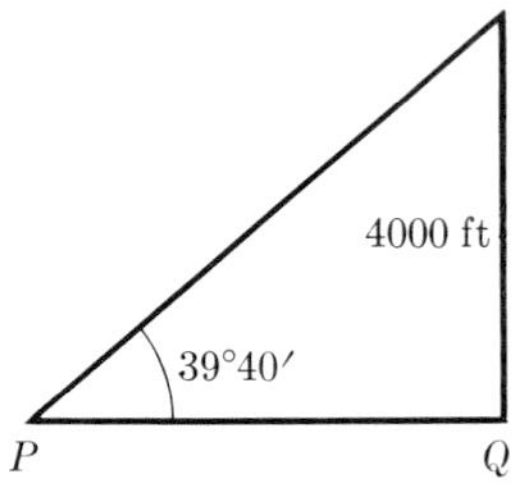

FIGURE 5-9

Example 1. The angle of elevation of an airplane from a point P on the ground is 39° 40′. Find the distance from P to the point on the ground directly beneath the plane, if the altitude of the plane is 4000 ft.

Solution. The situation is depicted in Fig. 5-9, with QP as the desired distance. We have at once, from right triangle PQR,

$$QP = 4000 \cot 39°\,40' = 4000 \times 1.206 = 4824 \text{ ft.}$$

A second type of application concerns the use of directions on the earth. Two modes of designating directions are in common use. One of these uses the angle by which the direction deviates from north or south to the east or west. Thus in Fig. 5-10 the direction of B from A in this system is written as N 40° E, while the direction of A from B is S 40° W. The second method simply uses the angle from the north direction to the given direction, *measured clockwise*. In this system the direction of B from A in Fig. 5-10 is given as 40°, and the direction of A from B is 220°. In either system the north direction which is used as the reference line is drawn through the point from which the direction is determined.

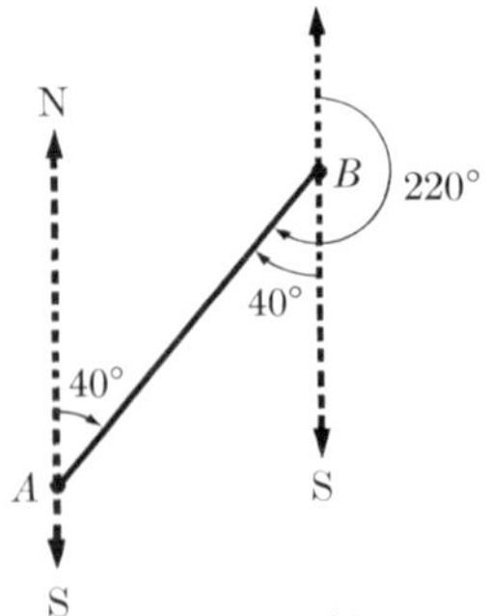

FIGURE 5-10

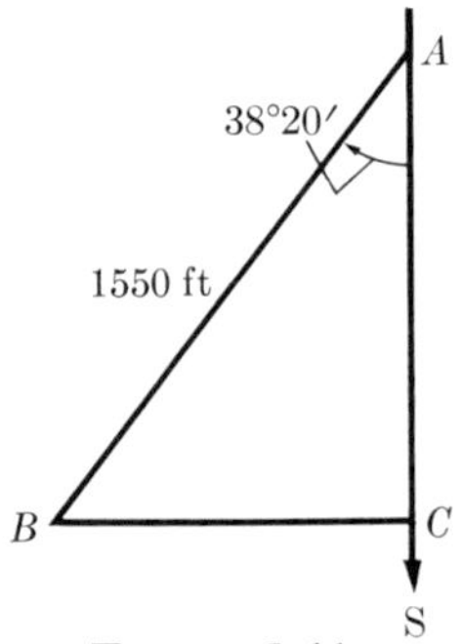

FIGURE 5-11

Example 2. A ship bears S 38° 20′ W from a point A on shore, at a distance of 1550 ft. How far south of A is the ship?

Solution. Figure 5–11 shows the relevant information, with point B representing the position of the ship. The desired distance is represented by AC. Then, from right triangle ABC, we have

$$AC = 1550 \cos 38^\circ 20' = 1550 \times 0.7844$$
$$= 1216 \text{ ft.}$$

However, if the given angle is correct only to the nearest 10′, the distance is given as 1220 ft.

Example 3. Two planes start at the same point at the same time, one flying due east at 180 mph, the second flying due south at 220 mph. What is the bearing of the second plane from the first at the end of two hours?

Solution. At the end of two hours plane P is 360 mi east of the starting point R, and plane Q is 440 mi south of R (Fig. 5–12). From right triangle PQR we have

$$\tan \measuredangle RPQ = \tfrac{440}{360} = 1.222.$$

Hence, since the given data present no greater accuracy in the angle than the nearest 10′, we obtain

$$\measuredangle RPQ = 50^\circ 40'.$$

The bearing of Q from P, indicated by θ in the figure, is then

$$\theta = 270^\circ - 50^\circ 40' = 219^\circ 20'.$$

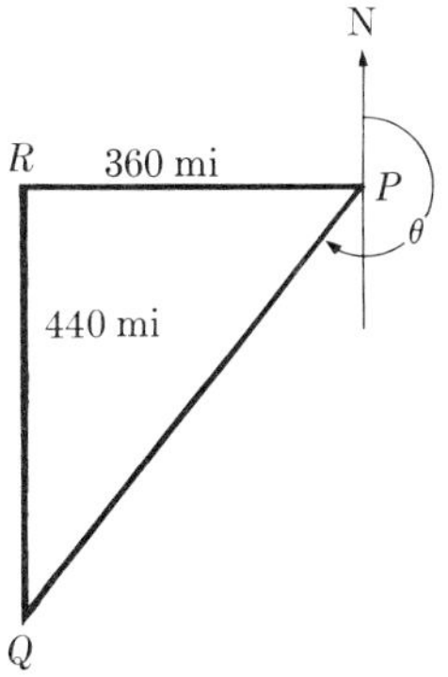

FIGURE 5–12

EXERCISE GROUP 5–5

1. From a point 153 ft from, and in the same horizontal plane with, the base of a flagpole, the angle of elevation of the top is 23°. Find the height of the flagpole.
2. From an observation balloon which is 250 ft high, the angle of depression of an object is 8° 50′. How far is the object from a point directly under the balloon and in the same horizontal plane with the object?
3. A pilot, wishing to check his speed, flies on a level course at an altitude of 2000 ft. He observes that an object on the ground straight ahead has an angle of depression of 10° and that 15 sec later the same object has an angle of depression of 21°. How fast is he traveling?
4. An airplane is observed flying directly toward us and at a given instant we observe the angle of elevation of the plane to be 8° 40′. Fifteen seconds later the plane is directly overhead and we estimate its speed to be 300 mph. Approximately how high is it flying (in feet)?
5. Two ships start from the same place at the same time and one sails for 3 hr on a course of 112° at 12 knots (nautical miles per hour), while the other sails for 3 hr on the course 202° at 15 knots. Determine the distance between the ships and the direction from the first to the second at the end of the 3 hr.

6. A ship sails for 5 hr on a course 87° at 15 knots and then sails for 7 hr on a course of 177° at 14 knots. At the end of the 12 hr, how far is the ship from its starting place and in what direction?

7. An aircraft carrier is sailing on a course of 263° with a speed of 30 knots. A plane takes off and flies on a course of 353° at a speed of 300 knots. What is the distance and direction from the plane to the carrier at the end of 5 hr?

8. An airplane pilot observes that two buoys in the water under him have angles of depression of 17° and 24°, respectively. If the buoys are known to be 2 mi apart and if a point directly under the plane is on the line joining the two buoys and between them, how high is the plane?

9. From the top of a lighthouse, 150 ft above sea level, the angle of depression to a buoy is 13° 24′ and to a point on shore, in the same vertical plane with the buoy and the lighthouse and between the two, is 63° 17′. How far from shore is the buoy?

10. An observer on the eleventh floor of a building determines that the angle of depression of the foot of a building across the street is 59° and that the angle of elevation of the top of the same building is 79°. If the street is 70 ft wide, find the height of the observed building.

11. The driver of a car observes that a forest ranger's lookout tower is in a direction which makes an angle of 15° with the highway. After driving 10 mi he notes that the direction to the lookout tower makes an angle of 30° with the highway. Assuming that the road is straight, how far is the lookout tower from the highway?

12. A motorist on a level highway observes that the angle of elevation of the top of a distant mountain is 5° and after driving 8 mi directly toward the mountain he observes that the angle of elevation of the top of the mountain is 7°. How high above the road is the top of the mountain?

13. An observer is 200 ft from a building that has a flagpole on top of it. He observes that the angle of elevation of the top of the building is 24° 10′ and that the angle of elevation of the top of the flagpole is 28° 50′. What is the approximate height of the flagpole?

14. While flying over a small lake, a pilot observes that he is at an altitude of 1000 ft, and that the angle of depression of a point on one side of the lake is 12° 30′ and that of a point on the opposite side of the lake is 14°. Assuming that the point directly under the plane is in the lake on the line joining the two points on the shore of the lake, how far is it across the lake?

15. The smaller angle between two intersecting lines is 43° 24′ and a circle whose radius is 3187 feet is tangent to both lines. Find the distance from the point of tangency to the point of intersection of the two lines when the circle is in the smaller angle, and also when it is in the larger angle.

16. Each side of a regular hexagon (six equal sides and six equal angles) is 24 in. long. Find the radius of the inscribed circle.

17. Two pulleys have diameters of 12 in. and 8 in., respectively, and their centers are 4 ft apart. If the two pulleys are to be belted together (the belt uncrossed), what must be the length of the belt?

18. If the belt in Exercise 17 is crossed, how long must it be?

19. A plane is flying over the ocean at an altitude of 5 miles. Assuming unlimited visibility, determine the distance along the earth's surface to a point on the horizon for an observer in the plane. (The radius of the earth is 3960 mi.)
20. Assuming that the earth is a sphere with a radius of 3960 mi, find the radius of the parallel of latitude which passes through Milwaukee. (The latitude of Milwaukee is 43° 03′.) What is the length of arc of 1° of this parallel of latitude?
21. Two points A and B on the earth (radius of 3960 mi) have the same latitude 24° 17′. Exactly one hour after the sun is directly over the north and south line through B it will be over the north and south line through A. How far west of B is A and what is the difference in longitude between the points A and B?

5–7 VECTORS

A further group of applications concerns problems involving such physical concepts as can be treated as examples of the general concept of vector. The idea of a vector, and the manner in which vectors are combined, will be introduced by a consideration of velocity.

Suppose that a plane is flying in a given direction with a given speed. If the direction is maintained while the speed is altered, the velocity is different. Likewise, if the speed is maintained while the direction is altered, the velocity is again different. In other words, the velocity of the plane is composed of both the speed and the direction; if either one is altered, the velocity is different.

It is then reasonable to represent a velocity by a directed line segment, drawn in the direction of the velocity, and with its length denoting the magnitude (speed) of the velocity. A directed line segment as thus described is called a *vector*. It is now apparent that a velocity may be represented by such a vector; we also say, more briefly, that a *velocity is a vector*. In the same sense, other physical concepts, such as force, acceleration, angular velocity, and directed distance, each of which involves a magnitude and a direction, are vectors.

Now suppose that the plane is flying due east. If a wind is blowing due north, the resulting motion of the plane will be in some direction between east and north, the actual direction and speed, and therefore the velocity, being in some manner a combination of the velocities of the plane and the wind. We shall accept the statement that experimentation shows that the combined effect of any two velocity vectors, or force vectors, or other similar vectors, is given by the *vector sum*, or *resultant*, which will now be defined.

***Definition* 5–1.** *If two vectors OA and OB have the same initial point O, the vector sum, or resultant, of OA and OB is defined as the diagonal OC of the parallelogram constructed with OA and OB as sides* (Fig. 5–13).

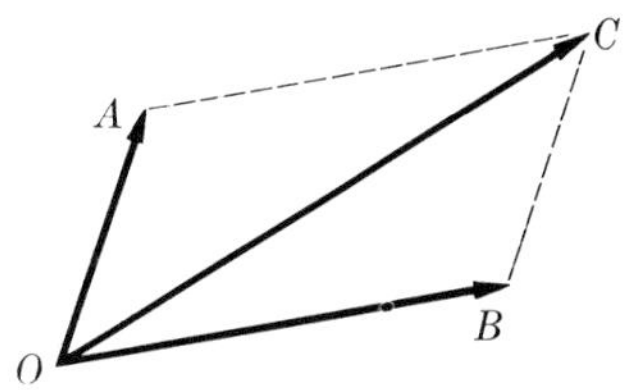

FIGURE 5–13

Often a problem at hand requires the breaking down of a vector rather than the addition of two vectors.

Whenever a vector is expressed as a resultant of two vectors, these two vectors are called *components* of the vector sum. The breaking down of a vector in this way is called a *resolution* of the vector into components. For example, we may say that the vector OC in Fig. 5–13 has been resolved into the two components OA and OB.

Example 1. A ship is headed due east at 30 knots (nautical miles per hour), while the current carries the ship due south at 4 knots. Find the resultant velocity of the ship.

Solution. The velocities combine as vectors, with the resultant vector OC in Fig. 5–14 representing in both magnitude and direction the actual velocity of the ship. From triangle OAC we have

$$\tan\theta = \tfrac{4}{30} = 0.1333, \qquad \theta = 8^\circ.$$

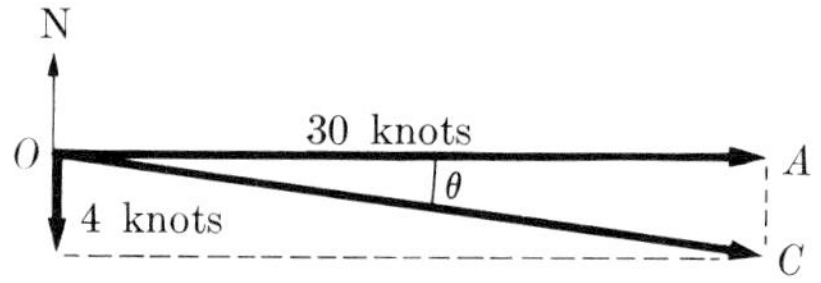

FIGURE 5–14

Hence the direction of OC, or the *course* of the ship, is

$$90^\circ + 8^\circ = 98^\circ.$$

To find the net speed, or the length of OC, we may, with the simple numbers involved, use the Pythagorean theorem, and obtain:

$$\text{speed} = \sqrt{4^2 + 30^2} = \sqrt{916} = 30 \text{ knots}.$$

A number of problems involve the following terminology, as used in air navigation. The *airspeed* is the speed the plane would have in still air, or the speed of the plane relative to the air; the *heading* is the direction of the plane relative to the air. Thus, if there is no wind, the magnitude and direction of the velocity are given by the airspeed and heading, but when a wind is blowing, the magnitude and direction of the resultant velocity are called the *groundspeed* and the *course*, respectively.

Example 2. A 20 mph south wind (that is, from the south) is blowing. At what speed should a plane head due west to be on course 279° 10′? What is the groundspeed?

FIGURE 5–15

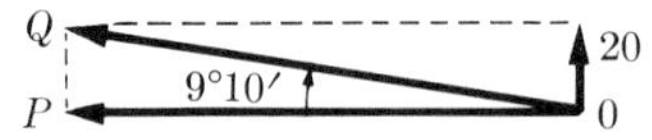

Solution. In the vector diagram in Fig. 5–15, the airspeed is given by the length OP, the groundspeed by the length OQ. From the triangle OPQ, we find

$$\begin{aligned} \text{airspeed} &= 20\cot 9^\circ\,10' = 20(6.197) = 124 \text{ mph}, \\ \text{groundspeed} &= 20\csc 9^\circ\,10' = 20(6.277) = 126 \text{ mph}. \end{aligned}$$

The resolution of a vector into components is illustrated in considering the weight of an object resting on an inclined plane. It was stated earlier that a force is a vector. The weight, which is a force acting vertically downward, can be resolved into two components, one acting perpendicular to the inclined plane, the other acting parallel to the plane.

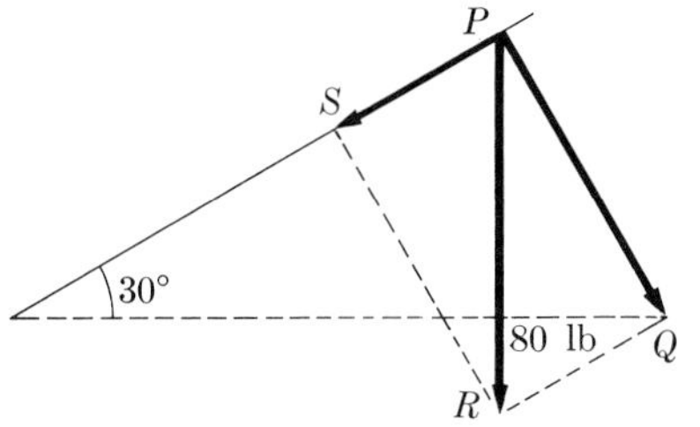

FIGURE 5–16

Example 3. What force, acting parallel to an inclined plane which makes an angle of 30° with the horizontal, is required to hold a weight of 80 lb stationary on the plane (assuming no friction)?

Solution. In Fig. 5–16, the vector *PR*, representing the weight, is the sum of the vectors *PS* and *PQ*, representing the components of the weight parallel to the plane and perpendicular to the plane, respectively. The required force F is equal to *PS* in length, but opposite in direction. Clearly, angle *PRS* is also 30°. Hence

$$F = 80 \sin 30° = 80 \times \tfrac{1}{2} = 40 \text{ lb}.$$

The principle of resolving a vector into components can be employed to find the resultant of any number of coplanar vectors acting at the same point. We choose two directions (usually perpendicular) and resolve each vector into its components in these directions. The sum of the components in either direction will be the component of the resultant vector in that direction. In particular, if the sum of a set of vectors is zero, the sum of the components in any direction must vanish.

Example 4. A weight of 1000 lb is supported by two cables which make angles of 30° and 40°, respectively, with the horizontal. Find the tension in each cable.

Solution. There are three forces acting on the weight: the pull of gravity, which is 1000 lb directed downward, and the two tensions, each acting along the respective cable. Since this system of forces is in equilibrium, their sum is zero. Hence, the sum of the horizontal components must vanish, and the sum of the vertical components must vanish. Stated differently, the sum of the horizontal components to the right must equal the sum of those to the left, and the sum of the upward vertical components must equal the sum of the downward ones. The tensions T_1 and T_2 can be resolved into horizontal components H_1 and H_2, respectively, and vertical components V_1 and V_2. Then, by the above principle,

$$H_1 = H_2 \quad \text{and} \quad V_1 + V_2 = 1000.$$

On expressing the components in terms of T_1 and T_2, we have, from Fig. 5–17,

$$H_1 = T_1 \cos 30°, \qquad H_2 = T_2 \cos 40°,$$
$$V_1 = T_1 \sin 30°, \qquad V_2 = T_2 \sin 40°,$$

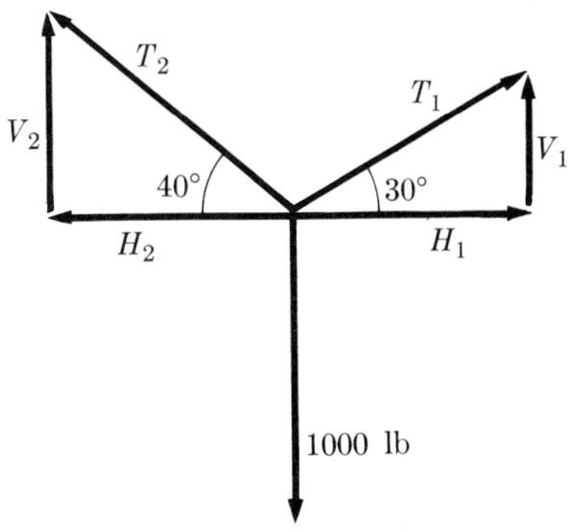

FIGURE 5–17

and the above equations become

$$0.8660T_1 = 0.7660T_2, \qquad 0.5000T_1 + 0.6428T_2 = 1000.$$

Solving these equations, we find from the first one that $T_1 = 0.8845T_2$. Substituting this value in the second equation, we obtain

$$1.0850T_2 = 1000,$$

which yields $T_2 = 922$ lb (to the nearest pound). Then $T_1 = 0.8845 \times 922 = 815$, and the desired tensions are

$$T_1 = 815 \text{ lb}, \qquad T_2 = 922 \text{ lb}.$$

EXERCISE GROUP 5–6

In each of Exercises 1–6, find the vertical and horizontal components of the vector whose magnitude M and angle θ which the vector makes with the horizontal are as indicated.

1. $M = 250, \theta = 33° 17'$
2. $M = 175, \theta = 37° 15'$
3. $M = 310, \theta = 62° 19'$
4. $M = 43.17, \theta = 85° 47'$
5. $M = 51.96, \theta = 83° 13'$
6. $M = K, \theta = \alpha$

In each of Exercises 7–10, find the vertical and horizontal components under the conditions stated for a force with magnitude M.

7. $M = 350$ and the vertical component is twice the horizontal component.
8. $M = 220$ and the horizontal component is five times the vertical component.
9. $M = 750$ and is double the magnitude of the vertical component.
10. $M = K$ and is r times the magnitude of the horizontal component.

Find the resultant of the forces shown in Fig. 5–18 under the stated conditions in each of Exercises 11–16.

11. $F_3 = 0, \theta_1 = \theta_2 = 30°$ and $F_1 = F_2 = 100$
12. $F_1 = 0, \theta_2 = 60°$ and $F_2 = F_3 = 100$
13. $F_3 = 0, \theta_1 = 30°, \theta_2 = 60°, F_1 = 200$, and $F_2 = 100$
14. $F_1 = 0, \theta_2 = 40°, F_2 = 100$, and $F_3 = 200$
15. $\theta_1 = 40°, \theta_2 = 75°, F_1 = 100, F_2 = 200$, and $F_3 = 300$
16. $\theta_1 = 180°, \theta_2 = 80°, F_1 = 300, F_2 = 200$, and $F_3 = 250$

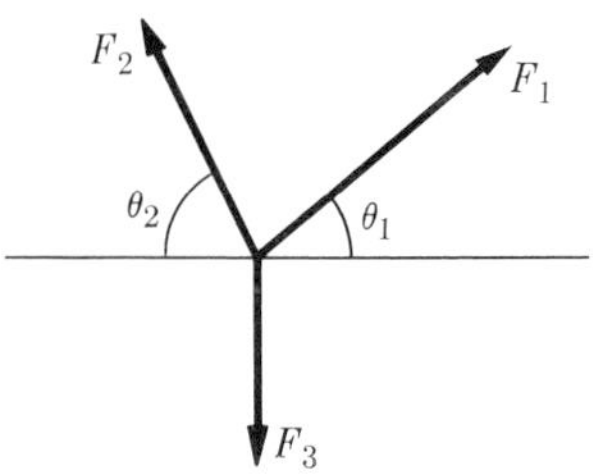

FIGURE 5–18

17. An airplane has an airspeed of 420 mph on a heading of 212° 10′. The wind is blowing at 25 mph from the direction 122° 10′. Find the groundspeed and course of the plane.

18. An airplane maintains an airspeed of 530 mph on a heading of 153° 12′. There is a 45 mph wind from the direction 243° 12′. Find the course flown by the plane and also its groundspeed.
19. A pilot must fly from A to B in $1\frac{1}{2}$ hr. The distance is 500 mi in the direction 52° 20′. If the wind is blowing 20 mph from the direction 142° 20′, what heading and airspeed must the pilot maintain?
20. A pilot wishes to fly 931 mi in the direction 272° 30′. The wind is blowing from the south at 22 mph and the pilot decides to fly on a heading of 270°. What airspeed must he maintain and how long will it take him to reach his destination?
21. An automobile weighing 3500 lb is standing on a smooth driveway which is inclined 3° with the horizontal. Find the force (parallel to the driveway) necessary to keep the car from rolling down the driveway.
22. A 1000-lb weight is to be supported by two cables, one of them with a tension of 700 lb and making an angle of 60° with the horizontal. Find the tension in the other cable, and the angle it should make with the horizontal.
23. A sphere of 1000 lb weight is supported by two smooth inclined planes, as shown in Fig. 5–19. Find the force which each plane exerts on the sphere.

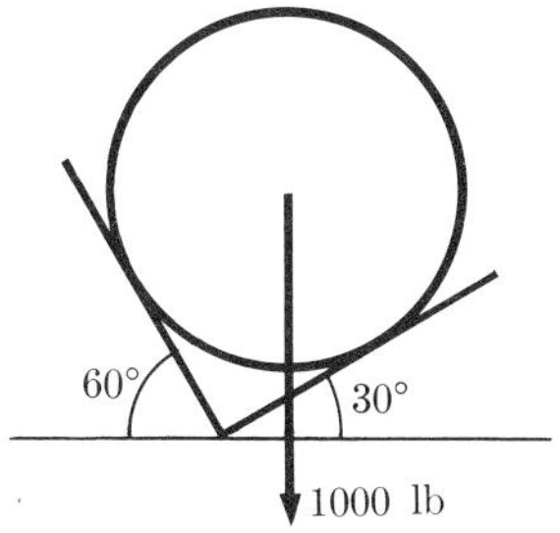

FIGURE 5–19

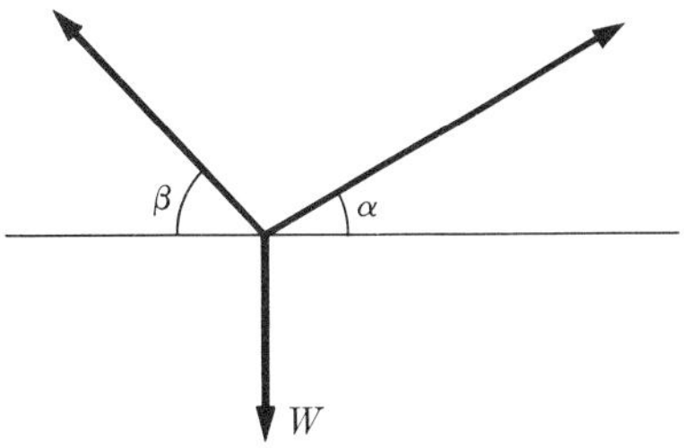

FIGURE 5–20

24. A weight W is supported by two cables, as shown in Fig. 5–20. Find the tension in each cable.

In Fig. 5–21 a beam BC of negligible weight is fastened to a wall AC with a hinge at C and is supported at B by a cable AB. A weight of 100 lb is supported at B. Find the tension T in the cable AB and the compression C in the beam BC under the following conditions:

25. $AC = BC = 4$ ft, $\theta = 90°$
26. $AC = BC = AB$
27. $AC = BC = 4$ ft, $\theta = 60°$
28. $AC = BC = 4$ ft, $\theta = 45°$
29. $AC = 4$ ft, $BC = 6$ ft, $\theta = 90°$
30. $AC = 3$ ft, $BC = 2$ ft, $\theta = 90°$

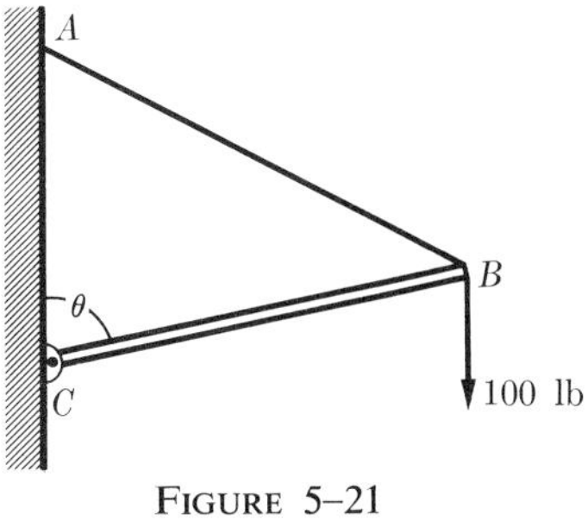

FIGURE 5–21

SUPPLEMENTARY EXERCISES FOR CHAPTER 5

Solve the right triangles in Exercises 1–4, and round off the results to the correct number of significant figures.

1. $a = 31.94$, $B = 23°$
2. $c = 1.3$, $A = 36° 03'$
3. $b = 2.3$, $c = 3.246$
4. $a = 3.942$, $b = 1.23$
5. At what airspeed should an airplane fly on a heading of 270° to maintain a course of 260° 32′, if a 15 mph north wind (i.e., from the north) is blowing?
6. A river has a current of 3.5 mph. A man in a motorboat, with a speed in still water of 8 mph, heads directly across the river. Find his speed and the direction in which he travels.
7. A force of 275 lb is acting at an angle of 47° with the horizontal. Find its horizontal and vertical components.
8. A ship is sailing due north at a speed of 15 mph. A man walks across the deck from west to east, at the rate of 5 ft/sec. Find the direction and magnitude of the man's actual velocity.
9. Find the height of a vertical pole which casts a shadow 73 ft long on the level ground when the altitude (angle of elevation) of the sun is 53° 12′.
10. A metal nut $\frac{1}{2}$ in. thick is in the shape of a regular hexagon, the distance between parallel sides being $1\frac{1}{2}$ in. There is a circular hole $\frac{1}{2}$ in. in diameter through the center. Find the volume of the metal in the nut.
11. Solve Example 4 of Section 5–7 under the conditions that the angles 30° and 40° are respectively 30° and 60°.
12. Determine a formula for the magnitude of the resultant of the three forces in Fig. 5–18, assuming that θ_1 and θ_2 are both positive acute angles.
13. A sphere of 2000 lb weight is supported by two smooth inclined planes, as shown in Fig. 5–19, but with angles α and β. Find the force which each plane exerts on the sphere.
14. An aircraft carrier is steaming due north at 30 knots. A plane takes off and flies on a course of 47° at 400 knots groundspeed for two hours in response to a distress signal. The plane spends $\frac{1}{2}$ hour with the ship in distress when a surface ship arrives and the plane heads back to the carrier. Because of a headwind the plane can maintain a groundspeed of only 370 knots on the return trip. Approximately what course should the plane fly to intercept the carrier, which has continued to steam due north at 30 knots?

CHAPTER 6

Inequalities

6–1 INTRODUCTION

The problem of solving an equation has been seen to involve the finding of values of a variable for which the values of two functions are equal. Perhaps equally important is the problem of finding values of a variable for which the value of one function is less than the value of a second function (in which case, of course, the value of the second function is greater than that of the first function). These ideas will be made more precise.

Axiom 7 of Section 1–2, for the natural numbers, was stated as follows:
If a and b are two natural numbers, then one and only one of the following holds:
(a) $a = b$.
(b) There is a natural number x such that $a = b + x$.
(c) There is a natural number y such that $b = a + y$.

In Section 1–3 it was stated that this property, suitably modified, holds for the set of all integers, and in Section 1–7 that it holds for the set of rational numbers. Finally in Section 1–8 the property was stated for the set of real numbers. On the basis of this property we may then establish an *ordering* relation for the real numbers, by defining the relation of "greater than," and hence "less than," between real numbers. The definition to be given involves the idea of positive real numbers, which were in turn defined in Section 1–8.

***Definition* 6–1.** *If a positive real number x exists such that $a = b + x$, we write $a > b$, and say, "a is greater than b."*

If a positive real number y exists such that $b = a + y$, we write $a < b$, and say, "a is less than b."

If $a < b$, then $b = a + y$, where y is positive; hence $b - a = y$, and we may write $b - a = 0 + y$. It follows that $b - a > 0$.

It is also clear that, *if a and b are any two real numbers, then one and only one of the relations*

$$a = b, \qquad a > b, \qquad \text{and} \qquad a < b$$

may hold.

We also use a *continued* inequality; thus $a < b < c$ *means that "b is simultaneously greater than a and less than c."*

It is convenient at times to use a notation that combines an inequality with an equality. Thus

$a \leqq b$ *means that "a is less than or equal to b,"*

$a \geqq b$ *means that "a is greater than or equal to b."*

For example, to express the requirement that a number x be positive, we write $x > 0$. On the other hand, if it is required simply that x not be negative (in which case it may be positive or zero) we write $x \geqq 0$.

In the treatment of inequalities it will be understood that *all numbers are real.* It is then instructive to represent numbers as points on a horizontal axis, with the positive direction to the right. Thus $a < b$ means geometrically that point a is to the left of b; $a < b < c$ means that point b lies between point a and point c, to the right of point a and to the left of point c.

6–2 OPERATIONS ON INEQUALITIES

Just as there are permissible operations on equations (Section 4–2), and solving an equation involves the correct application of these operations, so are there permissible operations on inequalities, which are then used in the solution of inequalities.

Theorem 6–1. *If $a < b$ and c is any real number, then*

$$a + c < b + c.$$

If $a > b$ and c is any real number, then

$$a + c > b + c.$$

Proof. To prove the first part we note that if $a < b$ then $b = a + y$, where y is some positive number. Then $b + c = (a + c) + y$, which means that

$$a + c < b + c,$$

and the first part is proved. For the second part, if $a > b$ then $a = b + x$ for some positive number x, and in a manner similar to the above we get

$$a + c > b + c.$$

Since c may be positive or negative, Theorem 6–1 implies that *the same quantity may be added to or subtracted from both members of an inequality without changing the sense of the inequality.*

Example 1. $7 > 5$; therefore

$$7 - 3 > 5 - 3, \quad \text{or} \quad 4 > 2;$$
$$7 + 3 > 5 + 3, \quad \text{or} \quad 10 > 8.$$

Example 2. If $2x + 5 < 0$, we may add -5 to both members to get $2x < -5$.

Theorem 6–2. (1) *If* $a < b$ *and* $c > 0$, *then* $ca < cb$.
(2) *If* $a > b$ *and* $c > 0$, *then* $ca > cb$.

Proof. We shall prove (1). Since $a < b$ we have $b = a + y$, where $y > 0$. Then we have $cb = ca + cy$, and since c is positive and y is positive, it follows that cy is positive, so that $ca < cb$. The proof of (2) is similar.

Example 3. $-3 < -2$; therefore $3(-3) < 3(-2)$, or $-9 < -6$.

Example 4. If $2x < -5$, as in Example 2, we may multiply both members by $\frac{1}{2}$ to get $x < -\frac{5}{2}$.

Theorem 6–3. (1) *If* $a < b$ *and* $c < 0$, *then* $ca > cb$.
(2) *If* $a > b$ *and* $c < 0$, *then* $ca < cb$.

Proof. Again we shall prove (1). Since $a < b$ we have $b = a + y$, where $y > 0$. Then we have $cb = ca + cy$. Since $c < 0$ and $y > 0$, it follows that $cy < 0$, so that $ca > cb$. The proof of (2) is similar.

Example 5. $-3 > -4$; therefore $(-2)(-3) < (-2)(-4)$, or $6 < 8$.

Example 6. If $-2x > 4$ we may multiply both members by $-\frac{1}{2}$ to get $x < -2$.

In effect these theorems state that (1) both members of an inequality may be multiplied (or divided) by the same (or equal) positive quantities; (2) both members of an inequality may be multiplied or divided by the same (or equal) negative quantities *if the inequality sign is reversed.*

To solve an inequality in the variable x shall mean to find all values of x for which the inequality is satisfied. In general the solution of an inequality will turn out to be one or more ranges of values of x, rather than one or more specific values.

Example 7. Determine the values of x for which $3x + 2 < 0$.

Solution. By Theorem 6–1 we may add -2 to both members, to give $3x < -2$. By Theorem 6–2 we may then multiply both members by $\frac{1}{3}$; hence $x < -\frac{2}{3}$, which is the solution. In other words, the solution consists of the set of all numbers which are less than $-\frac{2}{3}$.

Example 8. Solve the inequality $4x + 3 < 6x + 8$.

Solution. We may add $-6x - 3$ to both members (in other words we may transpose 3 and $6x$) and we get $-2x < 5$. Now we may divide by -2 and simultaneously reverse the inequality sign, and we have $x > -\frac{5}{2}$, which is the solution.

The inequalities of Examples 7 and 8 are linear. Other types of linear inequalities involve absolute or numerical values.

Let us denote the *numerical value* of x, or the *absolute value* of x, by $|x|$, and let us define it as follows:

$$\text{if } x \geqq 0 \quad \text{then} \quad |x| = x,$$
$$\text{if } x < 0 \quad \text{then} \quad |x| = -x.$$

For example, $|2| = 2$, and also $|-2| = 2$. We see from the definition that *an absolute value can never be negative.*

The relation $|x| < 2$ is equivalent to the inequality $-2 < x < 2$. On the other hand, the inequality $|x| > 2$ means that x may be in either of the ranges $x < -2$ or $x > 2$. These equivalences (a double arrow signifies "is equivalent to") may be stated as follows:

$$|x| < 2 \leftrightarrow -2 < x < 2, \tag{1}$$
$$|x| > 2 \leftrightarrow x < -2 \quad \text{or} \quad x > 2.$$

A related pair of equivalences is the following:

$$x^2 < 4 \leftrightarrow |x| < 2, \tag{2}$$
$$x^2 > 4 \leftrightarrow |x| > 2.$$

For, if $x^2 < 4$, then if $x \geqq 0$ we must have $x < 2$, and if $x < 0$ then $x > -2$, so that in any case $-2 < x < 2$, or $|x| < 2$. The second equivalence may be shown similarly.

Example 9. Write the inequality $|3x - 7| > 2$ in an equivalent form without absolute value signs.

Solution. A comparison with (1), but with x replaced by $3x - 7$, shows that we must have

$$3x - 7 < -2, \quad \text{or} \quad 3x - 7 > 2.$$

Transposing 7 in each inequality, and dividing by 3, we have as the solution the two ranges $x < \frac{5}{3}$ and $x > 3$.

EXERCISE GROUP 6–1

In each of Exercises 1–6, (a) rewrite the statement using inequality symbols, and (b) express by inequalities the real numbers not included in the given statement.

1. x lies to the right of 4.
2. x lies to the left of -2.
3. x lies to the left of 3.
4. x lies to the right of -6.
5. x lies between -2 and 3.
6. x lies between 3 and 10.

In each of Exercises 7–14, express by inequalities (a) the values of x which are common to the given inequalities, and (b) the real numbers which are not common to the given inequalities.

7. $x < 3, x > 2$
8. $x < -\frac{2}{3}, x < 5$

9. $x < 0, x < -3$

10. $x > -\frac{2}{3}, x > 5$

11. $-3 < x < 0.5, x > -1$

12. $-2 < x < 1, x < -3$

13. $-5.3 < x < -2.4, -4 < x < 2.7$

14. $-2 < x < 3, 0 < x < 4$

In each of Exercises 15–24, determine the values of x satisfying the given inequality.

15. $3x - 2 < 5$

16. $3x - 5 < 10$

17. $-3x - 5 < 2$

18. $-7x - 5 > 4$

19. $2(x + 3) > -1$

20. $x - 2 < 3x$

21. $2(x + 3) > 3(x + 4)$

22. $3(2 - x) > 4(x - 2)$

23. $x(x + 1) < x^2 + 3x + 2$

24. $2(2x - 1)(x - 3) < 4x(x - 2)$

In each of the following write an equivalent inequality for x without absolute value symbols.

25. $|x| < 4$

26. $|x| < 5$

27. $|x| > 5$

28. $|x| > a^2$

29. $|x + 1| < 3$

30. $|2x - 3| < \frac{1}{3}$

31. $|4 - 2x| > \frac{1}{2}$

32. $|3 - x| > b$

33. $2 < |x - 3| < 4$

34. $3 < |2x - 3| < 5$

35. $0 < |x + 2| < 2$

36. $0 < |2x - 1| < 4$

6–3 QUADRATIC INEQUALITIES

The method we shall present here may be used for the solution of any quadratic inequality and involves the technique of *completing the square*. In the next section we shall give a specialized method which applies to inequalities in factored form. The method will be explained by means of examples.

Example 1. Determine the values of x for which $3x^2 + 2x - 5 < 0$, and interpret the result graphically.

Solution. By the method of completing the square we have

$$x^2 + \frac{2}{3}x - \frac{5}{3} < 0, \qquad x^2 + \frac{2}{3}x + \frac{1}{9} < \frac{5}{3} + \frac{1}{9}, \qquad (x + \tfrac{1}{3})^2 < \tfrac{16}{9}.$$

Thus, as in (2), we have

$$|x + \tfrac{1}{3}| < \tfrac{4}{3} \quad \text{or} \quad -\tfrac{4}{3} < x + \tfrac{1}{3} < \tfrac{4}{3}.$$

If we now subtract $\frac{1}{3}$ from each member, we have the solution

$$-\tfrac{5}{3} < x < 1.$$

The graph of the function $3x^2 + 2x - 5$ is seen to have a vertex at $(-\frac{1}{3}, -\frac{16}{3})$, and the function vanishes at $x = -\frac{5}{3}$ and $x = 1$. With this information we can sketch the graph (Fig. 6–1), from which we see that

$$\begin{array}{rlll} \text{if } x < -\frac{5}{3} & \text{then} & y > 0 & \text{or} \quad 3x^2 + 2x - 5 > 0, \\ \text{if } -\frac{5}{3} < x < 1 & \text{then} & y < 0 & \text{or} \quad 3x^2 + 2x - 5 < 0, \\ \text{if } x > 1 & \text{then} & y > 0 & \text{or} \quad 3x^2 + 2x - 5 > 0. \end{array}$$

Example 2. Solve the inequality $\dfrac{2x - 3}{x + 2} > 0.$

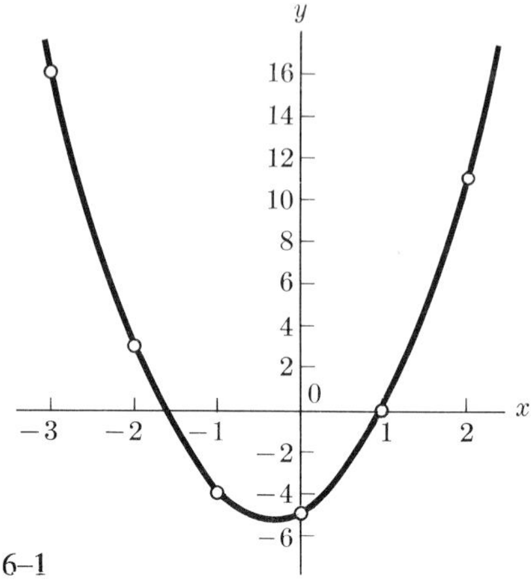

FIGURE 6-1

Solution. Since $(x + 2)^2 > 0$ for all $x \neq -2$, we may multiply both members of the inequality by $(x + 2)^2$ to give

$$(2x - 3)(x + 2) > 0 \qquad \text{or} \qquad 2x^2 + x - 6 > 0.$$

The method of completing the square in the latter inequality gives

$$|x + \tfrac{1}{4}| > \tfrac{7}{4},$$

which is equivalent to the pair of inequalities

$$x + \tfrac{1}{4} < -\tfrac{7}{4} \qquad \text{and} \qquad x + \tfrac{1}{4} > \tfrac{7}{4}.$$

Transposing $-\frac{1}{4}$ gives as the solution the two ranges of values

$$x < -2 \qquad \text{and} \qquad x > \tfrac{3}{2}.$$

Example 3. Solve the inequality $2x^2 + 3x + 2 < 0$.

Solution. Completing the square leads to the inequality

$$(x + \tfrac{3}{4})^2 < -\tfrac{7}{16}.$$

Since the square of a real number cannot be negative, the inequality has no solution.

In general, if the method of solution of an inequality leads to a relation of the form $(x + a)^2 < b$, where $b < 0$, the original inequality has no solution; if it leads to $(x + a)^2 > b$, where $b < 0$, the solution consists of all real numbers x.

EXERCISE GROUP 6-2

Determine the values of x satisfying each of the following inequalities.

1. $x^2 - x - 6 > 0$
2. $x^2 + x - 6 < 0$
3. $x^2 - 5x + 6 > 0$
4. $x^2 - 5x + 6 < 0$
5. $2x^2 - 3x - 7 > 0$
6. $3x^2 - 2x - 8 < 0$
7. $2x^2 - 3x - 7 < 0$
8. $6x^2 - 7x - 20 < 0$
9. $2x^2 < 5(x + 1)$
10. $x^2 - 10x > 171$
11. $3x^2 - 25x < 1128$
12. $x^2 + 6x - 891 > 0$

13. $3(x + 1) < 5x^2$
14. $2x^2 + 5 > 7x + 1$
15. $5x < 2 - 3x^2$
16. $2x^2 + 1 > 3x$
17. $x^2 + 2 < 2\sqrt{3}x$
18. $2x - 1 > x - x^2$
19. $x^2 - \sqrt{5}x - 1 > 0$
20. $6(x^2 + 1) > 13x$
21. $(3x - 1)(2x + 1) < 0$
22. $-x^2 + 2x + 3 > 0$
23. $2x^2 + 4x + 5 > 0$
24. $(2 - 3x)(x + 2) > 0$
25. $\dfrac{2x - 3}{3x - 1} > 0$
26. $\dfrac{5x + 1}{x + 5} < 0$
27. $\dfrac{3x + 2}{2x - 5} < 0$
28. $\dfrac{2x - 1}{x + 1/2} > 0$
29. $\dfrac{5x - 7}{7x + 2} > 0$
30. $\dfrac{3x - 5}{5x - 3} < 0$
31. $\dfrac{x + 3}{3x + 1} < 0$
32. $\dfrac{x}{2x - 5} < 0$
33. $\dfrac{2x + 4}{x} > 0$
34. $\dfrac{1}{(x - 2)(2x + 1)} > 0$
35. $\dfrac{1}{(4x + 3)(2x + 1)} < 0$
36. $-\dfrac{2}{(x + 1)(2 - x)} < 0$
37. $-\dfrac{3}{(1 - 2x)(1 - 4x)} > 0$

6-4 INEQUALITIES IN FACTORED FORM

When an inequality is in the form $f(x) < 0$ or $f(x) > 0$ where $f(x)$ is a polynomial in factored form, a solution can often be effected by considering the possible combinations of signs of the factors of $f(x)$.

Example 1. Solve the inequality $(2x - 1)(x + 2) < 0$.

Solution. Since the two factors must be of opposite sign for their product to be negative, we have the two tentative possibilities:

$$(1)\quad 2x - 1 < 0, \qquad x + 2 > 0,$$
$$(2)\quad 2x - 1 > 0, \qquad x + 2 < 0.$$

The pair (1) implies, for the same x, *both* $x < \frac{1}{2}$ *and* $x > -2$, or

$$-2 < x < \tfrac{1}{2},$$

which is then a solution range. The pair (2) implies, for the same x, *both* $x > \frac{1}{2}$ *and* $x < -2$, which are inconsistent, and yield no solution. The complete solution is then the continued inequality displayed above.

Example 2. Solve the inequality $(x + 2)(x - 1)(2x - 3) > 0$.

Solution. Using the method of Example 1, we must have either all three factors positive, or one factor positive and the other two negative. The tentative possibilities are:

$$(1)\quad x + 2 > 0, \qquad x - 1 > 0, \qquad 2x - 3 > 0,$$
$$(2)\quad x + 2 > 0, \qquad x - 1 < 0, \qquad 2x - 3 < 0,$$
$$(3)\quad x + 2 < 0, \qquad x - 1 > 0, \qquad 2x - 3 < 0,$$
$$(4)\quad x + 2 < 0, \qquad x - 1 < 0, \qquad 2x - 3 > 0.$$

The inequalities (1) yield, as the range satisfying all three linear inequalities, $x > \frac{3}{2}$; and (2) yields $-2 < x < 1$. In (3) the first two inequalities are inconsistent, and in (4) the second and third inequalities are inconsistent. Hence the complete solution consists of the ranges

$$-2 < x < 1 \quad \text{and} \quad x > \tfrac{3}{2}.$$

Another method, which is left to the reader, consists in treating the product $(x + 2)(x - 1)$, for example, as a single factor, and then considering the possible combinations of signs for this factor and the factor $2x - 3$.

An additional method may be used in solving inequalities in factored form, and also inequalities involving fractions such as in the following illustration.

Example 3. Solve the inequality $\dfrac{x^2(x + 3)}{x - 2} < 0.$

Solution. We note that the fraction vanishes at $x = 0$ and $x = -3$, and is undefined at $x = 2$. These three values of x are the only ones at which the value of the fraction may possibly (although not necessarily) change sign. For example, if the value of the fraction is of a certain sign at $x = -1$, it is of that same sign for $-3 < x < 0$. In fact, at $x = -1$ the value of the fraction is negative; therefore the fraction is negative for $-3 < x < 0$. Similarly, at $x = -4$ the fraction is positive, at $x = 1$ it is negative, and at $x = 3$ it is positive. The solution is then

$$-3 < x < 0; \qquad 0 < x < 2.$$

We may indicate the signs of the fraction for the various values of x in Fig. 6–2.

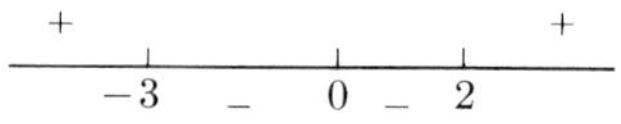

FIGURE 6–2

EXERCISE GROUP 6–3

Determine the values of x satisfying each of the following inequalities.

1. $(3x - 1)(2x + 1) < 0$
2. $(2x - 5)(3x + 2) < 0$
3. $(2x + 3)(x - 1) > 0$
4. $(1 - 2x)(x + 2) < 0$
5. $(3x - 4)(2x + 5) > 0$
6. $(1 - x)(x - 3) > 0$
7. $(2x - 1)(x + 2)(3x - 7) > 0$
8. $(x + 2)(x - 1)(x + 3) < 0$
9. $x(x + 1)(2x - 3) < 0$
10. $x(2x + 1)(2x - 5) > 0$
11. $x(2x - 1)(x - 2) < x(x - 2)$
12. $(x - 1)(x + 2)(x - 3) > (x + 2)(x - 3)$
13. $x^2(x - 3) < 0$
14. $x^2(x - 5) > 0$
15. $(x + 1)^2(x - 2) > 0$
16. $(2x + 3)^2(x - 1) < 0$
17. $(x + 1)^2(x - 2)(x + 3) < 0$
18. $(x - 1)^2(3x + 1)(x + 1) > 0$
19. $(x + 1)(x - 1)(x + 3)(x - 4) > 0$
20. $(2x - 3)(3x - 4)(x + 2)(x - 5) < 0$
21. $\dfrac{(2x + 5)(3x + 2)}{7x - 3} > 0$
22. $\dfrac{(2x - 3)(x + 4)}{x - 2} < 0$
23. $\dfrac{x(3x - 2)}{4x - 3} < 0$
24. $\dfrac{x(4x + 1)}{x - 3} > 0$

25. $\dfrac{2x - 5}{(x + 3)(2x + 3)} > 0$

26. $\dfrac{3 - 2x}{x(x - 3)} < 0$

27. $\dfrac{x(x + 1)}{(x + 2)(x + 3)} < 0$

28. $\dfrac{x(x - 1)}{(2x + 1)(x - 3)} > 0$

29. $\dfrac{(2x + 1)(2x - 1)}{(x + 1)(3x - 1)} > 0$

30. $\dfrac{(6x - 2)(x + 4)}{(2x - 1)(1 - 3x)} > 0$

6–5 ABSOLUTE INEQUALITIES

In the previous sections of this chapter we have been concerned with the problem of solving inequalities. Another aspect of this work is the establishment of certain inequalities, involving one or more variables, which are essentially independent of the values of the variables. Such inequalities are called *absolute inequalities.*

We shall present two basic absolute inequalities, whose proofs depend on the simple fact that the square of any nonzero real number is positive.

I. $a^2 + b^2 > 2ab$, for all a and b, if $a \neq b$.

Proof. Since $a \neq b$, we have $(a - b)^2 > 0$. This gives

$$a^2 - 2ab + b^2 > 0,$$

and the inequality follows.

II. $a^2 + b^2 + c^2 > ab + ac + bc$ if a, b, and c are not all equal.

Proof. From (I) above we have for the pairs a, b; a, c; and b, c the following inequalities,

$$a^2 + b^2 \geqq 2ab, \qquad a^2 + c^2 \geqq 2ac, \qquad b^2 + c^2 \geqq 2bc,$$

but with at least one of these without the equality sign, since the two members of at least one pair are unequal. Addition of the three inequalities gives

$$2(a^2 + b^2 + c^2) > 2ab + 2ac + 2bc$$

and the stated inequality follows.

No fixed procedure can be prescribed for proving absolute inequalities. An often fruitful technique, if a direct mode of proof is not apparent, is to assume the inequality valid, and then try to work it down to known inequalities, but with steps that are reversible. The valid proof then consists in applying the sequence of steps in reverse order. This will be made clear in the examples.

Example 1. Establish the inequality

$$\frac{x}{y} + \frac{y}{x} \geqq 2 \quad \text{if} \quad x > 0 \quad \text{and} \quad y > 0.$$

Solution. If the inequality is valid, we may multiply both members by xy since $xy > 0$. This gives

$$x^2 + y^2 \geqq 2xy,$$

which we know is valid, the inequality by (I) when $x \neq y$, and the equality when $x = y$. The proof then starts with this known relation, and the permissible division by xy establishes the inequality.

Example 2. Establish the inequality

$$\frac{x + y}{2} > \sqrt{xy} \qquad \text{if} \qquad x > 0, y > 0, \qquad \text{and} \qquad x \neq y.$$

Solution. Since x and y are positive we may set $x = a^2$ and $y = b^2$. In terms of a and b the desired inequality becomes, if a and b are both considered positive,

$$\frac{a^2 + b^2}{2} > ab.$$

This inequality is valid by (I), since $a \neq b$.

Example 3. Show that $x^3 > y^3$ if $x > y$.

Solution. If y^3 is transposed, the inequality may be written in the form

$$(x - y)(x^2 + xy + y^2) > 0.$$

If this inequality is valid we may divide by $x - y$, since $x - y > 0$, and obtain

$$x^2 + xy + y^2 > 0.$$

This latter inequality is valid since we may write

$$x^2 + xy + y^2 = (x + \tfrac{1}{2}y)^2 + \tfrac{3}{4}y^2.$$

The steps are all reversible and the given inequality is established.

EXERCISE GROUP 6-4

Establish the inequalities in each of Exercises 1–13, under the specified conditions.

1. $\dfrac{2xy}{x + y} < \sqrt{xy}$, $x > 0$, $y > 0$, $x \neq y$
2. $\dfrac{x + y}{2} > \dfrac{2xy}{x + y}$, $x > 0$, $y > 0$, $x \neq y$
3. $a^2 + \dfrac{1}{a^2} \geqq 2$, $a \neq 0$
4. $a^2 + 4b^2 \geqq 4ab$
5. $\left(\dfrac{a + b}{2}\right)^2 > ab$, $a \neq b$
6. $(1^r + 2^r)^2 \geqq 2^2 \cdot 2^r$
7. $x^3 - y^3 > (x - y)^3$, $x > 0$, $y > 0$, $x > y$
8. $x^3 - y^3 > 3xy(x - y)$, $x > 0$, $y > 0$, $x > y$

9. $x^3 + y^3 > xy(x + y)$, $x > 0$, $y > 0$, $x \neq y$

10. $a^3b + ab^3 < a^4 + b^4$, $a > 0$, $b > 0$, $a \neq b$

11. $\dfrac{a}{bc} + \dfrac{b}{ac} + \dfrac{c}{ba} > \dfrac{1}{a} + \dfrac{1}{b} + \dfrac{1}{c}$, $a > 0$, $b > 0$, $c > 0$; a, b, c not all equal.
[*Hint*: Use II.]

12. $a^2 - b^2 - c^2 < 2bc$, if a, b, c are the sides of a triangle.

13. $(x + y + z)^3 > 27xyz$; x, y, z not all equal. [*Hint*: Multiply both members of (II) by $a + b + c$, simplify, set $a^3 = x$, $b^3 = y$, $c^3 = z$.]

Establish each of the following inequalities. (These are somewhat more difficult than the preceding ones.)

14. $|ax + by| \leqq 1$ if $a^2 + b^2 = 1$, $x^2 + y^2 = 1$. [*Hint*: The inequality is equivalent to $(ax + by)^2 \leqq 1$.]

15. $(b + c)(c + a)(a + b) > 8abc$, a, b, c, all > 0, and not all equal

16. $(ab + xy)(ax + by) > 4abxy$, a, b, x, y, all > 0, not both $a = y$ and $b = x$

17. $\dfrac{1}{x} + \dfrac{1}{y} + \dfrac{1}{z} \geqq 9$, if $x + y + z = 1$, $x > 0$, $y > 0$, $z > 0$

CHAPTER 7

Graphs of the Trigonometric Functions

7-1 VARIATION OF THE TRIGONOMETRIC FUNCTIONS

In Chapter 3 we saw that each trigonometric ratio is defined for all angles, whether in radian or degree measure, with the exception of certain quadrantal angles. For any such angle the value of each trigonometric ratio is completely determined, and depends only on the angle. We now wish to define the *trigonometric functions* corresponding to the trigonometric ratios.

For any trigonometric function we assume that the domain consists of all real numbers θ for which the corresponding trigonometric ratio of θ radians is defined. The trigonometric function then consists of the pairs of numbers with θ in this domain and the value of the corresponding trigonometric ratio. The trigonometric functions and their domains may then be tabulated as follows:

Function	Representation	Domain
sine	$(\theta, \sin\theta)$	all real numbers θ
cosine	$(\theta, \cos\theta)$	all real numbers θ
tangent	$(\theta, \tan\theta)$	$\theta \neq (2n+1)\frac{\pi}{2}, n = 0, \pm 1, \ldots$
cotangent	$(\theta, \cot\theta)$	$\theta \neq n\pi, n = 0, \pm 1, \ldots$
secant	$(\theta, \sec\theta)$	$\theta \neq (2n+1)\frac{\pi}{2}, n = 0, \pm 1, \ldots$
cosecant	$(\theta, \csc\theta)$	$\theta \neq n\pi, n = 0, \pm 1, \ldots$

Our interest now turns to the behavior of the trigonometric functions "in the large," so to speak. We desire an over-all view of each function, apart from its

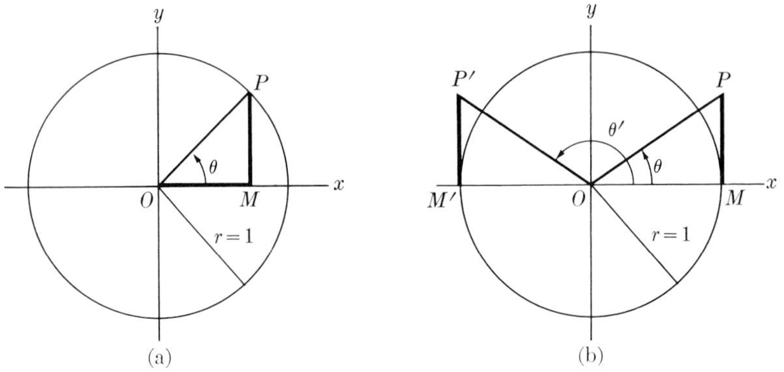

FIGURE 7–1

value for individual values of θ. The graphs of the functions serve ideally for this purpose. We shall first study the manner in which the trigonometric functions vary with θ, and then obtain the graphs. It will appear in the next section that it is sufficient to study this variation for values of θ between 0 and 2π.

In what follows it will be understood that, whenever reference is made to an angle θ, an angle of θ radians is meant. Similarly, a statement such as "θ is in Q_2" shall mean that "θ is a number such that an angle of θ radians is in Q_2," and so on.

In a coordinate system [Fig. 7–1(a)] draw a circle of radius 1 with center at O, and choose as the point P on the terminal line of any angle θ in standard position the intersection of this line with the circle. Let M be the intersection with the x-axis of a perpendicular from P to the x-axis. Then, by the definitions of Section 3–6, we have

$$\sin\theta = \frac{MP}{OP} = \frac{MP}{1} = MP, \qquad \cos\theta = \frac{OM}{OP} = \frac{OM}{1} = OM,$$

for θ in any quadrant.

To examine the variation of $\sin\theta$ we need merely examine the length MP as θ varies. We know that $\sin 0 = 0$. As θ increases from zero, $\sin\theta$ also increases, passing through $\sin\pi/6 = 0.500$, $\sin\pi/4 = 0.707$, $\sin\pi/3 = 0.866$, and reaching a maximum of 1 at $\pi/2$. As θ continues to increase from $\pi/2$ to π, $\sin\theta$ decreases from 1 to 0, in such a way that $\sin\theta = \sin(\pi - \theta)$. In other words, between $\pi/2$ and π, $\sin\theta$ retraces the values it assumed from 0 to $\pi/2$. For θ between π and $3\pi/2$, MP is directed downward and is negative, and $\sin\theta$ decreases from 0 to -1, repeating, but with a minus sign, the values that $\sin\theta$ assumed between 0 and $\pi/2$, and for θ varying from $3\pi/2$ to 2π, $\sin\theta$ increases from -1 to 0, repeating with a minus sign the values for θ between $\pi/2$ and π.

The variation of $\cos\theta$ can be traced similarly, by examining OM in Fig. 7–1(a) as θ increases. Thus, as θ increases from 0 to $\pi/2$, $\cos\theta$ decreases from 1 to 0, passing through $\cos\pi/6 = 0.866$, $\cos\pi/4 = 0.707$, and $\cos\pi/3 = 0.500$. In addition, we know from Section 3–9 that the behavior of $\cos\theta$ from 0 to $\pi/2$ is such that $\cos\theta = \sin(\pi/2 - \theta)$. For θ between $\pi/2$ and π, OM is directed to the left and is negative, and $\cos\theta$ decreases from 0 to -1. For θ between π and $3\pi/2$, $\cos\theta$ increases from -1 to 0, and for θ between $3\pi/2$ and 2π, $\cos\theta$ increases from 0 to 1.

For θ in Q_1 and Q_4 we have, from Fig. 7–1(b),

$$\tan\theta = \frac{MP}{OM} = \frac{MP}{1} = MP,$$

and for θ in Q_2 and Q_3 (shown in the figure as θ' just for this purpose),

$$\tan\theta = \frac{M'P'}{OM'} = \frac{M'P'}{-1} = -M'P'.$$

Hence, the variation of $\tan\theta$ can be studied by examining the length of MP for θ in Q_1 and Q_4, and of $M'P'$ for θ in Q_2 and Q_3. As θ increases from 0 to $\pi/2$, $\tan\theta$ increases from 0, passing through $\tan\pi/6 = 0.577$, $\tan\pi/4 = 1$, $\tan\pi/3 = 1.732$; then $\tan\theta$ increases indefinitely as θ gets closer to $\pi/2$, in such a manner that $\tan\theta$ *can be made larger than any preassigned number by taking* θ *close enough to, and less than,* $\pi/2$. For $\theta = \pi/2$ there is of course no value of the tangent. This behavior of $\tan\theta$ for θ in Q_1 and near $\pi/2$ is expressed in the statement

$$\tan\left(\frac{\pi}{2}\right)^- = \infty.$$

As soon as θ passes $\pi/2$, the tangent is negative, and very small algebraically (i.e., a large negative number) for θ close to but greater than $\pi/2$. We describe this behavior of $\tan\theta$ for θ in Q_2 and near $\pi/2$ by the statement

$$\tan\left(\frac{\pi}{2}\right)^+ = -\infty.$$

As θ increases to π, $\tan\theta$ increases to 0, and as θ increases from π to $3\pi/2$, $\tan\theta$ increases from 0 and repeats the behavior of $\tan\theta$ in Q_1. Finally, as θ increases from $3\pi/2$ to 2π, $\tan\theta$ increases from very small values to 0, duplicating the behavior in Q_2.

To study the variation of $\cot\theta$, $\sec\theta$, and $\csc\theta$, we use the following *reciprocal relations*, which follow at once from the definitions of the trigonometric ratios in Section 3–6,

$$\cot\theta = \frac{1}{\tan\theta}, \qquad \sec\theta = \frac{1}{\cos\theta}, \qquad \csc\theta = \frac{1}{\sin\theta},$$

for all angles for which the functions are defined.

Thus, $\cot\theta$ and $\tan\theta$ are *reciprocal functions;* as one increases the other decreases, and conversely. For $\theta = 0$ the cotangent is undefined. As θ increases from any value near, but greater than 0, $\cot\theta$ decreases from a very large value, and becomes very small (near zero) as θ nears $\pi/2$; we know that cot $\pi/2 = 0$ (see Section 3–8). As θ increases beyond $\pi/2$, cot θ becomes negative, decreasing from 0, and becoming very small algebraically as θ nears π, so that we may write

$$\cot \pi^- = -\infty.$$

The behavior of cot θ between π and 2π duplicates that between 0 and π.

It is left to the student to discuss in a similar fashion the variation of sec θ and csc θ for $0 \leqq \theta \leqq 2\pi$.

These results on the variation of the trigonometric functions are summarized in the following table, where the upward arrow $\nearrow$ indicates "increasing to," the downward arrow $\searrow$ indicates "decreasing to," and the behavior described is always for increasing θ.

	θ in Q_1	θ in Q_2	θ in Q_3	θ in Q_4
sin θ	$0 \nearrow 1$	$1 \searrow 0$	$0 \searrow -1$	$-1 \nearrow 0$
cos θ	$1 \searrow 0$	$0 \searrow -1$	$-1 \nearrow 0$	$0 \nearrow 1$
tan θ	$0 \nearrow \infty$	$-\infty \nearrow 0$	$0 \nearrow \infty$	$-\infty \nearrow 0$
cot θ	$\infty \searrow 0$	$0 \searrow -\infty$	$\infty \searrow 0$	$0 \searrow -\infty$
sec θ	$1 \nearrow \infty$	$-\infty \nearrow -1$	$-1 \searrow -\infty$	$\infty \searrow 1$
csc θ	$\infty \searrow 1$	$1 \nearrow \infty$	$-\infty \nearrow -1$	$-1 \searrow -\infty$

7–2 PERIODICITY OF THE TRIGONOMETRIC FUNCTIONS

We shall now show that the trigonometric functions manifest a kind of behavior, possessed also by other functions met in higher mathematics, by which there is a regular repetition of the values which each function has in a certain range of the angle. This behavior, known as *periodicity*, is expressed more explicitly in the following definition.

***Definition* 7–1.** *A function $f(\theta)$ is said to be periodic, with period α, if α is the smallest positive number for which*

$$f(\theta + \alpha) = f(\theta), \text{ for all } \theta \text{ for which } f(\theta) \text{ is defined.} \tag{1}$$

The number α is, for any trigonometric function, the range of the angle for which the values repeat. From the discussion of the variation of the functions in Section 7–1 the periodicity of these functions is almost apparent. The following theorem gives the precise statement.

Theorem 7–1. *The sine, cosine, secant, and cosecant functions have the period 2π. The tangent and cotangent functions have the period π.*

Proof. It has been shown, in Section 3–6, that any trigonometric function has the same value for coterminal angles. Hence, if $0 \leqq \theta \leqq 2\pi$, and n is any integer, the angle $\theta + 2n\pi$ is coterminal with θ, so that we may say:

Any trigonometric function of $(\theta + 2n\pi)$ = *the same-named function of* θ.

Thus, Eq. (1) holds with $\alpha = 2\pi$, for any trigonometric function. The remaining question is whether 2π is the smallest value that will serve. By Section 7–1 it is clear that for the sine, cosine, secant, and cosecant, no smaller value of α will suffice, and *these functions are periodic with period* 2π. Equation (1) holds also for the tangent and cotangent with $\alpha = 2\pi$, but the discussion of the preceding section has shown that $\alpha = \pi$ will suffice, and no smaller value will. Hence, the tangent and cotangent are periodic with period π, and the theorem is proved.

The importance of the periodicity of a function is that once the values of a periodic function are known for one period of the variable, the values of the function are then known for all values of the variable. Consequently, to draw the graphs of the trigonometric functions, as we shall do in the following section, it is sufficient to draw the graphs of the sine, cosine, secant, and cosecant for $0 \leqq \theta < 2\pi$, and of the tangent and cotangent for $0 \leqq \theta < \pi$, and to reproduce the portions thus obtained.

Example 1. Find the value of θ on the interval $-360° \leqq \theta < -180°$ for which $\tan\theta = \tan 246° 20'$.

Solution. Using the periodicity of the tangent function, we have $\tan 246° 20' = \tan(246° 20' + n \cdot 180°)$, for all integral values of n. We must choose a value of n such that the angle on the right is in the desired range. A few trials show that by choosing $n = -3$, we have

$$\tan 246° 20' = \tan(246° 20' - 540°) = \tan(-293° 40'),$$

and the desired angle in the given range is $\theta = -293° 40'$.

Example 2. Let $f(x)$ be the function defined in the following manner. In the interval $-\frac{3}{2} \leqq x \leqq 0$, $f(x)$ is defined by $f(x) = -x$, and in the interval $0 \leqq x \leqq \frac{3}{2}$, $f(x)$ is defined as $f(x) = x$. In addition, $f(x)$ is periodic with a period of 3. Find the values of $f(7)$, $f(-7.3)$, $f(9.7)$, $f(-8.7)$.

Solution. From the definition of periodicity, and the fact that in this case the period of $f(x)$ is 3, we have the relation

$$f(x) = f(x + 3n), \qquad \text{for all integral values of } n.$$

In each case, then, the problem becomes a matter of adding to or subtracting from x a suitable multiple of 3 to give a number between $-\frac{3}{2}$ and $\frac{3}{2}$. Thus, by subtracting 6 from 7 we get 1, which is in the desired range, so that $f(7) = f(1)$. Since the value $x = 1$ is in the range from 0 to $\frac{3}{2}$, the value of $f(x)$ is simply x, and we have

$$f(7) = f(1) = 1.$$

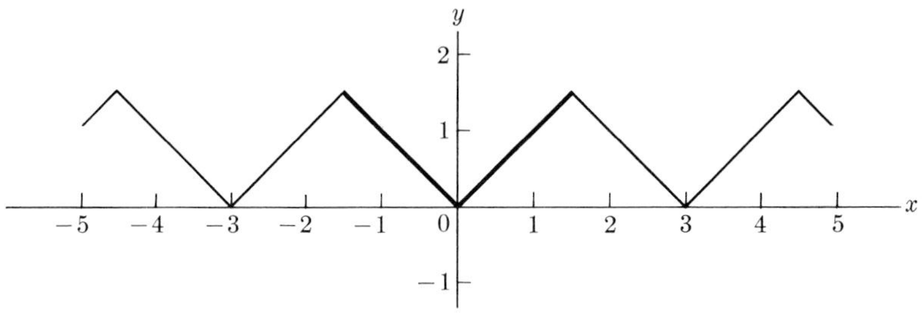

FIGURE 7–2

Similarly, we find

$$f(-7.3) = f(-7.3 + 6) = f(-1.3) = 1.3,$$
$$f(9.7) = f(9.7 - 9) = f(0.7) = 0.7,$$
$$f(-8.7) = f(-8.7 + 9) = f(0.3) = 0.3.$$

Figure 7–2 shows the graph of $f(x)$, with the periodicity clearly indicated.

EXERCISE GROUP 7–1

In Exercises 1–18, use either the table of Section 7–1, or the method by which the table was obtained, to answer the questions. For what values of θ, on the interval $0 \leqq \theta < 2\pi$,

1. is $\sin\theta$ increasing?
2. is $\cos\theta$ decreasing?
3. do $\sin\theta$ and $\cos\theta$ increase together?
4. do $\cos\theta$ and $\tan\theta$ increase together?
5. do $\sec\theta$ and $\csc\theta$ decrease together?
6. do $\sin\theta$, $\cot\theta$, and $\csc\theta$ decrease together?
7. is $\cot\theta$ decreasing?
8. is $\sec\theta \geqq 1$?
9. is $\csc\theta \leqq 1$?
10. is $\sin\theta \leqq \frac{1}{2}$?
11. is $0 \leqq \cos\theta \leqq \frac{1}{2}$?
12. is $0 \leqq \tan\theta \leqq 1$?
13. is $\tan\theta \geqq 1$?
14. is $-1 \leqq \sin\theta \leqq 0$?
15. is $-1 \leqq \tan\theta \leqq 0$?
16. is $-1 \leqq \cos\theta \leqq -\frac{1}{2}$?
17. is $\sin\theta \leqq \cos\theta$?
18. is $\tan\theta \leqq \cot\theta$?

In each of Exercises 19–36, use the periodic property of the trigonometric functions to find a value of θ on the interval $-\pi < \theta \leqq \pi$ or $-180° < \theta \leqq 180°$ for which

19. $\sin\theta = \sin(5\pi/3)$
20. $\cos\theta = \cos 638°$
21. $\tan\theta = \tan 1118°$
22. $\cot\theta = \cot(-9\pi/2)$
23. $\cos\theta = \cos(-17\pi/3)$
24. $\sin\theta = \sin(-647°)$
25. $\csc\theta = \csc 19\pi/4$
26. $\tan\theta = \tan(-873°)$
27. $\sec\theta = \sec(-873°)$
28. $\cos\theta = \cos(-19\pi/3)$
29. $\cot\theta = \cot 893°$
30. $\sin\theta = \sin(-21\pi/5)$
31. $\sec\theta = \sec 31(\pi/6)$
32. $\cot\theta = \cot(11\pi/3)$

33. $\tan\theta = \tan(9\pi/4)$

34. $\sec\theta = \sec 2114°$

35. $\csc\theta = \csc(37\pi/5)$

36. $\csc\theta = \csc 1937°$

37. $(x, f(x))$ is a function with a period of 4 and on the interval $-2 \leqq x < 2$, it is defined by the relation $f(x) = x$. Find $f(7.6)$, $f(-3.2)$, $f(11)$, $f(15)$.

38. $(x, f(x))$ is a function with a period of 2 and on the interval $-1 \leqq x \leqq 1$, it is defined by the relation $f(x) = \sqrt{1 - x^2}$. Find $f(3.2)$, $f(2.3)$, $f(1.1)$, $f(-3.7)$.

39. $(x, f(x))$ is a function with a period of 6 and on the interval $-3 \leqq x \leqq 3$, it is defined by the relation $f(x) = \frac{2}{3}\sqrt{9 - x^2}$. Find $f(13)$, $f(-12)$, $f(21)$, $f(-15)$.

40. $(x, f(x))$ is a function with a period of 2 and on the interval $-1 \leqq x \leqq 1$, it is defined by the relation $f(x) = 1 - x^2$. Find $f(2.3)$, $f(3.2)$, $f(-4.3)$, $f(-3.6)$.

41. $(x, f(x))$ is a function with period $2k$ and on the interval $-k \leqq x < k$, it is defined by the relation $f(x) = x^3$. Find $f(0.1 + 2k)$, $f(-0.2 - 2k)$, $f(2k)$, $f(-1 + 3k)$, $f(1.7 - 3k)$. Assume that $k \geqq 2$.

7-3 THE GRAPHS OF THE TRIGONOMETRIC FUNCTIONS

It is familiar from Chapter 2 that the graph of any equation in x and y consists of the aggregate of all points (x, y) whose coordinates satisfy the equation. In obtaining the graphs of the trigonometric functions, by setting y equal to each function and graphing the resulting equation, we shall use the knowledge of the variation of these functions, as discussed earlier, in addition to particular points on the graph.

Let us consider, as an example, the function

$$y = \sin x. \tag{2}$$

The graph of this function consists of the aggregate of all points (x, y) whose coordinates satisfy (2). Here x and y are numbers, and the meaning of this function is that when x is given a value, the corresponding value of y is obtained by finding the sine of x radians. Thus, if $x = \pi/3$, $y = \sin\pi/3 = 0.87$; if $x = \frac{3}{4}$, $y = \sin\frac{3}{4} = 0.68$. The fact that x represents the radian measure of an angle is no more significant for the graph than the fact that in the equation $A = x^2$ for the area of a square, the length of the side x may be in feet. The same scale is used on both axes, and the point on the x-axis representing π is placed, as nearly as possible, at $\pi = 3.1416$. For convenience, this point may often be placed at $x = 3$. Similar considerations apply to the other trigonometric functions.

In what follows we shall assume the truth of the statement that the graphs of the trigonometric functions are smooth curves, that is, that the curves have no corners or vertices. In view of our previous discussion of the variation of these functions, only a comparatively few points need actually be plotted. A table of values for special and quadrantal angles follows.

x	0	$\frac{\pi}{6}$	$\frac{\pi}{4}$	$\frac{\pi}{3}$	$\frac{\pi}{2}$	$\frac{2\pi}{3}$	$\frac{3\pi}{4}$	$\frac{5\pi}{6}$	π	$\frac{7\pi}{6}$	$\frac{5\pi}{4}$	$\frac{4\pi}{3}$	$\frac{3\pi}{2}$	$\frac{5\pi}{3}$	$\frac{7\pi}{4}$	$\frac{11\pi}{6}$
$y = \sin x$	0	.50	.71	.87	1	.87	.71	.50	0	−.50	−.71	−.87	−1	−.87	−.71	−.50
$y = \cos x$	1	.87	.71	.50	0	−.50	−.71	−.87	−1	−.87	−.71	−.50	0	.50	.71	.87
$y = \tan x$	0	.58	1	1.73	—	−1.73	−1	−.58	0							

The graph of $y = \sin x$. If the points (x, y), with $y = \sin x$ from the above table, are plotted and joined by a smooth curve, the portion of the graph of $y = \sin x$ between $x = 0$ and $x = 2\pi$ is obtained (Fig. 7–3). By the periodicity of the sine function (Section 7–2) the part of the graph thus obtained may be repeated indefinitely to the right and to the left, to give the complete graph.

The graph of $y = \cos x$. A similar procedure with the function $y = \cos x$ results in the graph in Fig. 7–4.

The graphs of $y = \tan x$ *and* $y = \cot x$. For the graph of $y = \tan x$, we plot the points (x, y) from the above table with $y = \tan x$ for $0 \leqq x < \pi$, and make use of our knowledge of the behavior of the tangent function for values of x near $\pi/2$. If the portion of the curve thus obtained for $0 \leqq x < \pi$ is continued in both directions (the period of $\tan x$ is π), the tangent curve in Fig. 7–5(a) is obtained. In a similar manner the graph of $y = \cot x$ is obtained, and is shown in Fig. 7–5(b).

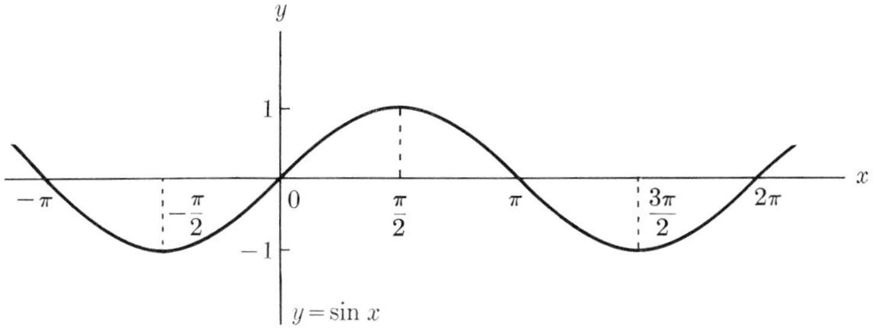

FIGURE 7–3

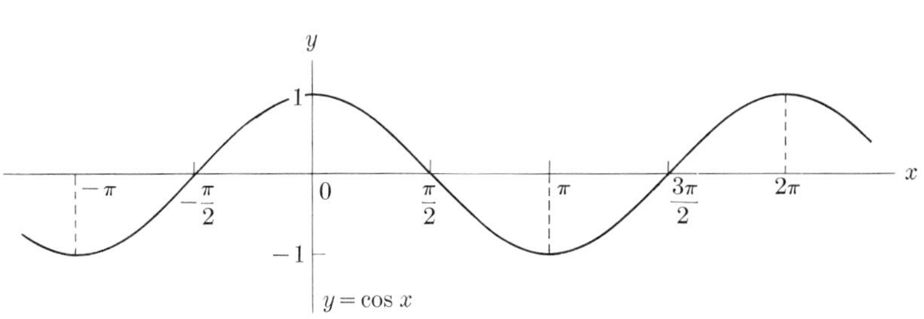

FIGURE 7–4

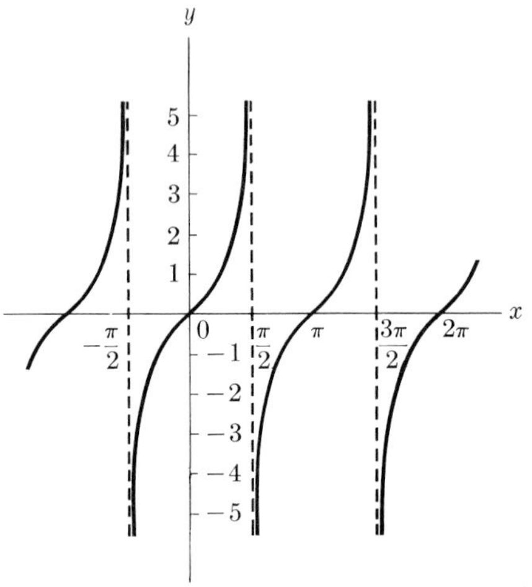

$y = \tan x$

(a)

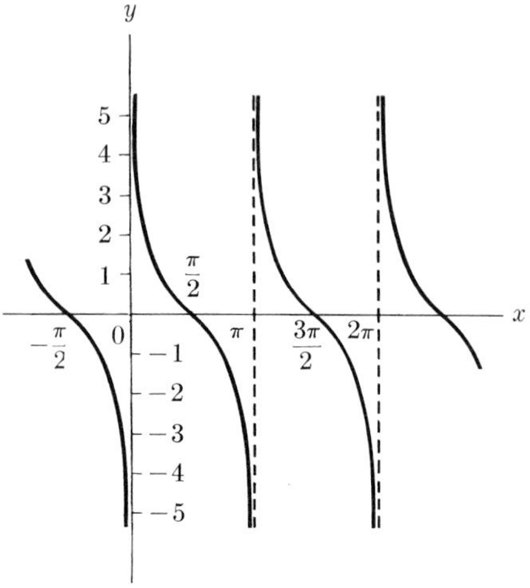

$y = \cot x$

(b)

FIGURE 7–5

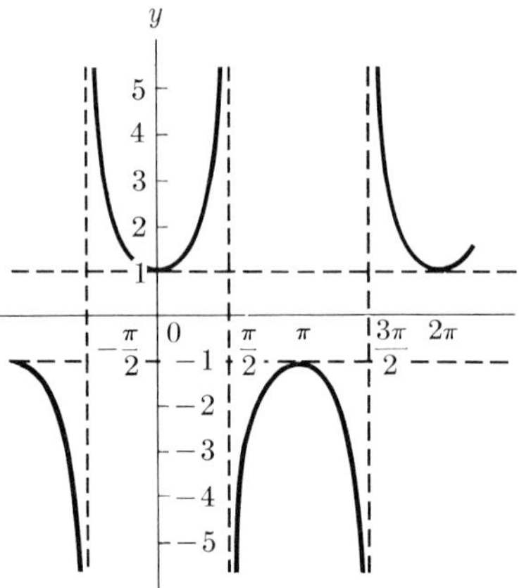

$y = \sec x$

(a)

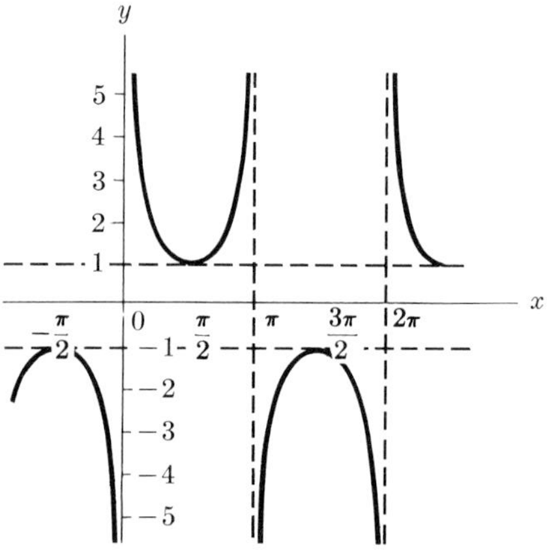

$y = \csc x$

(b)

FIGURE 7–6

The graphs of the remaining functions may also be obtained similarly, and appear in Fig. 7–6.

In addition to the periodicity of the trigonometric functions, an important feature of the sine and cosine curves is the regularity of the oscillation between the maximum and minimum values of the functions (Figs. 7–3 and 7–4).

***Definition* 7–2.** *The amplitude of a regularly oscillating function is one-half of the maximum minus the minimum values of the function.*

According to this definition, the amplitudes of $\sin x$ and $\cos x$ are both 1.

EXERCISE GROUP 7–2

In Exercises 1–21, construct the graph of each function by plotting the points obtained by assigning values to x on the interval $-\pi/2 \leqq x \leqq 2\pi$ corresponding to the special and quadrantal angles, and where applicable give the amplitude A.

1. $y = \sin x$
2. $y = \cos x$
3. $y = \tan x$
4. $y = \cot x$
5. $y = \sec x$
6. $y = \csc x$
7. $y = \cos(-x)$
8. $y = \sin(-x)$
9. $y = \tan(-x)$
10. $y = \frac{1}{2}\cos x$
11. $y = \frac{1}{3}\sin x$
12. $y = \frac{1}{4}\tan x$
13. $y = \frac{5}{2}\cos x$
14. $y = \frac{3}{5}\sin x$
15. $y = \frac{7}{3}\tan x$
16. $y = \sin\left(x - \frac{\pi}{2}\right)$
17. $y = \tan(x - \pi)$
18. $y = \cos\left(\frac{\pi}{3} + x\right)$
19. $y = 2\sin\left(\frac{\pi}{3} - x\right)$
20. $y = \tan\left(\frac{\pi}{3} - x\right)$
21. $y = \cos\left(\frac{\pi}{2} - x\right)$
22. Draw the graph of $y = \sin 2x$ by sketching a smooth curve through the points which are obtained by assigning to x those values on the interval $-\pi/4 \leqq x \leqq \pi$, for which $2x$ is a special or quadrantal angle.
23. Draw the graph of $y = \cos\frac{1}{2}x$ by sketching a smooth curve through the points which are obtained by assigning to x those values on the interval $-\pi \leqq x \leqq 4\pi$, for which $\frac{1}{2}x$ is a special or quadrantal angle.

By assigning suitable values to x, obtain a table of values for each of the following functions, and then construct the graph.

24. $y = \cos 3x$
25. $y = 3\cos 2x$
26. $y = \tan\frac{1}{2}x$
27. $y = \sin\frac{1}{3}x$
28. $y = \tan 2x$
29. $y = \sin 3x$

7–4 CONTRACTIONS AND EXPANSIONS, TRANSLATIONS, REFLECTIONS

A number of properties of the trigonometric functions (and functions in general) may be conveniently studied by considering the effects on the graphs of certain changes in the variables. This idea is, of course, new, and requires careful study. In particular, we shall consider the changes in the variable corresponding to contractions, expansions, translations, and reflections.

A *contraction* of a curve in the x-direction, or toward the y-axis, in a given ratio, means that each point of the curve is moved toward the y-axis in that ratio; if the ratio is $1:3$, each point is moved toward the y-axis to a new point which is $\frac{1}{3}$ of the former distance, while a ratio of $1:\frac{1}{3}$ means an expansion with each point moved in the direction from the y-axis to a point three times its former distance.

A *translation* of a curve in the x-direction by a given amount α means that each point of the curve is moved the amount α in the positive x-direction. For example, if $\alpha = 2$, each point is moved 2 units to the right, while if $\alpha = -2$, each point is moved -2 units to the right, or, in effect, 2 units to the left.

Finally, a *reflection* of a curve in some line means that a second curve is obtained, related to the first in such a way that if the paper were folded along that line, the two curves would coincide.

We shall now consider the particular change of variable for each geometric effect discussed.

Contractions and expansions. If, in a function of x, we replace x by ax, with $a > 0$, the effect is to contract the graph of the function in the x-direction, that is, toward the y-axis, in the ratio $1 : a$. For, if (m, n) are the coordinates of a point satisfying the equation $y = f(x)$, then the point $(m/a, n)$, which is obtained by moving (m, n) toward the y-axis in the ratio $1 : a$, will lie on the graph of the equation $y = f(ax)$.

Example 1. In Fig. 7-7 the graphs of $y = x^2$ and $y = 4x^2$ are drawn in the same coordinate system. It is clear that the second equation can be obtained by replacing x by $2x$ in the first equation. Thus the graph of $y = x^2$ can be contracted toward the y-axis in the ratio $1 : 2$ to give the graph of $y = 4x^2$. In particular, for any value of y we have $\overline{PM} = \frac{1}{2}\overline{PN}$.

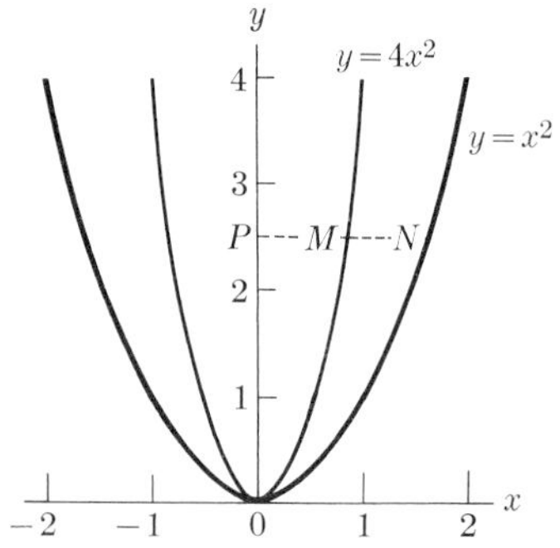

FIGURE 7-7

The number a as used here may be less than, equal to, or greater than 1. If $a < 1$, the ratio $1 : a$ is greater than 1, and the contraction, of course, becomes an expansion.

The principle employed in this discussion may be used to answer varied questions concerning variation of functions. The examples will amplify this.

Example 2. The period of $y = \tan 3x$ is $\pi/3$. For, a complete cycle of variation of the function $y = \tan x$ occurs in an x-interval of length π (one period); hence when x is replaced by $3x$, the graph is contracted toward the y-axis in the ratio $1 : 3$, and a cycle of variation will require an interval only $\frac{1}{3}$ as large, or $\pi/3$.

The same reasoning as above applies when y is replaced by cy, with $c > 0$. The effect of this substitution is to contract the curve in the y-direction in the ratio $1 : c$.

Example 3. The amplitude of $y = 2 \sin 4x$ is 2. For, the replacement of x by $4x$ changes only the period of $y = \sin x$, but not the amplitude. Thus $y = \sin 4x$ has amplitude 1, and period $\pi/2$. We may now obtain the equation $y = 2 \sin 4x$ by replacing y by $y/2$ in $y = \sin 4x$. This replacement of y by $y/2$ has the effect of contracting the curve in the y-direction in the ratio of $1 : \frac{1}{2} = 2 : 1$, which is actually an expansion. Hence, by Definition 7-2, the amplitude of $y = 2 \sin 4x$ is 2.

Translations. If, in a function $f(x)$, the variable x is replaced by $x - \alpha$, the effect on the graph of $f(x)$ is to translate the curve an amount α parallel to the x-axis, and in the positive direction. For, if (m, n) are the coordinates of a point on the graph of $y = f(x)$, then the point $(m + \alpha, n)$, which results from translating (m, n) an amount α in the positive x-direction, will lie on the graph of $y = f(x - \alpha)$. If $\alpha > 0$, the translation is to the right, and if $\alpha < 0$, the translation is to the left.

It is sometimes more convenient to think of the effect of replacing x by $x - \alpha$ as a translation of the coordinate axes an amount α in the negative x-direction, while leaving the curve unchanged.

Example 4. The graph of the function $y = \cos(x - \frac{1}{2}\pi)$ may be obtained, according to the principle just stated, by translating $y = \cos x$ an amount $\frac{1}{2}\pi$ to the right. Inspection of Figs. 7–3 and 7–4 would indicate that this translation yields the graph of $y = \sin x$. We shall see later (Section 10–3) that this is actually the case.

A corresponding translation of the curve in the y-direction by the amount β arises from a replacement of y by $y - \beta$. And a simultaneous replacement of x by $x - \alpha$ and y by $y - \beta$ translates the curve an amount α in the positive x-direction, and β in the positive y-direction.

Reflections. If (m, n) is a point in the plane, then the point $P_1(-m, n)$ is called its *reflection* or *image* in the y-axis (see Fig. 7–8), the point $P_2(m, -n)$ is its reflection in the x-axis, and $P_3(-m, -n)$ is its reflection in the origin. If each point of a curve is reflected in a line, the resulting curve is called the reflection or image of the original curve in the line. It follows from these statements that if x is replaced by $-x$ in the equation

$$y = f(x), \qquad (3)$$

the equation obtained, which is

$$y = f(-x), \qquad (4)$$

is the reflection of (3) in the y-axis.

Similarly, if y is replaced by $-y$ in Eq. (3), the resulting equation is

$$-y = f(x)$$

or

$$y = -f(x), \qquad (5)$$

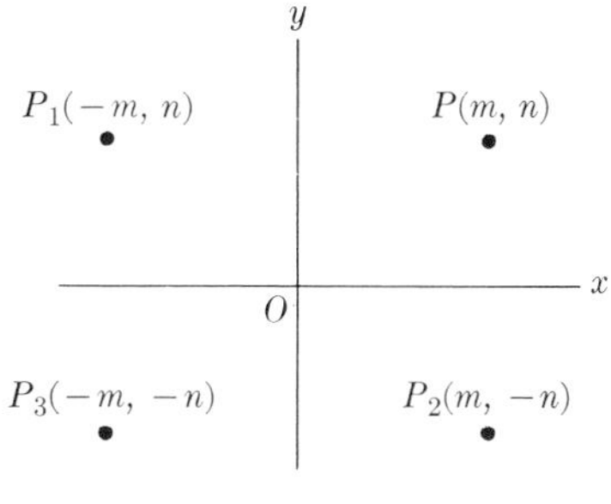

FIGURE 7–8

and the graph of (5) is the reflection of (3) in the x-axis.

Finally, if at the same time x is replaced by $-x$ and y by $-y$ in Eq. (3), the equation obtained is

$$-y = f(-x) \quad \text{or} \quad y = -f(-x),$$

and, although the physical idea of reflection does not persist, the graph of this equation is still called the reflection of (2) in the origin.

Example 5. The reflection of the straight line $y = 2x + 3$ in the y-axis is the line

$$y = 2(-x) + 3$$

or

$$y = -2x + 3.$$

The reflection of the first line in the x-axis is the line

$$-y = 2x + 3$$

or

$$y = -2x - 3.$$

Finally, the reflection of $y = 2x + 3$ in the origin is

$$-y = 2(-x) + 3$$

or

$$y = 2x - 3.$$

The four lines are shown in Fig. 7-9.

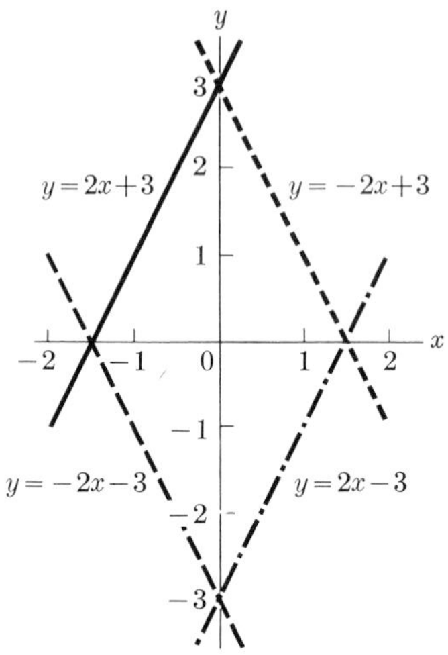

FIGURE 7-9

Example 6. Describe a sequence of changes in variable that will change the equation $y = \sin x$ into $y = 4 \sin (\pi - 3x)$.

Solution. In the first column the change in variable is given, and in the second column the resulting equation appears.

0. (Given equation)	$y = \sin x$
1. Replace y by $y/4$	$y = 4 \sin x$
2. Replace x by $3x$	$y = 4 \sin 3x$
3. Replace x by $-x$	$y = 4 \sin (-3x)$
4. Replace x by $x - \pi/3$	$y = 4 \sin [-3(x - \pi/3)]$
	$= 4 \sin (\pi - 3x)$

7-5 SYMMETRY. ODD AND EVEN FUNCTIONS

We shall introduce here, for future use, some concepts related to the previous section. It sometimes happens that the reflection of a curve in a line is the same curve as the original one; in such an event the curve is said to be *symmetric* in that line, or with respect to that line.

The test for symmetry is, then, that the change in variable which produces the reflection leaves the equation unaltered. Accordingly, we have the following tests for symmetry.

I. *If replacing y by $-y$ leaves an equation unaltered, the curve is symmetric in the x-axis.*

II. *If replacing x by $-x$ leaves an equation unaltered, the curve is symmetric in the y-axis.*

III. *If replacing x by $-x$ and y by $-y$ leaves an equation unaltered, the curve is symmetric in the origin.*

If the graph of $y = f(x)$ is symmetric in the y-axis, it follows that $f(x) = f(-x)$, and $f(x)$ is called an *even function* of x.

If the graph of $y = f(x)$ is symmetric in the origin, then $-y = f(-x)$, so that $f(-x) = -f(x)$ and $f(x)$ is called an *odd function* of x.

Example 1. The function $y = x^2$ is an even function of x. For, if $f(x) = x^2$, a replacement of x by $-x$ gives

$$f(-x) = (-x)^2 = x^2 = f(x),$$

and the criterion for evenness is established. Moreover, the graph of $y = x^2$ is symmetric in the y-axis.

Example 2. The function $f(x) = x^3 - 3x$ is an odd function of x. For,

$$f(-x) = (-x)^3 - 3(-x) = -x^3 + 3x = -(x^3 - 3x) = -f(x),$$

and the oddness of the function is proved. The graph of $f(x)$ is symmetric in the origin.

Example 3. The graph of $y = \cos x$ is seen from Fig. 7–4 to be symmetric in the y-axis. Hence, $\cos x$ *is an even function of* x, and we may write

$$\cos(-x) = \cos x, \qquad \text{for all } x.$$

EXERCISE GROUP 7–3

In each of Exercises 1–8, find the coordinates of each point after the indicated operation.

1. $(3, -2)$; a translation of 4 units to the right
2. $(-5, 6)$; a translation of 2 units up
3. $(3, -7)$; a translation of 4 units to the left and 2 units down
4. $(-2, 6)$; a translation of 3 units to the right and 4 units down
5. $(2, 10)$; a contraction in the y-direction in the ratio $1 : \frac{1}{5}$
6. $(5, -4)$; a contraction in the x-direction in the ratio $1 : 3$ and one in the y-direction in the ratio $1 : \frac{1}{3}$
7. $(2, -7)$; a reflection in the x-axis
8. $(-5, 3)$; a reflection in the y-axis

In each of Exercises 9–23, find the equation obtained from the given one by the indicated operation.

9. $3y = x + 5$; a translation of (a) 3 units to the right, (b) 3 units down
10. $y = x^2 + 2$; a translation of (a) 4 units to the left, (b) 4 units up
11. $y^3 = x^2$; a translation of one unit to the right and 2 units down
12. $y = \sin x$; a translation of π units to the right and one unit up
13. $y = \cos x$; a translation of $\pi/3$ units to the left and 4 units down
14. $y = \tan x$; a translation of $\pi/2$ units to the left and one unit up
15. $y = 2 \sin 3x$; a translation of 2π units to the left and 2 units up
16. $y = 3x$; a contraction in the x-direction in the ratio $1 : 3$

17. $y = x^3$; a contraction in the y-direction in the ratio $1 : \frac{1}{3}$
18. $y = \cos 3x$; a contraction in the x-direction in the ratio $1 : 2$
19. $y = 2 \tan x$; a contraction in the y-direction in the ratio $1 : \frac{1}{2}$
20. $y = x^2 + 2x$; a reflection in (a) the x-axis, (b) the origin
21. $y = x^4$; a reflection in (a) the y-axis, (*b*) the origin
22. $y = 4 \sin x$; a reflection in (a) the x-axis, (b) the y-axis
23. $y = \cos x$; a reflection in (a) the x-axis, (b) the y-axis, (c) the origin

Examine the graph of each function in Exercises 24–29 [see Figs. 7–3, 7–4, 7–5(a) and (b), 7–6(a) and (b)] to determine whether the function is odd or even and write the equation expressing your conclusion.

24. $\sin x$ 25. $\cos x$ 26. $\tan x$
27. $\cot x$ 28. $\sec x$ 29. $\csc x$

30. Derive the equation obtained from $y = x/(1 + x)$ under a translation of four units to the right, followed by a reflection in the y-axis.
31. Derive the equation obtained from $xy = 3y + 4$ under a translation of three units to the left, followed by a contraction in the y-direction in the ratio $1 : 2$.
32. Derive the equation obtained from $y = \sin x$ under a translation of $\pi/2$ units to the right, followed by a contraction in the y-direction in the ratio $1 : \frac{1}{2}$.
33. Derive the equation obtained from $y = \cos x$ under a contraction in the x-direction in the ratio $1 : 3$, followed by a translation in the x-direction of $\pi/6$ units to the right, and then followed by a reflection in the x-axis.

Describe the change of variable, or a sequence of such changes, that will lead from the first equation to the second in each of Exercises 34–41.

34. $y = x - 3,\ y = x + 1$
35. $y = 8x^2,\ y = -2x^2$
36. $y = x^2 - x,\ y = -\dfrac{(x + 2)^2}{9} + \dfrac{(x + 2)}{3}$
37. $y = \sin x,\ y = \sin\left(x - \dfrac{\pi}{2}\right)$
38. $y = \cos x,\ y = -2\cos\left(x + \dfrac{3\pi}{2}\right)$
39. $y = \sin x,\ y = 3 \sin 2(x - \pi)$
40. $y = \tan x,\ y = 3 - 2 \tan (5x - 2\pi)$
41. $y = \cos x,\ y = -1 + \frac{1}{2} \cos (-2x + \pi)$

In each of the following find the period P and, where applicable, the amplitude A.

42. $y = 2 \sin 3x$ 43. $y = 3 \cos \frac{1}{2}x$ 44. $y = 2 \tan 3x$
45. $y = 2 \sin 4(x - 2\pi)$ 46. $y = \cot 3(x - \pi)$ 47. $2y = \cos\left(x - \dfrac{\pi}{4}\right)$
48. $y - 1 = \sin x$ 49. $y = \cos (2x - 1)$ 50. $y = 2 + 4 \cos (3x - \pi)$

7-6 RAPID SKETCHING. THE GRAPHS OF $y = a \sin(bx + c)$ AND $y = a \cos(bx + c)$

We shall consider here a method of rapid sketching of certain graphs related to the basic trigonometric functions. The purpose of the rapid sketching of the graphs of functions is to show the essential features of these graphs, by relating the functions to certain basic functions, and by making use of the known graphs of the latter. More carefully drawn graphs can then be made, when necessary, by use of special values, or by use of a more extensive table of values.

In particular, the graphs of the functions

$$y = a \sin(bx + c) \quad \text{and} \quad y = a \cos(bx + c)$$

can be analyzed in terms of the changes in the sine and cosine curves caused by suitable changes in variable.

First we consider the graph of a function of this type in which $c = 0$.

Example 1. Draw the graph of $y = -\cos x/2$.

Solution. The equation $y = -\cos x/2$ may be obtained from the equation $y = \cos x$ by replacing x by $x/2$ and y by $-y$. Hence the desired graph is obtained by contracting the cosine curve in the x-direction in the ratio of $1 : \frac{1}{2}$ or $2 : 1$, and then reflecting in the x-axis. The graph, shown in Fig. 7–10, has a period of 4π, and amplitude of 1. The curve crosses the x-axis at $-\pi, \pi, 3\pi, \ldots$, has maximum points at $x = 2\pi, 6\pi, \ldots$, and minimum points at $x = 0, 4\pi, \ldots$.

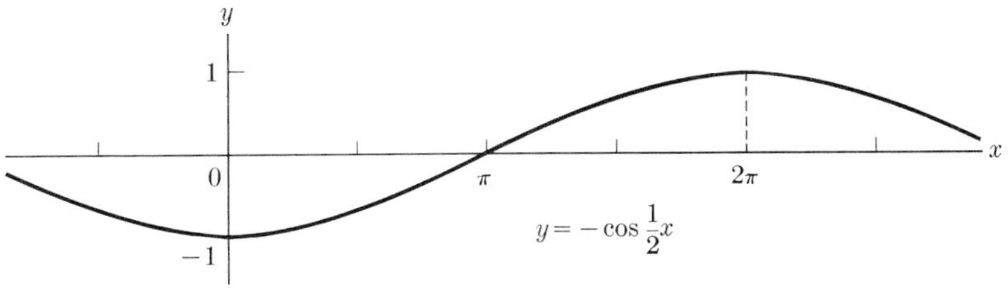

FIGURE 7–10

In the more general case, the effect of the constant c is to produce a translation of the curve $y = a \sin bx$ or $y = a \cos bx$ by an amount which depends on the values of b and c. The following example will illustrate this.

Example 2. Draw the graph of $y = 3 \sin(2x + \pi/2)$.

Solution. Let us write the function as

$$y = 3 \sin[2(x + \pi/4)].$$

This function can then be obtained from the function $y = \sin x$ by the following steps:

1. Replace y by $y/3$ to give $y = 3 \sin x$.
2. In $y = 3 \sin x$ replace x by $2x$ to give $y = 3 \sin 2x$.

3. In $y = 3 \sin 2x$ replace x by $x + \pi/4$ to give

$$y = 3 \sin [2(x + \pi/4)],$$

which is the desired function.

The effect of these steps on the graph of $y = \sin x$ is to contract the curve in the y-direction in the ratio of $1 : \frac{1}{3} = 3 : 1$, then to contract the resulting curve in the x-direction in the ratio of $1 : 2$, and finally to translate the curve the amount $\pi/4$ in the negative x-direction. The graph appears in Fig. 7–11, with period π and amplitude 3. A maximum occurs when $2x + \frac{1}{2}\pi = \frac{1}{2}\pi$, or $x = 0$; a minimum occurs when $x = \frac{1}{2}\pi$, etc.

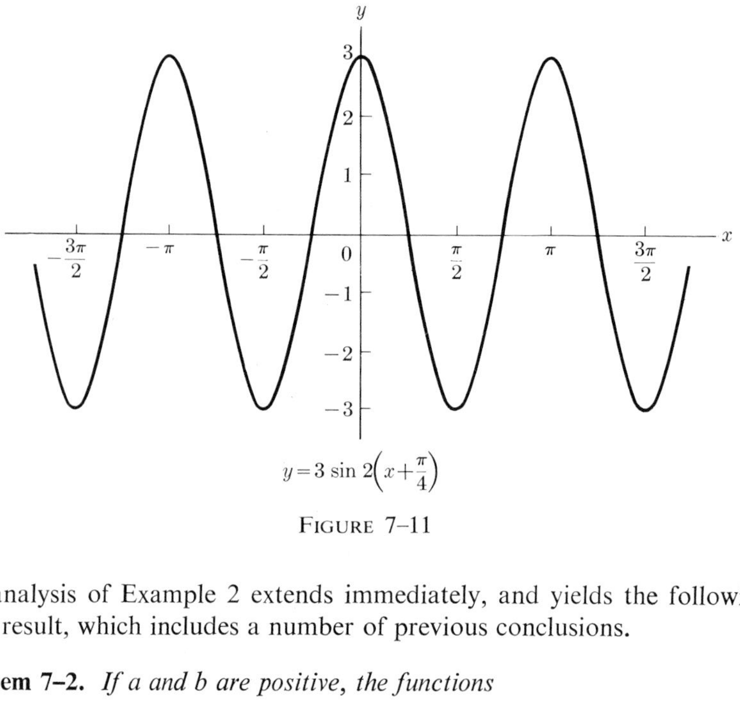

FIGURE 7–11

The analysis of Example 2 extends immediately, and yields the following important result, which includes a number of previous conclusions.

Theorem 7–2. *If a and b are positive, the functions*

$$y = a \sin (bx + c) \quad \textit{and} \quad y = a \cos (bx + c) \tag{6}$$

have the period $2\pi/b$, and amplitude a. The graphs of (6) *may be obtained by translating the graphs of $y = a \sin bx$ and $y = a \cos bx$, respectively, an amount c/b in the negative x-direction.*

If a or b is negative in a function of one of the types (6), the analysis of Example 2 need only be preceded by a reflection, as in the following example.

Example 3. Analyze the graph of $y = 3 \sin (-2x - \pi/2)$.

Solution. Starting with $y = \sin x$, we replace x by $-x$ to give $y = \sin (-x)$. Then the steps of Example 2 are followed, and the desired graph will turn out to be the image in the x-axis of the graph in Fig. 7–11.

EXERCISE GROUP 7–4

Sketch each of the following by the methods of Section 7–6, through at least one period. Check by finding, in the range of values used, those points for which the value of y is smallest, those for which the value of y is largest, and those for which the value of y is zero.

1. $y = 2\cos x$
2. $y = \sin \frac{1}{2}x$
3. $y = -2\sin x$
4. $y = -\frac{1}{2}\cos 2x$
5. $y = -3\cos \frac{1}{2}x$
6. $y = -2\sin \frac{1}{3}x$
7. $y = 2\cos(-x)$
8. $y = 3\sin(-x)$
9. $y = -3\cos(-x)$
10. $y = -2\sin(-x)$
11. $y = \sin\left(x - \frac{\pi}{2}\right)$
12. $y = \cos\left(x + \frac{\pi}{3}\right)$
13. $y = \sin\left(\frac{\pi}{3} - x\right)$
14. $y = \cos\left(\frac{\pi}{4} - x\right)$
15. $y = \cos(3x - \pi)$
16. $y = \sin(2x + \pi)$
17. $y = \cos(\pi - 3x)$
18. $y = \sin\left(\frac{\pi}{2} - 2x\right)$
19. $y = 2 + \sin 2x$
20. $y - 3 = \cos \frac{1}{2}x$
21. $y = 2 + 3\sin 4x$
22. $y = 3 - 2\cos \frac{1}{2}x$
23. $y = 2 + 3\cos(x - 1)$
24. $y = 3 + 2\sin(x - 1)$
25. $y = -1 + 2\sin(2 - x)$
26. $y = -\frac{1}{3} + \frac{1}{2}\sin\left(\frac{1}{4}x - \frac{\pi}{3}\right)$
27. $y = \frac{2}{3} - \frac{3}{2}\cos\left(\frac{1}{2}x + \frac{\pi}{3}\right)$
28. $y = -1 - 2\cos\left(\frac{\pi}{2} - x\right)$
29. $y = -2 - \sin(\pi - x)$
30. $y = \pi - 2\sin(\frac{1}{2} - 2x)$

7–7 GRAPHING BY ADDITION OF ORDINATES

A further method useful in the rapid sketching of certain functions is known as *addition of ordinates*. The method applies to a function $y = f(x)$ where $f(x)$ can be written as a sum of two functions,

$$y = f(x) = f_1(x) + f_2(x), \tag{7}$$

and where the graphs of $f_1(x)$ and $f_2(x)$ either are known or can be quickly obtained. Then if we set

$$y_1 = f_1(x), \qquad y_2 = f_2(x),$$

we have, of course,

$$y = y_1 + y_2. \tag{8}$$

By virtue of (8), points on the graph of (7) can be obtained by adding, for any value of x, the ordinates y_1 and y_2, and joining the points thus obtained by a smooth curve. For the best use of the method, the addition of ordinates should be done graphically, either with a pair of dividers, or with any straight edge on which the lengths of the ordinates can be marked. As many values of x may be used as are necessary; these should usually include values for which either y_1 or y_2

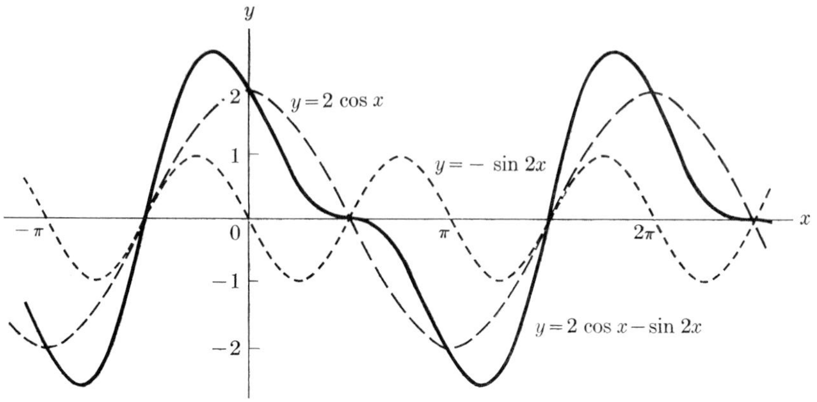

FIGURE 7-12

vanishes, values for which either y_1 or y_2 has a maximum or minimum, and values for which $y_1 = y_2$.

Example. Draw the graph of $y = 2\cos x - \sin 2x$.

Solution. Let us set $y = y_1 + y_2$, where

$$y_1 = 2\cos x, \qquad y_2 = -\sin 2x.$$

The minus sign is incorporated in y_2 because it is simpler to add ordinates than to subtract. We then draw the graphs of the functions y_1 and y_2 in the same coordinate system, as in Fig. 7-12. The addition of ordinates as described above yields the heavily drawn curve. Some of the values of x used in the construction of the curve are also indicated.

EXERCISE GROUP 7-5

Sketch the graph of each of the functions in Exercises 1-29 for x in at least the interval $-\pi \leqq x \leqq 2\pi$.

1. $y = x + \sin x$
2. $y = 2x + \cos x$
3. $y = \dfrac{x^2}{10} + \sin x$
4. $y = \dfrac{x^3}{25} + \cos 2x$
5. $y = -x + \sin 2x$
6. $y = -\dfrac{x^2}{8} + \cos x$
7. $y = \sin x + \cos x$
8. $y = \sin x + \sin 2x$
9. $y = \cos x - \sin 2x$
10. $y = \sin x - \cos 2x$
11. $y = \sin x + \cos 2x$
12. $y = 2\sin 2x + \cos \frac{1}{2}x$
13. $y = 2\cos \frac{1}{2}x - \sin 2x$
14. $y = \sin \frac{1}{2}x - \cos 2x$
15. $y = \sin \frac{1}{2}x - \cos \frac{1}{3}x$
16. $y = 2\sin \frac{1}{3}x - 3\cos \frac{1}{2}x$
17. $y = \frac{1}{2}\sin 2x + \frac{1}{3}\cos 3x$
18. $y = -\frac{1}{2}\sin 3x + \frac{1}{3}\cos 2x$
19. $y = \sin\left(x - \dfrac{\pi}{3}\right) + \cos x$
20. $y = \sin x + \cos\left(x + \dfrac{\pi}{3}\right)$
21. $y = \sin 2(x - \pi) + \cos 3(x + \pi)$

22. $y = \sin\left(\frac{1}{2}x - \frac{\pi}{3}\right) + \cos\left(\frac{1}{3}x - \frac{\pi}{2}\right)$

23. $y = 2\sin(3x - \pi) - 3\cos(4x + \pi)$

24. $y = 2\sin 2x - \cos\left(x - \frac{\pi}{3}\right)$

25. $y = 2\sin\frac{1}{2}x + \sin\left(x + \frac{\pi}{4}\right)$

26. $y = \sin(2x + \pi) - 2\sin\left(x - \frac{\pi}{2}\right)$

27. $y = \cos 3(x - \pi) + \sin 2(x + \pi)$

28. $y = 3\sin x + \sin 2x - \cos 3x$

29. $y = 2\cos x - \cos 2x + \sin 3x$

30. A 60-cycle alternating current ($i = 10\sin 120\pi t$) and a 25-cycle alternating current ($i = 5\sin 50\pi t$) are both fed into a circuit so that the current flowing in the circuit is given by the relation

$$i = 5\sin 50\pi t + 10\sin 120\pi t.$$

Draw the graph of this function and give its period and amplitude.

Two alternating currents, $i_1 = I_1 \sin k\pi t$ and $i_2 = I_2 \sin k\pi t$, of the same period $2/k$, are said to be *in phase* when both are zero for the same value of t. The current i_1 is said to *lead* current i_2 by T seconds if they are represented by the equations

$$i_1 = I_1 \sin k\pi(t - T), \qquad i_2 = I_2 \sin k\pi t;$$

and i_1 is said to *lag* T seconds behind i_2 if they are represented by the equations

$$i_1 = I_1 \sin k\pi(t + T), \qquad i_2 = I_2 \sin k\pi t.$$

Draw the graph of the current which results from combining the currents

$$i_1 = 10\sin 120\pi t \quad \text{and} \quad i_2 = 15\sin 120\pi t$$

if:

31. i_1 and i_2 are in phase.

32. i_1 leads i_2 by $\frac{1}{120}$ of a second.

33. i_1 lags behind i_2 by $\frac{1}{120}$ of a second.

34. i_1 lags behind i_2 by $\frac{1}{60}$ of a second.

SUPPLEMENTARY EXERCISES FOR CHAPTER 7

In each of Exercises 1–22, draw the graph of the function through at least one period. In each case, determine the period and also, where applicable, the amplitude.

1. $y = 2\tan x$
2. $y = 3\cos 2x$
3. $y = \frac{1}{2}\sin 3x$
4. $y = 3\sec x$
5. $y = 2\cot 3x$
6. $y = \frac{1}{3}\cos\frac{1}{2}x$
7. $y = 3\sin 2x$
8. $y = 2\sin\frac{1}{3}x$
9. $y = 3\tan 2x$
10. $y = 2\csc 3x$
11. $y = \cot\frac{1}{3}x$
12. $y = \sin\frac{2}{3}x$
13. $y = 2\cos(x + \pi)$
14. $y = 2\sin\left(x - \frac{\pi}{2}\right)$

15. $y = \frac{1}{2}\sin(2x - \pi)$

16. $y = \frac{1}{2}\cos\left(3x + \frac{\pi}{2}\right)$

17. $y = -3\sin\left(\frac{\pi}{3} - 2x\right)$

18. $y = -\cos(\pi - 3x)$

19. $y = \sin x + 2\cos x$

20. $y = \sin x - \cos 2x$

21. $y = \sin \frac{1}{2}x + \cos \frac{1}{3}x$

22. $y = 2\sin 2x + \cos \frac{1}{2}x$

Draw the graph of the function described in each of Exercises 23–26.

23. $(x, f(x))$ is a function with period π, and $f(x) = \sin x$ for $0 \leqq x < \pi$.

24. $(x, f(x))$ is a function with period π, and $f(x) = \cos x$ for $0 \leqq x < \pi$.

25. $(x, f(x))$ is a function with period 2π, and $f(x) = \sin x$ for $0 \leqq x < \pi/2$, $f(x) = 1$ for $\pi/2 \leqq x < 3\pi/2$, $f(x) = -\sin x$ for $3\pi/2 \leqq x < 2\pi$.

26. $(x, f(x))$ is a function with period 2π, and $f(x) = (2/\pi)x + 1$ for $-\pi/2 \leqq x < 0$, $f(x) = \cos x$ for $0 \leqq x < \pi$, $f(x) = (2/\pi)x - 3$ for $\pi \leqq x < 3\pi/2$.

In the following exercises, derive the equation obtained from the given equation under the indicated operations.

27. $y^2 = x^2 + 2$; a translation of 2 units to the right and 2 units down

28. $xy = 4$; a contraction in the x-direction in the ratio $1:2$, followed by a reflection in the x-axis

29. $x^2 + 2y^2 = 4$; a contraction in the x-direction in the ratio $1:\sqrt{2}$ and in the y-direction in the ratio $\sqrt{2}:1$

30. $x^2y = y + 2$; a contraction in the y-direction in the ratio $1:2$, followed by a reflection in the origin

31. $y + 2 = \cos x$; a translation of 2 units up and $\pi/2$ units to the left

32. $y = \sec x + \tan x$; a translation of $3\pi/2$ units to the right

33. $y = x\sin x$; a reflection in the y-axis, followed by a contraction in the x-direction in the ratio $2:3$

34. $y\sec x + x\tan y + 2 = 0$; a reflection in the x-axis, followed by a reflection in the origin

CHAPTER 8

Polynomials of Higher Degree

8–1 POLYNOMIALS

The linear and quadratic functions were discussed in Chapter 4. In the present chapter certain general methods will be presented for determining the real zeros of polynomial functions of higher degree.

Consider a function $(x, f(x))$, with domain consisting of all real numbers, and whose values may be written in the form

$$f(x) = a_0x^n + a_1x^{n-1} + a_2x^{n-2} + \cdots + a_n,$$

where $a_0 \neq 0$, the exponent n is a positive integer, and a_i $(i = 0, 1, \ldots, n)$ are real or complex numbers. This expression is called a *polynomial in x of degree n.* Since our study will be confined to polynomials, $f(x)$ as used in the present chapter will be understood as representing a polynomial.

8–2 GENERAL THEOREMS ABOUT POLYNOMIALS

In this section we shall present some basic theorems which find repeated application when we work with polynomials.

Remainder Theorem. *When a polynomial $f(x)$ is divided by $x - r$, where r is any number, until a constant remainder (free of x) is obtained, the resulting remainder is equal to $f(r)$.*

Proof. It is assumed that the reader is familiar with the division of one polynomial by another. In particular, if $f(x)$ is divided by $D(x)$, where $D(x)$ is of lower degree than $f(x)$, then there exist polynomials $Q(x)$, the *quotient*, and $R(x)$, the *remainder*, such that

$$f(x) = D(x) \cdot Q(x) + R(x),$$

and the degree of $R(x)$ is less than that of $D(x)$.

Let the quotient obtained when $f(x)$ is divided by $x - r$ be designated as $q(x)$ and let R designate the remainder. Then the function $f(x)$ can be expressed in the form

$$f(x) = (x - r) \cdot q(x) + R,$$

where the degree of R must be less than that of $x - r$; hence R is of degree zero and must be a *constant*. The equation holds for all values of x; in particular, if we set $x = r$, we have

$$f(r) = R,$$

which completes the proof of the theorem.

Example 1. Let $f(x) = 3x^4 - 2x^3 + 7x^2 - 5x + 2$, and $r = 3$. Division of $f(x)$ by $x - 3$ (by long division) gives a remainder of 239. By substituting $x = 3$ in $f(x)$, we find $f(3) = 243 - 54 + 63 - 15 + 2 = 239$, which is in accord with the theorem just proved. Again, we note that $f(1) = 5$. Hence if $f(x)$ is divided by $x - 1$ the remainder will be 5.

Factor Theorem. *If the remainder $R = f(r)$ is zero, then the division by $x - r$ is exact and $x - r$ is a factor of $f(x)$.*

Proof. Since by hypothesis $R = f(r) = 0$, then

$$f(x) = (x - r) \cdot q(x) + 0,$$

and, clearly, $x - r$ is a factor of $f(x)$.

Converse of Factor Theorem. *If $x - r$ is a factor of $f(x)$, then $f(r) = 0$ and $x = r$ is a zero of the function $f(x)$.*

Proof. It is assumed that $x - r$ is a factor of $f(x)$. Therefore, the division of $f(x)$ by $x - r$ is exact and the remainder $f(r) = 0$. Hence r is a zero of $f(x)$.

Example 2. Given $f(x) = 3x^3 + 2x^2 + 5x - 2$. Since $f(1) = 8 \neq 0$, we see that $x - 1$ is not a factor of $f(x)$. Again, $f(\frac{1}{3}) = 0$; hence $x - \frac{1}{3}$ is a factor of $f(x)$, and $x = \frac{1}{3}$ is a zero of the function $f(x)$ and a root of the equation $f(x) = 0$.

EXERCISE GROUP 8-1

In each of Exercises 1-18, use the Remainder Theorem to compute the remainder in each division.

1. $(3x^2 - 7x + 5) \div (x - 2)$
2. $(3x^2 - 7x - 5) \div (x + 1)$
3. $(x^3 - x^2 + 4x - 7) \div (x - 3)$
4. $(x^3 - 8x^2 + 12x + 17) \div (x + 2)$
5. $(3x^3 + 4x^2 - x - 11) \div (x + 2)$
6. $(5x^4 + 20x^3 + 18x^2 - 40x - 60) \div (x + 3)$
7. $(3x^4 + 2x^2 - 12x^3 + 11x + 10) \div (x + 5)$
8. $(x^4 - 2x^3 - x^2 + 4) \div (x - 3)$
9. $(x^4 + 2x^2 - x + 4) \div (x + 2)$

10. $(2x^5 + x^3 - 3x + 2) \div (x - 3)$
11. $(x^4 + 2x^2a^2 - 2xa^3 + 2a^4) \div (x + 2a)$
12. $(3x^4 - 5x^3 - 37x^2 + 4x - 17) \div (x - 3)$
13. $(4x^5 + 2x^4 - 2x^3 + 17x - 7) \div (x - \frac{3}{2})$
14. $(6x^4 + 2x^3a - x^2a^2 + 7xa^3 + 28a^4) \div (x - \frac{2}{3}a)$
15. $(5x^4 - 3x^3 + 7x^2 - 2x + 6) \div (5x - 3)$
16. $(x^4 - 5x^2 + 4x + 3) \div (3x + 2)$
17. $(7x^3 - 5x^2 + 4x - 32) \div (7x - 5)$
18. $(3x^4 - x^3 + 3x - 6) \div (3x + 5)$

In each of Exercises 19–35, use the Factor Theorem to determine whether the first quantity is a factor of the second.

19. $(x - 2), (x^4 - x^3 + x^2 - 4)$
20. $(x - 1), (x^4 + 2x^3 - x^2 + 2x - 4)$
21. $(x + 2), (x^4 - x^3 - 3x^2 + 4x + 4)$
22. $(x - 3), (x^3 - 4x^2 - 3x + 18)$
23. $(x + 2), (x^4 + 2x^3 - x - 2)$
24. $(x - 5), (x^4 - 6x^3 + 6x^2 - 4x + 5)$
25. $(x - 4), (x^4 - 6x^3 + 9x^2 + x - 19)$
26. $(x + 3), (2x^4 + 7x^3 - 12x - 9)$
27. $(x + 4), (3x^4 + 13x^3 + 7x^2 + 11x + 4)$
28. $(x + 3/5), (5x^5 - 2x^4 - 8x^3 + 2x^2 - 2x - 3)$
29. $(x + 2/3), (3x^5 - 4x^4 + 5x^3 - 7x + 2)$
30. $(x - 8a/3), (3x^4 - 5x^3a + x^2a^2 - 27xa^3 + 8a^4)$
31. $(x + 2a), (3x^4 + 4x^3a - 2xa^3 - 20a^4)$
32. $(2x + 7), (6x^5 + 15x^4 - 23x^3 - 27x^2 - 110x - 140)$
33. $(x + a), (x^n + a^n)$ [n a positive, odd integer]
34. $(x + a), (x^n + a^n)$ [n a positive, even integer]
35. $(x - a), (x^{2n} - a^{2n})$ [n a positive integer]
36. Let the polynomial $f(x)$ be divided by $ax + b$ until a constant remainder R is obtained. Show that $R = f(-b/a)$.

8-3 SYNTHETIC DIVISION

The problem of drawing the graph of a function $f(x)$ usually requires that a table be constructed showing pairs of values of x and y which satisfy the equation $y = f(x)$. The corresponding points (x, y) are then plotted on a coordinate system and a smooth curve is drawn through these points. Thus the construction of the table requires the computation of a number of values $f(r)$. The Remainder Theorem provides a method for such computation if $f(x)$ is a polynomial. The method involves long division, but this laborious process can be greatly simplified, when the dividend $f(x)$ is a polynomial and the divisor is of the form $x - r$, by the use of *synthetic division.* The simplicity of the technique of synthetic division makes the use of the Remainder Theorem for computing values of $f(r)$ very effective. Since synthetic division is a simplification (or, more accurately, an abbreviation) of long division, we shall start with an example of long division.

The division of $3x^4 - 2x^3 + 4x$ by $x - 3$ proceeds as follows:

$$
\begin{array}{lllll|l}
3x^4 & -\ 2x^3 & & +\ 4x & & x - 3 \quad \text{(Divisor)} \\
\underline{3x^4} & \underline{-\ 9x^3} & & & & 3x^3 + 7x^2 + 21x + 67 \quad \text{(Quotient)} \\
 & 7x^3 & & & & \\
 & \underline{7x^3} & \underline{-\ 21x^2} & & & \\
 & & 21x^2 & +\ 4x & & \\
 & & \underline{21x^2} & \underline{-\ 63x} & & \\
 & & & 67x & & \\
 & & & \underline{67x} & \underline{-\ 201} & \\
 & & & & 201 \quad \text{(Remainder)} &
\end{array}
$$

This process can be shortened greatly by omitting the x's and writing only the coefficients. However, in doing this we must place in the proper position a zero for the coefficient of any missing power of x (here x^2 and x^0).

$$
\begin{array}{rrrrr|l}
3 & -2 & +0 & +4 & +0 & 1 \ -3 \\
\underline{3} & \underline{-9} & & & & 3 \ +7 \ +21 \ +67 \\
 & 7 & +0 & & & \\
 & \underline{7} & \underline{-21} & & & \\
 & & 21 & +4 & & \\
 & & \underline{21} & \underline{-63} & & \\
 & & & 67 & +0 & \\
 & & & \underline{67} & \underline{-201} & \\
 & & & & 201 &
\end{array}
$$

We now see that it is unnecessary to write the first term in every second line, and the second term in the 3rd, 5th, . . . , lines. The remaining terms can then be compressed into two lines, and we have

$$
\begin{array}{rrrrr|l}
3 & -2 & +0 & +4 & +0 & 1 \ -3 \\
 & \underline{-9} & \underline{-21} & \underline{-63} & \underline{-201} & 3 \ +7 \ +21 \ +67 \\
 & +7 & +21 & +67 & +201 &
\end{array}
$$

If the first coefficient, 3, is written in the third line, the first four terms in the third line are the coefficients of the quotient, and we can omit writing these coefficients a second time. It should also be noted that the 1 of the divisor can be omitted. The process now becomes

$$\begin{array}{rrrrr|l} 3 & -2 & +0 & +4 & +0 & -3 \\ & -9 & -21 & -63 & -201 & \\ \hline 3 & +7 & +21 & +67 & +201 & \end{array}$$

The numbers in the third line result from subtractions. If the signs in the divisor and in the second line are all changed, the subtractions are replaced by additions, and we have

$$\begin{array}{rrrrr|l} 3 & -2 & +0 & +4 & +0 & 3 \\ & +9 & +21 & +63 & +201 & \\ \hline 3 & +7 & +21 & +67 & +201 & \end{array}$$

The last arrangement illustrates the method of *synthetic division*, of $3x^4 - 2x^3 + 4x$ by $x - 3$. A comparison with the above process of long division shows that the first four numbers in the third line are the coefficients of the terms in the quotient, starting with a term in x^3, and the last number is the remainder.

In summary, the steps in the synthetic division of $f(x)$ by $x - r$ are:

1. *Arrange $f(x)$ in descending powers of x, inserting each missing power of x with a coefficient of zero.*

2. *Write in order in a line the coefficients $a_0, a_1, a_2, \ldots, a_n$ of $f(x)$, retaining each sign as in $f(x)$. Leave the next line vacant and write a_0 in line* 3 *directly below a_0 in line* 1.

3. *Multiply a_0 by r and insert the product in line* 2 *under a_1. Add the product a_0r to a_1 and insert the result in line* 3. *Multiply this result by r and insert the product in line* 2 *under a_2. Add the product to a_2 and insert the result in line* 3. *Continue the process until finally a product is added to a_n and the result inserted in line* 3.

4. *The first n numbers in line* 3 *are the coefficients of the quotient in order of descending powers of x starting with x^{n-1}, and the $n + $* 1 *number is the remainder.*

Example 1. Divide $f(x) = 2x^5 - 3x^3 + 2x^2 - 7$ by $x - 2$. Arrange the work as follows:

$$\begin{array}{rrrrrr|l} 2 & +0 & -3 & +2 & +0 & -7 & 2 \\ & 4 & +8 & +10 & +24 & +48 & \\ \hline 2 & +4 & +5 & +12 & +24 & +41 & \end{array}$$

The quotient is then $2x^4 + 4x^3 + 5x^2 + 12x + 24$ and the remainder is 41. By the Remainder Theorem we have also $f(2) = 41$.

Example 2. Divide $3x^3 - 2x^2 + 9x - 6$ by $x + 2$.
Since $x + 2 = x - (-2)$ the value of r is -2. The synthetic division becomes:

$$\begin{array}{rrrr|l} 3 & -2 & +9 & -6 & \underline{-2} \\ & -6 & +16 & -50 & \\ \hline 3 & -8 & +25 & -56 & \end{array}$$

so that the quotient is $3x^2 - 8x + 25$ and the remainder is -56. It follows also that $f(-2) = -56$.

EXERCISE GROUP 8–2

In each of Exercises 1–16, use synthetic division to determine the quotient and remainder in each division.

1. $(3x^4 - 2x^3 + 5x - 6) \div (x - 2)$
2. $(3x^4 + x^3 - 27x^2 + 11x + 5) \div (x - 3)$
3. $(x^4 + 2x^3 + 2x^2 + 10x - 12) \div (x + 3)$
4. $(x^4 + 2x^3 - 13x^2 - 49) \div (x + 5)$
5. $(2x^3 - 4x - 9) \div (x - 2)$
6. $(2x^4 + 13x - 6) \div (x - 2)$
7. $(15x - 3x^5 + 25x^3 - 9) \div (x + 3)$
8. $(3x - 2x^5 - 250x^2 + 15) \div (x + 5)$
9. $(10x^2 - 19x + 4x^3 + 17) \div (x + 4)$
10. $(20x^2 - 5x - 6x^3 + 5) \div (x - 3)$
11. $(x^4 + 5x^3 + 4x^2 + 11x - 13) \div (x + 6)$
12. $(4x^5 + 19x^4 - 4x^3 + 7x^2 + 13x + 6) \div (x + 5)$
13. $(2x^5 - x^4a - 2x^3a^2 - 9x^2a^3 + 5a^5) \div (x - 2a)$
14. $(3x^4 - 4x^3a - 12x^2a^2 - 8xa^3 - 5a^4) \div (x - 3a)$
15. $(6x^5 + 15x^4 - 23x^3 - 27x^2 - 110x - 140) \div (2x + 7)$
16. $(3x^4 - 5x^3 - 3x^2 + 11x - 10) \div (2x - 5)$

Use synthetic division to compute the required quantities in each of the following exercises.

17. Compute $f(2)$, $f(0)$, $f(-3)$ if $f(x) = 3x^3 + 2x^2 - 7$.
18. Compute $f(-1)$, $f(\frac{1}{2})$, $f(-2)$ if $f(x) = 3x^2 - 4x^3 - 7 + 2x$
19. Compute $f(4)$, $f(-4)$, $f(3)$ if $f(x) = x^4 - 2x^3 - x + 2$
20. Compute $g(2)$, $g(3)$, $g(-5)$ if $g(z) = 4z^3 - 3z^2 + 7$
21. Compute $h(1)$, $h(-\frac{1}{2})$, $h(5)$ if $h(y) = y^2 - 3y^3 - 2$
22. Compute $f(-1)$, $f(5)$, $f(3)$ if $f(x) = x^3 - 2x^2 + x - 4$
23. Compute $f(2)$, $f(-1)$, $f(-3)$ if $f(x) = 3x^3 - 2x^2 + 3x - 5$
24. Compute $f(-0.7)$, $f(1.3)$, $f(1.1)$ if $f(x) = 2x^3 + 2x^2 - 2x + 3$
25. Compute $f(-2/3)$, $f(3/2)$, $f(-2)$ if $f(x) = 5x^3 + 6x^2 + 7x - 4$

8–4 GENERAL THEOREMS CONCERNING ZEROS OF POLYNOMIALS, OR ROOTS OF EQUATIONS

It is regrettable that a basic theorem, the so-called "Fundamental Theorem of Algebra," cannot be proved by elementary methods of algebra. Many proofs do exist, but they are all of an advanced character. For this reason we shall be content merely to state the theorem.

The Fundamental Theorem of Algebra. *Every polynomial* $f(x) = a_0x^n + a_1x^{n-1} + \cdots + a_n$, *with* $n \geqq 1, a_0 \neq 0$, *has at least one (real or complex) zero.*

Let r_1 be a zero of $f(x)$. Then by the Factor Theorem $x - r_1$ is a factor. If we designate the quotient of $f(x)$ by $x - r_1$ as $f_1(x)$, then $f_1(x)$ also has a zero which we may call r_2. The quotient of $f_1(x)$ by $x - r_2$ again has a zero, r_3, etc. Each new quotient is of degree one less than the degree of the preceding quotient, so that by continuing in the manner indicated we see that $f(x)$ has exactly n factors of the form $x - r$. It may happen that the factors are not all different, in which case $f(x)$ will have factors of the form $(x - r)^m$ with $m > 1$. Thus, in general, $f(x)$ can be written as a product,

$$f(x) = a_0(x - r_1)^{n_1}(x - r_2)^{n_2} \cdots (x - r_k)^{n_k},$$

where the exponents are positive integers such that $n_1 + n_2 + \cdots + n_k = n$. We say that r_1 is a *zero of* $f(x)$ *of multiplicity* n_1, etc., or that r_1 is *a root of the equation* $f(x) = 0$ *of multiplicity* n_1.

Taking into account the multiplicity of each root, we may now say that *the equation* $f(x) = 0$, *where* $f(x)$ *is of degree n, has exactly n roots.*

Example 1. If $f(x) = 2(x - 1)^2(x + 2)$, then $x = 1$ is a zero of $f(x)$ of multiplicity 2, or a *double* zero, and $x = -2$ is a zero of multiplicity 1, or a *simple* zero. Furthermore, $x = 1$ is a double root of $f(x) = 0$, and $x = -2$ is a simple root.

It has been noted that the zeros of a polynomial may be complex numbers. In this connection there is a special result, the proof of which may be omitted on first reading.

Theorem. *If the coefficients in the polynomial* $f(x)$ *are real, and if* $f(x)$ *has a zero* $a + bi$ *with a and b real and* $b \neq 0$ $(i = \sqrt{-1})$, *then* $a - bi$ *is also a zero of* $f(x)$.

Proof. We may divide $f(x)$ by the quadratic function $x^2 - 2ax + a^2 + b^2$ until a linear remainder is reached, and we have

$$f(x) = (x^2 - 2ax + a^2 + b^2)q(x) + mx + n, \tag{1}$$

where $q(x)$ is a polynomial with real coefficients, and m and n are real. Since $x^2 - 2ax + a^2 + b^2$ vanishes for $x = a + bi$, and $f(a + bi) = 0$, substitution of $a + bi$ for x in (1) gives

$$m(a + bi) + n = 0 \quad \text{or} \quad ma + n + mbi = 0.$$

Hence $ma + n = 0$ and $mb = 0$. Since $b \neq 0$, it follows from the second equation that $m = 0$, and then from either equation that $n = 0$. Equation (1) may then be written

$$f(x) = (x^2 - 2ax + a^2 + b^2)q(x).$$

Now, $x^2 - 2ax + a^2 + b^2$ vanishes also for $x = a - bi$. Hence $f(a - bi) = 0$, and $a - bi$ is a zero of $f(x)$.

A consequence of the theorems of this section is that *a real polynomial can always be expressed as a product of real linear and quadratic functions.*

Example 2. By direct substitution it can be verified that $2 + 3i$ is a zero of the polynomial

$$f(x) = x^3 - 5x^2 + 17x - 13,$$

so that $f(2 + 3i) = 0$. By the above theorem it follows also that $f(2 - 3i) = 0$, and by the observation following the theorem it is known that $x^2 - 4x + 13$ is a factor of $f(x)$.

8–5 RATIONAL ROOTS OF $f(x) = 0$

The theorems of Section 8–2, together with the process of synthetic division described in Section 8–3, provide an effective means of testing whether a number $x = r$ is a solution of $f(x) = 0$, when $f(x)$ is a polynomial of any degree n. Unfortunately, there is no general method for solving the equation $f(x) = 0$ if n is more than 4, and even when $n = 3$ or $n = 4$ the formulas which do exist are rather complicated and difficult to apply. However, if the equation has roots which are rational numbers, there is a guide as to the possible values of these rational roots, and the methods described above can establish the correct ones. The following theorem provides the desired guide for finding the rational roots.

Theorem. *If $f(x) = a_0x^n + a_1x^{n-1} + \cdots + a_n$ is a polynomial with integral coefficients, and if a rational number p/q, in lowest terms, is a root of $f(x) = 0$, then p is a factor of a_n and q is a factor of a_0.*

Proof. Since, by hypothesis, p/q is a root of $f(x) = 0$, we have

$$a_0(p/q)^n + a_1(p/q)^{n-1} + \cdots + a_n = 0. \tag{2}$$

Multiplication of both sides of this equation by q^n gives

$$a_0p^n + a_1p^{n-1}q + \cdots + a_nq^n = 0. \tag{3}$$

If now the term a_0p^n is subtracted from both members of (3), we have

$$q(a_1p^{n-1} + a_2p^{n-2}q + \cdots + a_nq^{n-1}) = -a_0p^n.$$

By hypothesis, all of the a_i $(i = 0, 1, \ldots, n)$ are integers. Therefore, since q is a factor of the left member it must also be a factor of the right member. Since p and q have no common factor (other than ± 1), no factor of q is a factor of p^n; it follows that q must be a factor of a_0.

If a_nq^n is subtracted from both members of (3), the equation becomes

$$p(a_0p^{n-1} + a_1p^{n-2}q + \cdots + a_{n-1}q^{n-1}) = -a_nq^n.$$

By the same reasoning as above, it follows that p is a factor of a_n. The proof of the theorem is now complete.

As a corollary, it follows that *if* $a_0 = 1$ *then any rational root of* $f(x) = 0$ *must be an integer; this integral root must be a factor of* a_n.

As soon as a rational root r_1 of the equation $f(x) = 0$ has been found, the division of $f(x)$ by $x - r_1$ should be performed, if it has not already been done by synthetic division in finding r_1. Let us designate the quotient by $f_1(x)$; the remaining roots of $f(x) = 0$ will then be the roots of $f_1(x) = 0$, and the subsequent search for roots should be continued in the equation $f_1(x) = 0$. An equation such as $f_1(x) = 0$, obtained by reducing a given equation after a root has been found, is called a *depressed* equation.

Example 1. Determine the rational roots of the equation

$$6x^5 + 13x^4 - 18x^3 - 37x^2 + 16x + 20 = 0.$$

Solution. We apply the Theorem of this section and determine that any rational roots must be found among the numbers

$$\pm\tfrac{1}{6},\ \pm\tfrac{1}{3},\ \pm\tfrac{1}{2},\ \pm\tfrac{2}{3},\ \pm 1,\ \pm\tfrac{4}{3},\ \pm\tfrac{5}{3},\ \pm\tfrac{5}{6},\ \pm 2,\ \pm\tfrac{5}{2},\ \pm\tfrac{10}{3},\ \pm 4,\ \pm 5,\ \pm\tfrac{20}{3},\ \pm 10,\ \pm 20.$$

Now we use synthetic division to test each of these numbers, discarding those for which the remainder is $\neq 0$. After a root is found the work is continued in the depressed equation. Thus (showing only the successful tries), we have

$$\begin{array}{rrrrrr|r}
6 & +13 & -18 & -37 & +16 & +20 & -\tfrac{2}{3} \\
 & -4 & -6 & +16 & +14 & -20 & \\ \hline
6 & +9 & -24 & -21 & +30 & & 1 \\
 & +6 & +15 & -9 & -30 & & \\ \hline
6 & +15 & -9 & -30 & & & -2 \\
 & -12 & -6 & +30 & & & \\ \hline
6 & +3 & -15 & & & &
\end{array}$$

The last depressed equation is $6x^2 + 3x - 15 = 0$, which reduces to

$$2x^2 + x - 5 = 0;$$

since this equation is quadratic it can be solved, and all five roots of the given equation are thus determined. These roots are

$$x = -\frac{2}{3}, \quad 1, \quad -2, \quad \frac{-1 \pm \sqrt{41}}{4}.$$

Comments: 1. When a rational root has been found, the subsequent tries should be made in the depressed equation.

2. When a rational root has been found, the same number should be tried again in the depressed equation; it may be a multiple root.

3. It may be laborious, as in the above example, to try all the possibilities, but this is seldom necessary, since we can find *limiting values* between which *all* real roots must lie. Thus, suppose we try $x = 2$ in the equation of Example 1. Synthetic division gives

$$\begin{array}{rrrrrr|l} 6 & +13 & -18 & -37 & +16 & +20 & \underline{2} \\ & +12 & +50 & +64 & +54 & +140 & \\ \hline 6 & +25 & +32 & +27 & +70 & +160 & \end{array}$$

Since the remainder and all the coefficients in the quotient are positive, a larger value of x will increase the numbers in the third row; it follows that no larger value of x can give a zero remainder. Hence 2 is an *upper limit* for the roots of the equation and we are relieved of the burden of examining any numbers greater than 2.

In a similar manner, when we try $x = -4$, we obtain

$$\begin{array}{rrrrrr|l} 6 & +13 & -18 & -37 & +16 & +20 & \underline{-4} \\ & -24 & +44 & -104 & +564 & -2320 & \\ \hline 6 & -11 & +26 & -141 & +580 & -2300 & \end{array}$$

Since the signs in the quotient and remainder are alternately plus and minus, it is clear that they will continue to be so for all numbers $x < -4$, and no such value can give a remainder zero. Therefore -4 is a *lower limit* for the roots of the equation, and all roots must lie between -4 and $+2$, or all real roots of the equation must lie in the range

$$-4 < x < 2.$$

Note that the test for an upper limit applies when a *positive* number gives positive coefficients in the quotient and remainder, and the test for a lower limit applies when a *negative* number gives alternating signs. Moreover, the tests apply to all real roots of the equation, and not only to the rational ones.

EXERCISE GROUP 8–3

Determine the rational roots of the following equations, and where the depressed equation is of degree 2, find all the roots. If there are no rational roots, prove that such is the case.

1. $6x^3 + x^2 - 21x - 10 = 0$
2. $4x^3 + 8x^2 - 27x - 45 = 0$
3. $12x^3 - 28x^2 - 9x + 10 = 0$
4. $21x^3 - 89x^2 + 14x + 24 = 0$
5. $6x^4 - 13x^3 + 51x^2 - 51x + 14 = 0$
6. $6x^3 - 7x^2 - 23x + 28 = 0$
7. $5x^3 + 3x^2 + 20x + 12 = 0$
8. $3x^3 - 8x^2 + 11x - 10 = 0$
9. $2x^4 + 17x^3 + 58x^2 + 100x + 75 = 0$
10. $2x^4 - 5x^3 + 6x^2 - x - 14 = 0$
11. $2x^5 + 9x^4 + 21x^3 + 28x^2 + 21x + 9 = 0$
12. $3x^7 - 3x^5 + 5x^4 + 2x^2 - 7 = 0$
13. $2x^6 + x^5 + 3x^4 + 7x^3 - 3x^2 - 4x - 6 = 0$
14. $2x^6 + x^5 - 2x^4 - 13x^3 - 37x^2 + 30x + 75 = 0$
15. $42x^5 + 205x^4 + 405x^3 + 438x^2 + 275x + 75 = 0$
16. $240x^5 - 668x^4 + 56x^3 + 1345x^2 - 1338x + 360 = 0$
17. $4x^4 - 12x^3 - 7x^2 + 24x - 8 = 0$
18. $9x^6 + 12x^5 - 53x^4 - 59x^3 + 88x^2 + 69x - 30 = 0$
19. $24x^8 - 28x^7 - 210x^6 + 99x^5 + 451x^4 - 57x^3 - 225x^2 - 54x = 0$
20. $6x^5 + 5x^4 - 25x^3 - 10x^2 + 24x + 1 = 0$

8–6 GRAPHS OF POLYNOMIALS

The depressed equation which remains after all rational roots have been removed cannot be solved by any of the methods developed thus far if it is of degree 3 or more. Methods for solving the general equations of degree 3 or 4 algebraically do exist,* but are rather complicated and are seldom used in practice. Moreover, *the general equation of degree 5 or more cannot be solved algebraically.* Hence the best procedure, if the depressed equation with no rational roots is of degree 3 or more, is to draw the graph of the appropriate function, to locate the real roots approximately from the graph, and then to compute any desired root more accurately. The real roots of $f(x) = 0$ are the abscissas of the points where the graph of $y = f(x)$ crosses or touches the x-axis.

The present section is devoted to a discussion of the graph of a polynomial, and in the next section the graph will be used to determine real roots to any desired accuracy.

The basic method of graphing the equation $y = f(x)$ is to assign values to x, to compute the corresponding values of y, to plot the points (x, y) thus obtained,

* G. Christal, *College Algebra*, Vol. 1. London: A. & C. Black, Ltd. (1926) pp. 549–553.

and to draw a smooth curve through these points. Some examples will illustrate this.

Example 1. Draw the graph of $y = x^5 + 5x^4 - 3x^3 - 29x^2 + 2x + 18$.

Solution. By synthetic division a table of values may be obtained as follows:

x:	-4	-3.5	-3	-2	-1	0	1	1.5	2	3
y:	-6	9.5	-6	-30	-6	18	-6	-21.5	-6	330

As x increases beyond 3 the value of y continues to increase, and as x decreases from -4 the value of y continues to decrease. We need only that part of the graph for $-4 < x < 3$, shown in Fig. 8–1. The values of x for which the curve crosses the x-axis are the zeros of the function y.

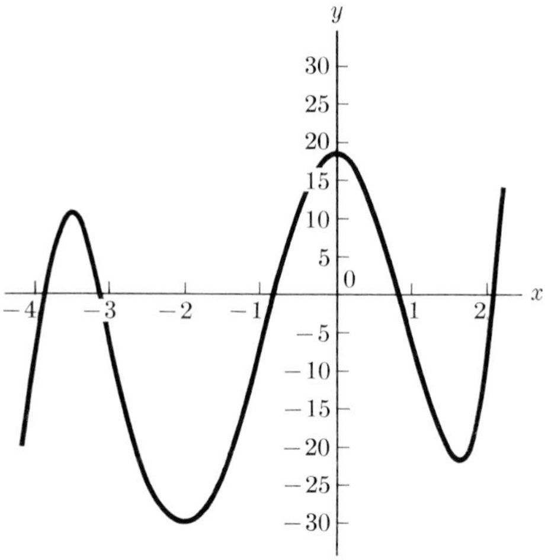

FIGURE 8–1

Care is required, in drawing a graph from a table of values, to be certain that an important feature of the graph is not overlooked. In Example 1 the points $(-3, -6)$ and $(-4, -6)$ were found. How is the curve to be drawn between these points? Does it remain below the x-axis, or does it extend above? To answer these questions, the value $x = -3.5$ was used, and the corresponding value of y showed that the curve rises above the x-axis. Thus it is often necessary to use values of x which are not integers, and often several such values, between two successive integral values. The need for these additional values must be gauged while the curve is being drawn.

Example 2. Draw the graph of $y = x^4 - x^2 - 4x - 3$.

Solution. As in Example 1, we use synthetic division to compute the values of the function corresponding to chosen values of x. The resulting table of values is :

x:	-2	-1	0	1	2	3
y:	17	1	-3	-7	1	57

The graph appears in Fig. 8–2.

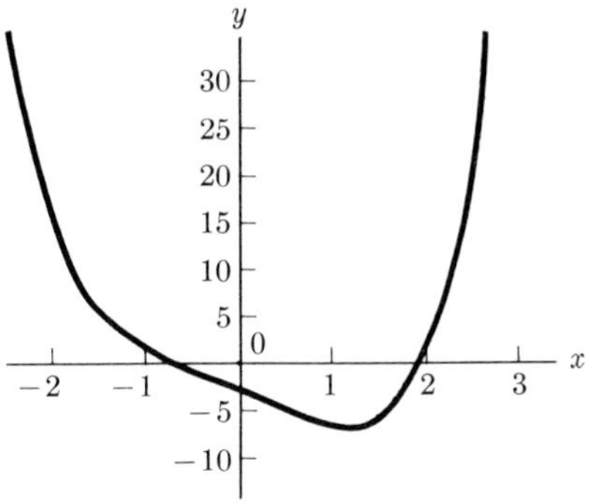

FIGURE 8–2

The equation obtained by setting y equal to zero has four (real or complex) roots. The graph crosses the x-axis twice, denoting two real roots; the other two roots are therefore complex.

Note. More precise information concerning the graph of a polynomial, such as maximum or minimum points on the curve, or matters relating to the direction of the tangent to the curve at different points, is often required. The study of such topics forms a part of the subject matter of Differential Calculus.

EXERCISE GROUP 8–4

In each of Exercises 1–10, draw the graph of the given function.

1. $(x, x^3 - x)$
2. $(x, x^3 + x + 1)$
3. $(x, 2x^3 + 3x^2 - 3x - 2)$
4. $(x, 2x^3 - x^2 - 8x + 4)$
5. $(x, 3x^3 + 8x^2 - 5x - 6)$
6. $(x, 6x^3 + 11x^2 - 3x - 2)$
7. $(x, x^4 - 2x^3 - 12x^2 + 18x + 27)$
8. $(x, x^4 - x^3 - 10x^2 + 4x + 24)$
9. $(x, 6x^4 - x^3 - 26x^2 + 4x + 8)$
10. $(x, 6x^4 - 7x^3 - 37x^2 + 8x + 12)$

In each of Exercises 11–20, draw the graph of the given function, and from the graph determine the approximate values of x for which the function is zero.

11. $(x, x^3 - 6x + 5)$
12. $(x, 7 + 4x - 4x^2 - x^3)$
13. $(x, 7x - x^3 + 3x^2)$
14. $(x, 2x^3 - x^2 - 6x + 3)$
15. $(x, 6x^3 + 4x^2 - 15x - 10)$
16. $(x, 6x^4 + 11x^3 - 22x^2 - 22x + 20)$
17. $(x, 24 - 2x^2 - 5x^4 + x^6)$
18. $(x, x^4 - 14x^2 + 1)$
19. $(x, x^4 - x^3 - 8x^2 - 3x + 5)$
20. $(x, x^4 - 2x^3 - 16x^2 + 18x + 63)$

8–7 IRRATIONAL ROOTS OBTAINED BY INTERPOLATION

From Fig. 8–1 it can be seen that the roots of the equation

$$x^5 + 5x^4 - 3x^3 - 29x^2 + 2x + 18 = 0$$

are approximately $x = -4, -3, -1, 1, 2$. More accurate approximations may be required. We shall now develop a method by which the value of any of these roots may be determined to any desired accuracy. Underlying the method is the principle that *if $f(a)$ and $f(b)$ are of opposite sign, then $f(x)$ must vanish for some value of x between a and b.* [Recall that $f(x)$ is a polynomial. The same principle applies to all *continuous* functions, a class of functions which includes the polynomials.]

For example, let us consider the root near $x = -1$. From Fig. 8–1 it appears that this root lies between $x = -1$ and $x = 0$, and we may estimate it to be $x = -0.8$, which must now be tested in the original function. Using synthetic division, we have

$$\begin{array}{rrrrrr|l} 1 & +5 & -3 & -29 & +2 & +18 & \underline{-0.8} \\ & -0.8 & -3.4 & +5.1 & +19.1 & -16.9 & \\ \hline 1 & +4.2 & -6.4 & -23.9 & +21.1 & +1.1 & \end{array} \qquad [f(-0.8) = 1.1]$$

Since $f(-0.8) > 0$, and near $x = -0.8$ the curve rises as x increases, it follows that the actual root must be less than -0.8. We now try $x = -0.9$, which gives $f(-0.9) = -2.4$:

$$\begin{array}{rrrrrr|l} 1 & +5 & -3 & -29 & +2 & +18 & \underline{-0.9} \\ & -0.9 & -3.7 & +6.0 & +20.7 & -20.4 & \\ \hline 1 & +4.1 & -6.7 & -23.0 & +22.7 & -2.4 & \end{array}$$

Since $f(-0.8)$ and $f(-0.9)$ are of opposite sign the root must lie between -0.9 and -0.8, and since $f(-0.8)$ is numerically less than $f(-0.9)$, the root is closer to -0.8.

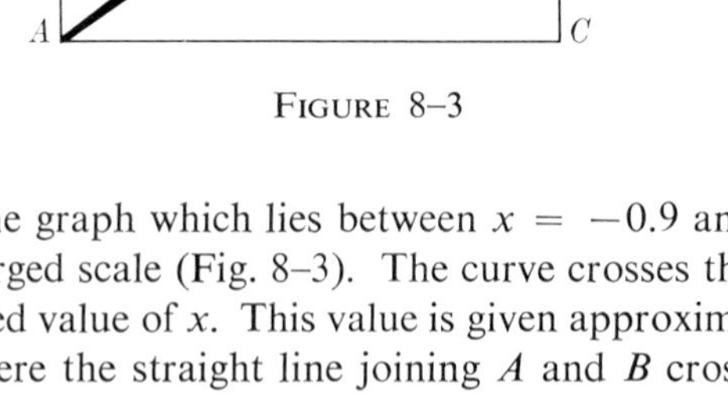

FIGURE 8–3

The portion of the graph which lies between $x = -0.9$ and $x = -0.8$ is now drawn with an enlarged scale (Fig. 8–3). The curve crosses the x-axis at P, whose abscissa is the desired value of x. This value is given approximately by the abscissa of Q, the point where the straight line joining A and B crosses the x-axis. The triangle QBR is similar to the triangle ABC. Hence corresponding sides are proportional, so that

$$\frac{h}{0.1} = \frac{1.1}{3.5}, \quad h = \frac{0.11}{3.5} = 0.03 \text{ approximately.}$$

The corresponding value of x is -0.83. We find $f(-0.83) = 0.06$, thus:

$$\begin{array}{rrrrrr|l} 1 & +5 & -3 & -29 & +2 & +18 & \underline{-0.83} \\ & -0.83 & -3.46 & +5.36 & +19.62 & -17.94 & \\ \hline 1 & +4.17 & -6.46 & -23.64 & +21.62 & +0.06 & \end{array}$$

Since $f(-0.83) > 0$ the exact root is less than -0.83. We next try $x = -0.84$, obtaining $f(-0.84) = -0.29$:

$$\begin{array}{rrrrrr|l} 1 & +5 & -3 & -29 & +2 & +18 & \underline{-0.84} \\ & -0.84 & -3.49 & +5.45 & +19.78 & -18.29 & \\ \hline 1 & +4.16 & -6.49 & -23.55 & +21.78 & -0.29 & \end{array}$$

Thus $f(-0.83)$ and $f(-0.84)$ are of opposite sign and the exact value of x lies between -0.83 and -0.84, closer to -0.83, since $f(-0.83)$ is smaller numerically than $f(-0.84)$. Hence to two decimal places the root is -0.83.

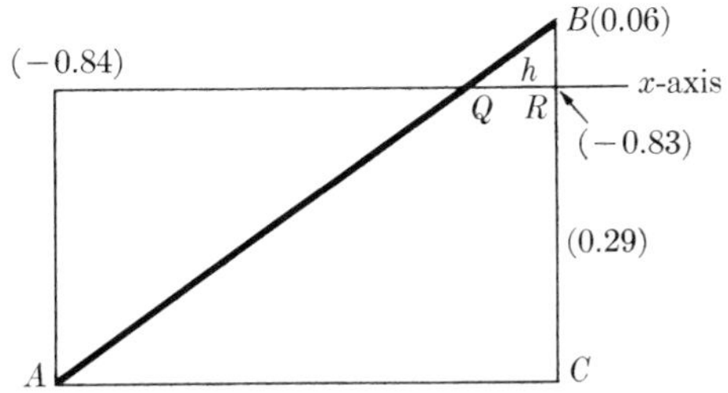

FIGURE 8–4

To find the next decimal we enlarge the scale again, between $x = -0.84$ and $x = -0.83$, and construct a new figure as in Fig. 8–4. From the similar triangles QBR and ABC, we find that

$$\frac{h}{0.01} = \frac{0.06}{0.35}, \quad h = \frac{0.0006}{0.35} = 0.002.$$

We compute $f(-0.832)$, which turns out to be $f(-0.832) = -0.014$, and then compute $f(-0.831) = +0.021$, from which we conclude that to three decimals $x = -0.832$.

Consider now the root near $x = 2$. From Fig. 8–1 it appears that this root is larger than 2, and very close to it. We know that $f(2) = -6$. If we try $x = 2.1$, we find by synthetic division that $f(2.1) = 4.6$, and we conclude that the root lies between $x = 2$ and $x = 2.1$. Enlarging the scale between these values of x as in Fig. 8–5, we find that

$$\frac{h}{0.1} = \frac{6}{10.6}, \quad h = \frac{0.6}{10.6} = 0.06 \text{ approximately.}$$

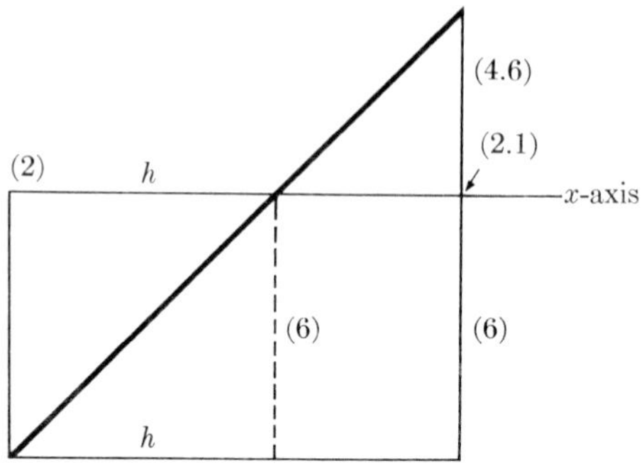

FIGURE 8–5

The corresponding value of x is 2.06, and $f(2.06) = -0.06$. Since this value of the function is negative, and near $x = 2.06$ the curve rises as x increases, the exact root is more than 2.06. We try next 2.07, and find $f(2.07) = 1.01$. It follows that the root is between 2.06 and 2.07, closer to 2.06, so that to two decimal places the root is 2.06. A continuation of the process would give the root to three decimal places as 2.060 and to four decimals as 2.0603.

The principle of the method described in this section is that of *linear interpolation*, since in each interval considered the curve is approximated by a straight line. The respective values of h can also be obtained graphically, if the enlarged figures are drawn to scale.

The method can be applied to any real root, provided the graph actually crosses the x-axis there. The roots to which the method is not applicable are those at which the graph is tangent to the x-axis without crossing it. While the method requires considerable effort, it is very simple and will give any real root, with the restriction previously mentioned, to any desired accuracy by repeated application.

EXERCISE GROUP 8–5

In each of Exercises 1–10, determine the specified root accurately to two decimal places.

1. The root of $x^3 + x^2 - 10x + 4 = 0$ between 0 and 1
2. The root of $2x^3 - 11x^2 + 15x - 1 = 0$ between 2 and 3
3. The root of $x^3 + 3x^2 + 3x - 10 = 0$ between 1 and 2
4. The root of $6x^4 - 13x^3 - 36x^2 + 91x - 42 = 0$ between 0 and 1
5. The root of $x^3 + 2x^2 - 7x + 1 = 0$ between -3 and -4
6. The root of $6x^3 - 4x^2 - 15x + 10 = 0$ between -1 and -2
7. The root of $4x^3 - 12x^2 + 8x - 1 = 0$ between 2 and 3
8. The root of $4x^4 + 13x^3 + 7x^2 - 7x - 2 = 0$ between 0 and 1
9. The root of $15x^3 + 34x^2 + 4x - 10 = 0$ between -1 and -2
10. The root of $6x^4 - 11x^3 - 23x^2 + 63x - 36 = 0$ between -2 and -3

Determine all of the real roots of the equations in Exercises 11–16, accurately to two decimal places.

11. $x^3 - x = 2x^2 - 1$

12. $3x^3 - 13x^2 + 5x + 15 = 0$

13. $35x^4 + 109x^3 + 619x^2 - 754x + 7 = 0$

14. $x^4 - 2x^3 + 3x^2 - 11x + 10 = 0$

15. $42x^4 + 113x^3 - 10x^2 - 71x + 8 = 0$

16. $x^5 - 8x^4 - 3x^3 - 24x^2 + 15x - 45 = 0$

Determine all of the real roots of the equations in Exercises 17–24, accurately to three decimal places.

17. $x^4 + x^3 - 4x^2 - 7x - 21 = 0$

18. $x^4 - x^3 + 2x^2 - 9x - 63 = 0$

19. $x^4 + 2x^3 - 4x^2 + 14x - 77 = 0$

20. $x^4 - x^3 - 17x^2 + 8x + 30 = 0$

21. $x^4 + x^3 - 5x^2 + 4x - 36 = 0$

22. $x^6 + 2x^5 + 2x^4 + 2x^3 - 24x^2 - 25 = 0$

23. $x^4 - 2x^3 - 9x^2 - 2x - 10 = 0$

24. $2x^5 - x^4 - 25x^3 - 14x^2 + 41x + 21 = 0$

SUPPLEMENTARY EXERCISES FOR CHAPTER 8

1. If the polynomial $P(x) = 2x^5 - 7x^4 + 8x^3 - 3x^2 - 50x + 75$ is divided by $x - \frac{1}{2}(1 - \sqrt{21})$, the remainder is zero, so that $\frac{1}{2}(1 - \sqrt{21})$ is a root of $P(x) = 0$. Show that $\frac{1}{2}(1 + \sqrt{21})$ is also a root of $P(x) = 0$, and find the other roots.
2. $x - i\sqrt{5}$ is a factor of the polynomial $x^4 + x^3 - 2x^2 + 5x - 35$. Find all the zeros of the polynomial.
3. Show that there are no rational roots of the equation

$$2x^6 + 2x^5 - 21x^4 - 7x^3 + 34x^2 - 15x + 105 = 0.$$

In each of Exercises 4–7, find for each equation (a) the smallest integral upper limit for the real roots of the equation, (b) the smallest, in absolute value, negative integral lower limit for the real roots of the equation.

4. $4x^3 + 8x^2 - 27x - 40 = 0$
5. $2x^6 + x^5 + 3x^4 + 7x^3 - 3x^2 - 4x - 5 = 0$
6. $6x^7 - 17x^6 - 27x^5 + 10x^4 - 2x^3 - 79x^2 + 41x - 6 = 0$
7. $24x^7 - 28x^6 - 130x^5 + 5x^4 + 12x^3 - 57x^2 - 225x - 15 = 0$

Determine the real roots of the following equations, correct to two decimal places.

8. $x^5 - x^4 - 9x^3 + 11x^2 + 13x - 15 = 0$
9. $2x^5 + x^4 - 19x^3 - 18x^2 + 39x + 45 = 0$
10. $x^6 - x^5 - 17x^4 + 22x^3 - 14x^2 - 96x + 480 = 0$
11. $2x^5 - 5x^4 - 28x^3 + 70x^2 + 66x - 165 = 0$

CHAPTER 9

Inverse Trigonometric, Exponential, and Logarithmic Functions

9-1 INVERSE FUNCTIONS AND THEIR GRAPHS

All functions which are studied in mathematics can be classified as either *algebraic functions* or *transcendental functions*. The class of algebraic functions includes the *polynomials* (also called rational integral functions), the *rational fractions* [functions of the form $f(x)/g(x)$, where $f(x)$ and $g(x)$ are polynomials with $g(x) \neq 0$], and certain *irrational functions* of which the simplest are obtained by extracting roots of rational functions. There are also a great many other, less simple, algebraic functions.

The class of *transcendental functions* consists of all functions which are not algebraic. In this class are the *trigonometric functions*, which were defined in Section 7–1. Other important categories of transcendental functions are the *inverse trigonometric functions*, the *exponential functions*, and the *logarithmic functions*, the subject of the present chapter.

In Section 2–5 a function was defined as a set of number pairs (x, y), such that no two distinct pairs have the same first number x. The set of numbers x constituted the *domain* of the function, and the set of numbers y, the *range*.

Suppose now that we further require that no two distinct pairs (x, y) have the same second number y. Then there is a one-to-one correspondence between the domain and the range, that is, to each number in the domain there corresponds one number in the range, and to each number in the range there corresponds one number in the domain. Under these conditions the set of number pairs (y, x), with x and y interchanged, also satisfies the requirements of a function. The new function is called the *inverse* of f, and is often written as f^{-1}; its domain is the range of f and its range is the domain of f.

Consider the function (x, x^2), x any real number. The set of number pairs (x^2, x) does not define a function, since two values of x, if $x \neq 0$, correspond to the same number x^2. However, if f is the function (x, x^2), $x \geqq 0$, then the pairs (x^2, x) do define a function, which is the inverse f^{-1} of f. If we wish the first number of the pairs of f^{-1} to be a single letter, say y, then we may set $y = x^2$, $x = \sqrt{y}$, and write the inverse function as $(y, \sqrt{y})$, $y \geqq 0$. Since it is immaterial which letter is used, the inverse function f^{-1} may then also be written as $(x, \sqrt{x})$, $x \geqq 0$.

To see this in another form, consider the function f whose values are given by $f(x) = x^2$, x any real number. This function has no inverse, since, if we set it equal to y we get the equation $y = x^2$, which may be solved for x to give $x = \pm\sqrt{y}$, and one value of y may give two values of x. On the other hand, if we write $y = x^2$ with $x \geqq 0$, then $x = \sqrt{y}$ does define an inverse function.

In general, if an equation

$$y = f(x),\ x \text{ in a set } A,\ y \text{ in a set } B, \tag{1}$$

can be solved for x in terms of y, written as

$$x = g(y), \tag{2}$$

where each value of y in B yields one value of x in A, the pairs $(y, g(y))$, and hence, the pairs $(x, g(x))$, constitute the inverse of the function $(x, f(x))$.

Using the equation $y = x^2$ again as an illustration, we may obtain the two solutions $x = \sqrt{y}$ and $x = -\sqrt{y}$. We have seen that $(x, \sqrt{x})$, $x \geqq 0$, is the inverse of (x, x^2), $x \geqq 0$. We may then also say that $(x, -\sqrt{x})$, $x \geqq 0$, is the inverse of the function (x, x^2), $x \leqq 0$.

It should be emphasized that what determines a function f: $(x, f(x))$ is the correspondence between x and $f(x)$. Thus $(x, f(x))$ and $(y, f(y))$ define the same function if the domains are the same. Similarly, we may say that $\sin x$ and $\sin y$ define the same function, and in general, so do $f(x)$ and $f(y)$, provided that x and y are in the same set.

The pairs of values (x, y) which satisfy (2) will also satisfy (1), so that the graph of (2) will coincide with the graph of (1).

We now wish to interchange the roles of x and y, and to consider the graph of the function

$$y = g(x). \tag{3}$$

This graph is then the same as that of

$$x = f(y), \tag{4}$$

where $f(x)$ is the inverse of $g(x)$. Thus, if f is a given function, we may assign values to y, compute the corresponding values of x from (4), and join the points (x, y) by a smooth curve. However, we may make a more direct use of the

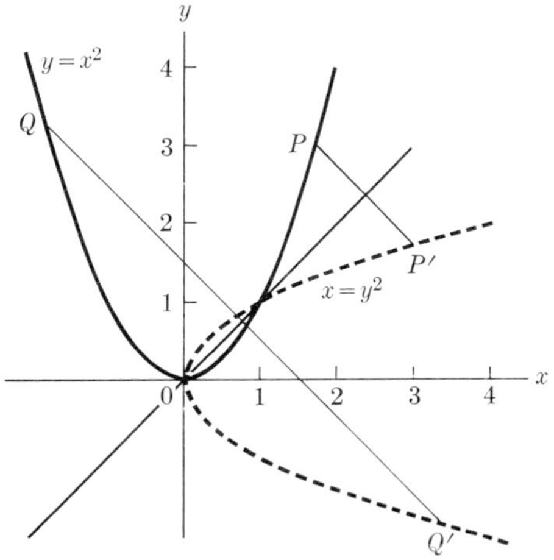

FIGURE 9–1

graph of (1). Since (1) and (4) differ only in that x and y are interchanged, *the graph of* (4) *may be obtained by reflecting the graph of* (1) *in the straight line* $y = x$.

For example, if the graph of the equation $y = x^2$ is shown in Fig. 9–1 as the solidly drawn curve, the graph of $x = y^2$, or $y = \pm\sqrt{x}$, will be the dotted curve. Under a reflection in the line $y = x$, a point such as P on $y = x^2$ goes into the point P' on $x = y^2$. The graph of the function $y = \sqrt{x}$ is then the part of the dotted curve for which $y \geqq 0$.

9–2 INTRODUCTION TO THE INVERSE TRIGONOMETRIC FUNCTIONS

For each of the trigonometric functions an inverse function may be defined. We write the general solution of the equation $y = \sin x$ as $x = \arcsin y$, with a similar notation applied to the other trigonometric functions. In general, in the discussion of the inverse trigonometric functions we should like to have x as the independent variable, and accordingly shall consider the equation

$$y = \arcsin x, \tag{5}$$

which is read just as it is written. Here x is a number such that $-1 \leqq x \leqq 1$, and y is also a number (actually, a number of radians). Because of the periodicity of the sine function, there are innumerably many values of $\arcsin x$ for any value of x. For example, if $x = \frac{1}{2}$, then $y = \arcsin \frac{1}{2}$ represents any number (of radians) such that $\sin y = \frac{1}{2}$. Thus, y may have any of the values $\pi/6 + 2n\pi$ or $5\pi/6 + 2n\pi$ $(n = 0, \pm 1, \pm 2, \ldots)$. We say that $\arcsin x$ is *multiple-valued*, and more particularly, that it is *infinitely many-valued.*

It is essential to realize that all knowledge concerning the equation $y = \arcsin x$ is derived from our knowledge of $\sin x$ and the complete equivalence of the equations $y = \arcsin x$ and $x = \sin y$. In this connection it is helpful to interpret $\arcsin x$ as "an angle whose sine is x." This equivalence, and similar ones for the other trigonometric functions, are shown in the following arrangement:

$y = \arcsin x \leftrightarrow x = \sin y$;	$y = \arccos x \leftrightarrow x = \cos y$;	
$y = \arctan x \leftrightarrow x = \tan y$;	$y = \operatorname{arccot} x \leftrightarrow x = \cot y$;	(6)
$y = \operatorname{arcsec} x \leftrightarrow x = \sec y$;	$y = \operatorname{arccsc} x \leftrightarrow x = \csc y$.	

In each case the two equations are equivalent.

We may now easily draw the graphs of equations such as (5). For example, to graph $y = \arccos x$ we need merely graph $y = \cos x$, and then interchange the roles of x and y. The graphs of the equations in (6), which appear in Fig. 9–2, may all be obtained in this fashion.

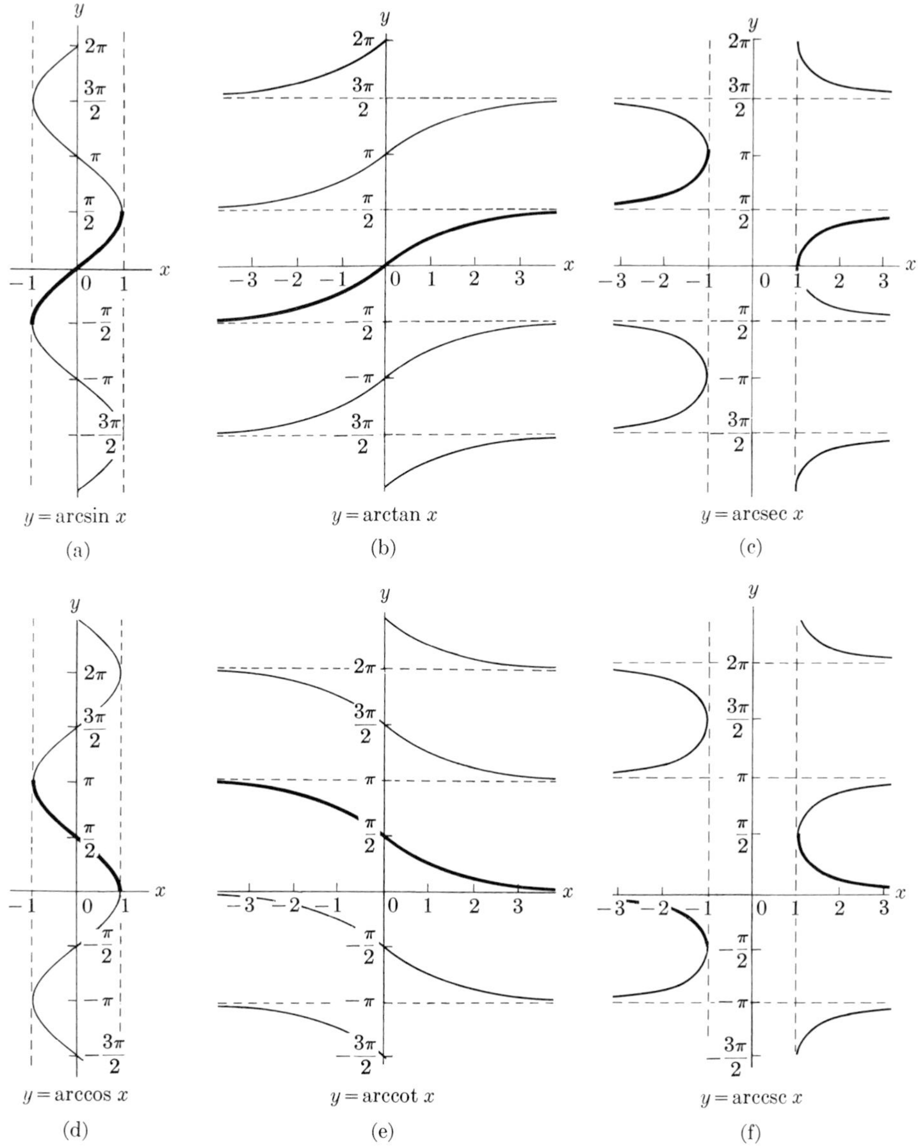

FIGURE 9–2

As an aid in sketching related functions, it will be helpful, when the terms period and amplitude apply to a trigonometric function, to apply the terms *inverse period* and *inverse amplitude* to the inverse function. For example, the equation $y = 2 \arcsin \frac{5}{6}x$ is equivalent to $x = \frac{6}{5} \sin y/2$, which has a period of 4π and amplitude of $\frac{6}{5}$. The same values then represent the inverse period and inverse amplitude of $y = 2 \arcsin \frac{5}{6}x$. The inverse period indicates regularity of behavior of the graph with respect to y, and inverse amplitude indicates the extent of the graph with respect to x.

Example 1. Draw the graph of the equation

$$y = 2 \arcsin \tfrac{5}{6}x.$$

Solution. As we have seen, the given equation has the inverse period 4π and the inverse amplitude $\frac{6}{5}$, since, for the equation $x = \frac{6}{5} \sin y/2$, the graph has a period of 4π and an amplitude of $\frac{6}{5}$. The graph appears in Fig. 9–3. Be sure to note the basic appearance of the sine curve, with the oscillation taking place along the y-axis.

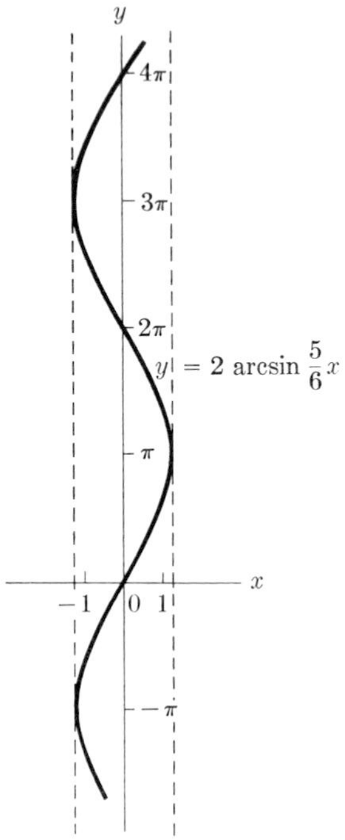

FIGURE 9–3

We give another example, which illustrates the application of our notation to the solution of certain equations.

Example 2. Express x in terms of y if

$$y = 2 \tan (3x + 1).$$

Solution. We require the solution of the equation for x. Solving first for $\tan (3x + 1)$, we obtain $\tan (3x + 1) = \frac{1}{2}y$, and by the definition of arctan, we find

$$3x + 1 = \arctan \tfrac{1}{2}y \qquad \text{and} \qquad x = \tfrac{1}{3}(-1 + \arctan \tfrac{1}{2}y).$$

EXERCISE GROUP 9–1

Express the values of the quantities in Exercises 1–15 in general form.

1. $\arcsin \dfrac{\sqrt{3}}{2}$
2. $\arctan 1$
3. $\operatorname{arcsec} 2$
4. $\operatorname{arccot} \sqrt{3}$
5. $\arccos \dfrac{\sqrt{2}}{2}$
6. $\operatorname{arccsc} 1$
7. $\arcsin \left(-\dfrac{\sqrt{3}}{2}\right)$
8. $\arccos (-\frac{1}{2})$
9. $\arctan (-\sqrt{3})$
10. $\operatorname{arccot} (-1)$
11. $\arcsin (-\frac{1}{2})$
12. $\operatorname{arcsec} (-1)$
13. $\arcsin 1$
14. $\arccos 0$
15. $\arctan 0$

In each of Exercises 16–27, solve for x in terms of y.

16. $y = 3 \sin x$
17. $2y = \tan 3x$
18. $y = 2 \sec \dfrac{x}{4}$
19. $3y = \cos \left(x + \dfrac{\pi}{2}\right)$
20. $y + 3 = \sin 2x$
21. $y = \cos (2x - 1)$
22. $y = 2 \arctan x$
23. $y = \arcsin \dfrac{x}{3}$

24. $3y = \arccos 2x$

25. $y + \frac{\pi}{3} = \arcsin x$

26. $3(y - 1) = \arctan \frac{x}{2}$

27. $y - \pi = \arcsin (x + 2)$

Construct the graph of each of the equations in Exercises 28–36 for $-\pi \leqq y \leqq 2\pi$.

28. $y = \arcsin x$

29. $y = \arccos x$

30. $y = \arctan x$

31. $y = 2 \arcsin x$

32. $y = \frac{1}{2} \arccos x$

33. $y = \arcsin \frac{x}{2}$

34. $y = \arccos 2x$

35. $y = 2 \arcsin 3x$

36. $3y = \arctan 2x$

Sketch the graph of each of the equations in the following exercises. In each case, give the inverse period and (where applicable) the inverse amplitude.

37. $y = 2 \arctan x$

38. $y = \arctan 2x$

39. $y = 2 \arccos \frac{x}{2}$

40. $2y = \arccos 3x$

41. $y = 3 \arcsin \frac{x}{2}$

42. $y = 2 \arcsin \frac{x}{3}$

43. $y = \frac{\pi}{2} + \arcsin x$

44. $y = \frac{1}{3} \arcsin 2x$

45. $y = \arcsin (x + 1)$

46. $y - \pi = 2 \arccos 3x$

47. $y - \frac{\pi}{3} = 3 \arcsin (2x - 1)$

9–3 THE INVERSE TRIGONOMETRIC FUNCTIONS

The fact that y is multiple-valued in an equation such as $y = \arcsin x$ can often be a hindrance. Hence we single out for each of these equations a range of values of y in which y can have only one value, and define the corresponding set of pairs of values (x, y) as the *inverse trigonometric function*. The corresponding portions of the curves in Fig. 9–2 are then called the *principal parts* of these curves. There is lack of uniformity among authors concerning the choice of these values. The reason for our choice is that thereby the sum of the values of an inverse function and the inverse cofunction is now $\pi/2$, which is consistent with, and even more general than, the result of Section 3–9 that any trigonometric ratio of a positive acute angle is equal to the coratio of the complementary angle. The principal part of each curve is shown more heavily in Fig. 9–2.

For purposes of illustration we shall sometimes give values of the inverse functions as angles in degrees, although they should be numbers.

We shall denote the actual inverse trigonometric functions as thus defined by capitalizing the initial letter of the name. The ranges for the inverse trigonometric functions follow:

$-\pi/2 \leqq \text{Arcsin } x \leqq \pi/2,$	$-\pi/2 \leqq \text{Arccsc } x \leqq \pi/2,$
$-\pi/2 < \text{Arctan } x < \pi/2,$	$0 < \text{Arccot } x < \pi,$
$0 \leqq \text{Arcsec } x \leqq \pi,$	$0 \leqq \text{Arccos } x \leqq \pi.$

Then, for example, $(x, \text{Arcsin } x)$, $-1 \leqq x \leqq 1$ is the inverse of the function $(x, \sin x)$, $-\pi/2 \leqq x \leqq \pi/2$.

Example 1.

$$\text{Arcsin } \tfrac{1}{2} = \pi/6, \qquad \text{Arccos } \tfrac{1}{2} = \pi/3,$$
$$\text{Arcsin } (-\tfrac{1}{2}) = -\pi/6, \qquad \text{Arccos } (-\tfrac{1}{2}) = 2\pi/3,$$
$$\text{Arctan } 1.437 = 55^\circ\ 10', \qquad \text{Arctan } (-0.2095) = -11^\circ\ 50'.$$

Example 2. Find Arctan (tan 120°).

Solution. The desired angle is the one in the range (in degrees) $-90° < \theta < 90°$ for which the tangent is the same as tan 120°, and is therefore $-60°$.

An important feature of inverse functions in general is that each function of a pair of inverse functions reverses the effect of the other. This idea is at first somewhat elusive, and the following two examples should be carefully studied.

Example 3. Find sin arcsin x.

Solution. Let us set

$$\arcsin x = \theta. \tag{7}$$

Then the problem is to find $\sin \theta$. But by definition, (7) is equivalent to the statement

$$\sin \theta = x,$$

and the answer is

$$\sin \arcsin x = x.$$

Example 4. Find Arcsin ($\sin x$) if $-\pi/2 \leqq x \leqq \pi/2$.

Solution. Let $\sin x = y$. Then by definition, and since x is in the range of values for the Arcsin function, we have $x = \text{Arcsin } y$, which becomes

$$x = \text{Arcsin } (\sin x);$$

this is the desired solution.

EXERCISE GROUP 9-2

Express each of the quantities in Exercises 1–18 in degrees and minutes.

1. Arcsin 0.5
2. Arctan 1
3. Arccos $\dfrac{\sqrt{2}}{2}$
4. Arccot $\sqrt{3}$
5. Arcsec 2
6. Arccsc $\dfrac{2\sqrt{3}}{3}$
7. Arcsin 0.6481
8. Arctan 1.788
9. Arccos 0.8679
10. Arccot 10.64
11. Arcsin $\left(-\dfrac{\sqrt{2}}{2}\right)$
12. Arctan $(-\sqrt{3})$
13. Arcsin (-0.1981)
14. Arctan (-0.3867)
15. Arcsec (-7.532)
16. Arccot (-9.345)
17. Arccos (-0.6700)
18. Arccsc (-1.740)

Express each of the quantities in Exercises 19–36 in radians.

19. Arcsin $\frac{\sqrt{2}}{2}$
20. Arctan (-1)
21. Arccos $(-\frac{1}{2})$
22. Arcsec (-2)
23. Arccot $(-\sqrt{3})$
24. Arcsin $\left(-\frac{\sqrt{3}}{2}\right)$
25. Arcsin (-1)
26. Arctan 0
27. Arcsec (-1)
28. Arcsin 0
29. Arccos 0
30. Arccot 0
31. Arccsc (-2)
32. Arcsec $\left(-\frac{2\sqrt{3}}{3}\right)$
33. Arcsin (-0.6483)
34. Arctan (-1.688)
35. Arcsec (-1.320)
36. Arccsc (-2.411)

Find the value of each expression in Exercises 37–51.

37. sin Arccsc $\frac{4}{3}$
38. sec Arcsin $(-\frac{1}{2})$
39. tan Arcsin $\left(-\frac{\sqrt{3}}{2}\right)$
40. sec Arctan 2
41. cos Arcsec (-1)
42. sec Arccos $\frac{2}{3}$
43. cos Arccot $(-\frac{12}{5})$
44. tan Arccos $\frac{3}{5}$
45. csc Arctan $(-\frac{7}{24})$
46. cot Arccos $(-\frac{2}{3})$
47. cot Arcsec (-2)
48. sin Arccot $(-\frac{3}{2})$
49. cos $[2 \text{ Arctan } \sqrt{3}]$
50. sin $[2 \text{ Arcsec } (-2)]$
51. tan $\left[2 \text{ Arcsin } \left(-\frac{\sqrt{2}}{2}\right)\right]$

9–4 INTRODUCTION TO LOGARITHMS

The definitions of exponents given in the Appendix, Sections A–2 and A–6, together with the five laws of exponents from Section A–2, will now be used to develop a process (defined in the following section) which may be used as a short cut for many arithmetical computations. The way in which exponents can serve in this manner will first be illustrated by some examples.

First let us note that from Table 1 of Appendix B we can obtain (accurate to three decimal places)

$$\sqrt{10} = 3.162 \quad \text{and} \quad \sqrt[3]{10} = 2.154.$$

Since $\sqrt{10} = 10^{1/2}$ and $\sqrt[3]{10} = 10^{1/3}$, we see that at least some numbers can be expressed as powers of 10. Once some numbers have been so expressed, additional numbers may be expressed as powers of 10 by use of the laws of exponents; some of these follow:

$$1 = 10^0, \qquad 10 = 10^1, \qquad 100 = 10^2$$

$$2.154 = 10^{1/3}, \qquad 21.54 = 10 \cdot 10^{1/3} = 10^{4/3}, \qquad 215.4 = 10 \cdot 10^{4/3} = 10^{7/3};$$

$$3.162 = 10^{1/2}, \qquad 31.62 = 10 \cdot 10^{1/2} = 10^{3/2}, \qquad 316.2 = 10 \cdot 10^{3/2} = 10^{5/2}.$$

It is clear how other numbers may be similarly expressed as powers of 10.

An indication of the way in which the above representations may be used in certain computations appears in the following example.

Example 1. Find the value of the product (3.162)(215.4).

Solution. Expressing the given values as powers of 10 we have

$$(3.162)(215.4) = (10^{1/2})(10^{7/3}) = 10^{1/2+7/3} = 10^{17/6} \text{ (Law 1 of exponents)}$$
$$= 10^{2.8333}.$$

Up to this point the product of 3.162 and 215.4 has been expressed as a power of 10. To complete the solution and obtain a numerical answer we need to be able to find the value of $10^{2.8333}$. It is beyond the scope of this book to compute the value of $10^{2.8333}$ but, as we shall see later, the value of $10^{2.8333}$ can be found from Table 3 to be 681.3.

Thus we see that the multiplication of two numbers can be accomplished by expressing each number as a power of 10, then expressing the product as a power of 10 by adding the exponents; the resulting power of 10 can then be converted into the desired numerical answer by the use of Table 3, after the use of this table is learned.

In a similar manner we can divide two numbers, and find the powers and roots of numbers, as illustrated in the following examples.

Example 2. Find the value of the quotient 31.62 ÷ 21.54.

Solution. Proceeding as in Example 1, we have

$$31.62 \div 21.54 = 10^{3/2} \div 10^{4/3} = 10^{3/2-4/3}$$
$$= 10^{1/6} = 10^{0.1667}.$$

Later, we shall be able to find from Table 3 that $10^{0.1667} = 1.468$.

Example 3. Find the value of $(2.154)^5$.

Solution. As in the preceding examples, we express the given number as a power of 10, getting

$$(2.154)^5 = (10^{1/3})^5 = 10^{5/3} = 10^{1.667} = 46.45 \quad \text{(from Table 3).}$$

Example 4. Find the value of $\sqrt[7]{3.162}$.

Solution. Since $3.162 = 10^{1/2}$ we have

$$\sqrt[7]{3.162} = (10^{1/2})^{1/7} = 10^{1/14} = 10^{0.0714}.$$

Turning again to Table 3, we find that $10^{0.0714} = 1.179$, which is then the value of $\sqrt[7]{3.162}$.

Thus we see that once numbers are expressed as powers of 10 the operations of multiplication, division, raising to powers, and the taking of roots are reduced to simple operations of addition, subtraction, multiplication, and division, respectively, performed on suitable exponents.

EXERCISE GROUP 9–3

Given $2 = 10^{0.3010}$, $3 = 10^{0.4771}$, $7 = 10^{0.8451}$, and $11 = 10^{1.0414}$, find the power of 10 which represents each of the following numbers.

1. $2 \cdot 3$	2. $2 \cdot 7$	3. $2 \cdot 3 \cdot 7$	4. $2 \cdot 7 \cdot 11$
5. $2 \div 3$	6. $3 \div 2$	7. $11 \div 7$	8. $7 \div 11$
9. $2^5 \cdot 3^2$	10. $3^4 \cdot 7^2$	11. $2^3 \cdot 7 \cdot 11^2$	12. $11^3 \cdot 7^2$
13. $3^3 \div 5^2$	14. $11^5 \div 7^3$	15. $2^5 \cdot 5^3 \cdot 7^{-4}$	16. $7^3 \cdot 11^2 \cdot 5^{-6}$
17. 63	18. 66	19. 432	20. 147
21. $11 \div 27$	22. $49 \div 33$	23. $99 \div 64$	24. 1980
25. 1782	26. $180 \div 121$	27. $891 \div 49$	28. $294 \div 77$
29. $\sqrt{2^3 \cdot 3^2}$	30. $\sqrt{77}$	31. $\sqrt[3]{294}$	32. $\sqrt[3]{1089}$
33. $\sqrt[5]{792}$	34. $\sqrt[7]{7^3 \cdot 6^5}$	35. $\sqrt[6]{1568}$	36. $\sqrt[4]{3234}$

9–5 EXPONENTIAL AND LOGARITHMIC FUNCTIONS

In the preceding section we encountered the problem of determining the value of a given power of 10. This problem is the determination of the value of y for a given value of x in the expression

$$y = 10^x. \tag{8}$$

However, this is a special case of the more general relation

$$y = b^x, \tag{9}$$

where b is any positive real number different from 1. We prefer to study this more general relation, since values of b other than 10 will prove both interesting and useful. We define the *exponential function* as the set of number pairs (x, b^x), x any real number. Note that this function involves a power, but differs fundamentally from the power function (x, y), $y = x^b$, in that in the exponential function *the exponent is variable.*

Exponential functions occur frequently in applications of mathematics, some of which will be considered in Section 9–13.

We may also write the exponential function as (x, y), $y = b^x$, x any real number. Since different values of x yield different values of y (all $\geqq 0$), the number pairs (x, y), $x = b^y$, $x \geqq 0$, define the *inverse* of the exponential function, this inverse being called the *logarithmic function.* The determination of y, for any value of x, in the logarithmic function, concerns the solution of the equation $x = b^y$ for y in terms of x. This type of problem was encountered in Section 9–4, with $b = 10$. The study of the logarithmic function is based on the meaning of logarithm, which we shall now define.

***Definition* 9–1.** *A number u is said to be the* logarithm *of a positive real number v to the base b (where b is real, positive, and different from* 1) *if u is the exponent of the power to which b must be raised to obtain v.*

In symbols, *the logarithm* is written as

$$\boxed{u = \log_b v}$$

and is read: "u equals the logarithm of v to the base b."

The number 1 cannot serve as a base of logarithms, since any power of 1 is equal to 1. The *logarithms of positive numbers only* will be considered here (logarithms of negative and imaginary numbers are defined in advanced courses).

It is important for the student to realize that *a logarithm is an exponent*, and that the following statements are valid.

The equations $u = \log_b v$ and $v = b^u$ are equivalent by definition. Each of the functions $u = \log_b v$ and $v = b^u$ is the inverse of the other.

Examples.

$\log_2 8 = 3$, since $8 = 2^3$; $\log_{10} 0.01 = -2$, since $0.01 = 10^{-2}$;
$\log_{1/3} 9 = -2$, since $9 = (\frac{1}{3})^{-2}$; $\log_{\sqrt{5}} 25 = 4$, since $25 = (\sqrt{5})^4$.

EXERCISE GROUP 9–4

Write each of the equations in Exercises 1–12 in logarithmic form.

1. $2^5 = 32$
2. $3^3 = 27$
3. $4^{-3} = \frac{1}{64}$
4. $(49)^{1/2} = 7$
5. $(125)^{1/3} = 5$
6. $(0.4)^{-3} = \frac{125}{8}$
7. $\sqrt{121} = 11$
8. $(27)^{2/3} = 9$
9. $(19)^0 = 1$
10. $(243)^{4/5} = 81$
11. $(\frac{1}{5})^{-2} = 25$
12. $(128)^{3/7} = 8$

Write each of the equations in Exercises 13–24 in exponential form.

13. $\log_2 256 = 8$
14. $\log_{64} 4 = \frac{1}{3}$
15. $\log_9 729 = 3$
16. $\log_{2.5} 15.625 = 3$
17. $\log_6 1296 = 4$
18. $\log_{16} 8 = 0.75$
19. $\log_{81} 243 = 1.25$
20. $\log_{0.5} 32 = -5$
21. $\log_{27} 9 = \frac{2}{3}$
22. $\log_{0.1} 10^5 = -5$
23. $\log_{32} 0.5 = -0.2$
24. $\log_a 1 = 0$

In each of Exercises 25–54, determine the values of b, x, or y, whichever is present.

25. $\log_3 81 = y$
26. $\log_2 32 = y$
27. $\log_4 (64)^{-1} = y$
28. $\log_{10} 10^a = y$
29. $\log_{10} 0.0001 = y$
30. $\log_{25} \frac{1}{125} = y$
31. $\log_{3\sqrt{2}} 324 = y$
32. $\log_{27} 81 = y$
33. $\log_{\sqrt[3]{b}} \sqrt[6]{b^5} = y$
34. $\log_5 x = 4$
35. $\log_{10} x = -3$
36. $\log_{10} x = 0.75$
37. $\log_3 x = -4$
38. $\log_4 x = -5$
39. $\log_5 x = \frac{3}{2}$

40. $\log_{81} x = \frac{5}{4}$
41. $\log_{64} x = -\frac{5}{6}$
42. $\log_{243} x = -\frac{4}{5}$
43. $\log_b 5 = 0.5$
44. $\log_b 25 = -\frac{2}{3}$
45. $\log_b a = 0.5$
46. $\log_b a = 1$
47. $\log_b a = -2$
48. $\log_b 49^{-1} = \frac{2}{3}$
49. $\log_b \sqrt[4]{3} = \frac{1}{5}$
50. $\log_b 10 = -\frac{1}{2}$
51. $\log_b \sqrt[3]{3} = 1$
52. $\log_b \sqrt[3]{b^2} = y$
53. $\log_b x^c = c$
54. $\log_a x^3 = c$

9–6 GRAPHS OF THE EXPONENTIAL AND LOGARITHMIC FUNCTIONS

Many properties of the exponential and logarithmic functions are most easily recognized from a graph. The graphs of the functions

$$y = b^x \qquad \text{and} \qquad y = \log_b x$$

will be obtained for certain values of b; these graphs will then illustrate the general situation. For a given value of b the graphs of the two functions are known to be reflections, or mirror images, of each other in the line $y = x$. It is also helpful to note that for each function there is a distinct graph for each suitable value of b, but all such graphs fall into certain types.

Example 1. Construct the graph of $y = 3^x$.

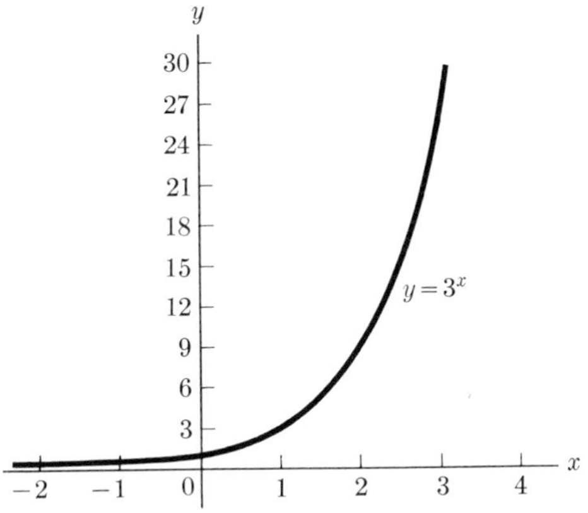

FIGURE 9–4

Solution. Assume values of x and compute the corresponding values of y, obtaining the following table of values:

x:	-3	-2	-1	0	1	2	3
y:	$\frac{1}{27}$	$\frac{1}{9}$	$\frac{1}{3}$	1	3	9	27

The points corresponding to these pairs of values are plotted on the coordinate system of Fig. 9–4 and these points are joined by a smooth curve, which is the desired graph of the function. Note that the values of y are all positive.

Example 2. Construct the graph of $y = \log_2 x$.

Solution. The relation $y = \log_2 x$ is equivalent to $x = 2^y$. Hence we assume values of y and compute the corresponding values of x, getting the table

x:	$\frac{1}{8}$	$\frac{1}{4}$	$\frac{1}{2}$	1	2	4	8
y:	-3	-2	-1	0	1	2	3

The points corresponding to these values are plotted on the coordinate system in Fig. 9–5. The smooth curve joining these points is the desired graph of $y = \log_2 x$. It should be noted that the graph lies entirely to the right of the y-axis.

The graph of $y = \log_b x$ for any $b > 1$ will be similar to that in Fig. 9–5. Some of the properties of this function which can be noted from the graph are:

I. $\log_b x$ is not defined for negative values of x or zero.

II. $\log_b 1 = 0$.

III. If $x > 1$, then $\log_b x > 0$.

IV. If $0 < x < 1$, then $\log_b x < 0$.

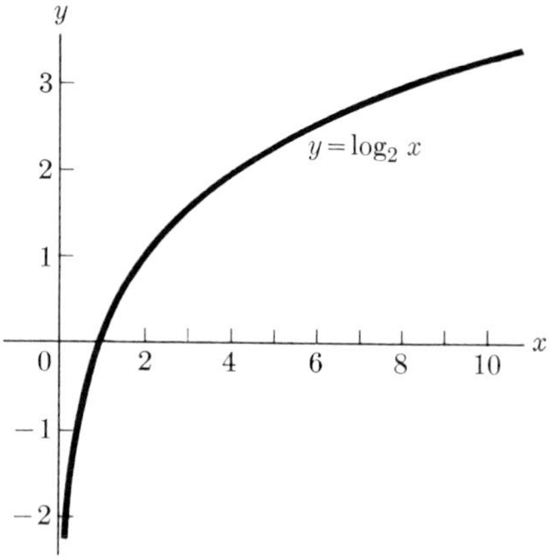

The knowledge of contractions, expansions, translations, and reflections as discussed in Section 7–4 can be used to good advantage in graphing certain exponential and logarithmic functions. Thus, the graph of $y = 3^{-x}$ is simply the image of the graph of $y = 3^x$ (Fig. 9–4) in the y-axis. Again, since $9^x = 3^{2x}$, the graph of $y = 9^x$ can be thought of as a contraction of the graph of $y = 3^x$ (Fig. 9–4) in the x-direction in the ratio 1 : 2.

As a further illustration we may apply these methods to the function 3^{1-x}. We may write 3^{1-x} as $3^{-(x-1)}$; since the latter function may be obtained from 3^x by replacing x by $-x$, and then replacing x by $x - 1$ in 3^{-x}, the graph of 3^{1-x} may be obtained from the graph of 3^x by reflecting in the y-axis, and then translating the resulting graph one unit to the right. We may also obtain the graph of 3^{1-x} by use of the relation $3^{1-x} = 3 \cdot 3^{-x}$; the graph of 3^{1-x} then becomes an expansion of the graph of 3^{-x} in the y-direction in the ratio 3 : 1.

If the methods indicated in these illustrations are kept constantly in mind, additional uses will be noticed. In particular, the application to certain logarithmic functions is immediate.

EXERCISE GROUP 9–5

In each of the following six exercises, graph the function for values of x from -3 to 3 and find at least some points for fractional values of x between -1 and 1.

1. 2^x
2. 3^x
3. 5^x
4. 10^x
5. 4^{-x}
6. 7^{-x}

In each of the following exercises, draw the graph of the given function. [*Hint:* The same values (x, y) satisfy the inverse relations $y = \log_b x$ and $x = b^y$.]

7. $\log_2 x$
8. $\log_3 x$
9. $\log_{10} x$
10. $\log_{10} \frac{1}{x}$
11. $\log_{10} (2x)$
12. $\log_{10} x^2$
13. $10^{\log_{10} x}$
14. $\log_{10} 10^x$
15. $\log_{10} (-x)$
16. $\frac{1}{2} \log_{10} x$

Use the properties of expansion, contraction, reflection, and translation, together with the graphs of the functions in Exercises 7–9, to construct the graph of each function in Exercises 17–27.

17. $\log_2 3x$
18. $\log_3 \frac{x}{2}$
19. $\log_{10} (x + 2)$
20. $\log_{10} (x - 3)$
21. $2 \log_{10} x$
22. $\frac{1}{3} \log_{10} x$
23. $\log_{10} (-x)$
24. $\log_2 (3 - x)$
25. $3 + \log_2 x$
26. $3 + 2 \log_{10} x$
27. $2 + 3 \log_{10} 5(x - 1)$

9–7 PROPERTIES OF LOGARITHMS

In this section we shall consider three additional general properties of logarithms, properties which are particularly useful for purposes of computation. The properties to be proved are a direct consequence of the laws of exponents and the fact that logarithms are actually exponents. More specifically, they may be considered as laws of exponents expressed in terms of logarithms. We shall first give the appropriate laws of exponents.

Laws of Exponents

A. $$b^p b^q = b^{p+q}.$$

B. $$\text{If } b \neq 0, \frac{b^p}{b^q} = b^{p-q}.$$

C. $$(b^p)^q = b^{pq}.$$

We proceed to the properties of logarithms.

I. $$\log_b uv = \log_b u + \log_b v.$$

Proof. Let $\log_b u = x$ and $\log_b v = y$. Then, by the definition of logarithms, $u = b^x$ and $v = b^y$. Hence

$$uv = b^x b^y = b^{x+y} \qquad \text{(Property A of exponents)},$$

and by applying the definition of logarithms to the last equation, we have

$$\log_b uv = x + y = \log_b u + \log_b v.$$

Example 1. $\log_{10} 6 = \log_{10} (2 \times 3) = \log_{10} 2 + \log_{10} 3.$

$$\text{II.} \quad \boxed{\log_b u/v = \log_b u - \log_b v.}$$

Proof. Proceed as in I above to obtain $u = b^x$ and $v = b^y$. Then $u/v = b^x/b^y = b^{x-y}$ (Property B of exponents). It follows that

$$\log_b u/v = x - y = \log_b u - \log_b v.$$

Example 2. $\log_{10} \frac{3}{7} = \log_{10} 3 - \log_{10} 7.$

$$\text{III.} \quad \boxed{\log_b u^r = r \log_b u.}$$

Proof. Let $\log_b u = x$; then, as above, $u = b^x$ and

$$u^r = (b^x)^r = b^{rx} \qquad \text{(Property C of exponents)}.$$

Hence

$$\log_b u^r = rx = r \log_b u.$$

Example 3. $\log_{10} \sqrt[3]{7} = \log_{10} 7^{1/3} = \frac{1}{3} \log_{10} 7.$

It will prove very helpful to the student to state the above properties of logarithms in words, and to learn the verbal statements.

Example 4. Express y in terms of x if

$$\log_b y = 2x + \log_b x.$$

Solution. Transposing $\log_b x$, we have

$$\log_b y - \log_b x = 2x,$$

and by Property II,

$$\log_b \frac{y}{x} = 2x.$$

Using the definition of logarithm, we obtain

$$\frac{y}{x} = b^{2x},$$

and the result is

$$y = x \cdot b^{2x}.$$

Example 5. Establish the following equation, and determine all values of x for which it is valid:

$$\log_b x + \log_b (x - 1) = \log_b (x^2 - x).$$

Solution. The equation

$$x(x - 1) = x^2 - x$$

is clearly valid for all x. Hence, by Property I, the relation which is to be established is valid for all values of x for which the logarithms exist. We must then find the values of x for which x, $x - 1$, and $x^2 - x$ are all positive. If $x > 0$ and $x - 1 > 0$, then certainly $x^2 - x > 0$. Hence we require the values for which at the same time $x > 0$ and $x - 1 > 0$; thus, the values being sought are all values for which $x > 1$.

9–8 COMMON LOGARITHMS. CHARACTERISTIC. MANTISSA

For purposes of computation by means of logarithms the base 10 is usually used, and it is customary to omit the designation of the base. Hence, when no base is indicated, it will be understood that the base is 10. Logarithms to the base 10 are called *common logarithms*.

We are familiar with the fact that any positive real number N can be expressed in *scientific notation*, that is, as the product of an integral (including zero) power of 10, and a positive real number m between 1 and 10. Thus,

$$N = m \cdot 10^c, \qquad 1 \leqq m < 10, \qquad c \text{ is an integer.} \tag{10}$$

For example, we have

$$31789.2 = 3.17892 \times 10^4, \qquad 0.00003219 = 3.219 \times 10^{-5},$$

where it is clear that the exponent of 10 is determined by the position of the decimal point in the original number. Application of Property I of Section 9–7 to the above relations gives

$$\begin{aligned} \log 31789.2 &= \log 10^4 + \log 3.17892 \\ &= 4 + \log 3.17892; \\ \log 0.00003219 &= \log 10^{-5} + \log 3.219 \\ &= -5 + \log 3.219. \end{aligned}$$

Moreover, if the position of the decimal point is changed in one of these numbers, the effect is to change the integer in the second expression for the logarithm. For each position the decimal point is moved to the left, the integer is decreased by 1, and for each position the decimal point is moved to the right, the integer is increased by 1.

Similarly, Eq. (10) gives, in general,

$$\log N = c + \log m, \qquad 1 \leqq m < 10. \tag{11}$$

Thus we see from (11) that if common logarithms are used, the logarithm of every positive real number N is the sum of an integer (positive, negative, or zero) and the logarithm of a number between 1 and 10. The integral part c is called the *characteristic* of $\log N$, and $\log m$ is the *mantissa* of $\log N$. Note that the base 10 is not being written; we shall continue this practice and omit the designation of the base except when a base other than 10 is used.

The characteristic of $\log N$ is obviously determined by the location of the decimal point in the number N, and is given by the following rule:

The first nonzero digit in N from the left is called the first *significant figure of N; the characteristic c of* $\log N$ *is the number of places from the first significant figure to the units place, being positive if the first significant figure is to the left of the units place, zero if it is at the units place, and negative if it is to the right of the units place.*

Example. The characteristic

of log 2156 is 3, since 3 significant figures are to the left of the units place,
of log 5.236 is 0, since the first significant figure is in the units place,
of log 0.00052 is -4, since the first significant figure is 4 places to the right of the units place.

To determine the mantissa of $\log N$, we must determine a number x such that

$$10^x = m, \qquad \text{where} \qquad 1 \leqq m < 10. \tag{12}$$

Since $1 = 10^0$ and $10 = 10^1$, it follows that the values of x satisfying (12) must satisfy the inequality

$$0 \leqq x < 1.$$

The mantissa x is thus seen to be the *positive* decimal part of the logarithm, or zero.

9-9 A TABLE OF LOGARITHMS

Some logarithms can be determined without a table. Thus,

$$\log 3.162 = 0.5000, \qquad \text{since } 10^{1/2} = \sqrt{10} = 3.162,$$
$$\log 2.154 = 0.3333, \qquad \text{since } 10^{1/3} = \sqrt[3]{10} = 2.154.$$

In general, however, mantissas are determined by methods which cannot be properly understood until the student has studied calculus. Hence we must accept values which have been computed and compiled in *tables of logarithms*. The first such table of common logarithms, that is, logarithms to the base 10, was published in 1624, having been computed by an Englishman, Henry Briggs (1561–1630).

Logarithm tables give only the logarithms of numbers between 1 and 10, or, more generally, the mantissas of the logarithms of positive numbers. We shall use a four-place table of logarithms; this will enable us to find the mantissas of the logarithms of four-digit numbers N. It should be understood that in a four-place table the mantissas, which are in fact infinite decimals, are given correct to four decimal places, that is, are *rounded off* to four decimal places.

The table of logarithms appears as Table 3 of the Appendix. We shall consider the *direct* use of the table, in which the logarithm of a number is found, and the *inverse* use, in which a number is to be found from the table when its logarithm is known. The table is arranged so that the first two significant figures of N appear in the column headed N, while the third significant digit of N appears in the row at the top of the table. The use of the table can now best be explained by examples. We illustrate first the direct use of the table.

Example 1. Determine log 213.

Solution. The characteristic is 2. To determine the mantissa, we look in the table in the column headed N and find 21. Directly to the right of this in the column headed 3, we find 3284. This number with a decimal point placed in front is the desired mantissa. Hence,

$$\log 213 = 2.3284.$$

When a logarithm is negative, we very often do not wish to lose the positive character of the decimal part; therefore we do not combine the characteristic and mantissa, although it is certainly correct to do so. If we add and subtract 10 we get what is known as the *standard form* of the logarithm. The following example will illustrate this.

Example 2. Determine log 0.00317.

Solution. The characteristic is -3 and the mantissa is 0.5011. Therefore, we have

$$\log 0.00317 = -3 + 0.5011 = (10 - 3 + 0.5011) - 10$$
$$= 7.5011 - 10. \quad \text{(This is in standard form.)}$$

Example 3. Determine the value of $\log \sqrt[3]{\frac{33}{14}}$.

Solution. From the table: $\log 33 = 1.5185$
$\log 14 = 1.1461$ $(-)$

By Property II, $\log \frac{33}{14} = 0.3724$

By Property III, $\log \sqrt[3]{\frac{33}{14}} = \frac{1}{3}(0.3724) = 0.1241.$

We now illustrate the *inverse* use of the table.

Example 4. Determine x when $\log x = 3.1818$.

Solution. We look in the *body* of the table for the mantissa 0.1818 and find it in row 15 and column 2, so that the digits of x are 152. Since the characteristic is 3, the decimal point must be placed so that the first significant figure is three places to the left of the units place. Hence $x = 1520$.

Example 5. Determine x when $\log x = 6.5490 - 10$.

Solution. Locate the mantissa 0.5490 in the table and note that the corresponding number is 354. The characteristic is $6 - 10$ or -4, and the decimal point must be placed so that the first significant figure is 4 places to the right of the units place. Hence $x = 0.000354$.

EXERCISE GROUP 9-6

In each of Exercises 1–24, make use of the properties of logarithms and Table 3 to find the value of the given logarithm.

1. $\log 3(11)$
2. $\log 5(12)$
3. $\log 3(5)7$
4. $\log 0.314(7.28)$
5. $\log 283(1.26)$
6. $\log 3.61(81.2)$
7. $\log 624(312)$
8. $\log 21.3(10^5)$
9. $\log \frac{13}{5}$
10. $\log \frac{31}{13}$
11. $\log \dfrac{3140}{217}$
12. $\log \dfrac{532}{726}$
13. $\log \dfrac{3.12}{1320}$
14. $\log \dfrac{21.3}{5170}$
15. $\log \dfrac{0.237}{0.0315}$
16. $\log \dfrac{0.00724}{0.427}$
17. $\log (19)^3$
18. $\log (37)^5$
19. $\log \sqrt[3]{31}$
20. $\log \sqrt{321}$
21. $\log (3.7)^3 \sqrt{41}$
22. $\log \sqrt{\dfrac{31}{19}}$
23. $\log \sqrt{\dfrac{19}{(37)^3}}$
24. $\log \sqrt{\dfrac{342(21.5)}{(19.1)^3}}$

In each of Exercises 25–34, use Table 3 to determine the value of x.

25. $\log x = 2.9581$
26. $\log x = 0.8779$
27. $\log x = 8.8982 - 10$
28. $\log x = 5.6920$
29. $\log x = 9.9987 - 10$
30. $\log x = 6.3874 - 10$
31. $\log x = 4.5977$
32. $\log x = 3.7966$
33. $\log x = 3.6263$
34. $\log x = 7.7589 - 10$

In each of Exercises 35–43, use the properties of logarithms and Table 3 to compute the value of x.

35. $x = (37)^2(26)$
36. $x = \sqrt{(395)^3}$
37. $x = (4.77)^{4/5}$
38. $x = \sqrt[3]{\dfrac{(792)^2}{29.2}}$
39. $x = \sqrt[5]{(613)^2(0.0504)}$
40. $x = \dfrac{(916)^2}{\sqrt[3]{1.57}}$
41. $x = \dfrac{17(19)(29)}{(31)(52)}$
42. $x = \dfrac{537(0.528)^3}{891}$
43. $x = \dfrac{2.88\sqrt{1.22}}{\sqrt[3]{6.67}}$

In Exercises 44–49, use the properties of logarithms to verify each equation.

44. $\log (4x^2 - 9) = \log (2x + 3) + \log (2x - 3)$
45. $\log (x^3 - 2x^2) = 2 \log x + \log (x - 2)$
46. $\log (x - 2) = \log (x^2 + x - 6) - \log (x + 3)$
47. $\log x = \log (x^3 + x^2 - 2x) - \log (x - 1) - \log (x + 2)$
48. $\frac{1}{2} \log (x + y) = \log \sqrt{\dfrac{x + y}{x - y}} + \log \sqrt{x - y}$
49. $a \log (x - y) = \log \dfrac{(x - y)^a}{(x - z)^b} + b \log (x - z)$

Rewrite each of the following equations so as to express y as a function of x; in each case reduce to simplest form.

50. $\log y = 2 \log x + \log 7$
51. $\log y = a \log x + \log b$
52. $\log y = 3x + \log 5$
53. $\log y = ax + \log b$
54. $\log y = mx + \log 10$
55. $\log y = 3x - \log 10$
56. $3 \log y = 4 \log x + 5 \log 2$
57. $a \log y = b \log x + c \log k$

9–10 INTERPOLATION IN THE TABLE OF LOGARITHMS

Table 3 gives all mantissas to four decimal places, while only three significant figures appear for the number N. The logarithms of numbers with four significant figures can be found from the table by the principle of linear interpolation.

The principle of linear interpolation, as applied here, is that a sufficiently small arc of the graph of the logarithmic function may be replaced by a straight line.

We may interpret this principle to mean that the difference between two sufficiently close values of x is proportional to the difference between the corresponding values of the logarithmic function $\log x$. We illustrate first *direct interpolation.*

Example 1. Determine log 3176.

Solution. The characteristic of the logarithm is 3, so that we may determine log 3.176 and then add 3. The value of log 3.176 must lie between log 3.17 and log 3.18, and by the principle of linear interpolation, the difference in the logarithms is proportional to the difference in the numbers, for small differences; hence we have

$$\frac{\log 3.176 - \log 3.17}{\log 3.18 - \log 3.17} = \frac{3.176 - 3.17}{3.18 - 3.17}.$$

From Table 3 we find that

$$\log 3.17 = 0.5011, \qquad \log 3.18 = 0.5024.$$

Substituting these values, we obtain the equation

$$\frac{\log 3.176 - 0.5011}{0.5024 - 0.5011} = \frac{0.006}{0.01},$$

which may be solved for log 3.176 as

$$\begin{aligned} \log 3.176 &= 0.5011 + \frac{0.006}{0.01}(0.0013) \\ &= 0.5011 + 0.6 \times 0.0013 \\ &= 0.5011 + 0.0008 = 0.5019. \end{aligned}$$

Hence the mantissa of log 3176 is 0.5019, and with a characteristic of 3, the value is

$$\log 3176 = 3.5019.$$

If log 0.3176 were desired, the mantissa would be determined in the same way, but with a characteristic of -1 the value would be

$$\log 0.3176 = 0.5019 - 1 = 9.5019 - 10.$$

Thus *the method for obtaining the mantissa of the logarithm of a four-digit number* can be described as follows:

1. *Disregard the decimal point and drop the fourth digit.*
2. *Subtract the mantissa corresponding to the remaining three-digit number from that corresponding to the next larger three-digit number.*
3. *Multiply the difference thus obtained by the fourth digit originally dropped, divide the product by* 10, *add the result to the smaller mantissa used in Step* 2, *and round off in the fourth decimal place.*

If the logarithm of a number with more than four digits is to be obtained from a four-place table, the number should first be rounded off in the fourth figure.

In the following example a self-explanatory schematic arrangement is used.

Example 2. Determine log 51.83.

Solution. With the fourth digit dropped, the remaining three-digit number is 518, and the next larger one is 519. Schematically, we have

$$10\left[\begin{array}{l} 3\left[\begin{array}{ll} 5180 & 7143 \\ 5183 & x \end{array}\right]h \\ \quad 5190 \quad 7152 \end{array}\right]9, \qquad \frac{h}{9} = \frac{3}{10},$$

$$h = 3 \text{ (in last decimal place).}$$

Thus $x = 7146$, and $\log 51.83 = 1.7146$.

There is also the *inverse* problem of determining a four-digit number whose logarithm is given, or the problem of *inverse interpolation*.

Example 3. Determine x when $\log x = 2.5615$.

Solution. We may find the number m such that $\log m = 0.5615$, and then place the decimal point as dictated by the characteristic. From the table we find that

$$\log 3.64 = 0.5611, \qquad \log 3.65 = 0.5623;$$

then $\log m$ must lie between these values. The equation of proportionality is

$$\frac{m - 3.64}{3.65 - 3.64} = \frac{0.5615 - 0.5611}{0.5623 - 0.5611},$$

which can be solved for m as

$$m = 3.64 + 0.01 \times \frac{0.0004}{0.0012} = 3.64 + 0.01 \times 0.3 = 3.64 + 0.003 = 3.643.$$

Since the characteristic of log x is 2, we obtain

$$x = 364.3.$$

In general, to determine the number corresponding to a mantissa not listed in the table, note the next smaller entry in the table and the next larger. Then subtract the next smaller mantissa from the given one and divide the result by the difference between the next larger and the next smaller, obtaining the quotient correct to one decimal. The digit thus obtained is the fourth digit of N. The first three digits correspond to the next smaller mantissa. The decimal point is then placed as dictated by the characteristic.

Example 4. Determine x when $\log x = 3.6112$.

Solution. The mantissa of the logarithm is 0.6112. The next smaller mantissa in the table is 0.6107 and the next larger one is 0.6117. Schematically, we have

$$10\left[\begin{array}{l} a\left[\begin{array}{cc} 4080 & 6107 \\ x & 6112 \end{array}\right]5 \\ \quad 4090 \quad 6117 \end{array}\right]10, \qquad \frac{a}{10} = \frac{5}{10}.$$

Hence $a = 5$ in the fourth figure and $x = 4085$.

EXERCISE GROUP 9–7

In each of Exercises 1–12, use Table 3 to find the given logarithm.

1. log 413.7
2. log 4.376
3. log 73.85
4. log 9365
5. log 0.8264
6. log 0.06472
7. log 84530
8. log 319300
9. log 0.0008421
10. log 0.001914
11. log 0.04569
12. $\log 8.334 \cdot 10^{-7}$

In each of Exercises 13–24, use Table 3 to find the value of x.

13. $\log x = 2.8289$
14. $\log x = 3.6596$
15. $\log x = 4.5497$
16. $\log x = 1.9794$
17. $\log x = 7.6596 - 10$
18. $\log x = 2.6556 - 7$
19. $\log x = 6.4633 - 10$
20. $\log x = 3.2979 - 9$
21. $\log x = 1.1580 - 4$
22. $\log x = 4.3955 - 10$
23. $\log x = 7.5099 - 12$
24. $\log x = 2.7656 - 7$

In Exercises 25–36, express each of the negative logarithms in standard form and then use Table 3 to find the value of x.

25. $\log x = -0.3149$
26. $\log x = \frac{1}{3}(9.0589 - 10)$
27. $\log x = 0.7(8.3214 - 10)$
28. $\log x = -3.7848$
29. $\log x = \frac{1}{3}(8.4302 - 10)$
30. $\log x = -1.2(3.0402)$
31. $\log x = 1.8423 - 2.4707$
32. $\log x = 3.7043 - 5.4$
33. $\log x = 2.1(4.0204 - 4.2)$
34. $\log x = (2.6 - 3.9) \div 3.5$
35. $\log x = 0.8(2.32516 - 3.2517)$
36. $\log x = \frac{1}{5}(3.2169 - 4.3247)$

9–11 COMPUTATION WITH LOGARITHMS

The method involved in the use of logarithms for the purpose of computing certain numbers is to employ the properties of logarithms to obtain the logarithm of the number, and then to find the number from the table when its logarithm is known. A neat and orderly arrangement of the work will be found to be very helpful, particularly in the less simple computations. The student should pay very close attention to the following examples, and should cultivate the habit of arranging his work in a similar manner.

Example 1. Compute the value of $Q = \dfrac{(315.7)^2\sqrt{23.46}}{\sqrt[3]{0.03128}}$.

Solution. From the properties derived in Section 9–7 we obtain

$$\log Q = 2 \log 315.7 + \tfrac{1}{2} \log 23.46 - \tfrac{1}{3} \log 0.03128.$$

The following form for the computation is self-explanatory.

$$\begin{array}{ll} \log 315.7 = 2.4993 & 2 \log 315.7 = 4.9986 \\ \log 23.46 = 1.3703 & \tfrac{1}{2} \log 23.46 = 0.6852 \quad (+) \\ \hline & \log N \text{ (numerator)} = 15.6838 - 10 \\ \log 0.03128 = 8.4952 - 10 & \tfrac{1}{3} \log 0.03128 = 9.4984 - 10 \quad (-) \\ \hline & \log Q \text{ (quotient)} = 6.1854 \\ & Q = 1532000. \end{array}$$

Notice that log N was changed from 5.6838 to 15.6838 — 10; the reason is that 9.4984 — 10 was to be subtracted from it and we wanted the positive part of log N to be larger than the positive part of the number to be subtracted.

Example 2. Compute the value of $\dfrac{3.142 \cdot 2031 \cdot \sqrt{3082}}{0.0231 \cdot \sqrt[3]{63.75}}$.

Solution. If we denote the number by Q, the logarithmic equation is

$$\log Q = \log 3.142 + \log 2031 + \tfrac{1}{2} \log 3082 - [\log 0.0231 + \tfrac{1}{3} \log 63.75].$$

The computation follows:

$$\begin{array}{ll} \log 63.75 = 1.8044 & \log 3082 = 3.4889 \\ (+)\left\{\begin{array}{l} \tfrac{1}{3} \log 63.75 = 0.6015 \\ \log 0.0231 = 8.3636 - 10 \end{array}\right. & (+)\left\{\begin{array}{l} \tfrac{1}{2} \log 3082 = 1.7444 \\ \log 3.142 = 0.4972 \\ \log 2031 = 3.3077 \end{array}\right. \\ \hline \log D = 8.9651 - 10 & (-)\ \begin{array}{l} \log N = 15.5493 - 10 \\ \log D = 8.9651 - 10 \end{array} \\ \hline & \log Q = 6.5842 \\ & Q = 3839000. \end{array}$$

EXERCISE GROUP 9–8

In each of the following exercises, compute the value of the given expression by the use of Table 3.

1. $(21.36)(8.076)$
2. $(293.2)(0.3847)$
3. $(0.04375)(28.47)$
4. $(79810)(0.004384)$
5. $2.397 \div 53860$
6. $27.94 \div 0.03897$
7. $(7.3 \cdot 10^{-3}) \div (8.746 \cdot 10^{6})$
8. $(3.964 \cdot 10^{-5})(7.342 \cdot 10^{-7})$
9. $(3.046)(0.6397)(0.07315)$
10. $(0.3914)(0.004371)(0.04322)$
11. $\dfrac{(43.79)(0.8365)}{75680}$
12. $\dfrac{(437.8)(2.967)}{0.004792}$
13. $\dfrac{(0.2973)(0.06738)}{0.007635}$
14. $\dfrac{(0.07586)(387.1)}{635400}$
15. $\sqrt{(9.347)(0.3982)}$
16. $\sqrt{(917.6)(0.3182)}$
17. $\sqrt[3]{3.967 \div 985.3}$
18. $\sqrt[3]{38.45 \div 0.01946}$
19. $\dfrac{\sqrt{(0.02165)(439.1)}}{\sqrt[3]{231.7}}$
20. $\dfrac{\sqrt{289.5}\,\sqrt[3]{0.3942}}{\sqrt[4]{0.08463}}$
21. $\dfrac{(0.03142)^2\,\sqrt[3]{4.375}}{(43.86)^4\,\sqrt{39810}}$
22. $\dfrac{(9.365)^2\,\sqrt[3]{5.387}}{(687.2)^3\,\sqrt{0.4371}}$
23. $\left[\dfrac{(7.389)^2(674.2)^3}{\sqrt{7.342}\,\sqrt[3]{0.4762}}\right]^{2/3}$
24. $\left[\dfrac{\sqrt{429.5}\,\sqrt[3]{0.07216}}{(0.3178)^3(987.5)^2}\right]^{3/4}$
25. $\dfrac{(0.3976)^{3/2}(47.86)^{2/3}}{(0.4785)^{3/5}(4.971)^{5/3}}$
26. $\left[\dfrac{(0.2476)^{1/3}(7.294)^{1/2}}{0.8347(976.3)^2}\right]^{7/5}$
27. $\dfrac{(0.04321)^3(3.142 \cdot 10^{-5})}{\sqrt{0.8463}\,\sqrt[3]{0.7392}}$
28. $\dfrac{2{,}397{,}000(1.035)^{18}}{(0.035)^{-15}}$
29. $\dfrac{124.7[(1.045)^{21} - 1]}{0.045}$
30. $\dfrac{2{,}319{,}000(1.025)^{15}}{(1.035)^{21}}$

9–12 LOGARITHMS OF THE TRIGONOMETRIC FUNCTIONS

The numerical work in applications of trigonometry can often be facilitated by the use of logarithms. For example, it may be necessary in the solution of a triangle to compute the value of $a = 143 \sin 29°\,20'$. From Table 2 we find $\sin 29°\,20' = 0.4899$. Then for $\log a$ we have

$$\log a = \log 143 + \log 0.4899 = 2.1553 + (9.6901 - 10) = 1.8454,$$

for which Table 3 gives

$$a = 70.0.$$

Two references to tables were required to find log sin 29° 20′. Table 4, on the other hand, gives directly the common logarithms of the trigonometric ratios, so that only one reference to a table is required. In those logarithms which are negative, the characteristic appears after the mantissa. We may always write such logarithms in standard form. Thus we find

$$\log \sin 29°\,20' = 9.6901 - 10$$

by one reference to a table. Otherwise, the table operates just as for the natural ratios, including the use of *linear interpolation.* We shall illustrate both *direct* and *inverse interpolation* in this table.

Example 1. Find log cos 78° 43′ from Table 4.

Solution. The desired value is between log cos 78° 40′ and log 78° 50′. Schematically, we have

$$10\left[3\begin{bmatrix}78^\circ\,40' & 2934\\ 78^\circ\,43' & x\end{bmatrix}h \atop 78^\circ\,50' \quad 2870\right]64, \qquad \frac{h}{64} = \frac{3}{10}, \qquad h = 19,$$

in which only the mantissas of the logarithms are indicated. Since log cos θ decreases as θ increases, $h = 19$ must be subtracted, in the last two decimal places, from log cos 78° 40′, and we find

$$\log \cos 78°\,43' = (9.2934 - 10) - 0.0019 = 9.2915 - 10.$$

Example 2. Use Table 4 to find θ if $\log \sin \theta = 9.7802 - 10$.

Solution. The angle must lie between 37° 00′ and 37° 10′. The interpolation is indicated in the scheme:

$$16\left[7\begin{bmatrix}7795 & 37^\circ\,00'\\ 7802 & \theta\end{bmatrix}h \atop 7811 \quad 37^\circ\,10'\right]10, \qquad \frac{h}{10} = \frac{7}{16}, \qquad h = 4.$$

Hence

$$\theta = 37°\,00' + 04' = 37°\,04'.$$

EXERCISE GROUP 9–9

Use Table 4 to find the value of the logarithm in each of Exercises 1–12.

1. log sin 32° 17′
2. log cos 48° 12′
3. log tan 57° 15′
4. log cot 41° 19′
5. log sec 73° 13′
6. log csc 16° 14′
7. log sec 69° 36′
8. log csc 129° 48′
9. log cot 181° 51′
10. log tan 234° 27′
11. log cos 347° 39′
12. log sin 98° 44′

Use Table 4 to find the smallest positive value of θ in each of Exercises 13–24.

13. $\log \cos \theta = 0.5659 - 1$
14. $\log \tan \theta = 0.7664 - 1$
15. $\log \cot \theta = 0.2339$

16. $\log \sin \theta = 0.5483 - 1$
17. $\log \sec \theta = 0.0719$
18. $\log \csc \theta = 0.2690$
19. $\log \sin \theta = 0.5958 - 1$
20. $\log \cos \theta = 0.9557 - 1$
21. $\log \tan \theta = 0.8000 - 1$
22. $\log \cot \theta = 0.3634$
23. $\log \sec \theta = 0.1120$
24. $\log \csc \theta = 0.1740$

Use logarithms to solve the right triangles having the parts given in Exercises 25–34. (In all cases C = 90°.)

25. $A = 43° 17'$, $a = 216.3$
26. $B = 59° 12'$, $c = 0.2365$
27. $a = 0.1392$, $b = 0.6314$
28. $a = 365900$, $c = 734100$
29. $A = 67° 45'$, $b = 34.23$
30. $b = 0.04127$, $c = 0.3524$
31. $B = 47° 34'$, $a = 4.381$
32. $a = 96.74$, $b = 18.39$
33. $B = 23° 13'$, $b = 42.73$
34. $A = 13° 16'$, $c = 1.327$

35. What airspeed should a pilot maintain on a heading of 270° to fly a course of 287° 30′, if a wind is blowing from the south at 25 mph?
36. A pilot notices that to fly a course of 98° 25′ he must maintain an airspeed of 210 mph on a heading of 90°. The wind is blowing from the north with what velocity?
37. A truck weighing 8926 lb moves up a ramp which is inclined 7° 14′ from the horizontal. What is the pressure of the truck against the ramp (perpendicular to the ramp)?
38. A weight of 2187 lb is suspended by two cables. One cable makes an angle of 35° 07′ with the horizontal and the other makes an angle of 28° 14′ with the horizontal. What is the tension in each cable?
39. A surveyor desires to find the distance from a point *B* to a point *A* on the opposite side of a river. He determines a point *C* which is 143.7 ft from *B* and such that the line *BC* is perpendicular to the line *AB*. He then measures angle *BCA* and finds it to be 29° 19′. What is the distance *AB*?
40. The navigator of a ship which is sailing due north notices a lighthouse in the direction N 26° 12′ W and after sailing one mile the bearing of the lighthouse is N 27° 15′ W. If the ship continues to sail a straight course, what will be the shortest distance between the ship and the lighthouse?
41. A force of 298.3 lb is directed at an angle of 43° 12′ with the horizontal. Compute the vertical and horizontal components of the force.
42. The cable on a vertical telegraph pole exerts a horizontal pull of 496.8 lb at a point 22.83 ft above the ground. A guy wire 27.8 ft long is attached to the pole at the same height above the ground and anchored to the ground at a point in the same horizontal plane with the foot of the pole. What is the tension in the guy wire required to counteract exactly the horizontal pull of the cable?

9–13 GRAPHS OF COMPOSITE FUNCTIONS

In the preceding section the logarithms of the trigonometric functions were considered. These are examples of *composite functions*, that is, functions in which the variable is replaced by another function. Other examples we have encountered are functions of quadratic form. Various combinations of the logarithmic, exponential, and trigonometric functions appear in mathematics. The properties of such functions must, of course, depend on the characteristics of the individual functions that appear in them. Our present concern is the graphing of some of these functions. For this purpose we make use of our knowledge of the component functions. In particular, we take into account the periodicity of the trigonometric functions, the fact that the exponential function is never negative, and the fact that the function $\log x$ is undefined for negative values of x. Moreover, we may always use specific points obtained by computing values of the composite function.

Example. Draw the graph of $y = \log \sin x$.

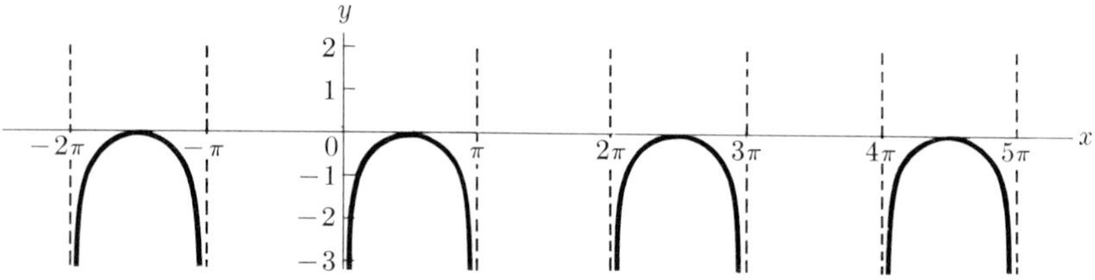

FIGURE 9-6

Solution. Since the logarithms of negative numbers are not defined, there are no values of y corresponding to any values of x in Q_3 or Q_4. Furthermore, since $\sin x \leqq 1$ for all x, and since $\log u < 0$ when $u < 1$, the curve lies below the x-axis except for values of x which are of the form $\pi/2 + 2n\pi$ with n an integer, for which values $y = 0$. Since the values of $\sin x$ repeat when x increases by 2π, the same is true of $\log \sin x$, which means that $\log \sin x$ is periodic with period 2π. The graph appears in Fig. 9-6.

EXERCISE GROUP 9-10

Draw the graph of each of the following functions.

1. $\log (2x + 1)$
2. $\log (x^2 + x)$
3. $\log (x^2 + 2x - 1)$
4. 5^{3x+1}
5. 3^{x^2-x}
6. $\log \sin (-x)$
7. $\log \tan x$
8. $\log \cos x$
9. $\log \cot x$
10. $\log \sin 2x$
11. $\log \cos 2x$
12. $\log \tan (x/2)$
13. $\log \csc (x/3)$
14. $\log \sec 3x$
15. $3^{\cos x}$
16. $3^{\tan x}$
17. $3^{\cot x}$
18. $3^{\sin x}$
19. $3^{\sec x}$
20. $3^{\csc x}$
21. $3^{\sin 2x}$
22. $2^{\cos 3x}$
23. $3^{\tan (x/2)}$
24. $\sin (\log x)$
25. $\cos 3^x$
26. $\cos (\log x^2)$
27. $\sin (\log 2x)$
28. $\tan 2^x$
29. $\tan (\log x)$
30. $\log (x \sin x)$
31. $\log \left(\dfrac{\sin x}{x}\right)$
32. $2^x \sin x$
33. $3^{x/2} \cos 2x$

9–14 EXPONENTIAL EQUATIONS. COMPOUND INTEREST

Formulas giving the *amount* of a sum of money invested at *compound interest* involve exponential functions. A few examples will illustrate this type of application.

Example 1. If \$100 is invested at 3% interest compounded annually, how much will it amount to at the end of 18 yr?

Solution. The \$100 will amount to $100(1 + 0.03)$ at the end of the first year. Since interest is compounded annually, the principal during the second year is \$103, and hence the amount at the end of the second year will be $103 + 0.03(103)$ or $103(1 + 0.03)$, which can be written as $100(1.03)^2$. A continuation of this reasoning shows that at the end of 18 yr the amount A_{18} will be given by

$$A_{18} = 100(1.03)^{18} = \$170 \text{ (computed by logarithms).}$$

Example 2. If \$100 is invested at 3% interest compounded quarterly, how much will it amount to in 18 yr?

Solution. Interest is now to be computed every 3 mos and added to the principal. However, the rate of 3% is the annual rate, so that the interest earned in 3 mos is $0.03/4 = 0.0075$. Hence, at the end of the first 3 mos, which is one interest period, the amount will be $100(1.0075)$. Then, as in Example 1, at the end of six mos, or two interest periods, the amount will be $100(1.0075)^2$, and at the end of 18 yr, or 72 interest periods, the amount A_{72} will be given by

$$A_{72} = 100(1.0075)^{72} = \$171.26 \text{ (by 7-place logarithms).}$$

In general, we see that $\$P$ at interest rate r compounded j times a year will amount in t years to A_{jt}, where A_{jt} is given by

$$\boxed{A_{jt} = P\left(1 + \frac{r}{j}\right)^{jt}.} \tag{13}$$

This is an exponential function when jt is a variable.

Example 3. How long will it take a sum of money (say \$1) to become doubled if invested at 4% interest compounded quarterly?

Solution. In Eq. (13) we set $P = 1$, $r = 0.04$, $j = 4$, $A_{4t} = 2$, and we have

$$2 = 1(1 + 0.01)^{4t}.$$

Then we apply logarithms to obtain

$$\begin{aligned}\log 2 &= \log 1 + \log (1.01)^{4t} \\ &= 0 + 4t \log 1.01.\end{aligned}$$

Solving this equation for $4t$ we have

$$4t = \log 2 \div \log 1.01,$$

so that we obtain for t the value

$$t = \frac{\log 2}{4 \log 1.01} = \frac{0.3010}{4(0.0043)} = \frac{0.3010}{0.0172} = 17.5 \text{ yr}.$$

Note that in this example the solution involves the division of one logarithm by another.

Example 4. Determine the value of x such that $10^x = 3.142$.

Solution. By the definition of logarithms,

$$x = \log 3.142 = 0.4972.$$

Example 5. Solve for x in the equation

$$3251 = 2184(1.02)^x.$$

Solution. Applying logarithms to both members of the given equation, we have

$$\log 3251 = \log 2184 + x \log 1.02.$$

Solving this last equation for x we obtain

$$x \log 1.02 = \log 3251 - \log 2184,$$

from which it follows that

$$x = \frac{\log 3251 - \log 2184}{\log 1.02} = \frac{3.5120 - 3.3393}{0.0086} = \frac{0.1727}{0.0086} = 20.08.$$

The method used in solving Example 3 involves the solution of the exponential equation $b = a^y$, which may also be thought of as finding the zero of a function containing an exponential. We shall consider another example of this type.

Example 6. Solve for x in the equation $7^{2x-1} - 5^{3x} = 0$.

Solution. Writing the equation as $7^{2x-1} = 5^{3x}$, and equating logarithms of both members, we have

$$(2x - 1) \log 7 = 3x \log 5 \tag{14}$$

or

$$(2x - 1)(0.8451) = 3x(0.6990).$$

Hence

$$1.6902x - 0.8451 = 2.097x, \qquad 0.4068x = -0.8451$$

and

$$x = -2.077.$$

In Example 3 the desired solution involves the quotient of two logarithms. In Example 6 we can solve Eq. (14) to give

$$x = \frac{\log 7}{2 \log 7 - 3 \log 5}.$$

These examples show that logarithms may be combined algebraically in the same manner as any other numbers and are added, subtracted, multiplied, or divided as the need arises; *the computation of any expression containing logarithms should be carried out in precisely the manner called for in that expression.*

EXERCISE GROUP 9–11

In each of Exercises 1–18, determine the value of x to four significant figures.

1. $x = (1.04)^{20}$
2. $x = (1.025)^{15}$
3. $x = (1.035)^{-16}$
4. $x = (1.045)^{-18}$
5. $x = 15.62(1.04)^{13}$
6. $x = 32.35(1.03)^{-15}$
7. $x = 1479(1.025)^{36}$
8. $3^x = 7$
9. $5^x = 2$
10. $13^x = 11$
11. $17^{2x} = 11(13^x)$
12. $19^{3x} = 17(11^x)$
13. $4976 = x(1.035)^{15}$
14. $2493 = 1200(1.025)^x$
15. $3916 = 1958(1.03)^{2x}$
16. $3 = (1 + x)^{17}$
17. $\dfrac{(1.025)^x - 1}{0.025} = 43.90$
18. $\dfrac{1 - (1.04)^{-x}}{0.04} = 17.29$
19. If \$100 is invested at 3.5% compounded annually, how much will it amount to at the end of 18 yr?
20. If \$2347 is invested at 4.5% compounded quarterly, how much will it amount to in 18 yr?
21. What sum of money, invested now at 4.5% interest compounded quarterly, will amount to \$5000 at the end of 18 yr?
22. How long will it take a sum of money (say \$1) to become doubled if invested at 4% compounded semiannually?
23. At what interest (compounded annually) must a sum of money (say \$1) be invested if it is to become doubled in 15 yr?
24. At what interest compounded quarterly must a sum of money be invested if it is to become trebled in 25 yr?

9–15 NATURAL LOGARITHMS. CHANGE OF BASE

It has been mentioned that the base 10 is usually used for computational purposes. In advanced mathematics, however, when purposes other than computation are concerned, a different base is used, which results in simpler formulas. This base, denoted by the letter e, is an irrational number, and will be defined in Section 11–8, but it is sufficient for our purposes to give it to a number of decimals as

$$e = 2.718281828\ldots$$

Logarithms to the base e are called *natural* or *Naperian* logarithms. Tables of natural logarithms exist, but it is desirable to be able to evaluate such logarithms by use of a table of common logarithms. To do this we shall develop a general formula for converting from one base to any other base.

Let us consider the logarithm

$$y = \log_a x. \tag{15}$$

The equivalent exponential relation is

$$x = a^y.$$

Taking logarithms of both members to the base b, we have $\log_b x = y \log_b a$, which can be solved for y as

$$y = \frac{\log_b x}{\log_b a}.$$

Substituting the value of y from (15), we have

$$\boxed{\log_a x = \frac{\log_b x}{\log_b a}.} \tag{16}$$

This is the formula used for converting from a logarithm with the base b to a logarithm with the base a.

In particular, the formula becomes, for changing from common to natural logarithms,

$$\boxed{\log_e x = \frac{\log_{10} x}{\log_{10} e} = 2.303 \log_{10} x,} \tag{17}$$

and for converting from natural to common logarithms the formula is

$$\boxed{\log_{10} x = \frac{\log_e x}{\log_e 10} = 0.4343 \log_e x.} \tag{18}$$

Example 1. Compute the value of $\log_{12} 17$.

Solution. By formula (16), with $a = 12$ and $b = 10$, we have

$$\log_{12} 17 = \frac{\log_{10} 17}{\log_{10} 12} = \frac{1.2304}{1.0792} = 1.1401.$$

Example 2. Compute the value of $\log_e 7$.

Solution. Formula (17) yields, with $x = 7$,

$$\log_e 7 = 2.303 \log_{10} 7 = 2.303 \times 0.8451 = 1.946.$$

EXERCISE GROUP 9-12

In each of Exercises 1-15, use Table 3 to determine the value of the given logarithm.

1. $\log_3 21.57$
2. $\log_3 2.157$
3. $\log_e 34.19$
4. $\log_2 3146$
5. $\log_5 0.0023$
6. $\log_e 0.7326$
7. $\log_4 0.4136$
8. $\log_4 413.6$
9. $\log_e 7e^{26}$
10. $\log_7 (32.54)^5$
11. $\log_3 (0.6549)^{-5}$
12. $\log_{13} (72.13)^{2/3}$
13. $\log_e 312e^7$
14. $\log_e \frac{8723}{219}$
15. $\log_e \sqrt[7]{832.4}$
16. Prove that $\log_u v = \dfrac{1}{\log_v u}$.
17. Show that $e^{\log_e x} = x$.

SUPPLEMENTARY EXERCISES FOR CHAPTER 9

In each of Exercises 1–6, determine the value of x, y, or b, whichever is present.

1. $\log_3 81 = y$
2. $\log_b 16 = 2$
3. $\log_5 x = -1$
4. $\log_{1/3} 27 = y$
5. $\log_b \frac{1}{64} = -6$
6. $\log_{\sqrt{3}} x = 6$

In each of Exercises 7–12, sketch the graph of the given function.

7. 3^x
8. $2(5^x)$
9. $3(2^{-x})$
10. $\log_2 x$
11. $\log_3 (-x)$
12. $\log_2 (2x)$

In Exercises 13–15, use the properties of logarithms to verify each statement.

13. $\log (3x^2 + 6x) = \log 3 + \log x + \log (x + 2)$, if x is positive.
14. $\log \dfrac{49x^3}{13} = 2 \log 7 + 3 \log x - \log 13$, if x is positive.
15. $\log \dfrac{x^2}{(x-1)^3} = 2 \log x - 3 \log (x - 1)$, if $x - 1$ is positive.

In Exercises 16–19, rewrite each of the given equations so as to express y as a function of x.

16. $\log y = 2 \log x + \log 3$
17. $\log y = 3x + \log 2$
18. $3 \log y - 2 \log x = 5 \log 4$
19. $2 \log y = 5x + 3 \log 10$

In each of Exercises 20–25, compute the value of the given expression by use of Table 3.

20. $\dfrac{(3.127)(428.3)}{\sqrt{0.002156}}$
21. $\dfrac{(314 \cdot 10^7)^{2/5}}{(31.78)^2\sqrt{917.6}}$
22. $\dfrac{\sqrt{31920}\,\sqrt{0.9346}}{\sqrt[4]{5172}}$
23. $\left[\dfrac{(0.03798)^2(8349)^3}{4351 \cdot 10^3}\right]^{1/7}$
24. $\dfrac{\sqrt{83.42}\,\sqrt[3]{0.3927}}{\sqrt[4]{1.234}\,\sqrt[5]{0.3416}}$
25. $\left[\dfrac{(3.127 \cdot 10^{-6})^2(72.31 \cdot 10^4)^3}{(317.4 \cdot 10^3)^4}\right]^{2/3}$

In Exercises 26–31 use Table 3 to determine the value of each given logarithm.

26. $\log_2 31.42$
27. $\log_3 2.346$
28. $\log_5 314.2$
29. $\log_e 1.285$
30. $\log_e 12.85$
31. $\log_e 245e^2$

In each of Exercises 32–37, determine the value of x, to three significant figures where possible.

32. $5^x = 17$
33. $(0.23)^x = 0.41$
34. $17^x = 7(3^x)$
35. $x = (0.9)^{0.4}$
36. $(1.03)^x = 2$
37. $(1 + x)^{18} = 2$

In each of Exercises 38–43, solve for x in terms of y.

38. $y = 3 \sin 2x$
39. $y = 2 \cos 2x$
40. $y = \arctan 3x$
41. $y = \arcsin 2x$
42. $y = 3 \arccos \frac{1}{2}x$
43. $y = a \tan bx$

Express each of the quantities in Exercises 44–49 in radians.

44. Arcsin $(-\frac{1}{2})$

45. Arctan $\dfrac{1}{\sqrt{3}}$

46. Arcsec (-2)

47. Arcsin 0.5225

48. Arctan (-0.65)

49. Arcsec 1.392

Find the value of each expression in Exercises 50–55.

50. sin Arctan $\frac{4}{3}$

51. tan Arcsin $(-\frac{5}{13})$

52. sec Arctan $\frac{5}{12}$

53. sin Arcsec $(-\frac{5}{4})$

54. tan Arcsec (-3)

55. sec Arcsin (-0.5)

CHAPTER 10

Properties of the Trigonometric Functions

10–1 THE FUNDAMENTAL IDENTITIES

In Section 3–6 it was seen that the values of the remaining trigonometric functions of a number can be found if the value of one function of that number is known. This would seem to indicate the existence of various relations among these functions, relations which are independent of the number involved.

***Definition* 10–1.** *A statement of equality which is valid for all values of the variable for which the functions involved are defined is called an identity.*

Identities are familiar from algebra. A factorization, such as

$$x^3 + 1 = (x + 1)(x^2 - x + 1),$$

involves a statement of identity, the equation being valid for all values of x. Another algebraic identity is the equation

$$\frac{1}{x-1} - \frac{1}{x+1} = \frac{2}{x^2-1},$$

which holds for all values of x except $x = \pm 1$, for which at least one term is undefined. On the other hand, an equation such as

$$x^2 - 4 = 0,$$

which holds only for isolated values of x (here, $x = \pm 2$), is called a *conditional equation.*

Identities do exist among the trigonometric functions, and their study comprises a major part of so-called analytical trigonometry. The fundamental identities fall into three types: the *reciprocal identities*, the *ratio identities*, and the *squares* or *Pythagorean identities.* The *reciprocal identities* are perhaps the simplest, and follow directly from the definitions of the trigonometric functions. They are as follows, with each written in three equivalent forms:

$$\boxed{\sin\theta = \frac{1}{\csc\theta}, \quad \sin\theta\csc\theta = 1, \quad \csc\theta = \frac{1}{\sin\theta};} \tag{1}$$

$$\boxed{\cos\theta = \frac{1}{\sec\theta}, \quad \cos\theta\sec\theta = 1, \quad \sec\theta = \frac{1}{\cos\theta};} \tag{2}$$

$$\boxed{\tan\theta = \frac{1}{\cot\theta}, \quad \tan\theta\cot\theta = 1, \quad \cot\theta = \frac{1}{\tan\theta}.} \tag{3}$$

For example, from the definitions of Section 3–6, we have, if θ is in standard position, and x, y, and r, with $r \neq 0$, are the coordinates and polar distance of a point on its terminal side,

$$\sin\theta = y/r, \qquad \csc\theta = r/y \qquad (y \neq 0),$$

from which it follows at once that

$$\sin\theta\csc\theta = 1.$$

The other two forms of (1) follow immediately. Equations (2) and (3) are proved similarly.

The *ratio identities* also follow at once from the definition of the trigonometric ratios (Section 3–6), and are

$$\boxed{\tan\theta = \frac{\sin\theta}{\cos\theta},} \tag{4}$$

$$\boxed{\cot\theta = \frac{\cos\theta}{\sin\theta}.} \tag{5}$$

Finally, to prove the *squares* or *Pythagorean identities*, let any angle θ be placed in standard position, and let x, y, r, with $r \neq 0$, be the coordinates and polar distance of a point on its terminal side. By Section 2–4, we have the relation

$$x^2 + y^2 = r^2. \tag{6}$$

Division of both members by r^2 gives

$$\left(\frac{x}{r}\right)^2 + \left(\frac{y}{r}\right)^2 = 1,$$

and since $\cos\theta = x/r$, and $\sin\theta = y/r$, the squares identity

$$\boxed{\sin^2\theta + \cos^2\theta = 1} \tag{7}$$

is obtained. Similarly, division of both members of (6) by x^2, with $x \neq 0$, yields the identity

$$\boxed{\sec^2\theta = 1 + \tan^2\theta.} \tag{8}$$

The third and final squares identity, derived in like manner, is

$$\boxed{\csc^2\theta = 1 + \cot^2\theta.} \tag{9}$$

10–2 ON PROVING IDENTITIES

In addition to the fundamental identities there are many other identities, some fairly complicated, involving the trigonometric functions. The need for them arises in various connections, in the study of calculus in particular. Facility in proving these identities depends to a large extent on great familiarity with the fundamental relations. No fixed procedure can be prescribed. In fact, a given identity can usually be proved in various ways. It is important, in the course of such a proof, to be able to look ahead, and foresee what a given step will yield. For example, by formula (8) we may replace $\sec^2\theta$ by $1 + \tan^2\theta$. By the same formula we may replace $\tan^2\theta$ by $\sec^2\theta - 1$, or $\sec^2\theta - \tan^2\theta$ by 1. However, it is not so easy to recognize that the number 1 may need to be replaced by $\sec^2\theta - \tan^2\theta$ or, by (7), by $\sin^2\theta + \cos^2\theta$.

Example 1. Can $\sqrt{1 + 2\sin\theta\cos\theta}$ be rationalized?

Solution. We may replace 1 by $\sin^2\theta + \cos^2\theta$. Then

$$\begin{aligned}\sqrt{1 + 2\sin\theta\cos\theta} &= \sqrt{\sin^2\theta + 2\sin\theta\cos\theta + \cos^2\theta}\\ &= \sqrt{(\sin\theta + \cos\theta)^2} = \pm(\sin\theta + \cos\theta).\end{aligned}$$

The generality of the identities has another aspect. The identities are stated in terms of θ, but any angle, such as 2θ, $\theta/2$, or even $\pi - \theta$, could appear, provided the same one is used throughout. Thus, the identities

$$\cos\frac{\theta}{2}\tan\frac{\theta}{2} = \sin\frac{\theta}{2} \qquad \text{and} \qquad \sin^2 3\theta = 1 - \cos^2 3\theta$$

follow at once from formulas (4) and (7), respectively, and the appearance of the angle $\theta/2$ or 3θ in these identities is not significant.

The proof of an identity can be achieved by transforming either member by the use of known identities, together with permissible operations, until the other member is obtained. By the same token, both members may be transformed independently until the same function results from the sequence of transformations. It is also possible to establish an identity by use of permissible operations on equations until a known identity is reached, but these steps must be reversible. For, as also with equations, each step involves the statement that *if the current relation is valid, then the resulting one is also valid.* In this manner, the final relation is merely shown to be possible, and must then be established either by direct substitution, or by a reversal of the steps.

We shall restrict the method of proof in what follows to working with one member of an identity until the other member is obtained. In the absence of a fixed method of procedure, the following suggestions should prove helpful.

1. *Choose the more complicated member as the one to be transformed.*
2. *If the member being transformed contains a sum of fractions, it may help to combine these fractions into a single fraction.*
3. *If the numerator of a fraction contains more than one term, it may help to express the fraction as a sum of fractions.*
4. *If the numerator or denominator of a fraction (or the entire member) can be factored, the factorization may suggest the next step.*
5. *In the absence of other steps to take, express each function in terms of sines and cosines.*
6. *At all times, in order to discover what step to take, keep in mind the other member of the identity, a comparison of which with the one being transformed may suggest what to do.*

Example 2. Prove the identity

$$\frac{\csc^2(\theta/2) - \cot^2(\theta/2)}{\sec^2(\theta/2)} = \cos^2\frac{\theta}{2}.$$

Solution. We choose the left member as the one to be transformed. By means of (9) we may replace $\csc^2(\theta/2) - \cot^2(\theta/2)$ by 1. Then the left member can be written as

$$\frac{1}{\sec^2(\theta/2)} = \cos^2\frac{\theta}{2} \quad \text{[by (2)]}$$

and the identity is established.

Example 3. Prove the identity $\cot 2\theta \cos 2\theta = \csc 2\theta - \sin 2\theta$.

Solution. With the use of (1) and (7), the right member may be written as

$$\frac{1}{\sin 2\theta} - \sin 2\theta = \frac{1 - \sin^2 2\theta}{\sin 2\theta} = \frac{\cos^2 2\theta}{\sin 2\theta} = \frac{\cos 2\theta}{\sin 2\theta} \cdot \cos 2\theta,$$

and by (5) this becomes $\cot 2\theta \cos 2\theta$.

Example 4. Prove the identity

$$\frac{\sec\theta + 1}{\tan\theta} = \frac{\tan\theta}{\sec\theta - 1}.$$

Solution. There is no apparent reason for preferring to transform either member. We arbitrarily choose to transform the left member. To obtain $\sec\theta - 1$ in the denominator (since it appears there in the right member), we multiply numerator and denominator of the fraction by that quantity, and have

$$\frac{\sec\theta + 1}{\tan\theta} \cdot \frac{\sec\theta - 1}{\sec\theta - 1} = \frac{\sec^2\theta - 1}{\tan\theta\,(\sec\theta - 1)} = \frac{\tan^2\theta}{\tan\theta\,(\sec\theta - 1)} \qquad \text{[by (8)]}$$

$$= \frac{\tan\theta}{\sec\theta - 1}$$

and the proof is complete.

The use of trigonometric identities is often involved in solving a (conditional) trigonometric equation.

Example 5. Solve the equation $\tan^2 x + \sec^2 x = 7$ for x, in terms of inverse trigonometric functions.

Solution. By Eq. (8) the left member of the equation becomes

$$\tan^2 x + \sec^2 x = \tan^2 x + (1 + \tan^2 x) = 2\tan^2 x + 1.$$

It follows that

$$2\tan^2 x + 1 = 7, \qquad \tan^2 x = 3, \qquad \text{and} \qquad \tan x = \pm\sqrt{3}.$$

In the notation of Section 9–2, the values of x can now be given as

$$x = \arctan(\pm\sqrt{3}).$$

In terms of inverse trigonometric functions we have

$$x = \text{Arctan}\,\sqrt{3} + n\pi \qquad \text{or} \qquad x = \text{Arctan}\,(-\sqrt{3}) + n\pi, \qquad n \text{ any integer.}$$

Example 6. Solve the equation $\cos^2\theta - \sin^2\theta = \cos\theta$ for θ.

Solution. By Eq. (7) the left member becomes

$$\cos^2\theta - \sin^2\theta = \cos^2\theta - (1 - \cos^2\theta) = 2\cos^2\theta - 1,$$

and the equation reduces to

$$2\cos^2\theta - \cos\theta - 1 = 0.$$

This is an equation of quadratic form, quadratic in $\cos\theta$, and can be solved by factoring. Thus, we obtain

$$(2\cos\theta + 1)(\cos\theta - 1) = 0.$$

We may equate each factor to zero, and obtain as the values of $\cos\theta$,

$$\cos\theta = -\tfrac{1}{2}, \qquad \cos\theta = 1.$$

The solutions are then

$$\theta = \arccos\left(-\tfrac{1}{2}\right) = 120^\circ + n\cdot 360^\circ \quad \text{or} \quad 240^\circ + n\cdot 360^\circ,$$

and

$$\theta = \arccos 1 = n\cdot 360^\circ, \quad \text{for any integer } n.$$

EXERCISE GROUP 10–1

In each of Exercises 1–10, reduce the first expression to the second, by use of the fundamental identities.

1. $\cos^2\theta\,(1 + \cot^2\theta),\ \cot^2\theta$
2. $\cos^2\theta\,(\sec^2\theta - 1),\ \sin^2\theta$
3. $\sec^2\theta\,(1 - \sin^2\theta),\ 1$
4. $\cos\theta\,(\sec\theta - \cos\theta),\ \sin^2\theta$
5. $\dfrac{\csc\theta}{\cos\theta} - \dfrac{\cos\theta}{\sin\theta},\ \tan\theta$
6. $\tan^2\theta\left(\dfrac{1 - \sin^2\theta}{1 - \cos^2\theta}\right), 1$
7. $2 + \tan^2\theta + \cot^2\theta,\ \sec^2\theta\csc^2\theta$
8. $\cot^2\theta - \cos^2\theta,\ \cot^2\theta\cos^2\theta$
9. $\sec\theta + \csc\theta,\ \dfrac{\sin\theta + \cos\theta}{\sin\theta\cos\theta}$
10. $\tan^2\theta - \cot^2\theta,\ \dfrac{\sin^2\theta - \cos^2\theta}{\sin^2\theta\cos^2\theta}$

Prove that the equations in Exercises 11–50 are identities.

11. $\cos\theta\cot\theta + \sin\theta = \csc\theta$
12. $\dfrac{\cos\theta\tan\theta + \sin\theta}{\tan\theta} = 2\cos\theta$
13. $\sin\theta\tan\theta + \cos\theta = \sec\theta$
14. $\sec^4\theta - \tan^4\theta = \sec^2\theta + \tan^2\theta$
15. $(1 - \cos\theta)(\csc\theta + \cot\theta) = \sin\theta$
16. $(\sec\theta - \tan\theta)(\csc\theta + 1) = \cot\theta$
17. $\sec^2\theta + \tan^2\theta + 1 = \dfrac{2}{\cos^2\theta}$
18. $\dfrac{\sin^2\theta}{1 + \cos\theta} = 1 - \cos\theta$
19. $\dfrac{\sin\theta + \cos\theta}{\cos\theta - \sin\theta} = \dfrac{\cot\theta + 1}{\cot\theta - 1}$
20. $\dfrac{\cos\theta}{\cos\theta - \sin\theta} = \dfrac{1}{1 - \tan\theta}$
21. $\dfrac{\csc^2\theta}{\csc\theta + 1} = \dfrac{\csc\theta - 1}{\cos^2\theta}$
22. $\dfrac{\cos^2\theta}{\cos^2\theta + \sin\theta} = \dfrac{\cot\theta}{\cot\theta + \sec\theta}$
23. $\dfrac{\csc\theta + 1}{\csc\theta - 1} = \dfrac{1 + \sin\theta}{1 - \sin\theta}$
24. $\dfrac{\cos\theta}{1 + \sin\theta} = \dfrac{1 - \sin\theta}{\cos\theta}$
25. $\dfrac{\cos\theta}{\cos\theta + \sin\theta} = \dfrac{\cot\theta}{1 + \cot\theta}$
26. $\dfrac{\cos\theta}{\csc\theta + 1} + \dfrac{\cos\theta}{\csc\theta - 1} = 2\tan\theta$
27. $\dfrac{1}{1 + \cot\theta} = \dfrac{\sin\theta}{\sin\theta + \cos\theta}$
28. $\dfrac{\sin\theta}{1 + \cos\theta} = \dfrac{1 - \cos\theta}{\cos\theta\tan\theta}$
29. $\sin^2\theta\cos^2\theta\,(\sec^2\theta + \csc^2\theta) = 1$
30. $\tan^2\theta\,(1 + \tan^2\theta) = \sin^2\theta\sec^4\theta$

31. $\csc^2\theta(\sec^2\theta - 1) = \sec^2\theta$

32. $\cot^2\theta - \cos^2\theta = \cot^2\theta\cos^2\theta$

33. $\sin^4\theta - \cos^4\theta = 2\sin^2\theta - 1$

34. $1 + \tan^2\theta\sec^2\theta = \sec^4\theta - \tan^2\theta$

35. $\dfrac{\tan\theta}{\csc\theta - \cot\theta} - \dfrac{\sin\theta}{\csc\theta + \cot\theta} = \sec\theta + \cos\theta$

36. $\dfrac{\cos\theta}{1 + \sin\theta} + \dfrac{1 + \sin\theta}{\cos\theta} = 2\sec\theta$

37. $\dfrac{\csc^4\theta - 1}{\cot^2\theta} = 2 + \cot^2\theta$

38. $\sec^4\theta - 2\sec^2\theta\tan^2\theta = 1 - \tan^4\theta$

39. $\dfrac{\sin^4\theta - \cos^4\theta}{1 - \cot^4\theta} = \sin^4\theta$

40. $\csc\theta + \cot\theta = \dfrac{\sin\theta}{1 - \cos\theta}$

41. $\sec^2\theta\cot^2\theta - \cos^2\theta\csc^2\theta = 1$

42. $\tan\theta + \cot\theta = \cot\theta\sec^2\theta$

43. $\sec\theta + \tan\theta = \dfrac{\cos\theta}{1 - \sin\theta}$

44. $1 - \cos\theta = \dfrac{\sin\theta}{\csc\theta + \cot\theta}$

45. $\sin^6\theta + \cos^6\theta = 1 - 3\sin^2\theta\cos^2\theta$

46. $\sec^6\theta - \tan^6\theta = 1 + 3\sec^2\theta\tan^2\theta$

47. $\csc\theta - \cot\theta = 2\csc\theta - \dfrac{1}{\csc\theta - \cot\theta}$

48. $\dfrac{\tan^2\theta - 2}{\tan^2\theta + 2} = \dfrac{1 - 3\cos^2\theta}{1 + \cos^2\theta}$

49. $\sin^2\theta(2 + \tan^2\theta) = \sec^2\theta - \cos^2\theta$

50. $\sin^2\theta(2 + \tan^2\theta) = \sin^2\theta + \tan^2\theta$

In Exercises 51–58, express the value of each of the quantities without radicals, under the given substitution ($0 \leqq \theta < \pi/2$).

51. $\sqrt{1 - x^2}$ if $x = \sin\theta$

52. $\sqrt{1 + 9x^2}$ if $3x = \tan\theta$

53. $\sqrt{3 - 2x^2}$ if $\sqrt{2}\,x = \sqrt{3}\sin\theta$

54. $\sqrt{6x - x^2}$ if $x = 3 + 3\sin\theta$

55. $\sqrt{4x + x^2}$ if $x = -2 + 2\sec\theta$

56. $(a^{2/3} - x^{2/3})^{3/2}$ if $x = a\cos^3\theta$

57. $\sqrt{x^2 + 8x - 9}$ if $x = -4 + 5\sec\theta$

58. $\sqrt{12 + 4x - x^2}$ if $x = 2 + 4\sin\theta$

In each of Exercises 59–68, solve for x in terms of arcsin, etc., by use of the fundamental identities.

59. $2\cos^2 x = \cos x$

60. $\sqrt{2}\sin^2 x = \sin x$

61. $\cos x = \cot x$

62. $2\cos^2 x - \cos x = 1$

63. $1 - 2\cos^2 x = \sin x$

64. $\sec^2 x - 1 = \sqrt{3}\tan x$

65. $\cos x = \dfrac{1 + \cos x}{2}$

66. $\sin x - \cos x = 0$

67. $\cos^2 x - \sin^2 x = \cos x$

68. $3(\tan^2 x + \tan x) = \sqrt{3}(1 + \tan x)$

10-3 REDUCTION FORMULAS

A number of formulas that were previously mentioned fall into a general category. For example, in Section 7-2 we had the formula $\sin(2\pi + x) = \sin x$. In Section 3-9 the formula $\sin(\pi/2 - x) = \cos x$ was obtained. In Section 7-1 we showed that $\sin(\pi - x) = \sin x$, at least for x between 0 and $\pi/2$. The discussion there also implied formulas such as $\cos(\pi/2 + x) = -\sin x$. Indeed, there is a wide variety of such formulas, each involving a number of the form $n\pi/2 \pm x$ (n is an integer, positive, negative, or zero), and expressing a trigonometric function of such a number as a function of x alone. The purpose of this section is to present a general procedure for deriving such formulas, and in the following section we shall prove that the formulas thus obtained are valid with no restriction on the magnitude of the number.

Let x, y, r, with $r \neq 0$, be the coordinates and polar distance of some point on the terminal side of an angle θ in standard position. The reference angle (Section 3-5) for θ is in Q_1, and it is clear that $|x|$, $|y|$, r are the corresponding quantities of some point on the terminal side of this angle in Q_1. It follows from the definition of the trigonometric functions that

Any function of θ is numerically equal to the same-named function of its reference angle, (10)

that is, the same-named functions of any angle and its reference angle differ at most in sign. For example, we have $\sec\theta = r/x$, which may be positive or negative, but the secant of the reference angle is $r/|x|$, which is always positive.

When (10) is applied, there remains only the determination of the proper sign. Since any function of the reference angle is positive, the required sign is simply the one determined by the sign of the given function for the quadrant in which the given angle lies.

Example 1. By (10) we have $\cos 247° = \pm\cos 67°$. But $\cos 67° > 0$, and, since 247° is in Q_3, $\cos 247° < 0$. Hence the minus sign applies, and

$$\cos 247° = -\cos 67°.$$

Example 2. $\tan(-592°) = -\tan 52°$, the minus sign applying since $-592°$ is in Q_2.

Example 3. $\cos(-83°) = \cos 83°$, since $-83°$ is in Q_4, and in Q_4 the cosine function is positive.

Related to (10) is a variety of so-called *reduction formulas* involving functions of numbers of the type $n\pi/2 \pm x$, where n is an integer, positive, negative, or zero. For example, we have seen that $\sin(\pi - x) = \sin x$ if x is between 0 and $\pi/2$. This follows also from (10) upon determination of the proper sign. It is also true, and will be proved in the following section, that *this relation holds for all values of x*. Similarly, the relation $\cos(\pi/2 + x) = -\sin x$ holds for all values of x. Both relations are examples of the following general theorem (to be proved in the next section).

Theorem. *Any trigonometric function of $n(\pi/2) \pm x$ is equal to*

(a) $\pm$ *(the same-named function of x), if n is even,*
(b) $\pm$ *(the corresponding cofunction of x), if n is odd,*

where, for a given integer n, the appropriate sign in the right member applies for all values of x for which the functions are defined.

In applying this theorem to determine any reduction formula, it is necessary to note the multiple of $\pi/2$ which appears, and then to ascertain the appropriate sign. The following examples will make this clear.

Example 4. Express $\tan(x - 3\pi/2)$ as a trigonometric function of x.

Solution. By the theorem we have at once, since an odd multiple of $\pi/2$ appears,

$$\tan\left(x - \frac{3\pi}{2}\right) = \pm\cot x,$$

where the applicable sign holds for all values of x except multiples of π. Since the sign that is determined by any value of x will then apply for all values of x, we may choose a value of x in Q_1 to make that determination. Accordingly, if $0 < x < \pi/2$, we have $\cot x > 0$; but then $x - 3\pi/2$ is in Q_2, and the tangent of an angle in Q_2 is negative. Hence the minus sign applies, and

$$\tan\left(x - \frac{3\pi}{2}\right) = -\cot x.$$

Thus, the sign in any of these *reduction formulas* can be determined by considering x in the range $0 < x < \pi/2$, (that is, as a positive, acute angle), and having been obtained in this manner, the sign applies generally.

Example 5. Express $\cos(\pi - x)$ as a trigonometric function of x.

Solution. By the above theorem, the multiple of $\pi/2$ being even, we have

$$\cos(\pi - x) = \pm\cos x.$$

If $0 < x < \pi/2$, then $\pi - x$ is in Q_2, $\cos(\pi - x) < 0$, and $\cos x > 0$. Hence the minus sign applies, and

$$\cos(\pi - x) = -\cos x.$$

The reduction formulas as obtained are of course not restricted to any range. Thus, if $x = 7\pi/4$, the result of Example 5 becomes

$$\cos(-3\pi/4) = -\cos(7\pi/4),$$

which can also be verified directly.

Example 6. The theorem of this section applies equally well when $n = 0$, and yields the following identities:

$$\begin{aligned} \sin(-x) &= -\sin x, & \cos(-x) &= \cos x, \\ \tan(-x) &= -\tan x, & \cot(-x) &= -\cot x, \\ \sec(-x) &= \sec x, & \csc(-x) &= -\csc x. \end{aligned}$$

The formulas of Example 6 express the oddness or evenness of the trigonometric functions (Section 7–5). Thus, $\sin x$, $\tan x$, $\cot x$, and $\csc x$ *are odd functions of* x, while $\cos x$ and $\sec x$ *are even functions of* x.

Example 7. Express $\cos 219^\circ\, 32'$ as the cosine of a positive acute angle.

Solution. The reference angle is $219^\circ\, 32' - 180^\circ = 39^\circ\, 32'$. By (10) we obtain $\cos 219^\circ\, 32' = \pm\cos 39^\circ\, 32'$. But $\cos 39^\circ\, 32' > 0$, and we know $\cos 219^\circ\, 32' < 0$ since $219^\circ\, 32'$ is in Q_3; hence $\cos 219^\circ\, 32' = -\cos 39^\circ\, 32'$.

Example 8. Express $\cos 219^\circ\, 32'$ as the coratio of a positive acute angle.

Solution. Since $219^\circ\, 32' = 3 \times 90^\circ - 50^\circ\, 28'$, we have by (10), $\cos 219^\circ\, 32' = \pm\sin 50^\circ\, 28'$. To determine the proper sign we note that $\cos 219^\circ\, 32' < 0$ and $\sin 50^\circ\, 28' > 0$. Hence the minus sign applies, and

$$\cos 219^\circ\, 32' = -\sin 50^\circ\, 28'.$$

10–4 PROOF OF THE THEOREM OF SECTION 10–3

We shall discuss the trigonometric functions in a general way, and shall use $f(x)$ here as a composite designation of all the trigonometric functions, so that in what follows $f(x)$ can mean $\sin x$, $\cos x$, $\tan x$, $\cot x$, $\sec x$, or $\csc x$. The graphs of these functions represent a visual account of the variation of the functions as discussed in Section 7–1, for all values of x. In the ensuing discussion of this section repeated reference should be made to the graphs of the trigonometric functions in Section 7–3. By Section 7–4 the function $f(x - \pi)$ represents a translation of each graph by the amount π in the positive x-direction. For the tangent and cotangent curves this translation again gives the original curve, and we have for these two functions the relation $f(x - \pi) = f(x)$. For each of the other trigonometric functions the translation gives a curve which is the reflection of the original curve in the x-axis, and for these functions we have $f(x - \pi) = -f(x)$. Hence we have in general

$$f(x - \pi) = \pm f(x), \tag{11}$$

where the sign is determined by the function. For each trigonometric function one of the signs holds in Eq. (11) for all values of x.

It was stated in Section 3–9 that the six trigonometric ratios fall into three *pairs of coratios*, which are the sine and cosine, the tangent and cotangent, and the secant and cosecant. *A similar statement applies to the trigonometric functions.* We shall denote the cofunction of any trigonometric function $f(x)$ by co$f(x)$. By Section 7–4 again the function $f(x - \pi/2)$ represents a translation of the corresponding graph of $f(x)$ by the amount $\pi/2$ in the positive x-direction. From the graphs of the functions we see that for the cosine and secant curves, $f(x - \pi/2) = \text{co}f(x)$, while for the others, $f(x - \pi/2) = -\text{co}f(x)$. In general, then, we have for each of the trigonometric functions $f(x)$ the relation

$$f(x - \pi/2) = \pm\text{co}f(x) \tag{12}$$

where, again, one of the signs holds for each $f(x)$ for all values of x.

Let us now consider a function of the form $f(x + n\pi)$, where n is any integer. If n is even, the periodicity (Section 7–2) of $f(x)$ shows that $f(x + n\pi) = f(x)$. If n is odd, we write

$$\begin{aligned} f(x + n\pi) &= f[x - \pi + (n + 1)\pi] \\ &= f(x - \pi) \quad \text{[by the periodicity of } f(x)\text{]}; \end{aligned}$$

and by (11) we obtain the relation

$$f(x + n\pi) = \pm f(x). \tag{13}$$

Hence (13) holds whether n is odd or even. The significant aspect of (13) is that for a given trigonometric function the applicable sign holds for all values of the variable for which the function is defined, since the same generality applies to the equations used in the derivation of (13). Thus, *the relation* (13) *is an identity.*

Now let us consider the function $f(x + n\pi/2)$, where n is an *odd* integer, positive or negative. We may write this as

$$\begin{aligned} f\left(x + n\frac{\pi}{2}\right) &= f\left[x - \frac{\pi}{2} + (n + 1)\frac{\pi}{2}\right] \\ &= \pm f\left(x - \frac{\pi}{2}\right); \end{aligned}$$

the second equality follows from (13), since $n + 1$ is even, and $(n + 1)(\pi/2)$ is a multiple of π. Applying (12) to the last result, we obtain

$$f\left(x + n\frac{\pi}{2}\right) = \pm\text{co}f(x), \tag{14}$$

with the same generality as in (13) regarding the sign.

Finally, if we set $x = -y$, Eq. (13) becomes

$$f(-y + n\pi) = \pm f(-y),$$

and Eq. (14) becomes, if n is odd,

$$f\left(-y + n\frac{\pi}{2}\right) = \pm\text{co}f(-y).$$

We know that each trigonometric function is either odd or even (Section 10-3). Hence

$$f(-y) = \pm f(y), \qquad \text{co}f(-y) = \pm \text{co}f(y),$$

and we obtain the following formulas, similar to (13) and (14):

$$f(-y + n\pi) = \pm f(y), \qquad \text{for any integer } n;$$
$$f\left(-y + n\frac{\pi}{2}\right) = \pm \text{co}f(y), \quad \text{for any odd integer } n.$$

The results that have been proved may now be combined in the following restatement of the theorem of Section 10-3.

Theorem. *If $f(x)$ is any trigonometric function, then*

$$f\left(\pm x + n\frac{\pi}{2}\right) = \begin{cases} \pm f(x), & \text{if } n \text{ is even}, \\ \pm \text{co}f(x), & \text{if } n \text{ is odd}, \end{cases} \tag{15}$$

where, for a given integer n, the appropriate sign in the right members applies for all values of x for which the functions are defined.

EXERCISE GROUP 10-2

Express the given quantity in each of Exercises 1-21 in terms of (a) the same trigonometric ratio of the reference angle, (b) a trigonometric ratio of an angle between 0° and 45°, and (c) the coratio of a positive acute angle.

1. cos 156°
2. cot 149°
3. csc 237°
4. cos 419°
5. sec 291°
6. tan 98°
7. cot 632°
8. cos 814°
9. sin 536°
10. tan (−127°)
11. sin (−218°)
12. csc (−620°)
13. sin 167° 13′
14. sin 314° 20′
15. sec 219° 8′
16. tan 143° 23′
17. tan 296° 47′
18. cot (−123° 13′)
19. sec (−241° 30′)
20. cos (−451° 12′)
21. cot (−88° 17′)

Verify each of the statements in Exercises 22-39.

22. $\sin(90° - \theta) = \cos\theta$
23. $\cos(90° - \theta) = \sin\theta$
24. $\tan(90° - \theta) = \cot\theta$
25. $\cot(90° - \theta) = \tan\theta$
26. $\sec(90° - \theta) = \csc\theta$
27. $\csc(90° - \theta) = \sec\theta$
28. $\sin\left(\theta + \frac{3\pi}{2}\right) = -\cos\theta$
29. $\sin(\theta + \pi) = -\sin\theta$
30. $\cos\left(\theta + \frac{5\pi}{2}\right) = -\sin\theta$
31. $\cos(\theta + 3\pi) = -\cos\theta$

32. $\sin\left(\theta - \frac{\pi}{2}\right) = -\cos\theta$ 33. $\cos\left(\theta - \frac{3\pi}{2}\right) = -\sin\theta$

34. $\sin(\theta - 3\pi) = -\sin\theta$ 35. $\cos(\theta - 5\pi) = -\cos\theta$

36. $\sin\left(\theta + \frac{n\pi}{2}\right) = (-1)^{(n-1)/2}\cos\theta$ (n an odd integer)

37. $\sin\left(\theta + \frac{n\pi}{2}\right) = (-1)^{n/2}\sin\theta$ (n an even integer)

38. $\cos\left(\theta + \frac{n\pi}{2}\right) = (-1)^{(n+1)/2}\sin\theta$ (n an odd integer)

39. $\cos\left(\theta + \frac{n\pi}{2}\right) = (-1)^{n/2}\cos\theta$ (n an even integer)

Express each of the following as a trigonometric ratio of θ and then verify each relation for (1) $\theta = 141°$, and (2) $\theta = -289°$.

40. $\sin(180° - \theta)$ 41. $\tan(270° - \theta)$ 42. $\sec(90° - \theta)$

43. $\tan(630° + \theta)$ 44. $\csc(90° + \theta)$ 45. $\cos(540° + \theta)$

46. $\tan(-180° - \theta)$ 47. $\cot(-270° + \theta)$ 48. $\cos(-270° - \theta)$

If $A + B + C = 180°$, prove the following statements.

49. $\sin A = \sin(B + C)$ 50. $\cos A = -\cos(B + C)$

51. $\tan A = -\tan(B + C)$ 52. $\cot A = -\cot(B + C)$

53. $\sec A = -\sec(B + C)$ 54. $\csc A = \csc(B + C)$

55. $\sin A = -\sin(2A + B + C)$ 56. $\sec B = -\sec(A + 2B + C)$

57. $\tan C = \tan(A + B + 2C)$ 58. $\cos A = \sin(\frac{3}{2}A + \frac{1}{2}B + \frac{1}{2}C)$

59. $\sin B = -\cos(\frac{1}{2}A + \frac{3}{2}B + \frac{1}{2}C)$ 60. $\sin(\frac{1}{2}A + B) = \cos\frac{1}{2}(B - C)$

61. $\cos(\frac{1}{2}B + C) = -\sin\frac{1}{2}(C - A)$ 62. $\cos\frac{1}{2}A = \sin\frac{1}{2}(B + C)$

63. $\tan\frac{1}{2}B = \cot\frac{1}{2}(A + C)$ 64. $\cot\frac{1}{2}C = \tan\frac{1}{2}(A + B)$

65. $\csc\frac{1}{2}A = \sec\frac{1}{2}(B + C)$ 66. $\sin\frac{1}{2}(A - B + C) = \cos B$

10–5 THE ADDITION FORMULAS

There are additional groups of identities which involve more than one angle, or multiples of an angle. The following are the *addition formulas*, which are identities involving two angles:

$$\boxed{\sin(A + B) = \sin A\cos B + \cos A\sin B,} \tag{16}$$

$$\boxed{\cos(A + B) = \cos A\cos B - \sin A\sin B,} \tag{17}$$

$$\boxed{\tan(A + B) = \frac{\tan A + \tan B}{1 - \tan A\tan B}.} \tag{18}$$

The corresponding formulas for functions of $A - B$ are

$$\sin(A - B) = \sin A \cos B - \cos A \sin B. \tag{19}$$

$$\cos(A - B) = \cos A \cos B + \sin A \sin B, \tag{20}$$

$$\tan(A - B) = \frac{\tan A - \tan B}{1 + \tan A \tan B}. \tag{21}$$

These identities will be established in the following section, without any restriction on the magnitudes of the angles. Here we wish to emphasize their application.

Example 1. Determine the values of $\sin(A + B)$, $\sin(A - B)$, $\cos(A + B)$, $\cos(A - B)$, $\tan(A + B)$, and $\tan(A - B)$ if $\cos A = -\frac{4}{5}$, A in Q_3 and $\tan B = -\frac{5}{12}$, B in Q_2.

Solution. Figure 10–1 shows an angle A in Q_3, and an angle B in Q_2. It follows that

$$\sin A = -\tfrac{3}{5}, \qquad \tan A = \tfrac{3}{4},$$
$$\sin B = \tfrac{5}{13}, \qquad \cos B = -\tfrac{12}{13}.$$

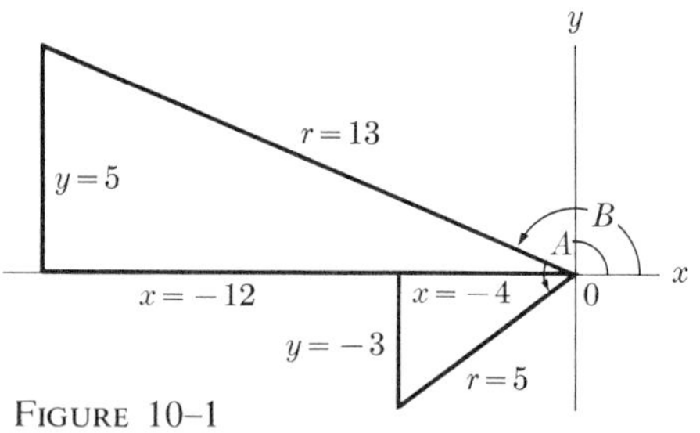

FIGURE 10–1

With the values for sin A, cos A, tan A, and sin B, cos B, tan B, we can substitute in formulas (16), (17), (18), (19), (20), and (21), to obtain

$$\sin(A + B) = \left(-\frac{3}{5}\right)\left(-\frac{12}{13}\right) + \left(-\frac{4}{5}\right)\left(\frac{5}{13}\right) = \frac{36 - 20}{65} = \frac{16}{65};$$

$$\sin(A - B) = \left(-\frac{3}{5}\right)\left(-\frac{12}{13}\right) - \left(-\frac{4}{5}\right)\left(\frac{5}{13}\right) = \frac{36 + 20}{65} = \frac{56}{65};$$

$$\cos(A + B) = \left(-\frac{4}{5}\right)\left(-\frac{12}{13}\right) - \left(-\frac{3}{5}\right)\left(\frac{5}{13}\right) = \frac{48 + 15}{65} = \frac{63}{65};$$

$$\cos(A - B) = \left(-\frac{4}{5}\right)\left(-\frac{12}{13}\right) + \left(-\frac{3}{5}\right)\left(\frac{5}{13}\right) = \frac{48 - 15}{65} = \frac{33}{65};$$

$$\tan(A + B) = \frac{\frac{3}{4} + \left(-\frac{5}{12}\right)}{1 - \left(\frac{3}{4}\right)\left(-\frac{5}{12}\right)} = \frac{\frac{9 - 5}{12}}{\frac{48 + 15}{48}} = \frac{1}{3}\cdot\frac{48}{63} = \frac{16}{63};$$

$$\tan(A - B) = \frac{\frac{3}{4} - \left(-\frac{5}{12}\right)}{1 + \left(\frac{3}{4}\right)\left(-\frac{5}{12}\right)} = \frac{\frac{9 + 5}{12}}{\frac{48 - 15}{48}} = \frac{7}{6}\cdot\frac{16}{11} = \frac{56}{33}.$$

Of course tan $(A + B)$ and tan $(A - B)$ can be found more easily by the ratio identities after sin $(A + B)$, cos $(A + B)$, sin $(A - B)$, and cos $(A - B)$ are known, but the example illustrates the use of the addition formulas if the other functions are not known.

Example 2. Use the appropriate addition formula to obtain the exact value of $\cos(3\pi/2 - \pi/3)$.

Solution. With the use of formula (20) it follows that

$$\cos\left(\frac{3\pi}{2} - \frac{\pi}{3}\right) = \cos\frac{3\pi}{2}\cos\frac{\pi}{3} + \sin\frac{3\pi}{2}\sin\frac{\pi}{3}$$

$$= 0 \cdot \frac{1}{2} + (-1)\cdot\frac{\sqrt{3}}{2} = -\frac{\sqrt{3}}{2}.$$

Example 3. Use the appropriate addition formula to prove the identity

$$\sin 3\theta \cos\theta - \cos 3\theta \sin\theta = \sin 2\theta.$$

Solution. If in formula (19) we set $A = 3\theta$ and $B = \theta$ we have

$$\sin(3\theta - \theta) = \sin 3\theta\cos\theta - \cos 3\theta\sin\theta,$$

which gives the desired identity, since $3\theta - \theta = 2\theta$.

Example 4. Prove the identity

$$\frac{\tan(C - D) + \tan D}{1 - \tan(C - D)\tan D} = \tan C.$$

Solution. In formula (18), let $A = C - D$ and $B = D$. Then we have

$$\tan[(C - D) + D] = \tan C = \frac{\tan(C - D) + \tan D}{1 - \tan(C - D)\tan D}.$$

10–6 PROOF OF THE ADDITION FORMULAS FOR GENERAL ANGLES

In proving the addition formulas we shall first give a general proof of the addition formula (20) for cos $(A - B)$. The other addition formulas will then be derived from this one. If we set $B = \theta$, $A = \theta + \phi$, the formula for cos $(A - B)$ becomes

$$\cos\phi = \cos(\theta + \phi)\cos\theta + \sin(\theta + \phi)\sin\theta, \tag{22}$$

which is the form in which we shall prove the formula.

It is clear that if ϕ is a multiple of 2π, the above relation becomes, by the periodicity of the sine and cosine functions, $1 = \cos^2\theta + \sin^2\theta$, which we know to be valid. If ϕ is not a multiple of 2π, we may add to ϕ a suitable positive, negative, or zero multiple k of 2π so that $\alpha = \phi + 2k\pi$ is an angle between 0 and 2π. The angle θ is now drawn in standard position in a coordinate system, and α is drawn with its vertex at 0, and initial side on the terminal side of θ. We also draw a circle

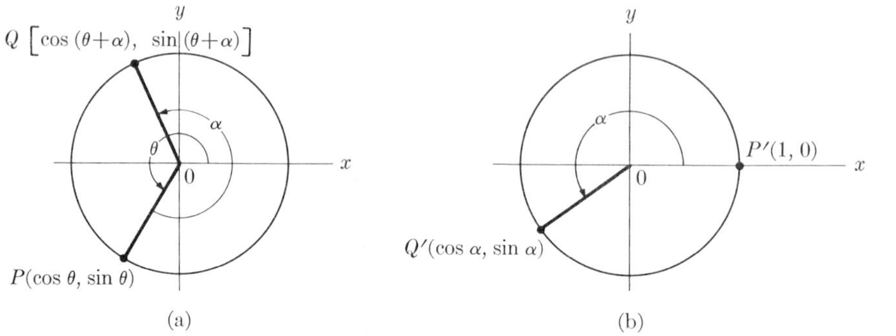

FIGURE 10–2

of radius 1 with center at 0. The point P in Fig. 10–2(a) on the terminal side of θ then has coordinates $(\cos\theta, \sin\theta)$, and the point Q on the terminal side of $\theta + \alpha$ has coordinates $[\cos(\theta+\alpha), \sin(\theta+\alpha)]$. Now rotate triangle OPQ through the angle $-\theta$, to assume the position $OP'Q'$ in Fig. 10–2(b), with (1,0) as the coordinates of P' and $(\cos\alpha, \sin\alpha)$ as the coordinates of Q'. Now, the lengths of PQ and $P'Q'$ are equal and so are their squares. Applying the distance formula of Section 2–4 in each case, we have

$$(\cos\alpha - 1)^2 + \sin^2\alpha = [\cos(\theta+\alpha) - \cos\theta]^2 + [\sin(\theta+\alpha) - \sin\theta]^2$$

or

$$\begin{aligned}\cos^2\alpha - 2\cos\alpha + 1 + \sin^2\alpha &\\ &= \cos^2(\theta+\alpha) - 2\cos(\theta+\alpha)\cos\theta + \cos^2\theta \\ &+ \sin^2(\theta+\alpha) - 2\sin(\theta+\alpha)\sin\theta + \sin^2\theta.\end{aligned}$$

If we apply the squares identity (7) to α on the left, and $\theta + \alpha$ and θ on the right, we obtain

$$\cos\alpha = \cos(\theta+\alpha)\cos\theta + \sin(\theta+\alpha)\sin\theta. \tag{23}$$

Now, $\cos(\theta+\alpha) = \cos(\theta+\phi+2k\pi) = \cos(\theta+\phi)$, by the periodicity of the cosine function, and similarly $\sin(\theta+\alpha) = \sin(\theta+\phi)$ and $\cos\alpha = \cos\phi$. Substitution of them in (23) gives (22), and the proof of (20) is complete.

To prove (19) we first obtain some incidental relations from (20). Let $B = \pi/2$ in (20). Since $\cos(\pi/2) = 0$ and $\sin(\pi/2) = 1$, we obtain

$$\cos\left(A - \frac{\pi}{2}\right) = \sin A, \quad \text{for any angle } A. \tag{24}$$

In (24) let $A = B - \pi/2$; we get $\cos(B - \pi) = \sin(B - \pi/2)$. But by (20) again, $\cos(B - \pi) = -\cos B$. Hence, it follows that

$$\sin\left(B - \frac{\pi}{2}\right) = -\cos B, \quad \text{for any angle } B. \tag{25}$$

To derive (19), we replace A by $A - \pi/2$ in (20), which then becomes

$$\cos\left(A - \frac{\pi}{2} - B\right) = \cos\left(A - \frac{\pi}{2}\right)\cos B + \sin\left(A - \frac{\pi}{2}\right)\sin B. \tag{26}$$

But by (24) and (25), $\cos(A - B - \pi/2) = \sin(A - B)$, $\cos(A - \pi/2) = \sin A$, $\sin(A - \pi/2) = -\cos A$, and (26) becomes

$$\sin(A - B) = \sin A \cos B - \cos A \sin B,$$

which is (19).

We derive (21) by dividing the members of (19) by the corresponding members of (20) as follows, if $A - B$ is not an odd multiple of $\pi/2$:

$$\begin{aligned}\tan(A - B) &= \frac{\sin(A - B)}{\cos(A - B)} = \frac{\sin A \cos B - \cos A \sin B}{\cos A \cos B + \sin A \sin B}\\ &= \frac{(\sin A \cos B)/(\cos A \cos B) - (\cos A \sin B)/(\cos A \cos B)}{1 + (\sin A \sin B)/(\cos A \cos B)}\\ &= \frac{\tan A - \tan B}{1 + \tan A \tan B}.\end{aligned}$$

Letting $A = 0$ in (19), (20), and (21), or by Example 6 of Section 10–3, we obtain

$$\sin(-B) = -\sin B, \qquad \cos(-B) = \cos B, \qquad \tan(-B) = -\tan B. \tag{27}$$

We can now obtain (16), (17), and (18), by replacing B by $-B$ in (19), (20), and (21) and using (27). For example, we have

$$\begin{aligned}\sin(A + B) = \sin[A - (-B)] &= \sin A \cos(-B) - \cos A \sin(-B)\\ &= \sin A \cos B + \cos A \sin B\end{aligned}$$

and (16) is established. Formulas (17) and (18) follow similarly.

EXERCISE GROUP 10–3

Find the values of $\sin(A + B)$, $\sin(A - B)$, $\cos(A + B)$, $\cos(A - B)$, $\tan(A + B)$, and $\tan(A - B)$ under the conditions stated in each of Exercises 1–6.

1. $\cos A = \frac{3}{5}$, A in Q_1; $\sin B = \frac{5}{13}$, B in Q_2
2. $\cot A = \frac{3}{4}$, A in Q_3; $\cos B = \frac{12}{13}$, B in Q_4
3. $\sin A = -\frac{7}{25}$, A in Q_4; $\sin B = \frac{4}{5}$, B in Q_2
4. $\cos A = -\frac{5}{13}$, A in Q_2; $\cot B = \frac{7}{24}$, B in Q_3
5. $\tan A = \frac{12}{5}$, A in Q_3; $\sin B = -\frac{4}{5}$, B in Q_3
6. $\cot A = -\frac{5}{12}$, A in Q_2; $\tan B = -\frac{24}{7}$, B in Q_4

Apply the addition formulas in Exercises 7–18 to obtain the exact value in each case.

7. $\cos(60^\circ - 45^\circ)$
8. $\sin(2\pi/3 - \pi/3)$
9. $\sin(\pi/2 - \pi/6)$
10. $\cos(270^\circ + 30^\circ)$
11. $\tan(135^\circ - 60^\circ)$
12. $\tan(\pi/4 - \pi/6)$
13. $\cos(270^\circ - 90^\circ)$
14. $\sin(\pi - \pi/6)$
15. $\tan(\pi/4 + \pi/6)$
16. $\tan(360^\circ - 135^\circ)$
17. $\cos(3\pi/2 + \pi/3)$
18. $\sin(450^\circ + 60^\circ)$

Use the addition formulas to prove the identities in each of Exercises 19–39.

19. $\cos(90^\circ + \theta) = -\sin\theta$
20. $\sin(180^\circ + \theta) = -\sin\theta$
21. $\tan(270^\circ + \theta) = -\cot\theta$
22. $\cos(2\pi - \theta) = \cos\theta$
23. $\sin(\pi/2 - \theta) = \cos\theta$
24. $\tan(180^\circ - \theta) = -\tan\theta$
25. $\cos(\pi/4 + \theta) = \dfrac{\cos\theta - \sin\theta}{\sqrt{2}}$
26. $\sin(\pi/3 + \theta) = \dfrac{\sqrt{3}\cos\theta + \sin\theta}{2}$
27. $\sin(240^\circ - \theta) = \dfrac{-\sqrt{3}\cos\theta + \sin\theta}{2}$
28. $\cos(300^\circ - \theta) = \dfrac{\cos\theta - \sqrt{3}\sin\theta}{2}$
29. $\tan(120^\circ - \theta) = \dfrac{\sqrt{3} + \tan\theta}{\sqrt{3}\tan\theta - 1}$
30. $\tan(225^\circ + \theta) = \dfrac{1 + \tan\theta}{1 - \tan\theta}$
31. $\cos 2\theta \cos 3\theta - \sin 2\theta \sin 3\theta = \cos 5\theta$
32. $\sin\theta \cos 2\theta + \cos\theta \sin 2\theta = \sin 3\theta$
33. $\cos 3\theta \cos 2\theta + \sin 3\theta \sin 2\theta = \cos\theta$
34. $\sin 2\theta \cos\theta - \cos 2\theta \sin\theta = \sin\theta$
35. $\sin(A + B)\cos B - \cos(A + B)\sin B = \sin A$ [*Hint*: Let $A + B = \theta$.]
36. $\cos(A - B)\cos B - \sin(A - B)\sin B = \cos A$
37. $\dfrac{\tan(A + B) - \tan B}{1 + \tan(A + B)\tan B} = \tan A$
38. $\sec\theta \sec 2\theta = \csc\theta \tan 2\theta - \sec\theta$
39. $\csc\theta(\tan 3\theta - \tan 2\theta) = \sec 2\theta \sec 3\theta$
40. Find $\tan(A - B)$ if $\tan A = \dfrac{x + ky}{kx - y}$ and $\tan B = \dfrac{y}{x}$.
41. Find $\tan(x + y)$ if $\tan x = \dfrac{a}{1 + a}$ and $\tan y = \dfrac{1}{1 + 2a}$.
42. If $\tan A + \tan B + \tan C = \tan A \tan B \tan C$, show that

$$\tan 2A + \tan 2B + \tan 2C = \tan 2A \tan 2B \tan 2C.$$

43. Use the result of Exercise 42 to show that if

$$x + y + z = xyz,$$

then

$$\frac{2x}{1 - x^2} + \frac{2y}{1 - y^2} + \frac{2z}{1 - z^2} = \frac{2x}{1 - x^2} \cdot \frac{2y}{1 - y^2} \cdot \frac{2z}{1 - z^2} \cdot$$

Derive the formulas displayed in Exercises 44 and 45.

44. $\cot (A + B) = \dfrac{\cot A \cot B - 1}{\cot A + \cot B}$

45. $\cot (A - B) = \dfrac{\cot A \cot B + 1}{\cot B - \cot A}$

46. Prove that: Arctan 1 = Arctan $\frac{1}{2}$ + Arctan $\frac{1}{3}$.

47. Prove that: Arctan 1 = Arctan $\frac{3}{4}$ + Arctan $\frac{1}{7}$.

10–7 THE DOUBLE-ANGLE FORMULAS

By setting $B = A$ in the addition formulas (16), (17), and (18) of Section 10–5, the *double-angle formulas* are obtained:

$$\boxed{\sin 2A = 2 \sin A \cos A,} \tag{28}$$

$$\boxed{\cos 2A = \cos^2 A - \sin^2 A,} \tag{29a}$$

$$\boxed{\cos 2A = 1 - 2 \sin^2 A,} \qquad \text{[by (7)]} \tag{29b}$$

$$\boxed{\cos 2A = 2 \cos^2 A - 1,} \tag{29c}$$

$$\boxed{\tan 2A = \frac{2 \tan A}{1 - \tan^2 A} \cdot} \tag{30}$$

For example, to prove (29a) we have

$$\cos 2A = \cos (A + A) = \cos A \cos A - \sin A \sin A = \cos^2 A - \sin^2 A.$$

These formulas possess a generality with regard to the angle which is perhaps not readily apparent. For example, if $A = \theta/2$, formula (28) gives

$$\sin \theta = 2 \sin \frac{\theta}{2} \cos \frac{\theta}{2},$$

and with $A = 2\theta$, formula (29a) becomes

$$\cos 4\theta = \cos^2 2\theta - \sin^2 2\theta.$$

10–8 THE HALF-ANGLE FORMULAS

Let formula (29b) be solved for sin A, and let A be replaced by $A/2$. There results, at once, the formula,

$$\boxed{\sin \frac{A}{2} = \pm\sqrt{\frac{1 - \cos A}{2}}\,;} \tag{31}$$

a similar procedure with (29c) gives

$$\boxed{\cos \frac{A}{2} = \pm\sqrt{\frac{1 + \cos A}{2}}\,;} \tag{32}$$

and division of the members of (31) by the corresponding members of (32) yields

$$\boxed{\tan \frac{A}{2} = \pm\sqrt{\frac{1 - \cos A}{1 + \cos A}}\,.} \tag{33}$$

The three formulas thus derived are known as the *half-angle formulas*. In a sense they reverse the processes of the double-angle formulas, and they possess the same kind of generality with regard to the angle.

An alternative form of (33), involving no radical, may be obtained as follows, the reasons for the steps to be supplied by the student:

$$\tan (A/2) = \frac{\sin (A/2)}{\cos (A/2)} = \frac{2 \sin (A/2) \cos (A/2)}{2 \cos^2 (A/2)},$$

so that we obtain the formula

$$\boxed{\tan \frac{A}{2} = \frac{\sin A}{1 + \cos A} = \frac{1 - \cos A}{\sin A}\,.} \tag{34}$$

The advantage of (34) over (33) is the lack of ambiguity of sign.

Example 1. Find the exact values of sin $(\theta/2)$, cos 2θ, and tan 3θ, if $\sin \theta = -\frac{24}{25}$, with θ in Q_3.

Solution. Figure 10–3 shows an angle θ drawn in standard position. It follows that

$$\cos \theta = -\tfrac{7}{25}, \qquad \tan \theta = \tfrac{24}{7}.$$

Then from formula (31) we have

$$\sin \frac{\theta}{2} = \pm\sqrt{\frac{1 - (-\frac{7}{25})}{2}} = \pm\sqrt{\frac{16}{25}} = \pm\frac{4}{5}.$$

Either sign may apply, since, with θ in Q_3, $\theta/2$ may be in Q_2 or in Q_4. (If θ is in Q_3, then $\theta = \alpha + 2n\pi$ where $\pi < \alpha < 3\pi/2$, n an integer. Hence

$$\frac{\theta}{2} = \frac{\alpha}{2} + n\pi,$$

where

$$\frac{\pi}{2} < \frac{\alpha}{2} < \frac{3\pi}{4}\Big).$$

Using formula (29c), we have

$$\cos 2\theta = 2(-\tfrac{7}{25})^2 - 1 = \tfrac{98}{625} - 1 = -\tfrac{527}{625}.$$

Finally, with $A = 2\theta$ and $B = \theta$ formula (18) gives

$$\tan(2\theta + \theta) = \tan 3\theta = \frac{\tan 2\theta + \tan\theta}{1 - \tan 2\theta \tan\theta}.$$

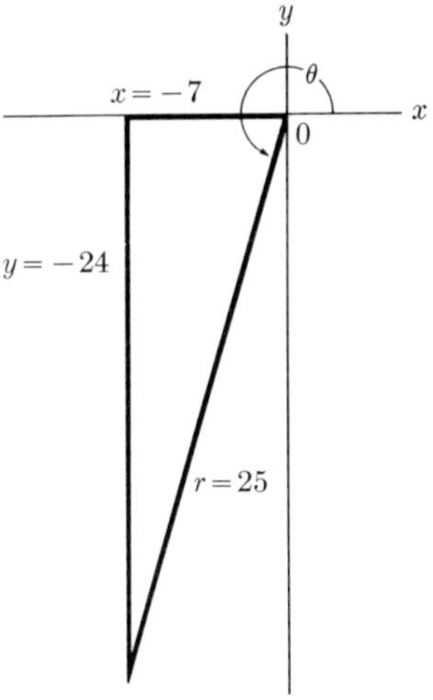

FIGURE 10–3

Thus, in order to find $\tan 3\theta$, we require the value of $\tan 2\theta$. Formula (30), together with the above value for $\tan\theta$, gives

$$\tan 2\theta = \frac{2(\frac{24}{7})}{1 - (\frac{24}{7})^2} = \frac{48}{7}\cdot\frac{49}{-527} = -\frac{336}{527}.$$

Hence the above expression for $\tan 3\theta$ gives

$$\tan 3\theta = \frac{-\frac{336}{527} + \frac{24}{7}}{1 + \frac{336}{527}\cdot\frac{24}{7}} = \frac{10296}{(7)(527)}\cdot\frac{(7)(527)}{11753} = \frac{10296}{11753}.$$

Example 2. Prove the identity

$$\cos\theta - \sin\frac{\theta}{2} = \left(1 - 2\sin\frac{\theta}{2}\right)\left(1 + \sin\frac{\theta}{2}\right).$$

Solution. We choose to work with the right member. Upon multiplying out, we obtain

$$\left(1 - 2\sin\frac{\theta}{2}\right)\left(1 + \sin\frac{\theta}{2}\right) = 1 - \sin\frac{\theta}{2} - 2\sin^2\frac{\theta}{2}$$

$$= \left(1 - 2\sin^2\frac{\theta}{2}\right) - \sin\frac{\theta}{2}$$

$$= \cos\theta - \sin\frac{\theta}{2} \qquad \text{[by (29b) with } A = \theta/2\text{]}.$$

Example 3. Prove the identity

$$\sec\frac{\theta}{2} + \csc\frac{\theta}{2} = \frac{2[\sin(\theta/2) + \cos(\theta/2)]}{\sin\theta}.$$

Solution. Since all angles are $\theta/2$, except in the denominator of the right member, the step that suggests itself is to use formula (28) with $A = \theta/2$ to obtain

$$\sin\theta = 2\sin\frac{\theta}{2}\cos\frac{\theta}{2}.$$

Then the right member can be written as

$$\frac{2[\sin(\theta/2) + \cos(\theta/2)]}{2\sin(\theta/2)\cos(\theta/2)} = \frac{1}{\cos(\theta/2)} + \frac{1}{\sin(\theta/2)}$$
$$= \sec\frac{\theta}{2} + \csc\frac{\theta}{2},$$

and the proof is complete.

Example 4. Evaluate the expression $\sin(2 \text{ Arctan } \frac{1}{2})$.

Solution. Let $\theta = \text{Arctan } \frac{1}{2}$. We then wish to find the value of $\sin 2\theta$, which may be done by use of formula (28). For this purpose we need $\sin\theta$ and $\cos\theta$. But $\tan\theta = \frac{1}{2}$, with θ in Q_1 since θ is the value of the inverse tangent of a positive number. Hence

$$\sin\theta = \frac{1}{\sqrt{5}}, \qquad \cos\theta = \frac{2}{\sqrt{5}},$$

and we obtain

$$\sin 2\theta = 2\sin\theta\cos\theta = 2\left(\frac{1}{\sqrt{5}}\right)\left(\frac{2}{\sqrt{5}}\right) = \frac{4}{5}.$$

EXERCISE GROUP 10–4

Simplify each of the expressions in Exercises 1–12, by using a half-angle or double-angle formula with the appropriate angle.

1. $\sqrt{\dfrac{1 + \cos 30^\circ}{2}}$
2. $\dfrac{1 - \cos 30^\circ}{\sin 30^\circ}$
3. $2\sin^2 A/2 - 1$
4. $\sin\theta\cos\theta$
5. $1 - 2\cos^2 2A$
6. $\sin^2\theta\cos^2\theta$
7. $\dfrac{2\tan 2\theta}{1 - \tan^2 2\theta}$
8. $\frac{1}{2}(1 + \cos 3\theta)$
9. $\cos^2 3\theta - \sin^2 3\theta$
10. $\dfrac{1 - \cos 3\theta}{2}$
11. $\dfrac{\sin 6\theta}{1 + \cos 6\theta}$
12. $\dfrac{1 - \cos 3\theta}{\sin 3\theta}$

In each of Exercises 13–22, compute the exact value of $\sin 2A$, $\cos 2A$, and $\tan 2A$ for:

13. $\sin A = \frac{3}{5}$, $0^\circ < A < 90^\circ$
14. $\cos A = -\frac{5}{13}$, $90^\circ < A < 180^\circ$
15. $\cot A = \frac{4}{3}$, $\pi < A < 3\pi/2$
16. $\csc A = -\frac{13}{12}$, $3\pi/2 < A < 2\pi$
17. $\tan A = -\frac{5}{12}$, A in Q_2
18. $\sec A = -\frac{5}{4}$, A in Q_3
19. $\sin A = \frac{3}{4}$, A in Q_2
20. $\cot A = \frac{3}{2}$, A in Q_3
21. $\csc A = -\frac{6}{5}$, A in Q_4
22. $\sin A = -\frac{3}{4}$, A in Q_4

In each of Exercises 23–32, compute the exact values of sin $(A/2,)$ cos $(A/2,)$ and tan $(A/2)$ for:

23. $\sin A = -\frac{1}{2}$, $180° < A < 270°$
24. $\cos A = -1$, $0° < A < 360°$
25. $\sin A = 0$, $90° < A < 270°$
26. $\cos A = -\frac{3}{5}$, $180° < A < 270°$
27. $\csc A = -1$, $0 < A < 2\pi$
28. $\tan A = -\frac{12}{5}$, $3\pi/2 < A < 2\pi$
29. $\csc A = -\frac{17}{8}$, $\pi < A < 3\pi/2$
30. $\sec A = -\frac{5}{4}$, $\pi < A < 3\pi/2$
31. $\cot A = -\frac{5}{12}$, $5\pi/2 < A < 3\pi$
32. $\sec A = -2$, $3\pi < A < 7\pi/2$

Evaluate each of the expressions in Exercises 33–41.

33. $\sin(2 \text{ Arctan } \frac{1}{2})$
34. $\sin(2 \text{ Arctan } \frac{3}{4})$
35. $\cos(2 \text{ Arcsin } \frac{3}{5})$
36. $\tan(\frac{1}{2}\text{Arcsin } \frac{3}{5})$
37. $\cos(2 \text{ Arccos } x)$
38. $\cos(2\text{Arcsin } x)$
39. $\tan(\frac{1}{2} \text{ Arcsin } x)$
40. $\tan(\frac{1}{2} \text{ Arctan } x)$
41. $\sin(2 \text{ Arccot } x)$

Prove that the equations in Exercises 42–62 are identities.

42. $(\sin A + \cos A)^2 = 1 + \sin 2A$
43. $\cos^4 A - \sin^4 A = 2\cos^2 A - 1$
44. $\cos 2A + 2\sin^2 A = 1$
45. $\dfrac{\cos A - \sin A}{\cos A + \sin A} = \sec 2A - \tan 2A$
46. $2\cos^2(A/2) = 1 + \cos A$
47. $2\csc 2A \tan A = 1 + \tan^2 A$
48. $2\cos A + \sin 2A = \dfrac{2\cos^3 A}{1 - \sin A}$
49. $\cot 3A \cos A - \sin A = \cos 4A \csc 3A$
50. $2\cot 2A = 2\cot A - \sec A \csc A$
51. $\cot 2A - \cot A + \csc 2A = 0$
52. $\cot(A/2) - \tan(A/2) = 2\cot A$
53. $\dfrac{\sin A - \cos 2A}{\cos^2 A} = \dfrac{2\sin A - 1}{1 - \sin A}$
54. $2\cos(A/2) = (1 + \cos A)\sec(A/2)$
55. $\tan(A/2) + \cot(A/2) = 2\csc A$
56. $\sin 4A(1 - 2\sin^2 2A) = \frac{1}{2}\sin 8A$
57. $\dfrac{2}{1 - \cos 2A} = \csc^2 A$
58. $\dfrac{\sin 3A}{\sin A} + \dfrac{\cos 3A}{\cos A} = 4\cos 2A$
59. $\dfrac{\sin 3A}{\sin A} - \dfrac{\cos 3A}{\cos A} = 2$
60. $\dfrac{3\cos A + \cos 3A}{3\sin A - \sin 3A} = \cot^3 A$
61. $\cos^6 A - \sin^6 A = (1 - \sin^2 A\cos^2 A)\cos 2A$
62. $\sec A + \sec 2A \sec A + \sec 3A \sec 2A = \csc A \tan 3A$

63. Find the values of $\sin\theta$ and $\cos\theta$ in terms of t if $\tan(\theta/2) = t$.
64. If $x = \cos 2\theta$ and $y = \cos\theta$, eliminate θ and thus find the relation that exists between x and y.
65. If $x = 2\cos\theta - \cos 2\theta$ and $y = 2\sin\theta - \sin 2\theta$, eliminate θ and thus show that

$$(x^2 + y^2)^2 - 6(x^2 + y^2) + 8x - 3 = 0.$$

10–9 THE PRODUCT AND FACTOR FORMULAS

Let us write the expressions for $\sin(A + B)$ and $\sin(A - B)$. We have

$$\sin(A + B) = \sin A \cos B + \cos A \sin B,$$
$$\sin(A - B) = \sin A \cos B - \cos A \sin B.$$

Adding corresponding members of these two equations, we obtain

$$\sin(A + B) + \sin(A - B) = 2 \sin A \cos B,$$

from which we obtain, on solving for $\sin A \cos B$, which appears in the right member,

$$\boxed{\sin A \cos B = \tfrac{1}{2}[\sin(A + B) + \sin(A - B)].} \tag{35}$$

Similarly, addition of Eqs. (17) and (20) yields the formula

$$\boxed{\cos A \cos B = \tfrac{1}{2}[\cos(A + B) + \cos(A - B)],} \tag{36}$$

and subtraction of Eq. (17) from Eq. (20) gives

$$\boxed{\sin A \sin B = \tfrac{1}{2}[\cos(A - B) - \cos(A + B)].} \tag{37}$$

Formulas (35), (36), and (37) are known as the *product formulas.*

Let us set $A + B = x$, and $A - B = y$. We may solve these equations to give $A = \frac{1}{2}(x + y)$, $B = \frac{1}{2}(x - y)$, and substitution of these in (35) gives

$$\boxed{\sin x + \sin y = 2 \sin \tfrac{1}{2}(x + y) \cos \tfrac{1}{2}(x - y).} \tag{38}$$

Replacing y by $-y$ in this formula gives, since $\sin(-y) = -\sin y$,

$$\boxed{\sin x - \sin y = 2 \sin \tfrac{1}{2}(x - y) \cos \tfrac{1}{2}(x + y).} \tag{39}$$

From (36) and (37) we obtain, by the above substitution,

$$\boxed{\cos x + \cos y = 2 \cos \tfrac{1}{2}(x + y) \cos \tfrac{1}{2}(x - y),} \tag{40}$$

$$\boxed{\cos x - \cos y = -2 \sin \tfrac{1}{2}(x + y) \sin \tfrac{1}{2}(x - y).} \tag{41}$$

Formulas (38), (39), (40), and (41) are called the *factor formulas.*

Note that *the product formulas express certain products of sines and cosines as sums, while the factor formulas express certain sums of sines and cosines as products.*

Example 1. Find the value of sin 75° sin 15°.

Solution. By formula (37) we have

$$\begin{aligned}\sin 75^\circ \sin 15^\circ &= \tfrac{1}{2}[\cos (75^\circ - 15^\circ) - \cos (75^\circ + 15^\circ)]\\ &= \tfrac{1}{2}(\cos 60^\circ - \cos 90^\circ)\\ &= \tfrac{1}{2} \times \tfrac{1}{2} = \tfrac{1}{4}.\end{aligned}$$

Example 2. Prove the identity

$$2 \cos \theta \sin 3\theta = \sin 4\theta + \sin 2\theta.$$

Solution. Formula (38) with $x = 4\theta$ and $y = 2\theta$ gives for the right member of the desired identity,

$$\begin{aligned}\sin 4\theta + \sin 2\theta &= 2 \sin \tfrac{1}{2}(4\theta + 2\theta) \cos \tfrac{1}{2}(4\theta - 2\theta)\\ &= 2 \sin 3\theta \cos \theta,\end{aligned}$$

and the identity is proved.

Alternative solution. Formula (35) with $A = 3\theta$ and $B = \theta$ gives, for the left member of the desired identity,

$$\sin 3\theta \cos \theta = \tfrac{1}{2}[\sin (3\theta + \theta) + \sin (3\theta - \theta)],$$

which becomes

$$2 \sin 3\theta \cos \theta = \sin 4\theta + \sin 2\theta.$$

Example 3. Prove the identity

$$\cos 3\theta = \cos \theta - 2 \sin 2\theta \sin \theta.$$

Solution. Formula (37) with $A = 2\theta$ and $B = \theta$ gives

$$\sin 2\theta \sin \theta = \tfrac{1}{2}[\cos (2\theta - \theta) - \cos (2\theta + \theta)].$$

Hence, the right member of the identity which is to be proved becomes

$$\cos \theta - 2[\tfrac{1}{2}(\cos \theta - \cos 3\theta)] = \cos \theta - \cos \theta + \cos 3\theta = \cos 3\theta,$$

which establishes the identity.

EXERCISE GROUP 10-5

Express the quantities in Exercises 1–10 as products.

1. $\sin 40^\circ + \sin 20^\circ$
2. $\cos 50^\circ + \cos 12^\circ$
3. $\sin 152^\circ - \sin 30^\circ$
4. $\sin 300^\circ + \sin 100^\circ$
5. $\cos 30^\circ - \cos 10^\circ$
6. $\sin 95^\circ - \sin 35^\circ$
7. $\sin 4\theta - \sin \theta$
8. $\cos 2\theta + \cos 4\theta$
9. $\cos 8\theta - \cos 2\theta$
10. $\sin (5\theta/2) + \sin (3\theta/2)$

Express the quantities in Exercises 11–22 as sums or differences.

11. $\sin 30° \cos 50°$
12. $\sin 30° \sin 50°$
13. $\cos 90° \cos 44°$
14. $\cos 60° \sin 38°$
15. $\sin 4\theta \cos 2\theta$
16. $\sin 2\theta \cos \theta$
17. $\cos 3\theta \cos 4\theta$
18. $\cos \theta \sin 4\theta$
19. $\sin 5A \cos 6A$
20. $\sin 9B \sin 11B$
21. $\cos 13C \cos 15C$
22. $\cos 8\theta \sin 22\theta$

Prove that the following statements are identities.

23. $\dfrac{\sin A - \sin B}{\sin A + \sin B} = \tan \dfrac{A - B}{2} \cot \dfrac{A + B}{2}$

24. $\dfrac{\sin 4A + \sin 3A}{\cos 3A - \cos 4A} = \cot \dfrac{A}{2}$

25. $\sin (A + B) \sin (A - B) = \sin^2 A - \sin^2 B$

26. $\cos (A + B) \cos (A - B) = \cos^2 A - \sin^2 B$

27. $\sin 7x - \sin (\pi/2 - x) = 2 \cos (3x + \pi/4) \sin (4x - \pi/4)$

28. $\cos 5x + \cos (\pi/2 - x) = 2 \cos (2x + \pi/4) \cos (3x - \pi/4)$

29. $\dfrac{\cos (2A - B) + \cos B}{\sin B - \sin (B - 2A)} = \cot A$

30. $\dfrac{\sin 2A - \sin 2B}{\cos 2A - \cos 2B} = -\cot (A + B)$

31. $\cos (3A - 2B) - \cos (3A + 2B) = 2 \sin 3A \sin 2B$

32. $2 \cos 2A + \sin A (\sin A - \sin 3A) = \cos A (\cos A + \cos 3A)$

33. $\sin A - \sin 2A + \sin 3A = -\sin 2A (1 - 2 \cos A)$

34. $\sin 7A = 2 \sin A \cos 6A + \sin 5A$

35. $\sin 5A = 2 \sin 4A \cos A - \sin 3A$

36. $\dfrac{\sin 3A + \sin A}{\sin A \cos A} = 4 \cos A$

37. $\dfrac{\sin 6A - \sin 4A}{\cos 5A} = 2 \sin A$

38. $\dfrac{\cos 3A + \cos A}{2 \cos^3 A - 2 \cos A} = 2 - \csc^2 A$

39. $\sin 4A = 2 \sin A \cos 3A + \sin 2A$

40. $\sin A + \sin 3A + \sin 5A = \dfrac{\sin^2 3A}{\sin A}$

41. $\dfrac{\sin 3A - \sin 2A}{2 \cos 2A + 4 \sin^2 (A/2) - 1} = \sin A$

42. $4 \cos \dfrac{A}{3} \cos \dfrac{2\pi + A}{3} \cos \dfrac{4\pi + A}{3} = \cos A$

43. $\cos \dfrac{A}{3} \cos \dfrac{2\pi + A}{3} + \cos \dfrac{2\pi + A}{3} \cos \dfrac{4\pi + A}{3} + \cos \dfrac{4\pi + A}{3} \cos \dfrac{A}{3} = -\dfrac{3}{4}$

44. $\cos \dfrac{A}{3} + \cos \dfrac{2\pi + A}{3} + \cos \dfrac{4\pi + A}{3} = 0$

45. $\sin (A - B) + \sin (B - C) + \sin (C - A)$
$$= -4 \sin \frac{A - B}{2} \sin \frac{B - C}{2} \sin \frac{C - A}{2}$$

10–10 TRIGONOMETRIC EQUATIONS

In certain connections (in the study of calculus, in particular) the need arises for solving equations containing trigonometric functions of some variable. The solutions of a trigonometric equation consist of the value or values of the variable which reduce the equation to a (numerical) identity. In other words, the solution consists of those values of the variable which satisfy the equation. Thus, the solution of the equation

$$\sin x = -\tfrac{1}{2}$$

consists of the angles

$$x = 210° + n \cdot 360° \quad \text{and} \quad x = 330° + n \cdot 360°,$$

where n is any integer.

An equation may involve functions other than trigonometric. For example, the equation

$$2x + \tan x = 0$$

contains the linear function $2x$. In such an equation we wish to find *the value of* x *in radians* that satisfies the equation. We must use approximate methods of solution, since no exact method exists. One such method would be to graph the equations $y_1 = -2x$ and $y_2 = \tan x$, and to find the intersections of the graphs obtained. The abscissas of these points are then the desired solutions, since, for any such value of x we have $y_1 = y_2$, and the above equation is satisfied. However, *we shall be concerned here with equations which contain only trigonometric functions and constants.*

Due to the great variety of trigonometric equations, it is hardly of advantage to define specific types and to develop methods of solution for these types. However, the following suggestions will prove helpful in a great many cases. In addition, we must make effective use of the identities among the trigonometric functions.

1. *If an equation can be expressed in terms of one trigonometric function of the same angle, an algebraic equation in that function results, and the methods for solving algebraic equations can be applied.*
2. *If an equation can be expressed in such a form that a product of trigonometric expressions is zero, then each factor should be set equal to zero, where possible. The solutions of the resulting equations will comprise the solution of the original equation.*

Example 1. Solve the equation $2\cos^2\theta + 3\sin\theta = 0$.

Solution. When we replace $\cos^2\theta$ by $1 - \sin^2\theta$, the equation reduces to

$$2\sin^2\theta - 3\sin\theta - 2 = 0.$$

This is a quadratic equation in $\sin\theta$, in which the left member can be factored, so that we obtain

$$(2\sin\theta + 1)(\sin\theta - 2) = 0.$$

The second factor cannot be set equal to zero, since $\sin\theta$ cannot be greater than 1. By setting the first factor equal to zero, we find that

$$\sin\theta = -\tfrac{1}{2},$$

and the solution is

$$\theta = 210^\circ + n\cdot 360^\circ \qquad \text{or} \qquad \theta = 330^\circ + n\cdot 360^\circ, \qquad n \text{ any integer.}$$

Example 2. Solve the equation $\tan 2\theta + \cot 2\theta = 2$, for angles θ such that $0 \leqq \theta < 2\pi$.

Solution. Since $\cot 2\theta = 1/\tan 2\theta$, the equation becomes

$$\tan 2\theta + \frac{1}{\tan 2\theta} = 2.$$

Multiplication of both members by $\tan 2\theta$ gives

$$\tan^2 2\theta + 1 = 2\tan 2\theta \qquad \text{or} \qquad \tan^2 2\theta - 2\tan 2\theta + 1 = 0.$$

The latter equation is quadratic in $\tan 2\theta$, and factorization yields

$$(\tan 2\theta - 1)^2 = 0, \qquad \text{so that} \qquad \tan 2\theta = 1.$$

Hence $2\theta = \pi/4 + n\pi$, from which we find $\theta = \pi/8 + n\pi/2$. The angles in the desired range occur for $n = 0, 1, 2$, and 3, and are

$$\theta = \pi/8, \quad 5\pi/8, \quad 9\pi/8, \quad 13\pi/8.$$

All of these values are solutions, since $\tan 2\theta$ and $\cot 2\theta$ are defined for them.

Another way of finding the values of θ in the desired range is to note that the values of 2θ must be sought in the range $0 \leqq 2\theta < 4\pi$. Hence we find that

$$2\theta = \pi/4, \quad 5\pi/4, \quad 9\pi/4, \quad 13\pi/4,$$

from which the above values of θ are again found.

Example 3. Solve the equation $\sin\theta = \sin(\theta/2)$ for θ in the range $0 \leqq \theta < 2\pi$.

Solution. By the identity $\sin\theta = 2\sin(\theta/2)\cos(\theta/2)$, we may express the equation in terms of $\theta/2$ alone. Thus, we obtain

$$2\sin\frac{\theta}{2}\cos\frac{\theta}{2} = \sin\frac{\theta}{2},$$

$$2\sin\frac{\theta}{2}\cos\frac{\theta}{2} - \sin\frac{\theta}{2} = 0,$$

$$\sin\frac{\theta}{2}\left(2\cos\frac{\theta}{2} - 1\right) = 0.$$

Setting each factor equal to zero, we have, on realizing that $\theta/2$ must lie between 0 and π,

$$\sin\frac{\theta}{2} = 0, \qquad \frac{\theta}{2} = 0; \qquad \theta = 0;$$

or

$$2\cos\frac{\theta}{2} - 1 = 0, \qquad \cos\frac{\theta}{2} = \frac{1}{2}, \qquad \frac{\theta}{2} = \frac{\pi}{3}, \qquad \theta = \frac{2\pi}{3}.$$

The solutions are then $\theta = 0$ and $\theta = 2\pi/3$.

A somewhat special type of trigonometric equation is of the form

$$A \sin \theta + B \cos \theta = C.$$

A method of solution is given in the following example.

Example 4. Solve the equation $2 \sin \theta + 3 \cos \theta = 3$, for θ in the range $0 \leqq \theta < 360°$.

Solution. We may replace $\cos \theta$ by $\pm\sqrt{1 - \sin^2 \theta}$. Then the equation becomes

$$2 \sin \theta \pm 3\sqrt{1 - \sin^2 \theta} = 3.$$

If the term $2 \sin \theta$ is transposed, and if both members are then squared, we have

$$9(1 - \sin^2 \theta) = (3 - 2 \sin \theta)^2.$$

Expanding and simplifying, we obtain

$$13 \sin^2 \theta - 12 \sin \theta = 0,$$

which can be solved by factoring to give $\sin \theta = 0$ or $\frac{12}{13}$. We then obtain, in the desired range, $\theta = 0°, 67° 13', 112° 57', 180°$. These values must now be tested in the original equation, since, due to the step involving squaring, some of them may not be solutions. Substituting,

for $\theta = 0$ we have $2(0) + 3(1) = 3$,

for $\theta = 67° 13'$ we have $2\left(\frac{12}{13}\right) + 3\left(\frac{5}{13}\right) = \frac{24 + 15}{13} = 3$,

for $\theta = 112° 57'$ we have $2\left(\frac{12}{13}\right) + 3\left(-\frac{5}{13}\right) = \frac{24 - 15}{13} \neq 3$,

for $\theta = 180°$ we have $2(0) + 3(-1) \neq 3$.

Hence the only solutions are $\theta = 0$ and $\theta = 67° 13'$.

10–11 THE FUNCTION $y = a \sin x + b \cos x$

In Section 7–7 certain functions of the type $a \sin x + b \cos x$ were sketched by the method of addition of ordinates, and the graph in each case turned out to be a curve with the appearance of a sine (or a cosine) curve. This type of function is of some importance, and we shall now prove a result which will verify our supposition, and make it precise. Let us consider a and b as the coordinates of a point P in a rectangular coordinate system, with $r = \sqrt{a^2 + b^2}$ as the polar distance of P. Then, if α is an angle in standard position with $\overline{OP}$ as its terminal line, we have

$$a = r \cos \alpha, \qquad b = r \sin \alpha.$$

We may then write

$$a \sin x + b \cos x = r(\cos \alpha \sin x + \sin \alpha \cos x), \tag{42}$$

so that, by the addition formula for $\sin(x + \alpha)$, Eq. (42) gives

$$a \sin x + b \cos x = r \sin(x + \alpha),$$

$$r = \sqrt{a^2 + b^2}, \qquad \cos \alpha = \frac{a}{r}, \qquad \sin \alpha = \frac{b}{r}.$$

On the other hand, if we consider the coordinates of a point P as b and a, we have

$$b = r \cos \alpha, \qquad a = r \sin \alpha,$$

and instead of (42) we obtain

$$a \sin x + b \cos x = r(\sin \alpha \sin x + \cos \alpha \cos x) = r \cos(x - \alpha),$$

the last equality arising from the addition formula for $\cos(x - \alpha)$. These results may be stated as follows.

Theorem. *The function $a \sin x + b \cos x$ may be written in either of the two following forms:*

$$r \sin(x + \alpha), \quad \textit{where } r = \sqrt{a^2 + b^2}, \quad \cos \alpha = \frac{a}{r}, \quad \sin \alpha = \frac{b}{r}$$

or

$$r \cos(x - \alpha), \quad \textit{where } r = \sqrt{a^2 + b^2}, \quad \cos \alpha = \frac{b}{r}, \quad \sin \alpha = \frac{a}{r}.$$

This theorem yields a simple method for solving an equation of the form

$$a \sin x + b \cos x = c,$$

which will be made clear in the following example. A different method was given in Example 4 of Section 10–10.

Example. Solve the equation $\sqrt{3} \sin x + \cos x = \sqrt{2}$ for the smallest nonnegative value of x which satisfies it.

Solution. By the theorem we have, since $r = \sqrt{3 + 1} = 2$,

$$\sqrt{3} \sin x + \cos x = 2 \cos(x - \alpha), \text{ where } \cos \alpha = \tfrac{1}{2}, \ \sin \alpha = \tfrac{1}{2}\sqrt{3}.$$

We may then take $\alpha = \pi/3$. Hence the given equation becomes $2 \cos(x - \pi/3) = \sqrt{2}$, so that the solution for $x - \pi/3$ becomes

$$x - \frac{\pi}{3} = \frac{\pi}{4} + 2k\pi \quad \text{or} \quad -\frac{\pi}{4} + 2k\pi,$$

where k is any integer; the general solution for x is then

$$x = \frac{\pi}{3} + \frac{\pi}{4} + 2k\pi = \frac{7\pi}{12} + 2k\pi \quad \text{or} \quad x = \frac{\pi}{3} - \frac{\pi}{4} + 2k\pi = \frac{\pi}{12} + 2k\pi.$$

Of these values, the smallest nonnegative value of x is given by $k = 0$ in the last expression for x, and the desired solution is $x = \pi/12$ or $x = 15°$.

EXERCISE GROUP 10–6

Solve each of the following equations for all values of θ such that $0 \leqq \theta < 2\pi$.

1. $2\cos\theta - 1 = 0$
2. $\tan\theta + 1 = 0$
3. $4\sin^2\theta - 3 = 0$
4. $3\cot^2\theta - 1 = 0$
5. $\sin 2\theta + \cos\theta = 0$
6. $\cos 2\theta - \sin\theta = 0$
7. $\cos^2\theta - \sin^2\theta = 1$
8. $\sin\theta + \sin(\theta/2) = 0$
9. $\cos\theta + \sin(\theta/2) = 0$
10. $2\sin^2\theta - \cos\theta - 1 = 0$
11. $2\cos^2\theta - 3\sin\theta - 3 = 0$
12. $\tan\theta + 2\cos\theta = \sec\theta$
13. $2\sin^2\theta + 2\cos 2\theta = 1$
14. $\cos 2\theta + 2\sin^2(\theta/2) = 3$
15. $\cos 2\theta\cos\theta + \sin 2\theta\sin\theta = 1$
16. $\sin 3\theta\cos\theta - \cos 3\theta\sin\theta = 0$
17. $\cot\theta - \tan(\theta/2) = 0$
18. $\tan 2\theta = \cot\theta$
19. $2\sin 2\theta - 2\cos\theta + 2\sin\theta = 1$
20. $2\cos^2 2\theta - 2\sin^2 2\theta = 1$
21. $\cot(\theta/2) = 1 + \cos\theta$
22. $\tan(\theta/2) + \sin\theta = 2\csc\theta$
23. $2\cos^2 2\theta + \cos 2\theta - 1 = 0$
24. $\cos^2(\theta/2) - \sin^2(\theta/2) = \cos 2\theta$
25. $\sin^2(\theta/2) = \cos^2\theta$
26. $2\sin^2(\theta/2) = 1 - \sin\theta$
27. $\sin 3\theta - \sin(3\theta/2) = 0$
28. $\cos^2 3\theta - \sin^2 3\theta = 1$
29. $2\sin^3 2\theta - \sin 2\theta = 1 - 2\sin^2 2\theta$
30. $\tan 2\theta + \cot 2\theta = 2$
31. $\dfrac{1 - \sin\theta}{\cos\theta} = \cos\theta$
32. $\dfrac{\cos\theta}{1 + \sin\theta} = 1 - \sin\theta$
33. $4\tan^2\theta = 3\sec^2\theta$
34. $1 + \sin^2(\theta/2) = \cos\theta$
35. $1 - 2\cos^2\theta = 2(1 - 2\sin^2\theta)$
36. $2\sin^2\theta - \sin\theta = 1$
37. $2\cos^2 2\theta - 3\cos 2\theta + 1 = 0$
38. $\cot\theta + 2\sin\theta = \csc\theta$
39. $\sin^2\theta - \sin\theta = 2$
40. $3\cos\theta + 4\sin\theta = 5$
41. $\tan\theta - 2\sec\theta = 3$
42. $2\cot\theta + 3\csc\theta = 4$
43. $5\sin\theta + 12\cos\theta = 13$
44. $24\cos\theta + 7\sin\theta = 25$
45. $5\cot\theta - 13\csc\theta = 12$
46. $7\tan\theta - 25\sec\theta = 24$
47. $\sin 7\theta + \sin 5\theta = 0$
48. $\sin 11\theta = \sin 3\theta$
49. $\cot 2\theta + \csc 2\theta = 7$
50. $\cos 3\theta + \cos\theta = 0$

SUPPLEMENTARY EXERCISES FOR CHAPTER 10

Prove that each of the equations in Exercises 1–32 is an identity.

1. $\dfrac{\csc\theta}{\sec\theta - \csc\theta} = \dfrac{\cos\theta}{\sin\theta - \cos\theta}$
2. $\dfrac{\sin^3\theta - \cos^3\theta}{1 + \sin\theta\cos\theta} = \sin\theta - \cos\theta$
3. $\dfrac{\csc\theta + 1}{\csc\theta - 1} = \dfrac{\cot\theta + \cos\theta}{\cot\theta - \cos\theta}$
4. $\cos^4\theta - \cos^6\theta = \sin^6\theta + \sin^2\theta\cos 2\theta$
5. $\cot\theta = \dfrac{1 + \cos 2\theta}{\sin 2\theta}$
6. $\cot\theta = \dfrac{\sin 2\theta}{1 - \cos 2\theta}$

7. $\sin 2\theta = \dfrac{2 \cot \theta}{1 + \cot^2 \theta}$

8. $\csc \theta = \dfrac{\csc^2 (\theta/2)}{2 \cot (\theta/2)}$

9. $1 + 2 \sin (\theta/2) = \dfrac{\sin (\theta/2) + \cos \theta}{1 - \sin (\theta/2)}$

10. $\cot 2\theta = \frac{1}{2}(\cot \theta - \tan \theta)$

11. $\dfrac{\cot 2\theta}{2 - \sec^2 \theta} = \frac{1}{2} \cot \theta$

12. $\dfrac{4 \cos 2\theta}{\sin^2 2\theta} = \csc^2 \theta - \sec^2 \theta$

13. $\sin 4\theta = 4 \sin \theta \cos \theta - 8 \sin^3 \theta \cos \theta$

14. $\sin 3\theta = 4 \sin \theta \cos^2 \theta - \sin \theta$

15. $\cos 3\theta = \cos \theta (2 \cos 2\theta - 1)$

16. $\cos 4\theta = 1 - 8 \sin^2 \theta + 8 \sin^4 \theta$

17. $\sec 2\theta = \dfrac{\csc^2 \theta \sec^2 \theta}{\csc^2 \theta - \sec^2 \theta}$

18. $2 \csc 2\theta = \sec \theta \csc \theta$

19. $\tan \theta \tan 2\theta = \sec 2\theta - 1$

20. $\csc \theta(\csc \theta + 2 \cos \theta) = (1 + \cot \theta)^2$

21. $\dfrac{2}{1 - \cos 2\theta} = \csc^2 \theta$

22. $-2 \sin 2\theta + \dfrac{\sin 2\theta}{\sin^2 \theta} = 2 \cot \theta \cos 2\theta$

23. $\dfrac{\sin^2 2\theta}{2(1 + \cos 2\theta)} = \sin^2 \theta$

24. $\dfrac{\sin^2 \theta}{\cos \theta - \cos 2\theta} = \dfrac{1 + \cos \theta}{1 + 2 \cos \theta}$

25. $\sin^2 2\theta = 4(\sin^2 \theta - \sin^4 \theta)$

26. $2 \sin^2 (\theta/2) + \cos \theta = 1$

27. $\dfrac{2 \cos 2\theta + 1}{2 \cos 2\theta - 1} = \dfrac{3 - \tan^2 \theta}{1 - 3 \tan^2 \theta}$

28. $\frac{1}{2}(1 + \tan \theta)^2 = \dfrac{1 + \sin 2\theta}{1 + \cos 2\theta}$

29. $\tan 4\theta = \dfrac{4 \tan \theta(1 - \tan^2 \theta)}{1 - 6 \tan^2 \theta + \tan^4 \theta}$

30. $\tan 3\theta = \dfrac{\tan \theta(3 - \tan^2 \theta)}{1 - 3 \tan^2 \theta}$

31. $\cos 2\theta \cos (\theta/2) - \sin 2\theta \sin (\theta/2) = \pm\sqrt{(1 + \cos 5\theta)/2}$

32. $\sin \theta \cos (\theta/2) + \cos \theta \sin (\theta/2) = \pm\sqrt{(1 - \cos 3\theta)/2}$

Express each ratio given in Exercises 33–47 in terms of (a) the same-named ratio of a positive acute angle and (b) a ratio of an angle between 0° and 45° or between 0 and $\pi/4$ radians, the latter value being permitted in each case.

33. $\cos 218° 42'$
34. $\sin (-213° 12')$
35. $\tan 987°$
36. $\cot (-893° 12')$
37. $\sin 7895°$
38. $\cos 2174°$
39. $\sin (13\pi/3)$
40. $\cos (17\pi/3)$
41. $\tan (17\pi/3)$
42. $\cot (19\pi/4)$
43. $\cos (13\pi/4)$
44. $\sin (-23\pi/3)$
45. $\tan (-17\pi/4)$
46. $\cot (-31\pi/3)$
47. $\cos (-19\pi/3)$

Solve the equations in Exercises 48–63 for all values of θ such that $0 \leqq \theta < 2\pi$.

48. $\sin \theta + \cos \theta = 0$

49. $\sin 2\theta - \sin \theta = 0$

50. $\sin 2\theta = \cos^2 \theta - \sin^2 \theta$

51. $6 \cos^2 \theta + \cos \theta = 2$

52. $2 \tan \theta = 1 + \sec \theta$

53. $\sin 5\theta + \sin 3\theta = 0$

54. $\cos 3\theta - \cos \theta = 0$

55. $\cos 2\theta = 2 - 2 \cos^2 \dfrac{\theta}{2}$

56. $3 \sin^2 \theta - 2 \cos \theta - 2 = 0$

57. $\sec^2 \theta - \tan \theta = 1$

58. $\dfrac{\tan 2\theta + \tan\theta}{1 - \tan 2\theta \tan\theta} = \sqrt{3}$

59. $2\cos^2 3\theta + \sin 3\theta - 1 = 0$

60. $3\sin\theta - 4\cos\theta = 1$

61. $2(\sin\theta - \cos\theta) = \sqrt{2}$

62. $\sin 2\theta + \sin\theta = 1 + 2\cos\theta$

63. $\tan\dfrac{\theta}{2} + \sin 2\theta = \csc\theta$

Prove each of the following:

64. $\text{Arctan } 1 = 2 \text{ Arctan } \frac{1}{3} + \text{Arctan } \frac{1}{7}$

65. $\text{Arctan } 1 = 4 \text{ Arctan } \frac{1}{5} - \text{Arctan } \frac{1}{239}$

66. $\text{Arcsin } 1 = \text{Arcsin } \dfrac{\sqrt{3}}{2} + \text{Arcsin } \dfrac{1}{2}$

67. $\text{Arcsin } 1 = \text{Arcsin } \dfrac{1}{3} + \text{Arcsin } \dfrac{2\sqrt{2}}{3}$

CHAPTER 11

Mathematical Induction and the Binomial Formula

11-1 INTRODUCTION

In algebra and in trigonometry, as in other parts of mathematics, there are theorems which can be formulated in terms of n so as to state that a certain equation or property holds when n is any positive integer. For many such theorems a particularly well-suited method of proof is the one known as "mathematical induction." In the first part of this chapter this method will be treated, and then later in the chapter the method will be used to prove the Binomial Theorem.

11-2 AN ILLUSTRATION

Suppose we wish to find a formula for the sum of the positive integers 1, 2, 3, . . . , n, that is, a formula which will give the value of $1 + 2 + 3$ when $n = 3$, the value of $1 + 2 + 3 + 4$ when $n = 4$, and so on, and suppose that in some manner we are led to believe that the formula $1 + 2 + 3 + \cdots + n = n(n + 1)/2$ is the correct one. How can this formula actually be proved? We can, of course, verify the statement for as many positive integral values of n as we like, but this process will not prove the formula for even one additional value of n. What is needed is some kind of "chain reaction" which will have the effect that once the formula is proved for a particular integer the formula will automatically follow for the next integer and the next and the next, indefinitely. Such a reaction may be considered as produced by the method of *mathematical induction.* The method will be explained, and will then be applied to the above formula.

11-3 THE METHOD OF MATHEMATICAL INDUCTION

If a theorem is formulated in terms of n and involves the statement that a formula or property holds when n is any positive integer, *a proof by mathematical induction consists of the following two steps.*

I. *Verify the theorem for* $n = 1$ (*or, in special cases, some other value of* n).

II. *Assume that the theorem holds for* $n = p$ *and then prove that it holds for* $n = p + 1$.

These two steps constitute the method of proof of a theorem by mathematical induction. Once they have been carried out, the "chain reaction" mentioned in the preceding section is set in motion.

The justification for this method of proof lies in Axiom 8 of Section 1–2, the *Principle of Finite Induction*. For, suppose that the above two steps have been carried out. Let M be the set of positive integers for which the theorem holds. By Step I, M contains the integer 1; by Step II, the set M contains $a + 1$ whenever it contains the positive integer a. By Axiom 8, the set M then consists of all the natural numbers, or positive integers.

More intuitively, we may say that by Step I the theorem is proved for $n = 1$. Then by Step II with $p = 1$, the theorem is proved for $n = 2$; by Step II again with $p = 2$, it follows for $n = 3$, then for $n = 4$, and so on for all the positive integers.

Let us apply this method to the proof of the formula of the preceding section, that is, to prove that the equation

$$1 + 2 + 3 + \cdots + n = \frac{n(n+1)}{2} \tag{1}$$

holds for any positive integer n.

I. Substituting $n = 1$ in Eq. (1), we have $1 = (1 \cdot 2)/2$, which is true, and therefore (1) is verified for $n = 1$.

II. *Assume* the formula valid for $n = p$; that is, assume that the equation

$$1 + 2 + 3 + \cdots + p = \frac{p(p+1)}{2} \tag{2}$$

is correct.

We wish to *prove* the formula for $n = p + 1$, that is, we wish to prove the correctness of the equation

$$1 + 2 + 3 + \cdots + p + (p + 1) = \frac{(p+1)(p+2)}{2}. \tag{3}$$

To do this we add $p + 1$ to both members of (2), which was assumed true, and we obtain

$$\begin{aligned}(1 + 2 + 3 + \cdots + p) + (p + 1) &= \left[\frac{p(p+1)}{2}\right] + (p + 1)\\ &= \frac{p(p+1) + 2(p+1)}{2}\\ &= \frac{(p+1)(p+2)}{2}.\end{aligned}$$

This proves Eq. (3), and completes the proof of (1) by mathematical induction.

In this way the formula has been proved in turn for $n = 1, n = 2, n = 3$, and for all the positive integers n.

Note: In our discussion of formula (1), we made no mention of the method by which the formula was discovered. This formula happens to be one which can be easily derived by other methods. But other theorems which lend themselves to proof by mathematical induction are often discovered by a trial-and-error method. Various values of n are used in turn until some pattern or formula becomes apparent. When such a pattern seems reasonable, the proof is attempted. This method of discovery can be compared with the inductive method as used in the natural sciences. Mathematical induction is sometimes called *complete induction* to distinguish it from the method of induction as used in science.

Example 1. Prove:

$$1 \cdot 2 + 2 \cdot 3 + 3 \cdot 4 + \cdots + n(n+1) = \frac{n(n+1)(n+2)}{3}.$$

Solution by mathematical induction:

I. For $n = 1$ the formula gives $1 \cdot 2 = (1 \cdot 2 \cdot 3)/3$, which is correct and completes Step I.

II. *Assume* the formula for $n = p$:

$$1 \cdot 2 + 2 \cdot 3 + 3 \cdot 4 + \cdots + p(p+1) = \frac{p(p+1)(p+2)}{3}.$$

To prove the formula for $n = p + 1$, that is, to prove

$$1 \cdot 2 + 2 \cdot 3 + \cdots + p(p+1) + (p+1)(p+2) = \frac{(p+1)(p+2)(p+3)}{3},$$

$(p+1)(p+2)$ is added to both members of the first equation in this step; this gives

$$\begin{aligned}
[1 \cdot 2 + 2 \cdot 3 + \cdots + p(p+1)] + (p+1)(p+2) \\
&= \left[\frac{p(p+1)(p+2)}{3}\right] + (p+1)(p+2) \\
&= (p+1)(p+2)\left(\frac{p}{3} + 1\right) \\
&= \frac{(p+1)(p+2)(p+3)}{3},
\end{aligned}$$

and Step II is completed, as is the proof by mathematical induction.

Example 2. Prove the following identity for all positive integers n:

$$\sin\left[\theta + \frac{(2n-1)\pi}{2}\right] = (-1)^{n-1}\cos\theta.$$

Solution by mathematical induction:

I. For $n = 1$ the identity becomes $\sin(\theta + \pi/2) = \cos\theta$; this is a reduction formula, and is valid by the theorem of Section 10-3 on reduction formulas.

II. Let us *assume* the identity valid for $n = p$, that is,

$$\sin\left[\theta + \frac{(2p-1)\pi}{2}\right] = (-1)^{p-1}\cos\theta. \tag{4}$$

We wish to prove the identity for $n = p + 1$, that is, we wish to *prove*

$$\sin\left[\theta + \frac{(2p+1)\pi}{2}\right] = (-1)^{p}\cos\theta.$$

We may write the left member as

$$\sin\left[\theta + \frac{(2p-1)\pi}{2} + \pi\right];$$

using the reduction formula $\sin(\alpha + \pi) = -\sin\alpha$ on this expression, with

$$\alpha = \theta + \frac{(2p-1)\pi}{2},$$

we obtain

$$\begin{aligned}\sin\left[\theta + \frac{(2p+1)\pi}{2}\right] &= -\sin\left[\theta + \frac{(2p-1)\pi}{2}\right]\\ &= -(-1)^{p-1}\cos\theta \quad \text{[by (4)]}\\ &= (-1)^{p}\cos\theta,\end{aligned}$$

and the desired relation is proved. This completes the proof by mathematical induction.

EXERCISE GROUP 11-1

Use mathematical induction to prove each of the following, where n is any positive integer.

1. $1^2 + 2^2 + 3^2 + \cdots + n^2 = \dfrac{n(n+1)(2n+1)}{6}$
2. $1^3 + 2^3 + 3^3 + \cdots + n^3 = \dfrac{n^2(n+1)^2}{4}$
3. $\dfrac{1}{1\cdot 2} + \dfrac{1}{2\cdot 3} + \dfrac{1}{3\cdot 4} + \cdots + \dfrac{1}{n(n+1)} = \dfrac{n}{n+1}$
4. $\dfrac{1}{1\cdot 3} + \dfrac{1}{3\cdot 5} + \dfrac{1}{5\cdot 7} + \cdots + \dfrac{1}{(2n-1)(2n+1)} = \dfrac{n}{2n+1}$
5. $1 + 2\cdot 2 + 3\cdot 2^2 + 4\cdot 2^3 + \cdots + n\cdot 2^{n-1} = 1 + (n-1)2^n$
6. $2 + 2^2 + 2^3 + \cdots + 2^n = 2^{n+1} - 2$
7. $1 + 2\cdot 3 + 3\cdot 3^2 + 4\cdot 3^3 + \cdots + n\cdot 3^{n-1} = \dfrac{(2n-1)3^n + 1}{4}$
8. $1\cdot 2\cdot 3 + 2\cdot 3\cdot 4 + 3\cdot 4\cdot 5 + \cdots + n(n+1)(n+2)$
   $= \frac{1}{4}n(n+1)(n+2)(n+3)$

9. $\dfrac{1}{2\cdot 3\cdot 4}+\dfrac{2}{3\cdot 4\cdot 5}+\dfrac{3}{4\cdot 5\cdot 6}+\cdots+\dfrac{n}{(n+1)(n+2)(n+3)}$
$=\dfrac{n(n+1)}{4(n+2)(n+3)}$

10. $\dfrac{1}{3\cdot 4\cdot 5}+\dfrac{2}{4\cdot 5\cdot 6}+\dfrac{3}{5\cdot 6\cdot 7}+\cdots+\dfrac{n}{(n+2)(n+3)(n+4)}$
$=\dfrac{n(n+1)}{6(n+3)(n+4)}$

11. $1+2r+3r^2+\cdots+nr^{n-1}=\dfrac{1-(n+1)r^n+nr^{n+1}}{(1-r)^2}$

12. $2+2\cdot 3r^2+3\cdot 4r^4+\cdots+n(n+1)r^{2n-2}$
$=\dfrac{2-(n+1)(n+2)r^{2n}+2n(n+2)r^{2n+2}-n(n+1)r^{2n+4}}{(1-r^2)^3}$

13. $1^2\cdot 2+2^2\cdot 2^2+3^2\cdot 2^3+\cdots+n^2\cdot 2^n=2^{n+1}(n^2-2n+3)-6$

14. $2\cdot 3^2+2^2\cdot 3^3+2^3\cdot 3^4+\cdots+2^n\cdot 3^{n+1}=\frac{18}{5}(6^n-1)$

15. $x+4x+7x+\cdots+(3n-2)x=\frac{1}{2}n(3n-1)x$

16. $(1-2x)+(3-4x)x^2+\cdots+(2n-1-2nx)x^{2n-2}$
$=\dfrac{1-(2n+1)x^{2n}-2nx^{2n+1}}{(1+x)^2}$

17. $\sin x+\sin 2x+\cdots+\sin nx=\dfrac{\cos\frac{1}{2}x-\cos(n+\frac{1}{2})x}{2\sin\frac{1}{2}x}$

18. $\cos x+\cos 2x+\cdots+\cos nx=\dfrac{\sin(n+\frac{1}{2})x}{2\sin\frac{1}{2}x}-\dfrac{1}{2}$

19. $\sin(\theta+n\pi)=(-1)^n\sin\theta$

20. $\cos(\theta+n\pi)=(-1)^n\cos\theta$

21. $\cos\left[\theta+\dfrac{(2n-1)\pi}{2}\right]=(-1)^n\sin\theta$

22. $(\cos\theta+i\sin\theta)^n=\cos n\theta+i\sin n\theta,\quad (i=\sqrt{-1})$

23. $\sec\theta\sec 2\theta+\sec 2\theta\sec 3\theta+\cdots+\sec n\theta\sec(n+1)\theta$
$=\csc\theta\tan(n+1)\theta-\sec\theta$

24. $\sin^3\theta+\sin^3 2\theta+\cdots+\sin^3 n\theta$
$=\dfrac{1}{8}\left[3\,\dfrac{\cos\frac{1}{2}\theta-\cos(n+\frac{1}{2})\theta}{\sin\frac{1}{2}\theta}-\dfrac{\cos\frac{3}{2}\theta-\cos 3(n+\frac{1}{2})\theta}{\sin\frac{3}{2}\theta}\right]$

25. $\cos^3\theta+\cos^3 2\theta+\cdots+\cos^3 n\theta$
$=\dfrac{1}{4}\left[\dfrac{3\sin(n+\frac{1}{2})\theta}{2\sin\frac{1}{2}\theta}+\dfrac{\sin 3(n+\frac{1}{2})\theta}{2\sin\frac{3}{2}\theta}-2\right]$

26. The sum of the interior angles of a polygon of n sides is equal to $(n-2)\cdot 180°$.

27. $10^{n+1}+10^n+1$ is divisible by 3.

28. $10^{n+1}+3\cdot 10^n+5$ is divisible by 9.

29. $10^{2n-1}+1$ is divisible by 11.

30. $2\cdot 10^{n+2}+4\cdot 10^n+3$ is divisible by 9.

31. $10^{2n}+2\cdot 10^{2n-1}+1$ is divisible by 11.

32. $4\cdot 10^{2n}+9\cdot 10^{2n-1}+5$ is divisible by 99.

11–4 THE BINOMIAL FORMULA

By direct multiplication the following formulas may be obtained:

$$\begin{aligned}
(u+v)^1 &= u+v,\\
(u+v)^2 &= u^2+2uv+v^2,\\
(u+v)^3 &= u^3+3u^2v+3uv^2+v^3,\\
(u+v)^4 &= u^4+4u^3v+6u^2v^2+4uv^3+v^4,\\
(u+v)^5 &= u^5+5u^4v+10u^3v^2+10u^2v^3+5uv^4+v^5.
\end{aligned}$$

A careful inspection of these expansions reveals certain properties which we shall assume (for the present) can be applied to the expansion of $(u+v)^n$ for any positive integer n. These properties are:

I. The first term in the expansion of $(u+v)^n$ is u^n.

II. The second term in the expansion of $(u+v)^n$ is $nu^{n-1}v$.

III. The exponent of u decreases by 1 from term to term, the exponent of v increases by 1 from term to term, and the sum of the exponents of u and v in each term is n.

IV. If the coefficient of any term is multiplied by the exponent of u in that term and if the product is divided by the number of that term, the quotient gives the coefficient of the next term.

V. There are $n+1$ terms in the expansion of $(u+v)^n$.

VI. The coefficients of terms equidistant from the ends of the expansion are equal.

Example 1. In the expansion of $(u+v)^{15}$, the second term is $15u^{14}v$, by Property II. By Property IV, the coefficient of the third term is $(15\cdot 14)\div 2 = 105$, so that by Property III the third term is $105u^{13}v^2$. By Property V there are 16 terms in the expansion. By Properties VI and III the last term is v^{15}, the 15th term is $15uv^{14}$, and the 14th term is $105u^2v^{13}$.

If the above properties are to be valid for any positive integer n, the resulting formula for $(u+v)^n$ must be

$$(u+v)^n = u^n + nu^{n-1}v + \frac{n(n-1)}{2}u^{n-2}v^2 + \frac{n(n-1)(n-2)}{2\cdot 3}u^{n-3}v^3 + \cdots + v^n. \tag{5}$$

This is the *binomial formula*. Its validity for the positive integers will be proved in Section 11–6. The case where n is a negative integer or a rational number will be discussed in Section 11–7.

The coefficients of the terms in the expansion of $(u+v)^n$ in Eq. (5) are known as the *binomial coefficients* corresponding to the exponent n.

Example 2. Expand $(2x + y)^8$.

Solution. In formula (5) set $u = 2x$, $v = y$, and $n = 8$. We then have

$$
\begin{aligned}
(2x + y)^8 &= (2x)^8 + 8(2x)^7 y + \frac{8 \cdot 7}{2}(2x)^6 y^2 + \frac{8 \cdot 7 \cdot 6}{2 \cdot 3}(2x)^5 y^3 \\
&\quad + \frac{8 \cdot 7 \cdot 6 \cdot 5}{2 \cdot 3 \cdot 4}(2x)^4 y^4 + \frac{8 \cdot 7 \cdot 6 \cdot 5 \cdot 4}{2 \cdot 3 \cdot 4 \cdot 5}(2x)^3 y^5 \\
&\quad + \frac{8 \cdot 7 \cdot 6 \cdot 5 \cdot 4 \cdot 3}{2 \cdot 3 \cdot 4 \cdot 5 \cdot 6}(2x)^2 y^6 + 8(2x)y^7 + y^8 \\
&= 256x^8 + 1024x^7 y + 1792x^6 y^2 + 1792x^5 y^3 + 1120x^4 y^4 + 448x^3 y^5 \\
&\quad + 112x^2 y^6 + 16xy^7 + y^8.
\end{aligned}
$$

Note that the coefficients in the final form of this expansion are not the binomial coefficients. They are products of the binomial coefficients and powers of the coefficients that appear in u and v.

Example 3. Expand $(ax - by)^7$.

Solution. We have $u = ax$, $v = -by$, and $n = 7$. The binomial formula gives

$$
\begin{aligned}
(ax - by)^7 &= (ax)^7 + 7(ax)^6(-by) + \frac{7 \cdot 6}{2}(ax)^5(-by)^2 + \frac{7 \cdot 6 \cdot 5}{2 \cdot 3}(ax)^4(-by)^3 \\
&\quad + \frac{7 \cdot 6 \cdot 5 \cdot 4}{2 \cdot 3 \cdot 4}(ax)^3(-by)^4 + \frac{7 \cdot 6 \cdot 5 \cdot 4 \cdot 3}{2 \cdot 3 \cdot 4 \cdot 5}(ax)^2(-by)^5 \\
&\quad + 7(ax)(-by)^6 + (-by)^7 \\
&= a^7x^7 - 7a^6bx^6y + 21a^5b^2x^5y^2 - 35a^4b^3x^4y^3 + 35a^3b^4x^3y^4 \\
&\quad - 21a^2b^5x^2y^5 + 7ab^6xy^6 - b^7y^7.
\end{aligned}
$$

Note that if the first term of the binomial has a plus sign and the second term has a minus sign, the signs of the terms of the expansion are alternately plus and minus.

EXERCISE GROUP 11–2

In each of Exercises 1–8, obtain the first five binomial coefficients for the given value of n.

1. $n = 13$
2. $n = 17$
3. $n = 23$
4. $n = 29$
5. $n = 37$
6. $n = 41$
7. $n = 53$
8. $n = 47$

Expand each of the expressions in Exercises 9–32, and simplify where possible.

9. $(x - y)^5$
10. $(x + y)^7$
11. $(u - v)^6$
12. $(a + b)^6$
13. $(x - ay)^5$
14. $(bx + y)^7$
15. $(x + 2y)^6$
16. $(3x - y)^4$
17. $(2x - 3y)^5$
18. $(2x - \frac{1}{3}y)^4$
19. $(\frac{1}{3}x - \frac{1}{2}y)^7$
20. $(\frac{1}{2}x - 3y^2)^4$

21. $\left(x+\frac{1}{x}\right)^7$ 22. $(-x^2+2y)^5$ 23. $(ax^{-1}-by^{-1})^5$

24. $(2x^{-1}+y)^4$ 25. $(x^2-2x^{-3})^4$ 26. $(ax^{-1}-b)^6$

27. $(1-i)^5$ 28. $(2-3i)^4$ 29. $\left(\frac{\sqrt{3}}{2}+\frac{1}{2}i\right)^6$

30. $(1-y^{1-x})^6$ 31. $(x^{-y}+y^{-x})^4$ 32. $(u^{1-x}-v^{1-x})^5$

Write the first three terms in the expansion of each of the expressions in Exercises 33–36.

33. $(1.04)^{15}$ 34. $(1.025)^{18}$ 35. $(1.03)^{25}$ 36. $[(a-b)+c]^k$

Use the binomial formula to obtain the value of the following expressions, using only enough terms to obtain a result accurate to three decimal places.

37. $(1.03)^{15}$ 38. $(1.04)^{12}$ 39. $(1.05)^{10}$ 40. $(1.025)^9$

11-5 THE GENERAL TERM IN THE EXPANSION OF $(u+v)^n$

Each term after the first in the binomial formula (5) may be obtained from the term which precedes it. However, no method has been described for obtaining a single term. We shall derive a formula which will give any term of the expansion independently of the others. In the binomial expansion (5), consider the term which contains v^r. By Property III it also contains u^{n-r}. By Property IV the denominator of the coefficient is the product of all the integers from 1 to r; this product is called *factorial* r and is written as

$$r! = 1\cdot 2\cdot 3\cdots(r-2)(r-1)r.$$

By Property IV again, the numerator of the coefficient contains r factors, the first being n, and each succeeding factor being one less than the preceding. The last or rth factor in the numerator is then $n-r+1$. The desired term is

$$\frac{n(n-1)(n-2)\cdots(n-r+1)}{r!}u^{n-r}v^r, \qquad r>0. \tag{6}$$

This is the $(r+1)$-*term* in the binomial expansion of $(u+v)^n$. An alternative form of (6) which can be obtained by multiplying the numerator and denominator by $(n-r)!$ is

$$\frac{n!}{r!(n-r)!}u^{n-r}v^r;$$

this form may also be used when $r=0$, if we *define* $0!=1$.

Example 1. Find the term involving y^5 in the expansion of $(2x^2 + y)^{10}$.

Solution. By formula (6), with $n = 10$ and $r = 5$, the desired term is

$$\frac{10 \cdot 9 \cdot 8 \cdot 7 \cdot 6}{1 \cdot 2 \cdot 3 \cdot 4 \cdot 5}(2x^2)^5 y^5 = 8064x^{10}y^5.$$

Since $r = 5$, this term is the sixth one.

Example 2. Find the 7th term in the expansion of $(x^2 - 3y)^{10}$.

Solution. We must have $r + 1 = 7$. Hence we use formula (6) with $r = 6$, $n = 10$, and obtain for the desired term

$$\frac{10 \cdot 9 \cdot 8 \cdot 7 \cdot 6 \cdot 5}{1 \cdot 2 \cdot 3 \cdot 4 \cdot 5 \cdot 6}(x^2)^4(-3y)^6 = 210x^8 \cdot 3^6 y^6 = 153090x^8y^6.$$

EXERCISE GROUP 11–3

In Exercises 1–21, find only the specified term in the expansion of each expression.

1. Term involving y^6 in $(x + y)^{10}$
2. Term involving v^5 in $(u - v)^{12}$
3. Term involving x^9 in $(x - 2y)^{15}$
4. Term involving y^{10} in $(x^3 - y^2)^{14}$ [*Hint:* $y^{10} = (y^2)^5$.]
5. Term involving y^{18} in $(ax^{1/2} - by^3)^{17}$
6. Term involving x^8 in $(\frac{1}{2}x^2 - 3y)^{14}$
7. Seventh term of $(2x - 3y)^{10}$
8. Sixth term of $(\frac{1}{3}x^2 - 2y^3)^{17}$
9. Fifth term of $(1 + 0.04)^{11} = (1.04)^{11}$
10. Fourth term of $(1.03)^{13}$
11. Middle term of $\left(x - \frac{1}{x}\right)^{14}$
12. Seventh term of $(2x^{1/2} - y^{1/3})^{12}$
13. Twentieth term of $\left(x - \frac{y}{x}\right)^{24}$
14. Middle term of $(u - v)^{14}$
15. Seventh term of $(\sqrt{3x} - \sqrt[3]{2y})^8$
16. Fifth term of $(u^{x+y} - v^{x-y})^{10}$
17. Term not involving x in $\left(x^2 + \frac{2}{x}\right)^{12}$
18. Term not involving x in $(2x^2 - x^{-1/2})^{10}$
19. Term not involving y in $(2u^{x+2y} - u^{x-y})^{15}$
20. Term involving x^2y^5 in $(x - y)^3(x + 2y)^4$
21. Term involving x^4y^5 in $(x + y^2)^4(x + y)^4$
22. If a_1, a_2, a_3, and a_4 are any four consecutive binomial coefficients for any n, prove that

$$\frac{a_1}{a_1 + a_2} + \frac{a_3}{a_3 + a_4} = \frac{2a_2}{a_2 + a_3}.$$

11-6 PROOF OF THE BINOMIAL FORMULA

To complete the treatment of the binomial formula, we shall now give a proof, by the method of mathematical induction. Throughout the proof, n is taken as a positive integer.

I. The formula has been verified for several values of n in Section 11-4.

II. *Assume* the formula for $n = p$; thus,

$$(u + v)^p = u^p + pu^{p-1}v + \frac{p(p-1)}{2!}u^{p-2}v^2 + \cdots + \frac{p(p-1)(p-2)\cdots(p-r+1)}{r!}u^{p-r}v^r + \cdots + v^p. \quad (7)$$

To *prove* the formula for $n = p + 1$, that is, to prove

$$(u + v)^{p+1} = u^{p+1} + (p+1)u^p v + \frac{(p+1)p}{2!}u^{p-1}v^2 + \cdots + \frac{(p+1)p(p-1)\cdots(p-r+2)}{r!}u^{p-r+1}v^r + \cdots + v^{p+1}, \quad (8)$$

let us multiply $(u + v)^p$ of (7) by $u + v$ in order to get $(u + v)^{p+1}$. It is clear that the first term of the product will be u^{p+1}. It is enough, then, to show that the term in the expansion of $(u + v)^{p+1}$ which involves v^r is as shown in (8). This term will be the term of (7) in v^r multiplied by u plus the term of (7) in v^{r-1} multiplied by v. Thus the desired term is

$$\frac{p(p-1)(p-2)\cdots(p-r+1)}{r!}u^{p-r}v^r \cdot u + \frac{p(p-1)\cdots(p-r+2)}{(r-1)!}u^{p-r+1}v^{r-1} \cdot v$$

$$= \frac{p(p-1)(p-2)\cdots(p-r+2)}{(r-1)!}\left(\frac{p-r+1}{r} + 1\right) \cdot u^{p-r+1}v^r$$

$$= \frac{p(p-1)(p-2)\cdots(p-r+2)}{(r-1)!} \cdot \frac{p+1}{r}u^{p-r+1}v^r$$

$$= \frac{(p+1)p(p-1)\cdots(p-r+2)}{r!}u^{p-r+1}v^r.$$

This is the same as the term in (8) involving v^r, and Step II is completed.

The proof of the binomial formula, by mathematical induction, has now been completed.

11-7 THE BINOMIAL SERIES

The validity of the binomial formula when n is not a positive integer depends on the ratio v/u. If we set $w = v/u$, we may write $(u + v)^n = u^n[1 + (v/u)]^n = u^n(1 + w)^n$ and we may discuss the expansion of $(1 + w)^n$. Applying the first four properties of Section 11-4 with $u = 1$ and with v replaced by w, we obtain (in a purely formal manner, without proof) the expansion

$$(1 + w)^n = 1 + nw + \frac{n(n-1)}{2!}w^2 + \cdots + \frac{n(n-1)\cdots(n-r+1)}{r!}w^r + \cdots. \quad (9)$$

If n is a positive integer, the coefficients of w^{n+1} and all higher powers of w vanish, and (9) becomes another form of the binomial formula. However, if n is any real number other than a positive integer or zero, the expansion in (9) does not end, and is called the *binomial series*. A detailed discussion of this series must be reserved for a more advanced course in mathematics, but the relevant result may be stated here. If n is not a positive integer, and if w is numerically less than 1, $(-1 < w < 1)$, then a finite number of terms of the expansion in the right member of (9) may be used to approximate the value of $(1 + w)^n$; in general, the greater the number of terms used, the better the approximation will be.

Example. Compute $\sqrt{23} = (23)^{1/2}$ correct to 4 decimal places.

Solution. $(23)^{1/2} = (25 - 2)^{1/2} = 25^{1/2}(1 - \frac{2}{25})^{1/2} = 5(1 - 0.08)^{1/2}$

$$= 5\left[1 + \tfrac{1}{2}(-0.08) + \frac{\frac{1}{2}(-\frac{1}{2})}{1 \cdot 2}(-0.08)^2 + \frac{\frac{1}{2}(-\frac{1}{2})(-\frac{3}{2})}{1 \cdot 2 \cdot 3}(-0.08)^3 + \cdots\right]$$

$$= 5\,[1 - 0.04 - 0.0008 - 0.000032 - \cdots].$$

To obtain 4 correct decimals it is advisable to take enough terms so that the first neglected term has a zero in the fifth decimal place, even when multiplied by the coefficient 5. The terms shown are accordingly sufficient, and the result, correct to 4 decimals, is

$$\sqrt{23} = 4.7958.$$

EXERCISE GROUP 11-4

In Exercises 1-12, write the first four terms of each expansion and simplify where possible.

1. $(1 + y)^{1/2}$
2. $(1 + v)^{-2}$
3. $(1 + 2x)^{-1/2}$
4. $(1 - v)^{-3/2}$
5. $(1 - x^2)^{-2/3}$
6. $(1 - 2x^2)^{3/2}$
7. $(1 + av)^{-3}$
8. $(1 + 3x^2)^{-3}$
9. $(1 - ax)^{5/2}$
10. $(1 + x)^{1/x}$
11. $\left(1 + \dfrac{1}{x}\right)^x$
12. $\left(x + \dfrac{1}{x}\right)^{5/2}$

Find the specified term in each of Exercises 13–16.

13. Term involving x^6 in $(1 - x)^{2/3}$
14. Term involving x^4 in $(1 + x)^{-3/2}$
15. Term involving x^9 in $(1 - 2x^{1/3})^{-1}$
16. Term involving $x^{7/2}$ in $(1 + x^{1/2})^{-2/3}$

Find the number of the first term with a minus sign in each of Exercises 17–19.

17. $(1 + \frac{2}{3}x)^{17/3}$
18. $(1 + 3x)^{8/3}$
19. $(1 + x^{1/2})^{9/2}$

Which terms are the first two consecutive ones with the same sign in Exercises 20–22?

20. $(1 - u)^{11/2}$
21. $(1 - v)^{13/3}$
22. $(1 - 3x)^{5/3}$

Compute the first three terms in the expansion of each expression in Exercises 23–28.

23. $(1.03)^{-15}$
24. $(1.04)^{15/2}$
25. $(17)^{1/4}$
26. $(1.05)^{-18}$
27. $(28)^{1/3}$
28. $(1.03)^{21/4}$

29. Find the first four terms in the expansion of $[1 + (x - 2)]^{1/2}$ in powers of $x - 2$, and tell for what values of x the expansion is valid.
30. Obtain the first four terms in the expansion of $(1 + x)^{-1}$ if $|x| > 1$. [*Hint:* Write the expression as $x^{-1}(1 + x^{-1})^{-1}$.]
31. Obtain the first four terms when $(1 + x)^{-2}$ is expanded so that the expansion is valid for $-1 < x < 3$. [*Hint:* Write the expression as $2^{-2}\,(1 + (x - 1)/2)^{-2}$.]

11-8 CONTINUOUS CONVERSION. THE LAW OF GROWTH

In Section 9–14 it was seen that if $\$P$ is invested at an interest rate r compounded j times a year, and if A_{jt} is the amount at the end of t years, then

$$A_{jt} = P\left(1 + \frac{r}{j}\right)^{jt}. \tag{10}$$

If we think of j in this expression as becoming greater and greater, or "increasing without limit," and at the same time the interest periods or *conversion periods* becoming shorter and shorter or approaching zero in length, we have the situation known as "continuous conversion." To express this analytically, let us write (10) as

$$A = P\left[\left(1 + \frac{r}{j}\right)^{j/r}\right]^{rt}.$$

If we replace r/j by x and j/r by $1/x$ and expand by means of the binomial series, we have

$$\begin{aligned}
A &= P[(1 + x)^{1/x}]^{rt}\\
&= P\left[1^{1/x} + \frac{1}{x}\cdot 1^{(1/x)-1}x + \frac{(1/x)[(1/x) - 1]}{2!}\,1^{(1/x)-2}x^2 + \cdots\right]^{rt}\\
&= P\left[1^{1/x} + 1^{(1-x)/x} + \frac{1 - x}{2!}\cdot 1^{(1-2x)/x} + \cdots\right]^{rt}\\
&= P\left[1 + 1 + \frac{1 - x}{2!} + \frac{(1 - x)(1 - 2x)}{3!} + \cdots\right]^{rt},
\end{aligned}$$

where in the last equation we use the fact that any power of 1 is 1; as j increases without limit x will approach zero, and it can be shown that the above relation reduces to

$$A = P\left(1 + 1 + \frac{1}{2!} + \frac{1}{3!} + \cdots\right)^{rt}.$$

If the value of the expression in parentheses is represented by the letter e, we obtain the formula

$$\boxed{A = Pe^{rt}.} \qquad (11)$$

This formula gives the total amount A at the end of t years if an initial amount P grows at a rate r compounded continuously.

Formula (11) *also gives the population A at any time t if P is the population at time $t = 0$, and r is the relative rate of growth per unit time.* This formula is accordingly sometimes called the *law of growth.*

Note: The number e as obtained here is the same number that was used in Section 9–15 as the base of natural logarithms. It is seen here that its value is given by

$$\boxed{e = 1 + 1 + \frac{1}{2!} + \frac{1}{3!} + \cdots.}$$

This expression, and others appearing above, are *infinite series*, which are studied in calculus. As with any infinite series, there is the question of the manner in which this series represents a number. Without attempting a proof here, we shall be content to state that the series does represent a number which can be approximated as closely as desired by using a sufficient number of terms of the series. The value of e, to five decimal places, is

$$e = 2.71828.$$

Example 1. Compare the amount of \$1 at 6% interest compounded quarterly with the amount at 6% compounded continuously, at the end of 2 yr.

Solution. By (10) the first amount is

$$A_1 = \left(1 + \frac{0.06}{4}\right)^8 = (1.015)^8 = 1.125 \quad \text{[by logarithms]}.$$

The second amount, by (11), is

$$A_2 = e^{2(0.06)} = e^{0.12}.$$

Using logarithms to compute A_2, we have

$$\log A_2 = 0.12 \log e = 0.12(0.4343) = 0.0521,$$

from which we find $A_2 = 1.127$. Thus the two amounts actually differ by little.

Example 2. If $A = Pe^{rt}$ is the law by which the number of bacteria in a culture increases and $r = 0.0001$ for t measured in seconds, find A at the end of 2 hr in terms of P.

Solution. For $t = 7200$ sec (i.e., 2 hr), we have

$$A = Pe^{0.0001(7200)} = Pe^{0.72} \quad \text{or} \quad A/P = e^{0.72}.$$

Taking logarithms, we have

$$\log A/P = 0.72 \log e = 0.72(0.4343) = 0.3127.$$

Therefore

$$A/P = 2.054 \quad \text{and} \quad A = 2.054P,$$

so that the population is slightly more than doubled.

EXERCISE GROUP 11–5

In Exercises 1–18, determine the value of x which satisfies the given equation.

1. $x = 1269e^{0.63}$	2. $x = 3.281e^{1.23}$	3. $x = 35.14e^{2.15}$
4. $x = 0.302e^{0.74}$	5. $x = 7.263e^{-18.3}$	6. $x = 317.2e^{-0.0312}$
7. $6129 = xe^{0.13}$	8. $382.1 = xe^{6.17}$	9. $27.83 = xe^{2.31}$
10. $8.396 = xe^{0.0094}$	11. $0.9387 = xe^{-0.73}$	12. $82.79 = xe^{-3.62}$
13. $27.13 = 32.21e^{x}$	14. $637.1 = 284.7e^{0.3x}$	15. $4823 = 2463e^{24x}$
16. $0.7136 = 0.0423e^{0.08x}$	17. $7.396 = 86.24e^{-2.4x}$	18. $78.13 = 3.462e^{-0.63x}$

19. If the population of a city increases from 2,861,190 to 3,900,000 in 25 yr, what is the rate of growth?

20. If a population increases at a rate $r = 0.002$ for time measured in years, how many years will be required for the population to double?

21. If the population of a city is assumed to grow in accordance with the law of growth and if the population was 1,250,000 in 1920 and 4,100,000 in 1950, what population should be expected in 1980?

22. If the number of bacteria in a bottle of milk doubles in 2 hr, determine the increase in 12 hr.

Radium decomposes according to the law

$$R = R_0 e^{kt},$$

where R represents the amount of radium present at any time t, R_0 is the value of R at time $t = 0$, and k is the rate of decomposition per unit of time.

23. If 8% of an amount of radium is lost in 324 yr, how long will it take for one-half of that amount to disappear?

24. After 25 yr a quantity of radium has decreased to 52.4 gm. At the end of the next 25 yr 51.8 gm remain. How many grams were there initially?

The temperature of a cooling body changes according to the law $T = T_0e^{kt}$, where T represents the difference in temperature between the cooling body and the surrounding air at any time t, T_0 is the value of T at time $t = 0$, and k is the rate of change of T per unit of time.

25. If T changes from 85° to 45° in 50 min, what will be the value of T at the end of 2 hr?

26. If $T_0 = 120°$, and $T = 70°$ after 50 min, how long will it take for T to reach 50°?

A chemical reaction transforms one substance into another according to the law $S = S_0e^{kt}$, where S represents the amount of the first substance untransformed at any time t, S_0 is the value of S at time $t = 0$, and k is the rate of the transformation per unit of time.

27. If at the end of one hour 55 gm of a substance remain and at the end of 4 hr 21 gm still remain, how many grams were there initially?

28. If two-thirds of a substance remains after 5 min, how much will remain after 12 min? How long will it take for half of the substance to be transformed?

29. What rate of continuous conversion would give the same return on an investment as 6% compounded quarterly?

30. What rate compounded annually is equivalent to 4% continuous conversion?

31. What rate compounded quarterly is equivalent to 6% continuous conversion? [*Hint:* $e^{0.015} = 1.0151$.]

32. What rate of continuous conversion would give the same return on an investment as 6% compounded semiannually?

33. Which would be worth more in 5 yr, $1000 invested at 4% compounded quarterly or $1000 invested at $3\frac{1}{2}$% continuous conversion? By how much?

SUPPLEMENTARY EXERCISES FOR CHAPTER 11

In Exercises 1–7, find only the specified term of each expansion.

1. The tenth term of $(2x - y)^{15}$
2. The sixth term of $(ax^2 + by)^{11}$
3. The fifteenth term of $\left(ax - \frac{b}{x}\right)^{21}$
4. The middle term of $(3x - 2y^2)^8$
5. The middle term of $(\frac{1}{2}x - 2y)^{16}$
6. The term involving x^7 in $(x + by)^{15}$
7. The term involving x^9 in $\left(x^2 - \frac{y}{x}\right)^{12}$

In Exercises 8–19, write the first four terms of each expansion and simplify where possible.

8. $(1 - 2x)^{2/3}$
9. $\left(1 + \frac{2}{x}\right)^{3/2}$
10. $\left(x - \frac{1}{x}\right)^{x}$
11. $\left(1 + \frac{x}{2}\right)^{2/x}$
12. $(1 + ax)^{-3}$
13. $\sqrt[3]{124} = (125 - 1)^{1/3}$
14. $(65)^{1/6}$
15. $\sqrt[5]{244}$
16. $(1.03)^{-18}$
17. $(1.025)^{22}$
18. $(1.035)^{20}$
19. $(1.05)^{35}$

Use mathematical induction to prove each of the statements in Exercises 20–23, where n is any positive integer.

20. $3 + 3^2 + 3^3 + \cdots + 3^n = \frac{3}{2}[3^n - 1]$

21. $1 + 2 \cdot 3 + 3 \cdot 3^2 + 4 \cdot 3^3 + \cdots + n \cdot 3^{n-1} = \frac{1}{4}[(2n - 1)3^n + 1]$

22. $\sin\left[\theta + \dfrac{(2n - 1)\pi}{2}\right] = (-1)^{n-1} \cos\theta$

23. $[\cos\theta - i\sin\theta]^n = \cos n\theta - i\sin n\theta, \quad i = \sqrt{-1}$

24. If the number of bacteria in a given culture doubles in 1.5 hr, determine the increase in 15 hr.

25. If 5%of a quantity of radium disappears in 156 yr, how long will it take for 25% to disappear?

26. What rate of continuous conversion is equivalent to 5% compounded semiannually?

CHAPTER 12

Systems of Equations

12–1 INTRODUCTION

In Chapters 4 and 8 we were interested in the problem of finding the zeros of polynomials, or, equivalently, of finding the abscissas of points where the graph of a polynomial either crosses or touches the x-axis. If, instead of the x-axis, the graph of a second function is involved in this manner, the problem becomes that of finding the points of intersection of two curves when they are drawn in the same coordinate system. Algebraically, this means that we are to find pairs of numbers which at the same time satisfy two equations in two unknowns. A *solution* of a system of two equations is a pair of numbers that satisfies both equations; such a pair of numbers constitutes *one* solution.

A term ax^my^n, where m and n are positive integers (or zero) and $a \neq 0$, is said to be of degree $m + n$ in x and y. A sum of terms of this form is a *polynomial in x and y*, and the *degree* of the polynomial is the degree of the term of highest degree.

Example. $2x + 3y^2 - 4xy + 7x^2y$ is a polynomial of degree 3 in x and y.

In this chapter we shall consider various cases of solving a pair of equations. The three most useful cases are: (1) both equations are of the first degree, or *linear*, in x and y; (2) one equation is linear in x and y and the other is of second degree in x and y; (3) both equations are linear in x^2 and y^2, that is, of the form

$$ax^2 + by^2 = c.$$

In addition, systems of 3 or 4 linear equations in 3 or 4 unknowns respectively will be considered. In cases where two unknowns are involved a geometric treatment of the problem may be instructive, and will often be included.

It is worthy of mention here that the methods to be developed will apply equally well to certain systems of equations involving trigonometric functions. However, a separate section will be devoted to these systems, in order to emphasize some special considerations.

12–2 SYSTEMS OF TWO LINEAR EQUATIONS IN TWO UNKNOWNS

Consider the equation $ax + by = c$ which, if $b \neq 0$, can be written in the form

$$y = -\frac{ax}{b} + \frac{c}{b}.$$

As was seen in Section 4–2 the graph of this equation is a straight line, with slope $m = -(a/b)$. If $b = 0$ and $a \neq 0$, then $ax + by = c$ reduces to

$$x = \frac{c}{a},$$

which also represents a straight line. If $a = b = 0$, then $ax + by = c$ reduces to $c = 0$, which is trivial. Hence the graph of $ax + by = c$ is always a straight line, and two such graphs will either (1) intersect in a single point, or (2) be parallel, or (3) be coincident. In case (1) the coordinates (x, y) of the point of intersection satisfy the equations of the two graphs and constitute the solution of the problem. In case (2) no solution exists and the two equations are said to be *inconsistent*. In case (3) the pair of equations has infinitely many solutions, since the coordinates of every point on the graph are a solution, and the equations are said to be *dependent*.

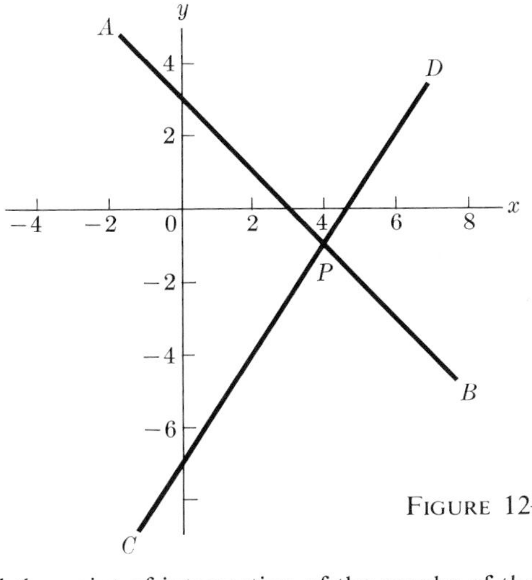

FIGURE 12–1

Example 1. Find the point of intersection of the graphs of the equations:

$$\begin{cases} x + y = 3, \\ 3x - 2y = 14. \end{cases}$$

Geometric solution. In Fig. 12–1, AB is the graph of the first equation, and CD is the graph of the second equation. The point of intersection P of the two graphs is the only point on both lines. The coordinates of P satisfy both equations and represent the desired solution of the problem. From the graph, P seems to be the point $(4, -1)$. These coordinates satisfy both equations, and hence are the exact coordinates of the point of intersection of the two lines.

Algebraic solution. Multiply both members of the first equation by 2, to make the term in y similar to that in the second equation, and add the resulting members to the corresponding members of the second equation. This eliminates y and gives

$$5x = 20 \qquad \text{or} \qquad x = 4.$$

Substitute this value in the first equation, and obtain

$$4 + y = 3 \qquad \text{or} \qquad y = -1.$$

Thus the desired solution is

$$x = 4, \qquad y = -1.$$

Example 2. Determine whether there is a point of intersection of the graphs of $2x - 3y = 5$ and $6x - 9y = 10$.

Geometric discussion. In Fig. 12–2, the graph of the first equation is the line AB through the point $(1, -1)$ with slope $\frac{2}{3}$, and the graph of the second equation is the line CD through the point $(\frac{2}{3}, -\frac{2}{3})$, with slope $\frac{2}{3}$. Since the slope is the same in both cases, the lines are parallel. Hence there is no point of intersection and the equations are *inconsistent*.

Algebraic discussion. If the members of the first equation are multiplied by 3, and if the members of the resulting equation are subtracted from the corresponding members of the second equation, we obtain the clearly absurd relation

$$0 = -5.$$

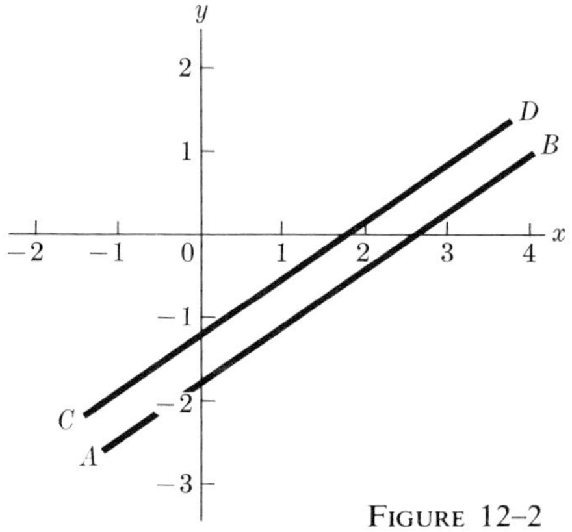

FIGURE 12–2

The steps that were taken were based on the assumption that the given equations had a solution. The fact that an impossible conclusion results proves that the assumption was false. In other words, the two equations have no common solution, and are therefore inconsistent.

Example 3. Find the point of intersection of the graphs of $3x - y = 5$ and $9x - 3y = 15$.

Solution. It is obvious that any pair of values (x, y) which satisfies the first equation also satisfies the second equation. Hence the same straight line is the graph of both equations. It follows that there is no unique solution, but rather that every point on the common line is a solution. The two equations are *dependent;* in fact, if both members of the first equation are multiplied by 3, the second equation is obtained.

To solve the pair of dependent equations algebraically it is sufficient to assign an arbitrary value to x (or y), and then to solve for y (or x) in either equation.

In the preceding examples the geometrical properties were described to illustrate the meaning of the algebraic solution. Frequently only algebraic solutions are required.

Example 4. Solve for x and y: $\begin{cases} 3x + 5y = 9, \\ 7x - 10y = 8. \end{cases}$

Solution. Multiply each member of the first equation by 2 and add each member of the resulting equation to the corresponding member of the second equation, getting $13x = 26$, or $x = 2$. Then set $x = 2$ in the first equation, obtaining $6 + 5y = 9$ or $y = \frac{3}{5}$. The desired solution is $x = 2$, $y = \frac{3}{5}$.

Example 5. Solve the following system for x and y:

$$\begin{cases} x \cos \alpha + y \sin \alpha = p, \\ x \sin \beta + y \cos \beta = q. \end{cases}$$

Solution. The system is linear in x and y. On multiplying the first equation by $\cos \beta$, the second by $\sin \alpha$, and subtracting corresponding members, y is eliminated and we obtain

$$x(\cos \alpha \cos \beta - \sin \alpha \sin \beta) = p \cos \beta - q \sin \alpha.$$

In a similar manner we may eliminate x, and obtain

$$y(\cos \alpha \cos \beta - \sin \alpha \sin \beta) = q \cos \alpha - p \sin \beta.$$

By the addition formula (17) of Section 10–5, the coefficients of x and y in these equations are equal to $\cos (\alpha + \beta)$. We then obtain, as the desired solution,

$$x = (p \cos \beta - q \sin \alpha) \sec (\alpha + \beta), \qquad y = (q \cos \alpha - p \sin \beta) \sec (\alpha + \beta).$$

EXERCISE GROUP 12–1

In Exercises 1–30, solve each system of equations for x and y.

1. $3x - 2y + 6 = 0$
   $2x + 3y = 9$
2. $5x - 3y + 2 = 0$
   $2x + 5y = 8$
3. $3x + 7y = 5$
   $5x + 2y = -2$
4. $2x + 7y = 9$
   $5x - 11y = 13$
5. $4x - 9y = 7$
   $7x - 11y = 5$
6. $10x + 75 = 21y$
   $7x + 3y = 36$
7. $\frac{5}{3}x - \frac{2}{5}y = -\frac{27}{5}$
   $3x + 17y = 8$
8. $6x + 10y = 1$
   $7y - \frac{3}{2}x + \frac{9}{2} = 0$
9. $\frac{1}{5}x - \frac{1}{7}y = \frac{2}{3}$
   $\frac{1}{7}x - \frac{1}{3}y = -\frac{4}{63}$
10. $\dfrac{2x - 1}{3} - \dfrac{3y + 1}{2} = -4$
    $\dfrac{3x + 1}{2} + \dfrac{1}{6} = \dfrac{4y - 1}{3}$
11. $\dfrac{3}{x} + \dfrac{5}{y} = 1$
    $\dfrac{7}{x} + \dfrac{11}{y} = 1$
12. $\dfrac{5}{x} - \dfrac{7}{y} + 9 = 0$
    $\dfrac{3}{x} + \dfrac{1}{y} = 2$
13. $\dfrac{2}{3x} + \dfrac{3}{5y} = 7$
    $\dfrac{7}{2x} - \dfrac{5}{3y} = \frac{38}{3}$
14. $5x - 7y = 3.1$
    $9x + 11y = -1.5$
15. $3x + 5y + 1.6 = 0$
    $7x + 2y = 1.1$
16. $-3x + 2y = -0.5$
    $5x + 7y + 6.4 = 0$

17. $bx + a^2 - ay = b^2 + by$
$ax - by = a^2$

18. $5x + 7y + ab = 0$
$3x - 4y - 2ab = 32ab/35$

19. $2ax - 3by = 2a^2 - 3bc$
$ay - cx = 3bc - 2a^2$

20. $2ax + by - cx = 3ab - bc$
$(a - b)x - by + 2cy = 2ac - b^2$

21. $0.3b^2x + 1.5c^2y = -2.91b^2c^2$
$1.7c^2x - 1.3b^2y = 3.06c^4 + 2.99b^4$

22. $0.4bx + 0.3ay = 0.05ab$
$1.3ax - 3.2by = 2.21a^2 + 6.72b^2$

23. $\dfrac{5x + 4y - 3}{9x - y + 5} + \dfrac{3}{4} = 0$
$\dfrac{2x - 3y + 3}{5x - 4y + 5} - \dfrac{2}{3} = 0$

24. $\dfrac{3x + 2y - 5}{2x - 3y + 4} - \dfrac{2}{3} = 1$
$\dfrac{x - 2y + 3}{-x + y - 5} - \dfrac{3}{4} = 1$

25. $\dfrac{1}{x - 1} + \dfrac{2}{y + 2} = 3$
$\dfrac{3}{2x - 2} + \dfrac{4}{y + 2} = 5$

26. $\dfrac{2}{2x + 3} + \dfrac{1}{y - 1} = 10$
$\dfrac{3}{2x + 3} + \dfrac{4}{y - 1} = 20$

27. $x \sin A + y \sin B = c$
$x \cos A + y \cos B = d$

28. $x \cos A + y \sin A = p$
$x \cos B + y \sin B = q$

29. $x \sin A + y \cos B = c$
$x \cos A + y \sin B = d$

30. $x \cos A + y \sin A = 3$
$x \sin A - y \cos A = 1$

31. If the larger of two numbers is divided by the smaller, the quotient is 3 and the remainder is 2. If the larger is divided by 40 more than the smaller, the quotient is 1 and the remainder is 6. Find the numbers.

32. Find two fractions, with numerators 3 and 4, whose sum is 41/35, and such that when their denominators are interchanged, their sum is 43/35.

33. Two points move at constant rates along the circumference of a circle whose length is 240 ft. When the points move in the same direction around the circle they are together every 12 sec, and when they move in opposite directions they meet every 3 sec. What is the rate of each?

34. Three alloys are as follows, by weight:

A is 50% lead, 20% zinc, and 30% copper;
B is 30% lead, 60% zinc, and 10% copper;
C is 20% lead, 30% zinc, and 50% copper.

How many ounces of *A*, *B*, and *C* must be melted and mixed together in order to obtain 15 oz of an alloy which contains equal amounts (by weight) of lead, zinc, and copper?

35. If 3 is added to both the numerator and denominator of a fraction, its value is $\frac{3}{4}$. If 1 is subtracted from both the numerator and denominator, its value is $\frac{1}{2}$. Find the fraction.

36. *A* takes 2 hr longer than *B* to walk *d* mi, but if *A* should increase his rate by 50% he would walk it in 1 hr less than *B*. Find the time *B* needs to walk the *d* mi.

37. A sum of money at simple interest amounted in 16 yr to $16,000, and in 18 yr to $17,000. What was the sum of money and the rate of interest?

38. The sums of \$1200 and \$1400 are invested at different rates and their annual interest is \$111. If the rates of interest were interchanged, the annual interest would be \$110. Find the rates of interest.

39. A takes 2 hr longer than B to walk d mi, but if A should double his speed, he would walk it in 1 hr less than B. Find the time B needs to walk the d mi.

40. If a rectangle were 100 ft longer and 25 ft narrower, its area would be 2500 ft^2 larger. If it were 100 ft shorter and 50 ft wider, its area would be 5000 ft^2 smaller. What are the dimensions of the rectangle?

41. The front wheel of a car makes 6 revolutions more than the rear wheel in going 120 yd. If the circumference of the front wheel is increased by 25%, and that of the rear wheel by 20%, the 6 becomes 4. Find the circumference of each wheel.

42. Find the linear function of x which has the values 8 and 10 when x has the values -2 and 3, respectively.

43. Find the function of the form $2x^2 + ax + b$ which has the values -5 and 61 when x has the values -1 and 5, respectively.

44. Find A and B if the equation $A(x - 1) + B(x - 2) = 3x - 2$ holds for all values of x. [*Hint:* The equation must be satisfied for any two values of x chosen at random.]

12–3 ALGEBRAIC SOLUTION OF THREE LINEAR EQUATIONS IN THREE UNKNOWNS

To solve a system of three linear equations in three unknowns, one of the unknowns is eliminated from a pair of the equations, and the same unknown is also eliminated from another pair of the equations. The resulting pair of two equations in two unknowns can then be solved.

Example. Solve the system of equations

$$\begin{cases} 2x - y - 4z = 3, \\ -x + 3y + z = -10, \\ 3x + 2y - 2z = -2. \end{cases}$$

Solution: To eliminate y from the first two equations, we multiply the first by 3, the second by 1, and add, getting

$$5x - 11z = -1.$$

Similarly, to eliminate y from the first and third equations, we multiply the first by 2, the third by 1, and add:

$$7x - 10z = 4.$$

We now have the system of two equations in two unknowns:

$$\begin{cases} 5x - 11z = -1, \\ 7x - 10z = 4. \end{cases}$$

Multiplying the first of this pair by 7, the second by -5, and adding, we have

$$-27z = -27, \qquad \text{hence} \qquad z = 1.$$

Substituting $z = 1$ in either of the equations in x and z, we find $x = 2$, and substituting $z = 1$ and $x = 2$ in one of the original equations, we find $y = -3$. The solution is $x = 2, y = -3, z = 1$.

To solve a system of four equations in four unknowns, the system is first reduced to a system of three equations in three unknowns.

EXERCISE GROUP 12–2

In each of Exercises 1–17, solve the system of equations for x, y, and z (and w in Ex. 17).

1. $3x - 4y + z = -2$
   $5x + y - 2z = 1$
   $7x + 3y + 2z = 19$

2. $x - 5y - 7z = 6$
   $2x + y + 5z = 9$
   $4x - 3y + 9z = 27$

3. $5x - y + 11z = 21$
   $-3x + 4y + 5z = 29$
   $2x - 7y + 9z = 9$

4. $6x + 7y - 10z = -3$
   $13x - 5y + 17z = 54$
   $-5x - 11y + 13z = 18$

5. $3x - 5y + 6z = -33$
   $5x + 7y - 2z = 39$
   $-7x + 3y + 5z = -25$

6. $-5x + 6y + 19z = 12$
   $3x - 4y - 8z = -4$
   $2x + 8y - 11z = -3$

7. $6x - 10y + 18z = 3$
   $12x + 20y - 3z = \frac{15}{2}$
   $-15x + 13y + 24z = \frac{8}{5}$

8. $9x - 8y + 10z = 8$
   $21x + 16y - 35z = -2$
   $-19x + 17y + 40z = \frac{385}{12}$

9. $x + 2y - z = a - b$
   $2x - y + z = 3a + 3b$
   $-x + y + 2z = 4a - 2b$

10. $-bx + ay + cz = c^2$
    $cx - by + az = 2ac - b^2$
    $ax - cy + bz = a^2$

11. $bx - ay + cz = \frac{1}{2}(c^2 - b^2)$
    $cx + ay - bz = ab - bc$
    $ax + cy - bz = \frac{1}{2}(a^2 - c^2)$

12. $ax + by - abz = a^2$
    $-bx + aby + az = a^2b^2$
    $bx - az = 0$

13. $x + 2y - 2z - 4u = 0$
    $6x - 5y + 2z - 21u = 0$
    $-2x + y - 16z + 23u = 0$

14. $3x + 2y + z - 10u = 0$
    $2x - 3y - z + 7u = 0$
    $5x - 7y + 2z + 3u = 0$

15. $\frac{3}{x} - \frac{2}{y} + \frac{5}{z} = \frac{25}{2}$
    $\frac{4}{x} + \frac{5}{y} - \frac{7}{z} = -9$
    $-\frac{5}{x} + \frac{3}{y} + \frac{2}{z} = \frac{19}{2}$

16. $\frac{2}{x} + \frac{5}{y} - \frac{7}{z} = 9$
    $\frac{5}{x} - \frac{1}{y} + \frac{3}{z} = 16$
    $\frac{7}{x} + \frac{6}{y} + \frac{1}{z} = 34$

17. $4x - y + z + 2w = 1$
    $3x + 2y - z + 2w = -12$
    $-2x + 3y + 2z - 3w = 10$
    $x + y + z + w = -2$

18. Find the quadratic function $ax^2 + bx + c$ which takes on the values -18, -4, and -13 when $x = -2, 0$, and 3, respectively.
19. Find the function of the form $a + b/x + c/x^2$ which takes on the values -14, -2, and $-\frac{1}{4}$ when $x = \frac{1}{3}$, 1, and 2, respectively.
20. Find the values of A, B, and C if the equation

$$A(x - 2)(x - 3) + B(x - 1)(x - 3) + C(x - 1)(x - 2) = x^2 - 3x + 8$$

holds for all values of x.
21. Find the values of A, B, and C if the equation

$$\frac{(x - 1)^2}{(x + 2)(x^2 - x + 1)} = \frac{A}{x + 2} + \frac{Bx + C}{x^2 - x + 1}$$

is an identity (that is, the equation holds for all values of x for which the functions are defined).
22. A sum of \$10,000 is partly invested at 5%, partly at 4%, and partly at 3%, bringing a total yearly interest of \$390. The 5% investment brings \$10 more interest yearly than the 4% and 3% investments together. How much money is invested at 3%, 4%, and 5%, respectively?
23. A, B, and C working together can do a piece of work in 1 day, A and C together in $1\frac{1}{2}$ days, and B and C together in 2 days. How many days would each of them require to do the work alone?
24. A tank can be filled by pipes A and B in 72 min, by pipes B and C in 120 min, and by pipes A and C in 90 min. How much time would be needed for each pipe to fill the tank?
25. The perimeter of a triangle is 39 in. The longest side is 7 in. less than the sum of the other two, and one of these two is twice as large as the difference of the remaining two. Find the length of each side.

12–4 GRAPH OF A QUADRATIC EQUATION IN x AND y

The geometric solution of all systems of equations of second degree is beyond the scope of this text, but a brief discussion of the geometry of the general equation of second degree in x and y will be very helpful of itself, and will also explain why we shall study only certain special cases.

The general quadratic equation in the two variables x and y is of the form

$$Ax^2 + Bxy + Cy^2 + Dx + Ey + F = 0, \tag{1}$$

where A, B, C, D, E, and F are constants with A, B, C not all zero.

It is shown in analytic geometry that if any real values of x and y satisy (1), then the graph of equation (1) will, apart from certain exceptional cases, be a *conic section*, that is, one of the curves in which a plane cuts a right circular cone. Moreover, it is also shown that if the coordinate axes are properly chosen with respect to the curve, Eq. (1) will reduce to one of the following standard forms:

A. $ax + by + c = 0$ (a and b not both zero). The graph of this is a straight line, which was discussed in Section 4–2.

B. $y = ax^2 + bx + c$ $(a \neq 0)$. The graph of this is the *parabola* which was discussed in Chapter 4.

C. $x^2/a^2 + y^2/b^2 = 1$. The graph of this equation is an *ellipse*, including a *circle* as a special case when $a = b$. The actual drawing of such a curve will be illustrated by an example.

Example 1. Draw the graph of $9x^2 + 25y^2 = 225$.

Solution. First divide the given equation by 225 to obtain a 1 as the right member. An equation of this type written in the form C is said to be in *standard form*, and in this instance the standard form is

$$\frac{x^2}{25} + \frac{y^2}{9} = 1.$$

From either form it is clear that if $y = 0$, $x = \pm 5$ and if $x = 0$, $y = \pm 3$. The four points $(5, 0)$, $(-5, 0)$, $(0, 3)$, and $(0, -3)$ are the points where the graph crosses the coordinate axes, and the distances of the points from the origin, each with its proper sign, are called the *intercepts* of the curve. Moreover, if $y^2 > 9$, then x^2 is negative and the values of x are imaginary and, if $x^2 > 25$, then y^2 is negative and the values of y are imaginary. Thus all the points of the graph are inside the rectangle bounded by the lines $x = 5$, $y = -3$, $x = -5$, and $y = 3$. Assigning admissible values to x and solving for the corresponding values of y we obtain the following table of values:

x:	-5	-4	-3	0	3	4	5
y:	0	$\pm\frac{9}{5}$	$\pm\frac{12}{5}$	± 3	$\pm\frac{12}{5}$	$\pm\frac{9}{5}$	0

To obtain the desired graph we plot the above points and draw a smooth curve through them, as in Fig. 12-3.

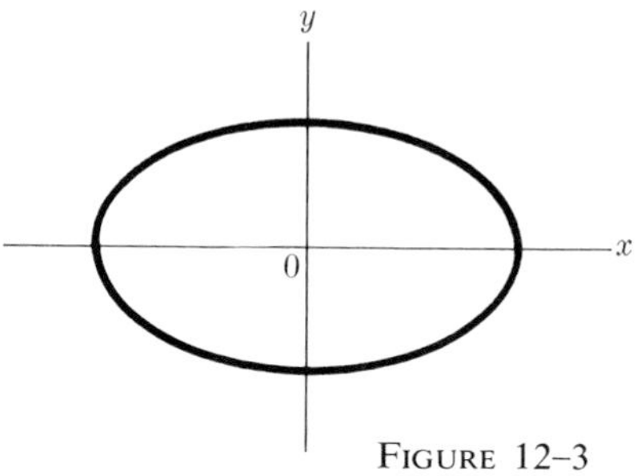

FIGURE 12-3

D. $x^2/a^2 + y^2/b^2 = 0$. The only real values of x and y satisfying this equation are $(0, 0)$ and therefore the graph consists of one point, the origin. Since the equation is similar to that of an ellipse, the graph is referred to as a *point ellipse*.

E. $x^2/a^2 + y^2/b^2 = -1$. Only imaginary values of x and y satisfy this equation, so there is no graph of it.

F. $xy = c$. The graph of this equation is a *hyperbola* for all nonzero real values of c. Again we shall illustrate the drawing of such a hyperbola by an example.

Example 2. Draw the graph of $xy = 6$.

Solution. Since the product is positive the values of x and y must have the same sign, that is, when x is positive y must also be positive and when x is negative then y is also negative. Moreover, neither x nor y can be zero, so that the graph never touches the coordinate axes. Assigning values to x and solving for the corresponding values of y we obtain the values:

x:	-6	-3	-2	-1	1	2	3	6
y:	-1	-2	-3	-6	6	3	2	1

Again the graph is obtained by plotting the above points and then joining them with a smooth curve, remembering that the curve can never cross a coordinate axis (Fig. 12–4).

Note: If c is negative then x and y must have opposite signs.

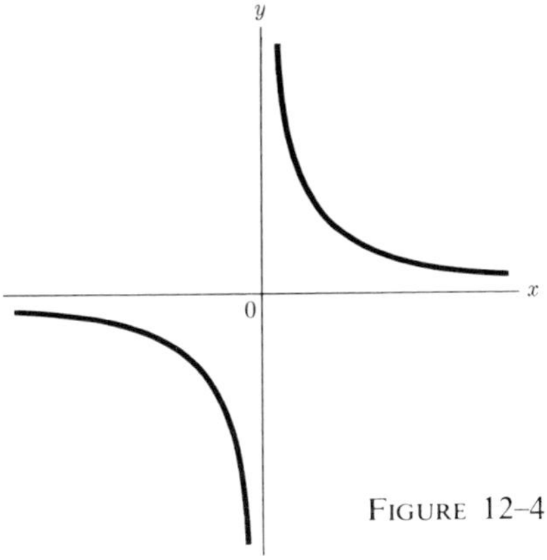

FIGURE 12–4

G. $x^2/a^2 - y^2/b^2 = 1$. The graph of this equation is also a *hyperbola* but, as will be seen, the curve is located differently with respect to the coordinate axes. To better understand the graph of this hyperbola consider the following example.

Example 3. Draw the graph of the equation $36x^2 - 64y^2 = 2304$.

Solution. Reducing the given equation to standard form we have $x^2/64 - y^2/36 = 1$. It is clear that if $y = 0$, then $x = \pm 8$ and if $y^2 > 0$ then $x^2 > 64$, so that there are no points on the graph for x between -8 and $+8$. If we assign admissible values to x and solve for the corresponding values of y we obtain

x:	-12	-10	-8	8	10	12
y:	$\pm 3\sqrt{5}$	$\pm\frac{9}{2}$	0	0	$\pm\frac{9}{2}$	$\pm 3\sqrt{5}$

In addition to plotting the above points it will also be helpful to draw the rectangle bounded by the lines $x = 8$, $y = -6$, $x = -8$, and $y = 6$. The diagonals of this rectangle are helpful as guide lines in drawing the graph (Fig. 12–5).

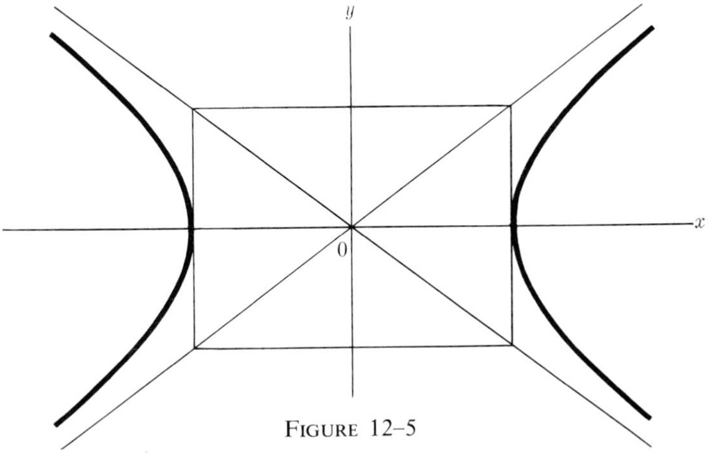

FIGURE 12–5

H. $x^2/a^2 - y^2/b^2 = 0$. The graph of this equation is a pair of straight lines through the origin.

Example 4. The equation $4x^2 - 9y^2 = 0$ is of the type H if both sides of the equation are divided by 36. We may, however, write the equation as

$$(2x + 3y)(2x - 3y) = 0,$$

so that either

$$2x + 3y = 0 \quad \text{or} \quad 2x - 3y = 0.$$

Each of these equations has a straight-line graph; the two straight lines obtained constitute the graph of the original equation.

EXERCISE GROUP 12-3

Draw the graph of each of the following equations.

1. $y = x^2 - 3x + 4$
2. $4x^2 + 9y^2 = 36$
3. $4x^2 - 16y^2 = 16$
4. $xy = 4$
5. $xy = -6$
6. $9y^2 - 16x^2 = 144$
7. $9x^2 + 16y^2 = 144$
8. $y = 2x - x^2$
9. $4x^2 + 4y^2 = 36$
10. $9x^2 - 9y^2 = 36$
11. $9x^2 + 4y^2 = 16$
12. $4x^2 - 9y^2 = 16$
13. $2xy = 4$
14. $9x^2 - 4y^2 = 0$
15. $16y^2 - 25x^2 = 0$

12-5 ONE LINEAR EQUATION AND ONE SECOND-DEGREE EQUATION

The algebraic solution of a pair of equations of which one is linear and the other is of the second degree can be applied equally well whether the second-degree equation is limited to one of the standard forms considered above or is of the general type.

Example 1. Determine the points of intersection of the curves represented by the equations

$$\begin{cases} 7x + 6y = 10, \\ 6x^2 - 19x - 6y = 38. \end{cases}$$

Geometric solution. The graph of the first equation is the straight line in Fig. 12-6. The second equation can be put in the form

$$y = x^2 - \tfrac{19}{6}x - \tfrac{19}{3}.$$

By the methods of Section 4-3, we know that the graph is a parabola with vertex at $[\frac{19}{12}, -(\frac{19}{12})^2 - \frac{19}{3}]$ or, approximately, (1.58, −8.84). We then compute the following table of values:

x:	−2	−1	0	1	2	3	4	5
y:	4	−2.17	−6.3	−8.5	−8.7	−6.9	−3	2.83

and draw the graph. From the figure it appears that the points of intersection, P and Q, have the coordinates $(-2, 4)$ and $(4, -3)$, respectively.

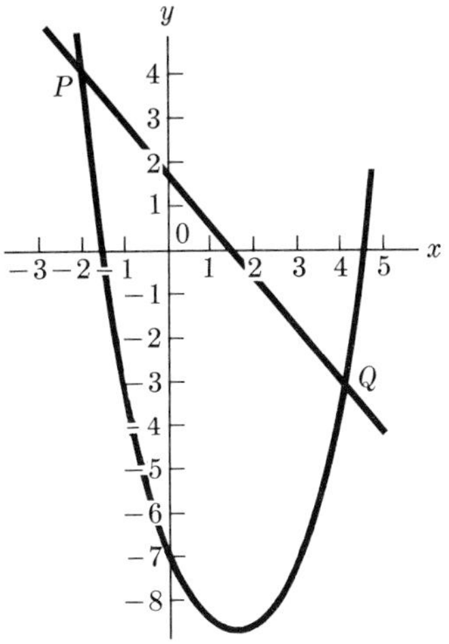

FIGURE 12–6

Algebraic solution. From the first equation, we have

$$6y = 10 - 7x.$$

Substituting this in the second equation, we obtain

$$6x^2 - 19x - 10 + 7x = 38,$$

or

$$6x^2 - 12x - 48 = 0.$$

Then

$$x^2 - 2x - 8 = 0, \qquad (x - 4)(x + 2) = 0,$$

and

$$x = 4, -2.$$

Substitution in the first equation gives the corresponding values $y = -3$ and $y = 4$. The two solutions are then $x = 4$, $y = -3$ and $x = -2$, $y = 4$.

Example 2. Solve for x and y: $\begin{cases} 5xy = 2x + 2y, \\ 2x + 2y = 5. \end{cases}$

Solution. The second equation gives

$$x = -y + \tfrac{5}{2}.$$

Substitution of this in the first equation gives

$$\begin{aligned} 5(\tfrac{5}{2} - y)y &= 2(\tfrac{5}{2} - y) + 2y, \\ \tfrac{25}{2}y - 5y^2 &= 5 - 2y + 2y, \\ 10y^2 - 25y + 10 &= 0 \qquad \text{or} \qquad 2y^2 - 5y + 2 = 0. \end{aligned}$$

Then $(2y - 1)(y - 2) = 0$, and $y = \frac{1}{2}, 2$. The values of x are then found from the second equation. Thus the two pairs of values (x, y) which satisfy the equations are $(2, \frac{1}{2})$ and $(\frac{1}{2}, 2)$.

The method for solving a pair of equations of which one is linear and the other is quadratic is now clear:

1. *Solve the linear equation for one of the unknowns in terms of the other.*
2. *Substitute this in the second-degree equation and solve for the second unknown.*
3. *Substitute in the linear equation the values found in Step 2 to find the corresponding values of the first unknown.*

Example 3. Solve for x and y: $\begin{cases} 9x^2 - 16y^2 = 144, \\ x - 2y = 4. \end{cases}$

Geometric solution. Construct the graph of each equation and note where the two graphs intersect. The graph of the first equation cuts the x-axis at $x = \pm 4$, and y is imaginary for any value of x between -4 and 4. The graph consists of the two curved branches in Fig. 12-7, and is a *hyperbola.*

The graph of the second equation is a straight line through the points (4, 0) and $(0, -2)$. This line intersects the hyperbola at the points P and Q, whose coordinates are approximately (4, 0) and $(-10, -7)$.

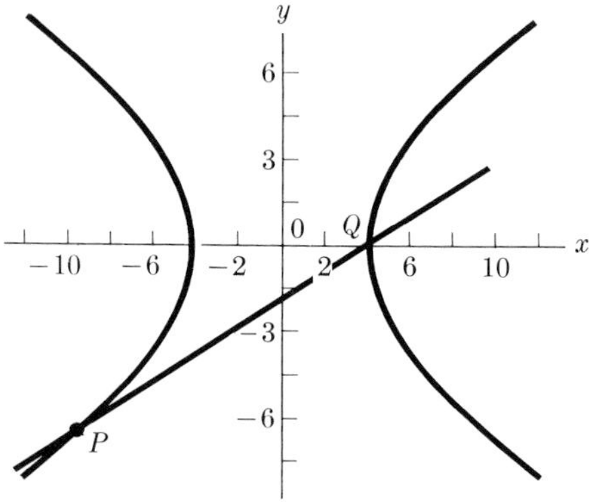

FIGURE 12-7

Algebraic solution. As in the preceding examples, we solve the linear equation for x and substitute the resulting expression in the second-degree equation. This gives

$$9(4 + 2y)^2 - 16y^2 = 144,$$

which reduces to

$$20y^2 + 144y = 0.$$

This can be solved by factoring to give

$$y = 0, \quad -\tfrac{36}{5}.$$

Placing these values in the *linear* equation gives $x = 4$ when $y = 0$ and $x = -\frac{52}{5}$ when $y = -\frac{36}{5}$, so that the two solutions of the equations are seen to be (4, 0) and $(-\frac{52}{5}, -\frac{36}{5})$, which are then the actual coordinates of the points of intersection of the line and the hyperbola.

Example 4. Solve for x and y: $\begin{cases} x^2 + 4y^2 - 8y + 2x - 3 = 0, \\ 3y - 2x = 12. \end{cases}$

Solution. From the second equation, we obtain

$$y = 4 + \tfrac{2}{3}x.$$

Substitution of this in the first equation gives

$$x^2 + 4(4 + \tfrac{2}{3}x)^2 - 8(4 + \tfrac{2}{3}x) + 2x - 3 = 0,$$

which reduces to

$$25x^2 + 162x + 261 = 0 \quad \text{or} \quad (25x + 87)(x + 3) = 0.$$

Hence $x = -3, -\frac{87}{25}$, and the two solutions are

$$x = -3, \quad y = 2; \quad x = -\tfrac{87}{25}, \quad y = \tfrac{42}{25}.$$

EXERCISE GROUP 12-4

In each of Exercises 1–6, draw the graphs of both equations on the same coordinate axes and find the points of intersection. In each pair of equations solve algebraically, also, for x and y, and compare results.

1. $x^2 + y^2 = 25$, $x - y + 1 = 0$
2. $9x^2 + 16y^2 = 144$, $3x + 4y = 12$
3. $x^2 - y^2 = 9$, $x + y = 1$
4. $xy = 6$, $y - 2x = 1$
5. $16x^2 + 4y^2 = 16$, $2x + \sqrt{3}y = 2$
6. $y = 4x^2 - 8x + 2$, $3x - y = 5$

In Exercises 7–22, solve each system of equations for x and y, algebraically.

7. $x^2 + 2xy - 2y^2 = -50$, $x - y = 5$
8. $y = 7 + 2x$, $x^2 + xy + 4 = 0$
9. $2x^2 + xy + y^2 = 2$, $x - 2y + 1 = 0$
10. $2x + 3y = 5$, $xy = 1$
11. $x^2 + y^2 = 109$, $x - y = 7$
12. $x^2 - y^2 = 11$, $x + 2y = 4$
13. $y^2 = xy + 4$, $x + 9 = 3y$
14. $x^2 + y^2 - xy = 169$, $x - y = 15$
15. $4x^2 + 3xy = 4$, $x + 3y - 4 = 0$
16. $x + 2y = 4$, $\dfrac{x + y}{x - y} = 3y$
17. $\dfrac{x^2}{a^2} + \dfrac{y^2}{b^2} = 1$, $\dfrac{x}{a} - \dfrac{y}{b} = 1$
18. $\dfrac{x^2}{16} + \dfrac{y^2}{9} = 1$, $\dfrac{x}{4} - \dfrac{y}{3} = 1$
19. $\dfrac{x^2}{16} - \dfrac{y^2}{25} = -1$, $\dfrac{x}{4} - \dfrac{y}{5} = 0$
20. $\dfrac{x^2}{a^2} - \dfrac{y^2}{b^2} = 1$, $\dfrac{x}{a} - \dfrac{y}{b} = 0$
21. $\dfrac{1}{x} + \dfrac{2}{y} = \dfrac{4}{3}$, $\dfrac{1}{x^2} + \dfrac{1}{y^2} = \dfrac{13}{36}$
22. $\dfrac{1}{x} + \dfrac{1}{y} = \dfrac{7}{6}$, $\dfrac{1}{xy} = \dfrac{1}{3}$

In each of Exercises 23–26, determine the values of k for which the values of x and y satisfying the pair of equations are (1) real, (2) imaginary.

23. $y^2/16 - x^2/9 = 1$, $y = kx$
24. $25x^2 + 16y^2 = 400$, $kx + y = 8$
25. $y^2 - 2y - x + 2 = 0$, $kx + y = 5$
26. $x^2/a^2 - y^2/b^2 = 1$, $x/a - y/k = 0$

27. Find two numbers for which the sum is 2 and the product is 4.
28. Find two positive numbers such that the quotient of one by the other is 3, and the quotient of their product by their difference is 6.
29. Find the dimensions of a rectangle whose perimeter is 160 ft and whose area is 1500 ft^2.
30. The hypotenuse of a right triangle exceeds one side by 6 in., and the third side is 12 in. Find the sides of the triangle.
31. To enclose a rectangular field 73,200 ft^2 in area, 1460 ft of fence are required. Find the dimensions of the field.
32. The perimeter of a right triangle is 56 ft, and the area is 84 ft^2. Find the three sides.
33. The area of a rectangle is 3780 ft^2, and a diagonal is 87 ft. Find the lengths of the sides.
34. The radii of two spheres differ by 18 in., and the difference of the spherical surfaces is equal to the surface of a sphere whose radius is 48 in. Find the radii (the surface of a sphere is $4\pi R^2$).
35. An integer less than 100 is equal to four times the sum of its digits, and the sum of the squares of the digits is 20. Find the number. [*Hint:* If t and u are the tens and units digits, respectively, of an integer, then the integer has the form $10t + u$.]
36. Determine k so that the straight line $x - 2y = k$ is tangent to the hyperbola $-4x^2 + 9y^2 = 36$.
37. Find the value m such that the line $y = mx - 2$ is tangent to the hyperbola $x^2 - y^2 = 1$.

12–6 TWO EQUATIONS OF THE FORM $ax^2 + by^2 = c$

An equation of the form $ax^2 + by^2 = c$ may be considered as *linear in* x^2 *and* y^2. By this we mean that if we make the substitution $u = x^2$ and $v = y^2$, then the resulting equations are linear in u and v. However, once this fact is recognized it is not necessary to make the actual substitution; the given system of equations can be solved for x^2 and y^2 by the method of Section 12–2, and then x and y can be found.

Example. Solve for x and y: $\begin{cases} x^2 + y^2 = 25, \\ x^2 - y^2 = 7. \end{cases}$

Solution: By adding corresponding members of the two equations, we get

$$2x^2 = 32, \qquad x^2 = 16.$$

Substitution of this value of x^2 in the first equation gives $16 + y^2 = 25$, $y^2 = 9$. The four solutions for x and y are

$$x = 4,\ y = -3; \qquad x = -4,\ y = -3,$$
$$x = 4,\ y = 3; \qquad x = -4,\ y = 3;$$

as can be verified by substitution in the given equations.

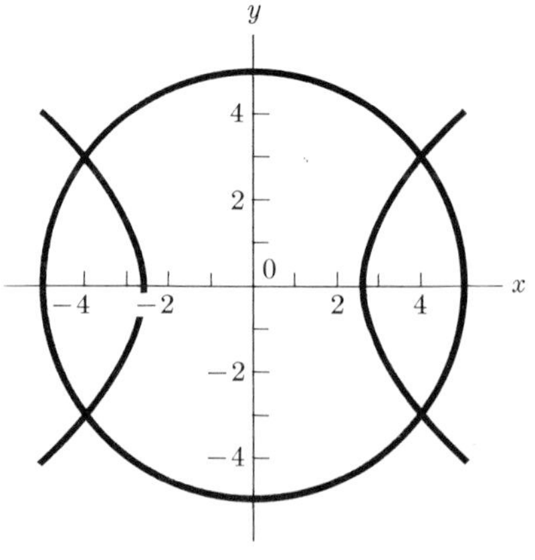

FIGURE 12–8

Graphical solution. If the graph of the first equation is constructed by finding pairs of values (x, y) which satisfy the equation and plotting the corresponding points, the circle shown in Fig. 12–8 is obtained. In a similar manner, the hyperbola shown in the figure is obtained as the graph of the second equation. The circle and hyperbola are seen to intersect in the four points $(4, 3)$, $(-4, 3)$, $(-4, -3)$, $(4, -3)$.

EXERCISE GROUP 12–5

In each of Exercises 1–3, draw the graph of both equations on the same coordinate axes and find the points of intersection; also solve each pair of equations algebraically for x and y.

1. $x^2 + 3y^2 = 37$, $2x^2 - 9y^2 = 14$
2. $5x^2 - 4y^2 = 16$, $x^2 + y^2 = 32$
3. $4x^2 + 9y^2 = 36$, $15x^2 + 9y^2 = 80$

Solve each of the following systems of equations for x and y, algebraically.

4. $3x^2 + 5y^2 = 57$, $7x^2 - 4y^2 = -8$
5. $5x^2 - 2y^2 = 47$, $3x^2 + 7y^2 = 184$
6. $6x^2 + 5y^2 = 7$, $7y^2 - 4x^2 = \frac{23}{15}$
7. $8x^2 + 5y^2 - 11 = 0$, $7x^2 - 6y^2 + 63 = 0$
8. $b^2x^2 - a^2y^2 = a^2b^2(1 - c^2)$, $c^2x^2 + y^2 = c^2(a^2 + b^2)$
9. $ax^2 + by^2 = c$, $bx^2 - ay^2 = 0$
10. $3x^2 + 4y^2 = 7$, $7x^2 + 12y^2 = 3$
11. $x^2 + y^2 = 8$, $7x^2 + 4y^2 = 72$
12. $3x^2/5 - 2y^2 = 0$, $7x^2/34 + 11y^2/17 = 2$
13. $3x^2 + 2y^2 = 30$, $7x^2 - 5y^2 + \frac{421}{6} = 0$
14. $2x^2/3 + 29y^2/27 = 5$, $-7x^2/2 - 73y^2/18 = 7$
15. $\frac{13}{5}x^2 - \frac{17}{3}y^2 = 4$, $\frac{29}{9}y^2 - \frac{31}{15}x^2 = \frac{2}{3}$
16. $\dfrac{x^2}{4a^2} + \dfrac{y^2}{b^2} = 1$, $\dfrac{x^2}{a^2} - \dfrac{y^2}{b^2} = 1$
17. $\frac{2}{3}x^2 - \frac{3}{5}y^2 = 18$, $\frac{5}{6}x^2 + \frac{7}{10}y^2 = 50$
18. $\dfrac{x^2}{16} - \dfrac{y^2}{25} = 1$, $\dfrac{x^2}{25} + \dfrac{y^2}{16} = 1$
19. $\dfrac{x^2}{25} - \dfrac{y^2}{9} = 1$, $\dfrac{y^2}{25} - \dfrac{x^2}{36} = 1$
20. $5x^2 - 3y^2 + 206 = 0$, $7y^2 - 15x^2 - 614 = 0$
21. $15x^2 - 19y^2 + \frac{27}{2} = 0$, $13y^2 - 27x^2 + \frac{15}{2} = 0$
22. $4x^2 - 3y^2 = 43$, $3x^2 + y^2 = 3$
23. $x^2 + y^2 = 2(a^2 + b^2)$, $2x^2 - 3y^2 = 10ab - a^2 - b^2$
24. $(x + y)^2 + (x - y)^2 = 85$, $2(x + y)^2 - 3(x - y)^2 + 10 = 0$
25. $4(2x + y)^2 - x^2y^2 = 28$, $4(2x + y)^2 + x^2y^2 = 100$

26. $\dfrac{2}{x^2} - \dfrac{1}{y^2} + 17 = 0$

$\dfrac{1}{x^2} + \dfrac{2}{y^2} = 54$

27. $\dfrac{5}{x^2} + \dfrac{3}{y^2} = 30$

$\dfrac{5}{x^2} - \dfrac{1}{y^2} + 70 = 0$

12–7 TWO QUADRATIC EQUATIONS, WITH ONE HOMOGENEOUS

A homogeneous quadratic equation in x and y is an equation of the form

$$ax^2 + bxy + cy^2 = 0,$$

in which only second-degree terms in x and y appear. If we wish to solve a system of two quadratic equations, of which one is homogeneous, we can always reduce the homogeneous equation to two linear equations, either by solving for one of the variables in terms of the other, or by factoring the left member and setting each factor equal to zero. Each of these linear equations, taken with the other given equation of the system of two quadratic equations, gives a pair of equations of which one is linear and one is quadratic. Each of the resulting pairs of equations can be solved by the method of Section 12–5, and there will be in general four solutions of the original system.

Example. Solve the following system of equations completely:

$$\begin{cases} x^2 - 5xy + 6y^2 = 0, \\ xy - y^2 = 2. \end{cases}$$

Solution. The first equation is homogeneous. Upon factoring the left member, we have $(x - 3y)(x - 2y) = 0$, which yields the two linear equations

$$x - 3y = 0 \qquad \text{and} \qquad x - 2y = 0.$$

Each of these is taken with the second given equation, and we obtain the following systems of equations:

$$\begin{cases} xy - y^2 = 2, \\ x - 3y = 0, \end{cases} \qquad \text{and} \qquad \begin{cases} xy - y^2 = 2, \\ x - 2y = 0. \end{cases}$$

These systems are of the type of Section 12–5. Any solution of either system will be a solution of the given system. By the method given in Section 12–5, we find the four solutions,

$$(3, 1), \quad (-3, -1), \quad (2\sqrt{2}, \sqrt{2}), \quad (-2\sqrt{2}, -\sqrt{2}),$$

where the first two are the solutions of the first system above, and the second two are the solutions of the second system.

While there are in general four solutions for the kind of system of equations considered in this section, there may in special cases turn out to be fewer than four solutions.

EXERCISE GROUP 12-6

In Exercises 1–18, solve each system of equations for x and y.

1. $x^2 + 2xy = 0$
   $3x^2 + xy + y^2 = 44$
2. $3x^2 + 5xy - 2y^2 = 0$
   $5y^2 - 8xy = 21$
3. $3x^2 + xy - 2y^2 = 0$
   $7x^2 - 3xy = 10$
4. $6x^2 + xy - 2y^2 = 0$
   $8x^2 + 3xy - 14 = 0$
5. $3x^2 - 8xy - 3y^2 = 0$
   $2x^2 - 4xy - y^2 = 5$
6. $6x^2 - xy - y^2 = 0$
   $y^2 - 3x^2 + 8x + y = 11$
7. $2x^2 + 5xy - 3y^2 = 0$
   $3xy - y^2 = 2$
8. $6x^2 - 5xy - 6y^2 = 0$
   $xy = 24$
9. $3x^2 + xy = 2y^2$
   $7x^2 + 2xy = 5$
10. $3x^2 - 7xy + 2y^2 = 0$
    $2x^2 - 4xy + 5y^2 = 35$
11. $3x^2 + 8xy - 3y^2 = 0$
    $5x^2 - 4y^2 = 5 - 12xy$
12. $x^2 + 5xy - 6y^2 = 0$
    $15y^2 - 8xy = 7$
13. $4x^2 - xy - 3y^2 = 0$
    $7x^2 - 5y^2 - 32 = 0$
14. $15x^2 - 22xy - 5y^2 = 0$
    $x^2 - y^2 = 1$
15. $3x^2 - 17xy + 10y^2 = 0$
    $3x^2 + 5y^2 + x = 7$
16. $6x^2 + xy - 35y^2 = 0$
    $2xy + 5y + 10 = 0$
17. $8x^2 - 10xy - 3y^2 = 0$
    $2x^2 - xy - 12 = 0$
18. $2x^2 + 4xy - 6y^2 = 0$
    $x^2 + y^2 + 3y = 2$

12-8 TWO EQUATIONS OF THE FORM $ax^2 + bxy + cy^2 = d$

A system of two equations of the form

$$ax^2 + bxy + cy^2 = d$$

can always be solved by the method of the preceding section, upon eliminating the constant terms from the two equations to obtain a quadratic equation which is homogeneous in x and y. The homogeneous equation thus obtained is then solved together with either of the given equations. There will be, in general, four solutions.

Example 1. Solve the system of equations,

$$\begin{cases} 2x^2 - xy + y^2 = 16, \\ x^2 - xy + 2y^2 = 44. \end{cases}$$

Solution. To eliminate the constant, we multiply both members of the first equation by 11, the members of the second equation by -4, and add corresponding members of the equations obtained. We obtain the equation $18x^2 - 15xy + 3y^2 = 0$. If both members are then divided by 3, the resulting left member can be factored, and the equation becomes

$$(3x - y)(2x - y) = 0.$$

Using the first of the given equations with the one just obtained, we see that the given system is equivalent to the two following ones:

$$\begin{cases} 2x^2 - xy + y^2 = 16, \\ 3x - y = 0, \end{cases} \quad \text{and} \quad \begin{cases} 2x^2 - xy + y^2 = 16, \\ 2x - y = 0. \end{cases}$$

By the method of Section 12-5 the solutions of these systems are, respectively,

$$(\sqrt{2}, 3\sqrt{2}), \quad (-\sqrt{2}, -3\sqrt{2}) \quad \text{and} \quad (2, 4), \quad (-2, -4),$$

which are the four solutions of the original system.

Special methods often apply to systems of equations of special types. The following example illustrates one such type, with an appropriate method of solution.

Example 2. Solve the system of equations,

$$\begin{cases} x^2 + y^2 = 25, \\ xy = 12. \end{cases}$$

Solution. If the second equation of the system is multiplied by 2 and subtracted from the first we get $x^2 - 2xy + y^2 = 1$, which can be written as $(x - y)^2 = 1$. This last equation is equivalent to the two equations $x - y = 1$ and $x - y = -1$. Thus the solutions of the given system may be found by solving the two systems

$$\begin{cases} xy = 12, \\ x - y = 1, \end{cases} \quad \text{and} \quad \begin{cases} xy = 12, \\ x - y = -1. \end{cases}$$

These latter systems are solved by the methods of Section 12-5 and the results are

$$(4, 3); \quad (-3, -4); \quad (-4, -3); \quad (3, 4).$$

The methods developed in this chapter are adequate for the systems of equations which are most frequently encountered. However, the subject has not been exhaustively treated. The solution of a pair of general equations of the second degree,

$$ax^2 + bxy + cy^2 + dx + ey + f = 0,$$
$$Ax^2 + Bxy + Cy^2 + Dx + Ey + F = 0$$

can be shown* to depend on the solution of a fourth-degree equation in one variable.

---

* For an extended treatment of this topic, the student is referred to *College Algebra*, by H. B. Fine, Boston: Ginn and Co., 1904, pp. 324-339; and *Algebra*, by G. Chrystal, Vol. I., London: A. & C. Black, Ltd., 1926, pp. 400-416.

EXERCISE GROUP 12–7

In Exercises 1–18, solve each system of equations for x and y.

1. $6x^2 + xy = 10$
   $2y^2 + 3xy - 4x^2 = 40$

2. $10x^2 - xy + 16y^2 = 72$
   $4x^2 + 5y^2 = 24$

3. $x^2 + 2xy - 4y^2 = 16$
   $2x^2 + 7xy + 4y^2 = 104$

4. $xy + y^2 = 10$
   $2x^2 + 3xy - 2y^2 = 40$

5. $x^2 + 7 = 2xy + y^2$
   $x^2 + y^2 + 5 = 3xy$

6. $2x^2 - 7xy - 2y^2 + 20 = 0$
   $4x^2 + 7xy + 2y^2 = 5$

7. $8x^2 - 7xy + 10 = 0$
   $25x^2 - 24xy + y^2 = -35$

8. $15x^2 + 29xy + 38y^2 = 120$
   $2x^2 + 4xy + 5y^2 = 15$

9. $y^2 + 2xy = 12$
   $2x^2 - xy + 1 = 0$

10. $x^2 + y^2 = (x - y + 1)^2$
    $x^2 + y^2 = (x + y + 2)^2$

[*Hint:* In Exercises 11, 12, 13, 14 use the method of Example 2.]

11. $9x^2 + 4y^2 = 37$
    $xy = 3$

12. $4x^2 + y^2 = 17$
    $xy = 4$

13. $x^2 + y^2 = 13$
    $xy = 2$

14. $x^2 + 9y^2 = 22$
    $xy = 3$

15. $x^2 + y^2 + 2x - 2y = 23$
    $xy = -6$

16. $x^2 - 3xy + 2y^2 = 15$
    $4x^2 + 5y^2 = 24$

17. $8x^2 + 7xy + 10 = 0$
    $9xy + 8y^2 = 18$

18. $x^2 - xy = 12$
    $2y^2 + xy + 1 = 0$

19. The sum of the squares of two numbers is $\frac{41}{36}$ and the product of the same numbers is $\frac{5}{9}$. Find the numbers.
20. The hypotenuse of a right triangle is 25 ft, and the area is 84 ft^2. What are the lengths of the sides of the triangle?
21. The sum of the squares of two numbers plus four times their product is equal to 382; the sum of their squares minus twice their product is equal to 4. Find the two numbers.
22. If the numerator of a simple fraction is increased by 5 and the denominator is decreased by 5, the resulting fraction equals the reciprocal of the original fraction. If 3 is added to the numerator and 6 is added to the denominator, the fraction is doubled. Find the fraction.

12–9 SYSTEMS OF TRIGONOMETRIC EQUATIONS

As was pointed out in Section 12–1, the methods that apply to solving systems of algebraic equations apply equally well to solving systems of trigonometric equations. Systems of trigonometric equations are of so many types that very little is gained in trying to classify them, apart from those which are combinations of linear and quadratic equations in the trigonometric functions. A special feature of systems of trigonometric equations, however, is the use that can be made of the many identities among the trigonometric functions. In fact, the clue to the solution of many such systems is the attempt to use the trigonometric identities either to eliminate one of the unknowns directly, or to obtain equations which are simpler than the given ones.

The examples, which can, of course, illustrate only certain types of systems, are intended to demonstrate the use of the identities in effecting a solution.

Example 1. Solve the following system for r and θ:

$$\begin{cases} r\cos\theta = a, \\ r\sin\theta = b. \end{cases}$$

Solution. Dividing the members of the second equation by the corresponding members of the first equation, we obtain $\tan\theta = b/a$, so that

$$\theta = \arctan\frac{b}{a}\cdot$$

Squaring the members of the given equations, and adding, we obtain, since $\cos^2\theta + \sin^2\theta = 1$,

$$r = \pm\sqrt{a^2 + b^2},$$

where the sign of r depends on the quadrant in which θ is taken. These values of r and θ are the desired solution.

Example 2. Solve the following system for x and y:

$$\begin{cases} \sin x - \sin y = a, \\ \cos x - \cos y = b. \end{cases}$$

Solution. Applying the factor formulas (Section 10–9) to the left members, we obtain

$$\begin{cases} 2\cos\tfrac{1}{2}(x+y)\sin\tfrac{1}{2}(x-y) = a, \\ -2\sin\tfrac{1}{2}(x+y)\sin\tfrac{1}{2}(x-y) = b. \end{cases} \tag{2}$$

Dividing the members of the second equation by those of the first, we obtain $\tan\frac{1}{2}(x+y) = -b/a$, which yields, since the inverse tangent is an odd function,

$$\tfrac{1}{2}(x+y) = -\arctan\frac{b}{a}\cdot \tag{3}$$

With the value of $\tan\frac{1}{2}(x+y)$ we find

$$\cos\tfrac{1}{2}(x+y) = \pm\frac{a}{\sqrt{a^2+b^2}},$$

and substitution of this value in (2) gives $\sin\frac{1}{2}(x-y) = \pm\frac{1}{2}\sqrt{a^2+b^2}$, or

$$\tfrac{1}{2}(x-y) = \pm\arcsin\tfrac{1}{2}\sqrt{a^2+b^2}. \tag{4}$$

Eqs. (3) and (4) yield immediately, by addition and subtraction,

$$x = -\arctan \frac{b}{a} \pm \arcsin \tfrac{1}{2}\sqrt{a^2 + b^2},$$

$$y = -\arctan \frac{b}{a} \mp \arcsin \tfrac{1}{2}\sqrt{a^2 + b^2},$$

where the upper signs are taken together, as are the lower signs.

EXERCISE GROUP 12–8

Solve each of the following systems of equations for r and θ or for x and y, whichever appear. (In Exercises 11, 13, 14, 15, find the angles in the range $0 \leqq x, y < 2\pi$.)

1. $r \sin \theta = a$
   $r \cos \theta = b$
2. $r \tan \theta = a$
   $r \sec \theta = b$
3. $r \tan \theta = a$
   $r \sin \theta = b$
4. $\sin x + \sin y = \sin A$
   $\cos x + \cos y = 1 + \cos A$
5. $\sin x + \sin y = a$
   $\cos x + \cos y = b$
6. $\sin x + \sin y = 2a \sin A$
   $\cos x + \cos y = 2b \cos A$
7. $\sin x + \cos y = a$
   $\cos x + \sin y = b$
8. $\sin^2 x + \sin^2 y = a$
   $\cos^2 x - \cos^2 y = b$
9. $\cos x + \cos y = a$
   $\cos 2x + \cos 2y = b$
10. $a \sin^4 x - b \sin^4 y = a$
    $a \cos^4 x - b \cos^4 y = b$
11. $\sin x = \sqrt{2} \sin y$
    $\tan x - \sqrt{3} \tan y = 0$
12. $r + \sin^2 \theta = a$
    $r + \cos^2 \theta = b$
13. $\cot x - \cot y = 2$
    $\csc x + \csc y = 0$
14. $\tan x + \tan y = 0$
    $\sec x + \sec y = 4$
15. $\tan x + \tan y = 0$
    $\sin x + \sin y = 1$

SUPPLEMENTARY EXERCISES FOR CHAPTER 12

In Exercises 1–14, solve each of the systems of equations.

1. $5x + 3y = -1$
   $7x + 5y = 1$
2. $\frac{3}{2}x + \frac{5}{3}y = 2$
   $\frac{5}{4}x + \frac{7}{3}y = \frac{9}{2}$
3. $\frac{3}{2}x + \frac{10}{3}y = 2$
   $3x + \frac{5}{2}y = -\frac{1}{2}$
4. $4x - 3y = 0.1$
   $0.5x + 0.2y = 0.04$
5. $bx - ay = 0$
   $ax + by = a^2 + b^2$
6. $cx - dy = ac + bd$
   $ax + cy = a^2 - bc$
7. $2x + 3y + z = -1$
   $3x - 4y - 2z = 5$
   $5x - 3y - 3z = 2$
8. $5x + 4y + 3z = 1$
   $2x - 3y + 11z = 1$
   $x + 2y - z = 1$

9. $ax + cy + bz = a^2 + 2bc$
$bx + ay + cz = 2ab + c^2$
$cx - by + az = 2ac - b^2$

10. $x + y + z = a$
$bx + by + az = \frac{3}{2}ab - \frac{b^2}{2}$
$x - y + z = a + b$

11. $2x - 3y - 2z = 2$
$3x + y + z = 4$
$x + 2y + z = 0$

12. $x + y + z = 1$
$2x + 3y - z = 1$
$3x + 2y + 3z = 1$

13. $x + y + z = b$
$x + y = 0$
$2x + z = a + b$

14. $bx - ay + z = c$
$x + cy - bz = a$
$cx + y - az = b$

In each of the pairs of equations in Exercises 15–18, draw the graphs of both equations on the same coordinate axes and find the points of intersection. Solve algebraically for x and y and compare results.

15. $2x - 5y + 2 = 0$
$4x^2 + 25y^2 = 100$

16. $4x^2 - 9y^2 = 19$
$25x^2 + 9y^2 = 706$

17. $y = 2x - x^2$
$2y = x^2 - 4x$

18. $16x^2 + 25y^2 = 3300$
$4x^2 + y^2 = 300$

In Exercises 19–28, solve each of the systems of equations for x and y algebraically.

19. $2x + 3y = 5$
$4x^2 + 9y^2 = 25$

20. $xy = 7$
$2x - 3y = 4$

21. $9x^2 + 4y^2 = 36$
$12xy = 11$

22. $6x^2 + xy - 15y^2 = 0$
$x^2 + 2xy + 3y^2 + x = y$

23. $x^2 + 4y^2 = 4$
$4xy = 21$

24. $3x^2 - 7xy + 2y^2 = 0$
$x^2 + y^2 = xy + x - y$

25. $3x^2 + 4xy + y^2 = 0$
$4x^2 - y^2 + x + 5y = 7$

26. $x^2 - xy - y^2 = 2$
$x^2 + 4xy - 6y^2 = 6$

27. $4x^2 - 9y^2 = 0$
$xy - 5y = 0$

28. $x^2 + xy + y^2 = 3$
$2x^2 - 13xy - 7y^2 = 0$

29. An airplane took 4 hr to fly 1800 mi, flying with a tail wind, and $4\frac{1}{2}$ hr for the return flight with a head wind. Find the wind velocity and the airspeed of the airplane.

30. We wish to obtain a 50% solution of alcohol by mixing a 40% solution and a 65% solution of alcohol. What percentage of the final solution should be taken from each of the two given solutions?

CHAPTER 13

Progressions

13–1 SEQUENCES

Any collection of numbers of which one is designated as the first, another as the second, another as the third, and so on, indefinitely, is called a sequence of numbers. As an example we may give the sequence of odd, positive integers

$$1, 3, 5, 7, \ldots, \tag{1}$$

where the three dots indicate that the succession continues indefinitely. The first number, or *term*, of the sequence is 1, and the second term is 3. It is clear that the third term is $2 \cdot 3 - 1 = 5$, and the fourth term is $2 \cdot 4 - 1 = 7$. We see that if the nth term is desired, that is, the term in nth position, it is given by $2n - 1$. Thus the 20th term is $2 \cdot 20 - 1 = 39$. In fact, if $f(n)$ designates the nth term of the sequence (1) we have

$$f(n) = 2n - 1.$$

The terms of a sequence may, in general, be considered to be the values of a function whose domain is the set of positive integers. It is customary to write the terms in a sequence as

$$a_1, a_2, a_3, \ldots, a_n, \ldots$$

so that a_n may be identified with the $f(n)$ above. For the sequence (1),

$$a_1 = 1, \quad a_2 = 3, \quad a_{20} = 39, \quad a_{47} = 93.$$

Example 1. Find the first four terms of the sequence for which $a_n = 2n^2 - 4$.

Solution. We have

$$a_1 = 2(1)^2 - 4 = -2, \qquad a_2 = 2(2)^2 - 4 = 4,$$
$$a_3 = 2(3)^2 - 4 = 14, \qquad a_4 = 2(4)^2 - 4 = 28.$$

It should be emphasized that if a few terms at the beginning of a sequence are given, the value of a_n or $f(n)$ is not uniquely determined. For example, if

$$a_n = n^4 - 10n^3 + 35n^2 - 48n + 23, \tag{2}$$

we get $a_1 = 1$, $a_2 = 3$, $a_3 = 5$, $a_4 = 7$, as in the sequence of odd, positive integers (1). However, $a_5 = 33$, which is not the fifth odd integer. On the other hand, if one were asked to give a_n for the sequence (1), $a_n = 2n - 1$ would be a simpler answer than (2).

Example 2. Find a_n for the sequence 1, 4, 7, 10, . . .

Solution. It is easily verified that $a_n = 3n - 2$ will suffice.

EXERCISE GROUP 13-1

In each of Exercises 1–12, write the first four terms of the sequence for which a_n is given; also find the indicated term.

1. $a_n = 2n + 4; a_{80}$
2. $a_n = 5n - 3; a_{76}$
3. $a_n = \dfrac{1}{2n}; a_{43}$
4. $a_n = \dfrac{1}{3n+1}; a_{38}$
5. $a_n = \dfrac{2n-1}{2n+1}; a_{123}$
6. $a_n = \dfrac{3n}{2n+3}; a_{96}$
7. $a_n = \dfrac{1}{n^2}; a_{71}$
8. $a_n = \dfrac{n}{n^2+1}; a_{48}$
9. $a_n = \dfrac{1}{2^n}; a_{11}$
10. $a_n = \dfrac{2^n}{3^n - 1}; a_7$
11. $a_n = \sin \dfrac{n\pi}{6}; a_{14}$
12. $a_n = \cos \dfrac{(2n-1)\pi}{4}; a_{10}$

In each of the following sequences, find an expression for a_n.

13. 3, 5, 7, 9, . . .
14. 2, 5, 8, 11, . . .
15. $1, \frac{1}{2}, \frac{1}{3}, \frac{1}{4}, \ldots$
16. $\frac{1}{3}, \frac{1}{7}, \frac{1}{11}, \frac{1}{15}, \ldots$
17. $\frac{1}{4}, \frac{1}{9}, \frac{1}{16}, \frac{1}{25}, \ldots$
18. $\frac{2}{3}, \frac{3}{4}, \frac{4}{5}, \frac{5}{6}, \ldots$
19. $\dfrac{2}{3 \cdot 4}, \dfrac{3}{4 \cdot 5}, \dfrac{4}{5 \cdot 6}, \dfrac{5}{6 \cdot 7}, \ldots$
20. 2, 4, 8, 16, . . .
21. $2, \dfrac{3}{1 \cdot 2}, \dfrac{4}{1 \cdot 2 \cdot 3}, \dfrac{5}{1 \cdot 2 \cdot 3 \cdot 4}, \ldots$
22. $\dfrac{1}{2}, \dfrac{1 \cdot 2}{5}, \dfrac{1 \cdot 2 \cdot 3}{8}, \dfrac{1 \cdot 2 \cdot 3 \cdot 4}{11}, \ldots$

13-2 ARITHMETIC PROGRESSIONS

It can be shown that, neglecting air resistance, a falling body which starts from rest will travel 16 ft the first second, 48 ft the next second, 80 ft the third second, 112 ft the fourth second, and so on. How far will the object fall in 10 sec? during the tenth second? We could compute the distance fallen in each second, and add as many of these distances as necessary, but this would be tedious and would give the solution to this one problem only. We shall seek a general method which will apply to all similar problems.

Consider the distances given above,

$$16, 48, 80, 112, \ldots$$

We note that each number after the first is obtained from the preceding one by adding the same number, 32, called the *common difference*. Such a sequence is called an *arithmetic progression*.

***Definition* 13–1.** *An arithmetic progression is a sequence of numbers in which each one after the first is obtained from the preceding one by adding a fixed number, called the common difference.*

Let the common difference of an arithmetic progression be designated by d, the first term by a_1, and the nth term by a_n. The terms, up to and including the nth term, can be written

$$a_1, a_1 + d, a_1 + 2d, \ldots, a_1 + (n - 1)d.$$

The formula for a_n is now clear, and may be written

$$a_n = a_1 + (n - 1)d. \tag{3}$$

Let S_n designate the sum of the first n terms of an arithmetic progression. The values of S_n for $n = 1, 2, 3, \ldots$ also form a sequence, but we are usually interested in S_n for a particular value of n. Let us write S_n as

$$S_n = a_1 + (a_1 + d) + (a_1 + 2d) + \cdots + [a_1 + (n - 2)d] + [a_1 + (n - 1)d]. \tag{4}$$

If the terms in the right member are written in reversed order, we have

$$S_n = [a_1 + (n - 1)d] + [a_1 + (n - 2)d] + \cdots + (a_1 + d) + a_1. \tag{5}$$

If Eqs. (4) and (5) are added, the sum of corresponding terms is the same, and there are n terms; hence

$$2S_n = n[2a_1 + (n - 1)d] \quad \text{or} \quad S_n = \frac{n}{2}[2a_1 + (n - 1)d].$$

Formula (3) may be used to give $2a_1 + (n - 1)d = a_1 + a_n$. Thus two formulas for S_n are obtained:

$$S_n = \frac{n}{2}[2a_1 + (n - 1)d] = \frac{n}{2}(a_1 + a_n). \tag{6}$$

To summarize these results, we note that the five quantities a_1, a_n, d, n, S_n of an arithmetic progression (A.P.) are related by the equations

$$\boxed{a_n = a_1 + (n - 1)d,}$$

$$\boxed{S_n = \frac{n}{2}(a_1 + a_n),}$$

$$\boxed{S_n = \frac{n}{2}[2a_1 + (n - 1)d].}$$

These formulas involve two independent relations, and can therefore be used to determine the remaining two quantities whenever the other three are known.

It is possible now to answer the questions raised above about the falling body. To determine how far it will fall in 10 sec, use the formula

$$S_n = \frac{n}{2}[2a_1 + (n - 1)d],$$

with $n = 10$, $a_1 = 16$, and $d = 32$. This gives $S_{10} = 1600$ ft. To determine how far it will fall during the tenth second, use

$$a_n = a_1 + (n - 1)d,$$

with the same values for a_1, n, and d. This gives $a_{10} = 304$ ft.

Example. Determine the 97th term and the sum of the first 150 terms of the arithmetic progression (A.P.) 5, 2, −1, . . .

Solution. The first term is 5, hence $a_1 = 5$. The second term minus the first term gives $d = -3$. To find the 97th term, we apply Eq. (3) with $n = 97$, and find

$$\begin{aligned} a_{97} &= 5 + (97 - 1)(-3) = 5 + 96(-3) \\ &= 5 - 288 = -283. \end{aligned}$$

For the second part of the problem we must find S_{150}. Since a_{150} has not been given and is not required, it is convenient here to use the first expression for S_n in Eq. (6). Thus

$$\begin{aligned} S_{150} &= \tfrac{150}{2}[2 \cdot 5 + (150 - 1)(-3)] = 75[10 - 447] = 75(-437) \\ &= -32775. \end{aligned}$$

The terms of an arithmetic progression between a_1 and a_n are called *arithmetic means*. Thus the insertion of m arithmetic means between two numbers requires the finding of an arithmetic progression of $(m + 2)$ terms. For example, if five arithmetic means are to be inserted between 2 and 20, the progression will have seven terms and will be

$$2, a_2, a_3, a_4, a_5, a_6, 20,$$

where the arithmetic means $a_2, \ldots, a_6$ are to be found. To find these means, Eq. (3) is employed with

$$a_7 = 20, \qquad n = 7, \qquad a_1 = 2,$$

so that

$$20 = 2 + (7 - 1)d; \qquad 6d = 18; \qquad \text{and} \qquad d = 3.$$

Then from the definition of an A.P., we have as the desired arithmetic means:

$$a_2 = 2 + d = 5, \qquad a_3 = a_2 + d = 5 + 3 = 8, \qquad a_4 = 8 + 3 = 11,$$
$$a_5 = 14, \qquad a_6 = 17.$$

EXERCISE GROUP 13–2

In each of Exercises 1–6, write the first three terms of an arithmetic progression for which:

1. $a_1 = 7, d = 3$
2. $a_1 = 13, d = \frac{3}{2}$
3. $a_1 = 9, d = -2$
4. $a_1 = -11, d = \frac{2}{3}$
5. $a_1 = \frac{5}{3}, d = -\frac{4}{3}$
6. $a_1 = b, d = c$

In each of Exercises 7–12, the first three terms of an arithmetic progression are given; find the indicated term and sum of terms.

7. 5, 9, 13; find a_{23} and S_{23}
8. $-2, -5, -8$; find a_{19} and S_{19}
9. 3, $3\frac{1}{4}$, $3\frac{1}{2}$; find a_{101} and S_{101}
10. 13, 10, 7; find a_{48} and S_{48}
11. $-15, -12, -9$; find a_{15} and S_{15}
12. $b, b + d, b + 2d$; find a_n and S_n

In each of Exercises 13–17, determine the arithmetic mean of the given numbers; that is, insert one arithmetic mean between them.

13. 9, 27
14. 11, 46
15. $\frac{3}{2}, \frac{2}{3}$
16. $-\frac{5}{3}, \frac{13}{5}$
17. u, v

18. Insert three arithmetic means between 5 and 27.
19. Insert six arithmetic means between -2 and -23.
20. Insert eight arithmetic means between 2 and -25.
21. Insert thirteen arithmetic means between 3 and $\frac{13}{2}$.

In each of Exercises 22–37, find the values of the missing elements among a_1, a_n, d, n, and S_n.

22. $a_1 = 13, d = 3, n = 19$
23. $a_n = -7, d = -\frac{1}{3}, n = 35$
24. $a_1 = 7, a_n = -45, n = 27$
25. $S_n = -237, a_1 = 23, n = 79$
26. $d = -2, a_n = -61, n = 23$
27. $S_n = -315, a_1 = -2, n = 63$
28. $a_1 = 17, a_n = 173, d = 3$
29. $S_n = 3720, a_1 = 15, d = 7$
30. $a_1 = -5, a_n = 2, d = \frac{1}{3}$
31. $S_n = 874, a_1 = 5, d = 3$
32. $a_1 = 3, d = -2, S_n = -525$
33. $a_1 = 2, d = -3, S_n = -1245$
34. $a_1 = -6, d = 4, n = 17$
35. $a_n = 68, d = 3, S_n = 805$
36. $a_n = -35, d = -2, S_n = -323$
37. $a_1 = -7, n = 19, S_{19} = 380$

38. Find $f(1) + f(2) + f(3) + \cdots + f(30)$ if $f(x) = 2x + 3$.
39. Find $f(-\frac{3}{2}) + f(1) + f(\frac{7}{2}) + \cdots + f(21)$ if $f(x) = -x + 2$.
40. Determine the first term and the common difference of an A.P. whose 12th term is 25 and 45th term is 91.
41. Determine the 27th term of an A.P. whose 7th term is 11 and whose common difference is $\frac{5}{2}$.
42. Find the sum of all the even integers from 12 to 2832 inclusive.
43. Find the sum of all the odd integers from 9 to 6381 inclusive.
44. A person saved 50 cents more each month than in the preceding one, and in 15 yr all of his savings amounted to \$10,305. How much did he save the first month? How much the last month?

45. A man accepts a position at a salary of \$3000 for the first year with an increase of \$100 per year each year thereafter. How many years will he have to work for his total earnings to equal \$60,000?

46. The sum of the first four terms of an A.P. is 20 and their product is 384. Find the numbers. [*Hint:* Let $x - 3y$, $x - y$, $x + y$, and $x + 3y$ represent the numbers.]

47. A man contracts to drill a 600-ft well at \$2.50 for the first foot and for each foot thereafter 1¢ more than for the preceding one. How much does he receive for drilling the well?

48. If a body falls 16.1 ft during the first second, 3 times as far during the next second, 5 times as far during the third second, and so on, how far will it fall during the 14th second? How far in t seconds?

49. At the ends A and B of a line 50 ft long, lines AC and BD of lengths 2 ft and 5 ft, respectively, are drawn on the same side of AB and perpendicular to it. At intervals of $\frac{1}{2}$ ft along AB, perpendiculars are drawn to meet the line CD. Find the sum of the lengths of the perpendiculars, including AC and BD.

50. How many terms of the sum $1 + 3 + 5 + \cdots$ are needed to give 1234321?

51. The 2nd, 31st, and last terms of an A.P. are $\frac{31}{4}$, $\frac{1}{2}$, $-\frac{13}{2}$. Find a_1 and n.

13-3 GEOMETRIC PROGRESSIONS

In Section 9-14 the amount of \$1 invested at compound interest for a period of years was determined. An extension of this topic might lead us to ask the following, as an illustration. If \$1 is invested each year at 3% interest compounded annually, what will be the total amount immediately after the eighteenth dollar has been invested? Such a series of equal payments made periodically is called an *annuity*, and the value sought here is called the *amount* of the annuity. The amount of each dollar can be considered as a separate problem and can be treated as in Chapter 9. The sum of all these values is the desired amount immediately after the investment of the eighteenth dollar. Hence the value is

$$(1.03)^{17} + (1.03)^{16} + (1.03)^{15} + \cdots + 1$$

(there is no interest on the last dollar). This sum can be computed term by term and the results added, but a preferable method is to have a formula that works directly. Such a formula will be developed.

The terms of the above sum are seen to have a *common ratio*; that is, the quotient of any term except the first by the next preceding term is the same, specifically $(1.03)^{-1}$. Any sequence of numbers which has a common ratio in this sense is called a *geometric progression* (G.P.). Let this common ratio be designated by r, the first term by a_1, the number of terms by n, the nth term by a_n, and the sum of n terms by S_n. Thus the sum of a general geometric progression can be written as

$$S_n = a_1 + a_1r + a_1r^2 + \cdots + a_1r^{n-1}. \tag{7}$$

The nth term, which has been designated by a_n, is thus seen to be a_1r^{n-1}, and we have the formula

$$a_n = a_1r^{n-1}. \tag{8}$$

Let us multiply both members of Eq. (7) by r and subtract the result, term by term, from the corresponding terms of (7); this gives

$$S_n - rS_n = a_1 - a_1r^n,$$

from which, by solving for S_n, we obtain as a formula for the sum of n terms:

$$S_n = \frac{a_1 - a_1r^n}{1 - r}. \tag{9}$$

If the value for a_n given by Eq. (8) is used in Eq. (9), another formula for S_n is obtained:

$$S_n = \frac{a_1 - ra_n}{1 - r}. \tag{10}$$

To summarize the above results, we note that in any geometric progression there are five quantities a_1, r, a_n, n, S_n which are related by the three equations

$$\boxed{a_n = a_1r^{n-1},}$$

$$\boxed{S_n = \frac{a_1 - a_1r^n}{1 - r},}$$

$$\boxed{S_n = \frac{a_1 - ra_n}{1 - r}.}$$

Two of these equations are independent, so that if any three of the five quantities are given the other two can be found from the above relations.

We can now answer the question raised at the beginning of this section. Let us rewrite the sum in reverse order; we may then set $a_1 = 1$, $r = 1.03$, $n = 18$, and by use of Eq. (9) we obtain

$$S_{18} = \frac{1 - 1(1.03)^{18}}{1 - 1.03} = \frac{(1.03)^{18} - 1}{0.03}.$$

Using logarithms to evaluate the power $(1.03)^{18}$, we find that

$$S_{18} = \$23.40.$$

Example. Determine the fifth term and the sum of the first ten terms of the geometric progression

$$2, \quad -\tfrac{3}{2}, \quad \tfrac{9}{8}, \quad -\cdots$$

Solution. The terms have the common ratio $r = -\frac{3}{4}$, and $a_1 = 2$. Hence the fifth term is given by

$$a_5 = 2\left(-\frac{3}{4}\right)^4 = \frac{2 \cdot 3^4}{4^4} = \frac{81}{128}.$$

For the second part of the problem, $n = 10$, $a_1 = 2$, $r = -\frac{3}{4}$, and from Eq. (9) we have

$$S_{10} = \frac{2 - 2(-\frac{3}{4})^{10}}{1 - (-\frac{3}{4})} = \frac{2 - 2(-\frac{3}{4})^{10}}{\frac{7}{4}} = \frac{4 \cdot 2}{7}\left(1 - \frac{3^{10}}{4^{10}}\right)$$
$$= \frac{4^{10} - 3^{10}}{7 \cdot 2 \cdot 4^8} = \frac{989{,}527}{917{,}504}.$$

The terms of a geometric progression between a_1 and a_n are called *geometric means*. For example, if three geometric means are inserted between 3 and 48, we have a geometric progression of five terms:

$$3, a_2, a_3, a_4, 48.$$

Equation (8) gives (since $a_5 = 48$)

$$48 = 3 \cdot r^4, \qquad r^4 = 16, \qquad r = \pm 2.$$

Hence the desired geometric means are

$$a_2 = 3 \cdot 2 = 6, \qquad a_3 = 6 \cdot 2 = 12, \qquad a_4 = 12 \cdot 2 = 24,$$

or a second set,

$$a_2 = -6, \qquad a_3 = 12, \qquad a_4 = -24.$$

EXERCISE GROUP 13-3

In each of Exercises 1-6, write the first three terms of a G.P. for which:

1. $a_1 = 11, r = 3$
2. $a_1 = -5, r = 2$
3. $a_1 = \frac{3}{2}, r = \frac{2}{3}$
4. $a_1 = 3, r = -\frac{3}{2}$
5. $a_1 = -5, r = -\frac{2}{5}$
6. $a_1 = b, r = c$

In each of Exercises 7-18, the first three terms of a G.P. are given; find the indicated term and sum of terms.

7. 3, 6, 12; find a_{19} and S_{19}
8. $-2, -6, -18$; find a_{11} and S_{11}
9. $10, -5, \frac{5}{2}$; find a_{17} and S_{17}
10. $18, -6, 2$; find a_{15} and S_{15}
11. $-\frac{1}{5}, \frac{3}{5}, -\frac{9}{5}$; find a_9 and S_9
12. $1, \sin\theta, \sin^2\theta$; find a_n and S_n
13. $1, \sin^2\theta, \sin^4\theta$; find a_n and S_n
14. $1, \cos\theta, \cos^2\theta$; find a_n and S_n

15. $\sin^2 \theta, 1, \csc^2 \theta$; find a_n and S_n

16. $\cot^4 \theta, \cot^2 \theta, 1$; find a_n and S_n

17. $\cos^6 \theta, \cos^4 \theta, \cos^2 \theta$; find a_n and S_n

18. $\csc^n \theta, \csc^{n-2} \theta, \csc^{n-4} \theta$; find a_n and S_n

19. Insert three geometric means between $\frac{4}{9}$ and $\frac{9}{4}$.

20. Insert four geometric means between $\frac{81}{2}$ and $\frac{16}{3}$.

21. Insert six geometric means between 2 and $\frac{1}{64}$.

22. Insert four geometric means between 243 and $\frac{1}{32}$.

23. Insert seven geometric means between 10 and 100.

24. Insert seven geometric means between $\csc^2 \theta$ and $\sin^6 \theta$.

25. Insert four geometric means between $\sin 2\theta$ and $32 \sin^{10} \theta \csc^4 2\theta$.

26. Insert three geometric means between $\cot^2 \theta$ and $4 \csc^2 2\theta$.

27. Insert three geometric means between $\tan^2 (\theta/2)$ and $(1 - \cos \theta)^2/\sin^6 \theta$.

In each of Exercises 28–38, determine the values of the missing elements among a_1, r, a_n, n, S_n.

28. $a_1 = 5, r = 2, n = 6$

29. $a_1 = 256, r = \frac{1}{2}, a_n = 1$

30. $S_n = 1785, a_1 = 7, a_n = 896$

31. $a_1 = 3, r = \frac{3}{2}, a_n = 6561/128$

32. $a_1 = \frac{5}{8}, a_n = 40, S_n = \frac{215}{8}$

33. $a_n = -6561, r = -3, S_n = -4914$

34. $a_1 = 3/\sqrt{2}, r = \sqrt{2}/3, n = 8$

35. $a_1 = 1/25, r = 5/2, S_n = 5187/800$

36. $a_n = \csc^6 \theta, r = \csc^2 \theta, S_n = (\csc^{14} \theta - 1) \div (\csc^6 \theta \cot^2 \theta)$

37. $a_1 = \cot^{20} \theta, r = -\tan^2 \theta, a_n = 1$

38. $a_1 = \cot^2 (\theta/2), a_n = \dfrac{(1 + \cos \theta)^2}{\sin^{11} \theta}, S_n = \dfrac{(1 + \cos \theta)(1 - \sin^{10} \theta) \csc^9 \theta}{(1 - \cos \theta)(1 - \sin \theta)}$

39. Find r if $a_2 = 4$ and $a_8 = 256$.

40. Find a_4 if $a_8 = \frac{1}{576}$ and $a_{10} = \frac{1}{2304}$.

41. Find r if $a_5 = \sin 2\theta$, $a_9 = 2 \cot \theta + 2 \cot^3 \theta$.

42. Find a_3 if $a_6 = \tan^3 \dfrac{\theta}{2}$, $a_{12} = \dfrac{1}{8} \sin^3 \theta$.

43. Find the sum of seven terms of the progression $1 + 2, 3 + 2^2, 5 + 2^3, \ldots$

44. Find the sum of nine terms of the progression $3 - 1, 4 - \frac{1}{2}, 5 - \frac{1}{4}, \ldots$

45. A man invests \$1000 at the end of each year. If the investments yield 4% interest compounded annually, how much are his investments worth at the end of 20 yr?

46. How long would it take the investments in Exercise 45 to amount to \$16,626.80?

47. If your father had deposited \$100 in an account for you on your first birthday and \$100 on each birthday thereafter, and if the account earned interest at the rate of 4% compounded annually, how much would be in your account on your 18th birthday?

48. A golf ball is dropped from a height of 6 ft. On each rebound it rises $\frac{2}{3}$ of the height from which it last fell. What distance has it traveled at the instant it strikes the ground for the 7th time?

13–4 GEOMETRIC PROGRESSIONS WITH INFINITELY MANY TERMS

Let us consider the geometric progression

$$1, \frac{1}{3}, \frac{1}{9}, \frac{1}{27}, \ldots, \frac{1}{3^{n-1}}, \ldots,$$

in which $r = \frac{1}{3}$. Here $a_n = 1/3^{n-1}$, and it is clear that the larger the value of n the smaller the value of a_n. In fact, if n can increase without bound, the value of a_n can be made smaller than any preassigned value by taking n large enough. In particular, if the preassigned value is 10^{-9}, then in order that $a_n < 10^{-9}$, we must have

$$\frac{1}{3^{n-1}} < \frac{1}{10^9}.$$

Since the numerators of the fractions are equal, it follows that the smaller fraction must have the larger denominator. Hence, it follows that

$$3^{n-1} > 10^9,$$

and taking the logarithm of both sides (also making use of the properties of logarithms), we have

$$(n - 1) \log 3 > 9 \log 10 = 9.$$

If we now solve this last relation for n, we have

$$n - 1 > \frac{9}{\log 3} \quad \text{and} \quad n > \frac{9}{0.4771} + 1 = 19.9.$$

Thus we see that whenever $n \geqq 20$, $a_n < 10^{-9}$.

The indicated sum of the terms of a geometric progression in which n can increase without bound is called an infinite geometric series, or simply a *geometric series.*

Consider now the geometric series

$$1 + \frac{1}{3} + \frac{1}{9} + \frac{1}{27} + \cdots + \frac{1}{3^{n-1}} + \cdots$$

Let S_n designate the sum of the first n terms of this series:

$$S_n = 1 + \frac{1}{3} + \frac{1}{9} + \cdots + \frac{1}{3^{n-1}}.$$

This is a *finite* sum and is called the nth *partial sum* of the series. By Eq. (9) we find the value of S_n to be

$$S_n = \frac{1}{1 - \frac{1}{3}} - \frac{1 \cdot (\frac{1}{3})^n}{1 - \frac{1}{3}}.$$

Only the second term of S_n contains n, and as n increases the value of this term decreases and becomes closer and closer to zero. Hence as n increases, the value of S_n gets closer and closer to the first term $1/(1 - \frac{1}{3})$. This fact is expressed in the statement

$$\lim_{n\to\infty} S_n = \frac{1}{1 - \frac{1}{3}} = \frac{1}{\frac{2}{3}} = \frac{3}{2}.$$

The left member is read "limit of S_n as n becomes infinite." *The value of this limit is defined as the sum or value of the geometric series.*

In the general case, let us designate the geometric series by S:

$$S = a_1 + a_1r + a_1r^2 + \cdots + a_1r^{n-1} + \cdots \tag{11}$$

We again define S_n as the *finite, partial sum* of the first n terms:

$$S_n = a_1 + a_1r + a_1r^2 + \cdots + a_1r^{n-1}$$

and apply Eq. (9) to find this sum:

$$S_n = \frac{a_1}{1 - r} - \frac{a_1r^n}{1 - r}.$$

If $|r| < 1$, that is, if $-1 < r < 1$, the value of the second term in S_n will decrease numerically, and approach zero as n increases indefinitely. Hence if $-1 < r < 1$, the value of S_n gets closer and closer to the number $a_1/(1 - r)$, and

$$\boxed{S = \lim_{n\to\infty} S_n = \frac{a_1}{1 - r}.} \tag{12}$$

The series is then said to converge and to have the value $S = a_1/(1 - r)$. When $|r| \geqq 1$, which means that when either $r \geqq 1$ or $r \leqq -1$, the partial sums S_n do not approach any value; in this event the series does not converge and is said to *diverge*. We collect these results in the following statement.

Theorem 13–1. *The geometric series* (11) *converges when and only when* $|r| < 1$, *that is,* $-1 < r < 1$, *and when convergent it has the value* $S = a_1/(1 - r)$.

By use of this theorem, the sum of the geometric series treated earlier in this section is $S = 1/(1 - \frac{1}{3}) = \frac{3}{2}$.

EXERCISE GROUP 13–4

In Exercises 1–10 find the sum of each geometric series.

1. $3 + \frac{1}{2} + \frac{1}{12} + \cdots$
2. $4 - \frac{1}{2} + \frac{1}{16} - \cdots$
3. $11 - 1 + \frac{1}{11} - \cdots$
4. $a - 0.1a + 0.01a - \cdots$
5. $6 + \frac{6}{5} + \frac{6}{25} + \cdots$
6. $4.509 + 3.006 + 2.004 + \cdots$

7. $0.171 - 0.114 + 0.076 - \cdots$

8. $\frac{2}{5} - \frac{1}{15} + \frac{1}{90} - \cdots$

9. $\dfrac{1}{1 - \sqrt{2}} + 1 + (1 - \sqrt{2}) + \cdots$

10. $\dfrac{\sqrt{3} + 1}{\sqrt{3} - 1} + \dfrac{2}{3 - \sqrt{3}} + \dfrac{2}{3} + \cdots$

In Exercises 11–18 find the sum of each infinite geometric series, and determine the values of x for which each series converges.

11. $1 - x + x^2 - x^3 + \cdots$

12. $1 + x^2 + x^4 + x^6 + \cdots$

13. $x + x^3 + x^5 + x^7 + \cdots$

14. $\dfrac{\sqrt{x}}{2} - \dfrac{x}{4} + \dfrac{\sqrt{x^3}}{8} - \cdots$

15. $(x + 3) + 2(x + 3)^2 + 4(x + 3)^3 + \cdots$

16. $(x^2 - 2) - 0.1(x^2 - 2)^2 + 0.01(x^2 - 2)^3 - \cdots$

17. $1 + \dfrac{1}{1 - x} + \dfrac{1}{(1 - x)^2} + \cdots$

18. $\dfrac{1}{1 + x} + \dfrac{x}{(1 + x)^2} + \dfrac{x^2}{(1 + x)^3} + \cdots$

Prove that:

19. $1 + \sin^2 x + \sin^4 x + \cdots = \sec^2 x$

20. $1 + \cos^2 x + \cos^4 x + \cdots = \csc^2 x$

21. $1 - \tan^2 x + \tan^4 x - \cdots = \cos^2 x$

22. $1 - \cot^2 x + \cot^4 x - \cdots = \sin^2 x$

13–5 REPEATING DECIMALS

An interesting application of convergent geometric series occurs in the case of *repeating infinite decimals*, that is, decimals in which, after some decimal place, a fixed group of digits repeats indefinitely. Thus the repeating decimal 0.333 . . . can be written as

$$0.3 + 0.03 + 0.003 + \cdots,$$

which is a geometric series with $r = 0.1$. Hence, by (12), the value is

$$S = \frac{a_1}{1 - r} = \frac{0.3}{1 - 0.1} = \frac{0.3}{0.9} = \frac{1}{3}.$$

The general result, of which an example has just been presented, is expressed in the following theorem.

Theorem 13–2. *Every repeating decimal represents a rational number.*

Proof. A repeating decimal can be expressed as the sum of a finite decimal and an infinite repeating part. The infinite repeating part is a geometric series with $0 < r \leqq 0.1$, hence can be written as a quotient of two finite decimals, and is therefore equal to a rational number. The finite decimal part is also a rational number. The sum of the two parts is thus a rational number also, and the theorem is proved.

Example 1. Express $a = 3.0342342\ldots$ as a rational number, that is, as a quotient of two integers.

Solution. Write the decimal in the form

$$a = 3 + (0.0342 + 0.0000342 + 0.0000000342 + \cdots).$$

The part in parentheses is a geometric series with $a_1 = 0.0342$ and $r = 0.001$. Hence by Eq. (12) its value is

$$\frac{0.0342}{1 - 0.001} = \frac{0.0342}{0.999} = \frac{342}{9990} = \frac{19}{555} \quad \text{and} \quad a = 3 + \frac{19}{555} = \frac{1684}{555}.$$

This result can be checked by long division.

For the sake of completeness we present the converse of Theorem 13–2 above.

Theorem 13–3. *Any rational number can be expressed as a repeating decimal.*

Proof. By definition, a rational number can be expressed in the form p/q, where p and q are integers. It is enough to prove the theorem for a positive proper fraction, that is, a fraction in which p and q are positive, and p is smaller than q. If the division of p by q is carried out, the remainder at each step will be either a positive integer smaller than q, or zero. Hence there are q possible remainders, and a remainder will be repeated after at most q steps in the division. At this step the digits in the quotient start repeating, and the quotient will be a repeating decimal.

Note that a number such as $0.783 = 0.783000\ldots$ may be thought of as a repeating decimal in which the digit zero repeats.

Example 2. $\frac{3}{7} = 0.428571428571428571\ldots$

```
    0.428571 . . .
 7)3.0
   2 8
    20
    14
     60
     56
      40
      35
       50
       49
        10
         7
         3
```

In the division of Example 2, the first remainder is 2, the second is 6, the third is 4, the fourth is 5, the fifth is 1, and the sixth is 3, which was the starting number. In this example, the six possible remainders were obtained before 3 was repeated.

Example 3. $\frac{2}{5} = 0.400000\ldots$, which is a repeating decimal with the digit zero repeating indefinitely.

EXERCISE GROUP 13–5

Reduce each of the following repeating decimals to a rational fraction in lowest terms.

1. 1.51515 . . .
2. 36.3636 . . .
3. 0.072072072 . . .
4. 0.102102102 . . .
5. 5.999 . . .
6. 0.603603603 . . .
7. 0.8777 . . .
8. 0.818181 . . .
9. 0.792792792 . . .
10. 7.545454 . . .
11. 0.0515151 . . .
12. 0.711711711 . . .
13. 1.62162162 . . .
14. 2.34323432343 . . .
15. 0.714285714285714285 . . .
16. 0.153846153846153846 . . .

SUPPLEMENTARY EXERCISES FOR CHAPTER 13

1. Show that the sum of any $2n + 1$ consecutive integers is divisible by $2n + 1$.
2. Prove that the squares of $x^2 - 2x - 1$, $x^2 + 1$, and $x^2 + 2x - 1$ form an A.P.
3. Prove that $\dfrac{1}{b+c}, \dfrac{1}{c+a}, \dfrac{1}{a+b}$ form an A.P. if a^2, b^2, c^2 form an A.P.
4. The sum of m terms of an A.P. is n, and the sum of n terms is m. Find the sum of $m + n$ terms.
5. Find the sum $\dfrac{1}{1+\sqrt{x}} + \dfrac{1}{1-x} + \dfrac{1}{1-\sqrt{x}} + \cdots$ to n terms.
6. If the sum of an A.P. is the same for m terms as for n terms, $m \neq n$, show that the sum of $m + n$ terms is zero.
7. If $\theta - A, \theta, \theta + A$ are three angles whose secants are in A.P., show that $\cos\theta = \sqrt{2}\cos(A/2)$.
8. Prove that values of θ satisfying $\tan m\theta \tan n\theta = 1$ are in A.P. with a common difference of $\pi/(m + n)$.
9. Prove that values of θ satisfying $\sin m\theta \cos n\theta = 0$ are in A.P. with a common difference of π/m or π/n.
10. Prove that values of θ satisfying $\sin m\theta + \sin n\theta = 0$ are in A.P. with a common difference of $2\pi/(m + n)$ or $2\pi/(m - n)$.
11. Show that for $0 < \theta < \pi/2$, $\log\sin\theta$, 0, $\log\csc\theta$ are in A.P.
12. Show that $\dfrac{1}{1-\sin\theta}, \dfrac{1}{2}, \dfrac{1}{1-\csc\theta}$ are in A.P.
13. If the arithmetic mean of a and b is twice as much as their geometric mean, show that $\dfrac{a}{b} = \dfrac{2+\sqrt{3}}{2-\sqrt{3}}$.
14. Show that the logarithms of the terms of any G.P. with positive terms form an A.P.
15. If a, b, c, is a G.P., show that $\dfrac{1}{b-a}, \dfrac{1}{2b}, \dfrac{1}{b-c}$ is an A.P.
16. Show that if each term in a G.P. is subtracted from the following one, the differences obtained also form a G.P.
17. Find three numbers in G.P. whose sum is 38 and whose product is 1728.

18. Find r if the sum of the first six terms of a G.P. of real terms is 9 times the sum of the first three terms.

19. Show that $\dfrac{4\cos\theta}{1+\sin\theta}$, $\dfrac{2\sin 2\theta}{1+\sin\theta}$, $\dfrac{\sin^2 2\theta}{\cos\theta(1+\sin\theta)}$ are in G.P.

Prove each relation in Exercises 20–23.

20. $1 + \cos 2x + \cos^2 2x + \cdots = \csc 2x \cot x$

21. $1 - \cos 4x + \cos^2 4x - \cdots = \csc 4x \tan 2x$

22. $1 + \sin 2x + \sin^2 2x + \cdots = \dfrac{1}{2}\sec^2\left(\dfrac{\pi}{4} + x\right)$

23. $1 + \cos x + \cos^2 x + \cdots = \dfrac{1}{2}\csc^2\dfrac{x}{2}$

24. Find the sum of the infinite series $(1 + \frac{1}{2}) + (\frac{1}{3} + \frac{1}{4}) + (\frac{1}{9} + \frac{1}{8}) + \cdots$

25. Find the sum of the infinite series $(2 - \frac{1}{4}) + (\frac{1}{2} - \frac{1}{12}) + (\frac{1}{8} - \frac{1}{36}) + \cdots$

26. Find r for an infinite geometric series in which each term is twice the sum of all the terms which follow it.

27. Find r for an infinite geometric series in which each term is ten times the sum of all the terms which follow it.

28. A golf ball is dropped from a height of 6 ft. Its center rebounds each time $\frac{2}{3}$ of the height from which it last fell. Find the limit of the distance traveled by the center of the ball in coming to rest.

29. Find the limit of the time the center of the ball of Exercise 28 will travel. [*Hint:* Recall that in Exercise 8 of Exercise Group 2–6, we found that s (the distance a body falls) $= 16t^2$ (t = time of falling in seconds). Hence $t = \frac{1}{4}\sqrt{s}$.]

CHAPTER 14

The Solution of Oblique Triangles

14–1 INTRODUCTION

In Chapter 5 we considered various types of problems which arise in surveying, navigation, and physics. The solutions of these problems were effected by solving appropriate right triangles. In less restricted situations similar problems can be solved if we have methods for solving *oblique* triangles, that is, triangles which contain no right angle. We shall discuss such methods in this chapter.

The formulas to be developed express certain relations among the sides and angles of a triangle; some of them have an importance apart from their use in the solution of triangles. Although the formulas are designed for use with oblique triangles, they do apply to right triangles as well. We shall, accordingly, not exclude right triangles when referring to oblique triangles, unless such exclusion is specifically mentioned.

14–2 THE LAW OF SINES

In the derivation of the various formulas which apply to oblique triangles, a *standard lettering* will be used. The vertices will be A, B, and C, the corresponding angles will be named similarly, and the side of the triangle opposite any vertex will be labeled with the corresponding lower-case letter.

Let ABC be either triangle in Fig. 14–1. The altitude h is drawn from B to AC, with D as the foot of this altitude. From right triangle ABD in Fig. 14–1(a) we have

$$h = c \sin (180^\circ - A),$$

which becomes, since $\sin (180^\circ - A) = \sin A$,

$$h = c \sin A. \tag{1}$$

For the triangle ABD of Fig. 14–1(b), Eq. (1) follows directly. From right triangle CBD in either figure we also have

$$h = a \sin C. \tag{2}$$

By equating the values of h in Eqs. (1) and (2) we have at once $a \sin C = c \sin A$, which in turn, upon division of both members by $\sin A \sin C$, gives

$$\frac{a}{\sin A} = \frac{c}{\sin C}. \tag{3}$$

A similar derivation (or a relettering of the triangle) yields the equation

$$\frac{a}{\sin A} = \frac{b}{\sin B}, \tag{4}$$

and a combination of (3) and (4) gives the *Law of Sines:*

$$\boxed{\frac{a}{\sin A} = \frac{b}{\sin B} = \frac{c}{\sin C}.} \tag{5}$$

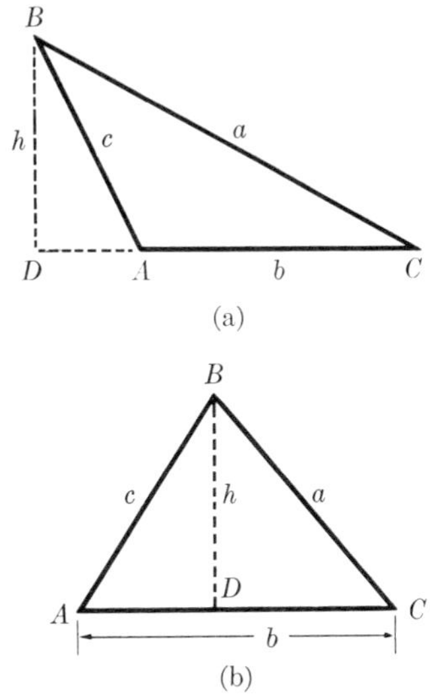

FIGURE 14–1

It is helpful to state this relation in words.

The Law of Sines. *In a triangle the ratio of any side to the sine of the opposite angle is constant.*

If one of the angles in a triangle is a right angle, the Law of Sines still applies, and in fact reduces to formulas obtained in Section 5–3.

14–3 THE LAW OF COSINES

Any triangle with standard lettering may be placed on a coordinate system as in Fig. 14–2. Since angle A is in standard position, the definitions of $\cos A$ and $\sin A$ give, if u and v are the coordinates of B, $\cos A = u/c$, $\sin A = v/c$. Hence $u = c \cos A$, $v = c \sin A$.

We now apply the distance formula of Section 2–4 to finding the square of the length BC, and we have

$$\begin{aligned} a^2 &= (b - c \cos A)^2 + (c \sin A)^2 \\ &= b^2 - 2bc \cos A + c^2 \cos^2 A + c^2 \sin^2 A \\ &= b^2 + c^2 - 2bc \cos A \\ &\quad (\text{since } \cos^2 A + \sin^2 A = 1). \end{aligned}$$

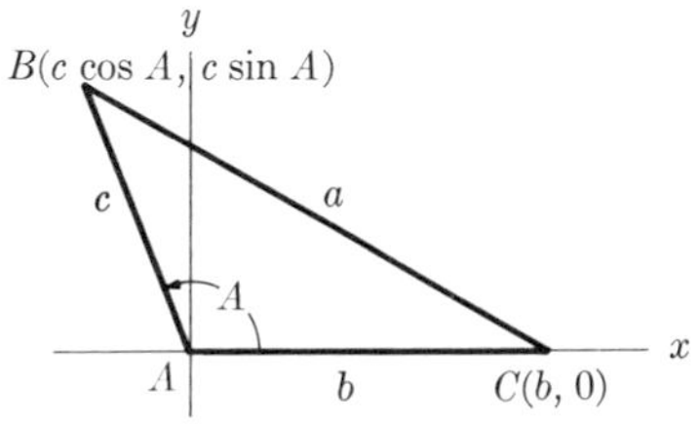

FIGURE 14–2

We have thus obtained one form of the *Law of Cosines*,

$$a^2 = b^2 + c^2 - 2bc \cos A. \tag{6}$$

By relettering the triangles, we may at once write down the other forms of the Law of Cosines,

$$b^2 = a^2 + c^2 - 2ac \cos B, \tag{7}$$

$$c^2 = a^2 + b^2 - 2ab \cos C. \tag{8}$$

The three equations (6), (7), and (8) are all contained in the following statement.

The Law of Cosines. *In a triangle the square of any side is equal to the sum of the squares of the other two sides minus twice the product of these sides and the cosine of the angle included between them.*

In the case of a right triangle the Law of Cosines reduces either to the theorem of Pythagoras, or to one of the formulas of Section 5-3. It should be realized that the Law of Cosines has important applications apart from the solution of triangles.

Example. Prove that if $(\cos A)/b = (\cos B)/a$, the triangle is either an isosceles or a right triangle.

Solution. We may solve Eqs. (6) and (7) to give

$$\cos A = \frac{b^2 + c^2 - a^2}{2bc}, \qquad \cos B = \frac{a^2 + c^2 - b^2}{2ac}.$$

Substitution of these in the given equation yields

$$\frac{b^2 + c^2 - a^2}{2b^2c} = \frac{a^2 + c^2 - b^2}{2a^2c}.$$

Multiplying both members by $2c$, and then clearing fractions, we have

$$a^2b^2 + a^2c^2 - a^4 = a^2b^2 + b^2c^2 - b^4,$$

which may be written as

$$a^2c^2 - b^2c^2 = a^4 - b^4,$$

and, on partial factorization, as

$$c^2(a^2 - b^2) = (a^2 + b^2)(a^2 - b^2).$$

One possibility is $a^2 - b^2 = 0$, in which case $a = b$ and the triangle is isosceles. If $a^2 - b^2 \neq 0$, we may divide both members of the above equation by $a^2 - b^2$, and we obtain

$$c^2 = a^2 + b^2,$$

from which it follows that the triangle is a right triangle (with $C = 90°$).

EXERCISE GROUP 14–1

In the following exercises the standard lettering of an oblique triangle is used unless otherwise specified.

1. Use the Law of Sines to prove that $\cos C = b/(2c)$ if $B = 2C$.
2. Prove the following relations from either triangle of Fig. 14–1:

$$b \cos A + a \cos B = c, \qquad c \cos B + b \cos C = a,$$
$$a \cos C + c \cos A = b.$$

3. Derive the Law of Cosines by eliminating $\cos B$ from the first two equations of Exercise 2, and then eliminating $\cos C$ from the resulting equation and the third equation of Exercise 2.
4. Show that $a^2 + bc = b^2 + c^2$ if $A = 60°$.
5. Show that $b^2 - ac = c^2 + a^2$ if $B = 120°$.
6. Show that $ab = c^2 - a^2$ if $C = 2A$ and $A \neq B$.
7. In an isosceles triangle in which the equal sides are designated by a and the angle between them by θ, use the Law of Cosines to show that the third side x is given by $x = 2a \sin(\theta/2)$.
8. Use the Law of Cosines to prove that the square of the length of the median drawn from A is given by $\frac{1}{4}[2(b^2 + c^2) - a^2]$.
9. Prove that $b \sin A/\sin(A + \frac{1}{2}C)$ is the length of the internal bisector of angle C.
10. Use the Law of Sines to prove that the bisector of an angle of a triangle divides the opposite side into parts which are proportional to the adjacent sides.
11. Prove that $a^2 + b^2 + c^2 = 2bc \cos A + 2ca \cos B + 2ab \cos C$.
12. Prove that $a^4 + b^4 + c^4 = 2a^3b \cos C + 2b^3c \cos A + 2c^3a \cos B$.
13. Prove that (a) $c(a \cos B - b \cos A) = a^2 - b^2$,
 (b) $a(b \cos C - c \cos B) = b^2 - c^2$,
 (c) $b(c \cos A - a \cos C) = c^2 - a^2$.
14. Show that the diameter of the circumscribed circle of a triangle is given by the relations $d = a \csc A = b \csc B = c \csc C$. (This may be used as an alternative proof of the Law of Sines.)
15. Show that the diameter of the inscribed circle of a triangle is given by the relations

$$d = \frac{2a \sin B \sin C}{\sin(B + C) + \sin B + \sin C} = \frac{2b \sin C \sin A}{\sin(C + A) + \sin C + \sin A}$$
$$= \frac{2c \sin A \sin B}{\sin(A + B) + \sin A + \sin B}.$$

16. One expression for c^2 may be obtained by squaring the first equation of Exercise 2, and another from the Law of Cosines involving $\cos C$. By equating these expressions, derive the Law of Sines. [*Hint:* The relation $\cos A \cos B + \cos C = \sin A \sin B$ holds for the angles of a triangle.]

14–4 ON SOLVING OBLIQUE TRIANGLES

The three angles and the three sides of any triangle are called the *parts* of the triangle. If three parts of a triangle (including at least one side) are known, the remaining parts may in general be found, by methods which we shall now present. *To solve a triangle shall mean to find those parts of the triangle which are not known.* It is convenient to consider the following four cases in the discussion of the methods of solving an oblique triangle.

A. *Two angles and one side are known.*
B. *Two sides and the angle opposite one of them are known.*
C. *Two sides and the included angle are known.*
D. *The three sides are known.*

It is clear, in regard to Case A, that if any two angles of a triangle are known, the third one can be found immediately by using the fact that the sum of the angles of a triangle is 180°.

Case B is known as the *ambiguous case*, for under certain conditions two triangles, distinct in the sense of not being congruent, exist with the same three given parts. In fact, this case is the only one of the four for which there is no corresponding theorem in plane geometry expressing a condition for congruence of triangles. For each of the other cases a theorem on congruence of triangles insures that only one triangle exists with the given parts.

In each of Cases C and D two methods of solution will be considered, one of which is well suited to logarithmic computation, while the other uses the highly important Law of Cosines.

14–5 CASE A. TWO ANGLES AND ONE SIDE

We may assume in this case that the three angles of the triangle are known, in addition to a side. The Law of Sines may then be used to find in turn each of the remaining sides. To find either unknown side we use the Law of Sines with the ratio which involves that side and the one which involves the given side.

Example. Solve the triangle ABC if

$$A = 23^\circ\ 09', \qquad B = 108^\circ\ 43', \qquad c = 123.2.$$

Solution. Angle C can be found at once:

$$C = 180^\circ - (23^\circ\ 09' + 108^\circ\ 43') = 48^\circ\ 08'.$$

Let us find side a. Using the Law of Sines with the ratios which involve a and c, we have

$$\frac{a}{\sin A} = \frac{c}{\sin C},$$

which may be solved for a to give

$$a = \frac{c}{\sin C} \cdot \sin A. \tag{9}$$

We shall use logarithms to evaluate a. Equating logarithms of both members of (9) we have

$$\log a = (\log c - \log \sin C) + \log \sin A.$$

The logarithmic computation follows:

$$\begin{aligned} \log c &= \log 123.2 = 12.0906 - 10 \quad (-) \\ \log \sin C &= \log \sin 48^\circ\, 08' = \underline{9.8720 - 10} \\ \log (c/\sin C) &= 2.2186 \quad (+) \\ \log \sin A &= \log \sin 23^\circ\, 09' = \underline{9.5945 - 10} \\ \log a &= 11.8131 - 10 \\ a &= 65.03. \end{aligned}$$

To find side b we have an equation similar to (9), involving b and c, namely,

$$b = \frac{c}{\sin C} \cdot \sin B,$$

and the corresponding logarithmic equation, $\log b = \log (c/\sin C) + \log \sin B$. Using the value of $\log (c/\sin C)$ from the above computation, we have

$$\begin{aligned} \log (c/\sin C) &= 2.2186 \quad (+) \\ \log \sin B &= \log \sin 71^\circ\, 17' = \underline{9.9764 - 10} \\ \log b &= 12.1950 - 10 \\ b &= 157.7. \end{aligned}$$

EXERCISE GROUP 14-2

In Exercises 1–20 solve the triangle ABC having the given parts.

1. $A = 62^\circ\, 23'$, $C = 34^\circ\, 14'$, $b = 324.1$
2. $B = 36^\circ\, 51'$, $A = 83^\circ\, 13'$, $c = 132.4$
3. $C = 25^\circ\, 32'$, $B = 47^\circ\, 37'$, $a = 31.02$
4. $B = 71^\circ\, 35'$, $C = 28^\circ\, 51'$, $a = 39.71$
5. $C = 99^\circ\, 26'$, $A = 58^\circ\, 21'$, $b = 7.312$
6. $A = 113^\circ\, 54'$, $B = 62^\circ\, 15'$, $c = 0.03165$
7. $C = 123^\circ\, 52'$, $B = 42^\circ\, 19'$, $a = 0.5631$
8. $A = 15^\circ\, 29'$, $C = 132^\circ\, 41'$, $b = 1253$
9. $B = 63^\circ\, 18'$, $A = 102^\circ\, 13'$, $c = 15.23$
10. $a = 0.6314$, $B = 14^\circ\, 49'$, $C = 32^\circ\, 19'$
11. $b = 3819$, $C = 39^\circ\, 11'$, $A = 84^\circ\, 50'$
12. $c = 0.04321$, $A = 126^\circ\, 19'$, $B = 35^\circ\, 22'$
13. $a = 26.35$, $A = 37^\circ\, 23'$, $B = 43^\circ\, 31'$
14. $b = 5317$, $B = 125^\circ\, 17'$, $C = 19^\circ\, 23'$
15. $c = 0.9513$, $C = 46^\circ\, 32'$, $A = 82^\circ\, 36'$
16. $a = 0.03819$, $A = 16^\circ\, 13'$, $B = 99^\circ\, 32'$

17. $b = 7.193$, $B = 91° 47'$, $C = 58° 12'$

18. $c = 38.12$, $C = 56° 39'$, $A = 52° 37'$

19. $c = 714.5$, $C = 123° 11'$, $A = 42° 06'$

20. $b = 0.4238$, $B = 14° 33'$, $C = 78° 16'$

21. A pilot flies with an airspeed of 450 mph on a heading of 134°. The wind is blowing from the direction 255°. If the resulting course is 130°, find the velocity of the wind and the groundspeed of the plane.

22. A tree standing (vertically) on a slope inclined at an angle of 7° to the horizontal casts a shadow 32 ft in length up the slope. If the angle of elevation of the sun is 63°, find the height of the tree.

23. Two points A and B on the bank of a river are 30 ft apart. A point C across the river is located so that angle CAB is 75° and angle ABC is 85°. How wide is the river?

24. A pilot maintains an airspeed of 450 mph on a heading of 328° 15'. The wind is blowing from the northeast (from direction 45°) and the course flown by the pilot is 325° 12'. Find the velocity of the wind and the groundspeed of the plane.

25. A side of a regular polygon of seven sides is 176.2 in. long. Find the radius of the circumscribed circle.

26. A body is acted upon by a force of 978 lb and by a force of unknown magnitude which makes an angle of 113° 54' with the direction of the first force. The direction of the resultant force can be measured and is found to make an angle of 62° 19' with the direction of the first force. Find the magnitude of the resultant, and also of the second force.

27. An aircraft carrier is sailing at 25 knots on a course of 26° 35'. A plane takes off and flies a course of 303° 30' to a point P. The pilot then flies on course 115° 10' until he reaches the carrier again, which has continued to sail with its original velocity during the elapsed time of 5 hr. How far did the pilot fly?

28. An engineer in town A must be in town B, which is 1256 mi east of A, in 12 hr. He decides to go by way of C to visit a branch plant. The direction from A to C is 59° 30' and the direction from C to B is 120°. If he averages 300 mph in his plane, how much time will he have for his visit at the branch plant at C?

29. To keep on his schedule a pilot must have an average groundspeed of 300 mph on a course of 282° 13'. The wind is blowing from the direction 132° 46' and the pilot decides to fly on a heading of 280°. Find the airspeed the pilot must maintain and also the wind velocity.

30. A pilot, who is flying on a straight course of 43°, observes a flashing beacon in the direction 76°, and after flying 30 mi he observes that the beacon is in the direction 110° 30'. How far is he from the beacon on his second observation?

14-6 CASE B. THE AMBIGUOUS CASE

We shall assume for the discussion of the case in which two sides and the angle opposite one of them are known, that the known parts of the triangle are A, a, and b. *If angle A is obtuse*, side a must be larger than side b in order for a triangle to exist, and in that case there is exactly one triangle [Fig. 14-3(a)]. A similar statement applies if A is a right angle.

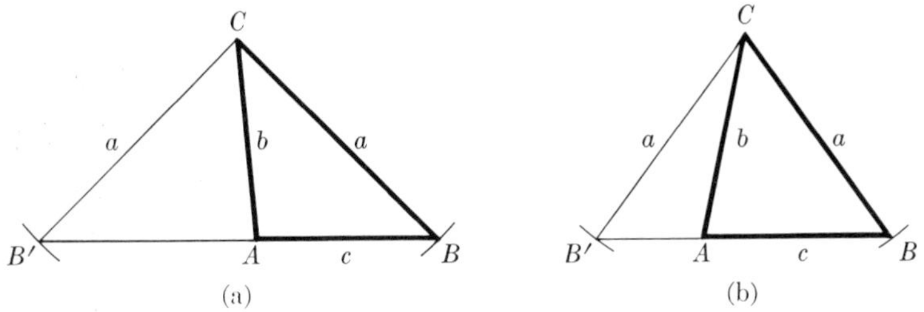

FIGURE 14–3

If A is an acute angle, and $a > b$, again only one triangle exists, as in Fig. 14–3 (b).

If A is an acute angle, and $a < b$, one of three possibilities may occur. As extended from vertex C, (1) a line of length a may be too short to reach AB, so that no triangle exists, or (2) the line of length a may be precisely the distance from C to the opposite side and one triangle, a right triangle, exists, or (3) a line of length a drawn from C may intersect the side opposite C in two points B and B', forming triangles $AB'C$ and ABC, each of which contains the given parts. The three possibilities are indicated in Fig. 14–4.

Criteria may be established to determine which possibility occurs in a given situation. However, this determination may be effectively made during the process of attempting a solution, as will appear in the examples.

The general method of solution in Case B is to use the Law of Sines to find the unknown angle opposite a given side, then to find the third angle, and finally to find the third side by the Law of Sines again.

Example 1. Solve the triangle ABC if $A = 30°$, $a = 3.4$, $b = 7$.

Solution. From the Law of Sines (Section 14–2) we find that

$$\sin B = \frac{b \sin A}{a}.$$

Hence, *if a triangle exists*, we must have

$$\sin B = \frac{7 \sin 30^\circ}{3.4} = \frac{3.5}{3.4} > 1.$$

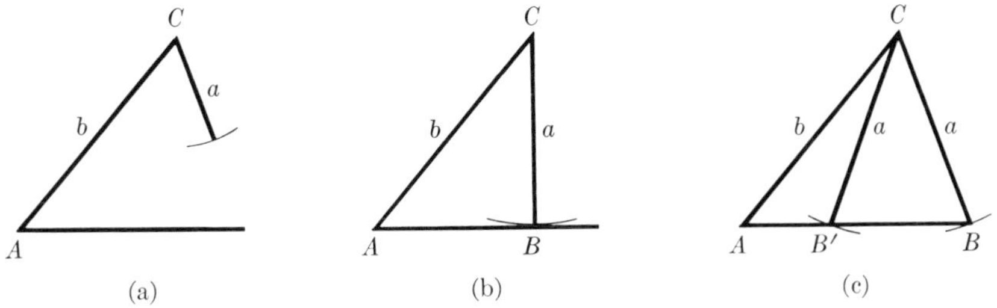

FIGURE 14–4

However, a value of sin B which is greater than 1 is clearly impossible, so that no solution exists.

If the attempt to compute sin B in Example 1 is made by use of logarithms, the indication that no solution exists will be the emergence of a value of log sin B which is greater than zero. For, since the sine of any angle must be not greater than 1, the logarithm of the sine must be not greater than zero.

Example 2. Solve the triangle ABC for which

$$C = 38° \; 17', \qquad a = 2.304, \qquad c = 1.520.$$

Solution. To find angle A we employ the Law of Sines in the form

$$\sin A = \frac{a \sin C}{c},$$

which becomes, in logarithmic form,

$$\log \sin A = \log a + \log \sin C - \log c.$$

The logarithmic computation follows:

$$\begin{aligned} \log a &= \log 2.304 = 0.3625 \\ \log \sin C &= \log \sin 38° \; 17' = \underline{9.7921 - 10} \quad (+) \\ \log (a \sin C) &= 10.1546 - 10 \\ \log c &= \log 1.520 = \underline{0.1818} \\ \log \sin A &= 9.9728 - 10. \end{aligned}$$

There are thus two possible values of angle A, which will be called A and A',

$$A = 69° \; 56' \quad \text{and} \quad A' = 110° \; 04'.$$

The corresponding values of the third angle are then

$$B = 71° \; 47' \quad \text{and} \quad B' = 31° \; 39'.$$

Finally, to find the remaining side we use the Law of Sines in the form (as in Case A),

$$b = \frac{a \sin B}{\sin A},$$

together with logarithmic computation for each of the possible triangles,

$$\begin{aligned} \log 2.304 &= 0.3625 \\ \log \sin 71° \; 47' &= \underline{9.9777 - 10} \quad (+) \\ & 10.3402 - 10 \\ \log \sin 69° \; 56' &= \underline{9.9728 - 10} \quad (-) \\ \log b &= 0.3674 \\ b &= 2.330 \end{aligned} \qquad \begin{aligned} \log 2.304 &= 0.3625 \\ \log \sin 31° \; 39' &= \underline{9.7199 - 10} \quad (+) \\ & 10.0824 - 10 \\ \log \sin 110° \; 04' &= \underline{9.9728 - 10} \quad (-) \\ \log b' &= 0.1096 \\ b' &= 1.288 \end{aligned}$$

Example 3. There can be only one triangle ABC with $A = 18°$, $a = 4.6$, $b = 3.1$, since the side a opposite the known angle A is the larger of the two given sides. If this were overlooked, and the attempt made to solve the triangle, the same conclusion would appear. Thus, angle B is found to be $12° \ 00'$ to the nearest $10'$; the supplement B' of B gives no triangle, since $A + B' > 180°$. Finally, angle C is 150°, and side c turns out to be 7.44.

These examples indicate that whenever the Law of Sines is used to find an angle, two supplementary values are possible initially for the angle. Other considerations will then determine whether one of these possibilities must be discarded.

EXERCISE GROUP 14–3

In each of Exercises 1–22, solve the triangle ABC having the given parts.

1. $A = 24° \ 21'$, $a = 6.312$, $b = 3.216$
2. $B = 96° \ 15'$, $b = 6.332$, $c = 3.269$
3. $C = 52° \ 18'$, $b = 502.7$, $c = 237.5$
4. $B = 127° \ 31'$, $b = 19.03$, $a = 17.13$
5. $C = 36° \ 19'$, $c = 23.25$, $b = 25.69$
6. $A = 133° \ 37'$, $a = 0.7893$, $c = 0.1973$
7. $a = 0.9346$, $b = 0.6372$, $B = 58° \ 39'$
8. $b = 0.08962$, $c = 0.07513$, $C = 47° \ 23'$
9. $c = 0.09268$, $a = 0.3624$, $A = 46° \ 43'$
10. $b = 9.234$, $a = 2.943$, $A = 134° \ 18'$
11. $c = 325.7$, $b = 314.9$, $B = 71° \ 16'$
12. $a = 0.3849$, $c = 0.2378$, $C = 17° \ 53'$
13. $b = 2.613$, $a = 3.513$, $A = 63° \ 49'$
14. $c = 0.02354$, $a = 0.1734$, $A = 134° \ 36'$
15. $c = 19.83$, $b = 14.07$, $C = 94° \ 38'$
16. $a = 322.8$, $b = 196.7$, $B = 31° \ 08'$
17. $B = 19° \ 13'$, $b = 84.02$, $a = 139.4$
18. $C = 97° \ 28'$, $c = 268.3$, $b = 159.8$
19. $A = 124° \ 16'$, $a = 6.284$, $b = 3.367$
20. $A = 14° \ 39'$, $a = 59.26$, $c = 243.7$
21. $C = 8° \ 54'$, $c = 0.8493$, $a = 1.932$
22. $B = 84° \ 47'$, $b = 38.31$, $a = 21.97$
23. A and B are two points on opposite sides of a body of water. A third point C is located so that AC and BC are found to be 193 ft and 236 ft, respectively, and the angle BAC is 43°. Compute the distance AB to the degree of accuracy the data justify.
24. A pilot wishes to fly from A to B, which is in the direction 50°. The wind is blowing 20 mph from the direction 290° and the airspeed will be 300 mph. Find the heading that the pilot must fly to reach the point B, and the average groundspeed for the flight.

25. A pilot must fly a course of 213° 24′, and the wind is blowing 23 mph from the direction 196° 41′. If he maintains an average airspeed of 293.8 mph, what will be his average groundspeed, and what heading should he fly?

26. The longer side of a parallelogram is 179.8 ft and the shorter side is 136.9 ft. The longer diagonal makes an angle of 34° 17′ with the longer side. Find the length of the longer diagonal, and the angle which the two given sides make with each other.

27. Two forces F_1 and F_2 have magnitudes of 3298 and 2597 lb, respectively, and their resultant F_3 makes an angle of 42° 45′ with F_2. Assuming that the direction of F_2 is horizontal, find the direction of F_1 and the magnitude of F_3.

28. A force F_1 has a magnitude of 173.6 lb, and a second force F_2 has a magnitude of 87.92 lb and is in the direction 59° 38′. The resultant F_3 of the two forces is in the direction 45° 42′. Find the magnitude of the resultant F_3 and the direction of F_1.

29. A pilot leaves an airport at A and flies a course of 241° for a distance of 298.5 mi when he finds himself in a very heavy fog bank with a compass that is out of order. He attempts to turn back, but is unable to judge his direction accurately. He flies for approximately 175 mi on a straight course until the fog thins out enough for him to observe a double-track railroad and he realizes that he is directly west of his starting point, and heading in a northeasterly direction. What course has he been flying, and how far is he from the airport at A?

30. The mean distance of the planet Mars from the sun (center to center) is 1.524 Astronomical Units. One *Astronomical Unit* is the mean distance from the earth to the sun, and is 92.9×10^6 mi. On a certain date it was observed that the line joining the earth to Mars (center to center) made an angle of 59° 32′ with the line joining the earth to the sun (center to center). How far was it from the earth to Mars on that date?

14–7 CASE C. TWO SIDES AND THE INCLUDED ANGLE

In Case C, as defined in Section 14–4, two sides and the included angle are known and the Law of Cosines may be used to find the third side. A second angle may be found by the Law of Sines (or by the Law of Cosines again as in the next section).

If the Law of Sines is used, there may be ambiguity regarding the angle. In general, *the order of magnitude of the angles of a triangle is the same as the order of magnitude of the sides*, the smallest angle being opposite the smallest side. Moreover, the two smallest angles in a triangle must be acute. Hence we shall find the smaller of the two unknown angles by finding the angle opposite the smaller of the corresponding sides, and are assured that this angle must be acute.

Example 1. Solve the triangle ABC if $a = 4$, $b = 6$, $C = 60°$.

Solution. Using the Law of Cosines in the form

$$c^2 = a^2 + b^2 - 2ab \cos C,$$

we have

$$c^2 = 16 + 36 - 2(4)(6)(\tfrac{1}{2}) = 28, \qquad c = \sqrt{28} = 5.29.$$

Since A is the smaller of the unknown angles, we use the Law of Sines in the form

$$\sin A = \frac{a \sin C}{c},$$

and have

$$\sin A = \frac{4 \times 0.866}{5.29} = 0.6548, \qquad A = 41°.$$

Finally, $B = 180° - (60° + 41°) = 79°$.

The method of Example 1 for finding the third side of a triangle becomes rather involved if the given sides are four or five place numbers, and the angle is other than one of the special angles. For such cases another method, to which logarithms can be applied, will be developed in Section 14–9. There are times, however, when we are not concerned with obtaining a numerical value for the third side, but we wish to express that side as a function of the opposite angle.

Example 2. Express the length of a chord of a circle as a function of the central angle θ.

Solution. Using the Law of Cosines, we have from Fig. 14–5,

$$\begin{aligned} c^2 &= r^2 + r^2 - 2r \cdot r \cos \theta \\ &= 2r^2 - 2r^2 \cos \theta \\ &= 2r^2(1 - \cos \theta), \end{aligned}$$

and

$$c = r\sqrt{2(1 - \cos \theta)}.$$

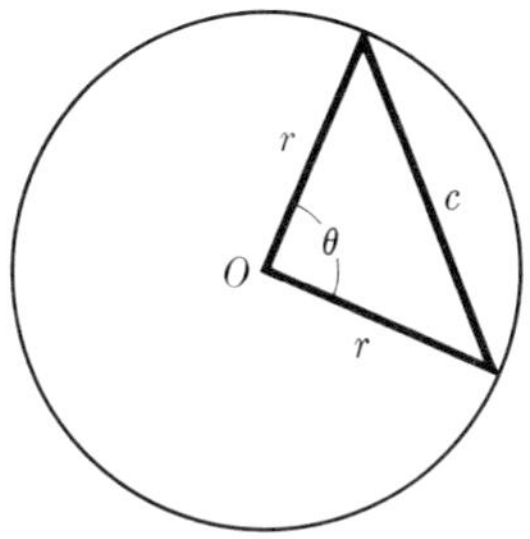

FIGURE 14–5

14–8 CASE D. THREE SIDES

When the three sides of a triangle are known (Case D), an angle may be found with the formula obtained by solving one of the forms of the Law of Cosines for the cosine which appears.

Example. Solve the triangle ABC if $a = 8$, $b = 17$, $c = 13$.

Solution. Equation (6) of Section 14–3 may be solved for $\cos A$ as

$$\cos A = \frac{b^2 + c^2 - a^2}{2bc}.$$

Then

$$\cos A = \frac{289 + 169 - 64}{2(17)(13)} = \frac{394}{442} = 0.8914, \qquad \text{and} \quad A = 27°.$$

Similarly,

$$\begin{aligned} \cos B &= \frac{a^2 + c^2 - b^2}{2ac} \\ &= \frac{64 + 169 - 289}{2(8)(13)} = -\frac{56}{208} = -0.2692, \quad \text{and} \quad B = 106°. \end{aligned}$$

Finally,

$$\cos C = \frac{a^2 + b^2 - c^2}{2ab}$$

$$= \frac{64 + 289 - 169}{2(8)(17)} = \frac{184}{272} = 0.6765, \qquad \text{and} \quad C = 47^\circ.$$

As a check, we verify that $A + B + C = 180°$.

EXERCISE GROUP 14-4

In Exercises 1–20, use the Law of Cosines to solve each triangle ABC having the given parts.

1. $a = 4, b = 3, C = 120°$
2. $b = 4, c = 5, A = 60°$
3. $a = 15, c = 32, B = 60°$
4. $a = 200, b = 300, C = 135°$
5. $b = 500, c = 300, A = 115° 10'$
6. $a = 8, c = 2.1, B = 70°$
7. $a = 200, b = 150, C = 130°$
8. $b = 120, c = 300, A = 40° 10'$
9. $c = 0.015, a = 0.15, B = 27°$
10. $a = 0.25, b = 0.14, C = 38° 20'$
11. $a = 2, b = 5, c = 6$
12. $a = 10, b = 15, c = 20$
13. $a = 100, b = 120, c = 130$
14. $a = 200, b = 310, c = 400$
15. $a = 350, b = 400, c = 450$
16. $a = 40, b = 70, c = 100$
17. $a = 0.12, b = 0.25, c = 0.3$
18. $a = 0.016, b = 0.024, c = 0.036$
19. $a = 3.2, b = 4.5, c = 5.6$
20. $a = 0.22, b = 0.33, c = 0.23$

21. The exact distance between two points A and B, which are on opposite sides of a building, is desired. A third point C is located so that AC is 150 ft and BC is 200 ft; the angle ACB is found to be 68° 20′. Compute distance AB.
22. A pilot desires to fly a heading of 225° at an airspeed of 100 mph. If the wind is blowing from the north at 15 mph, find the course and the groundspeed.
23. Two ships leave port at the same time; one sails on a course of 49° at a speed of 15 knots while the second sails on a course of 169° at a speed of 12 knots. How far apart are they after 5 hr and what is the direction of the second relative to the first?
24. Two forces F_1 and F_2 have magnitudes of 10 and 15 lb, respectively, and are directed in such a way that their resultant F_3 has a magnitude of 20 lb. Find the angles that the directions of the three forces make with each other.
25. Three airports A, B, and C are so located that A is 300 mi directly east of B, the distance AC is 250 mi, the distance BC is 150 mi, and C is north of line AB. What course would a plane fly in going from B to C? in going from C to A?
26. The adjacent sides of a parallelogram are 15 and 11 in., respectively, while the shorter diagonal is 13 in. What is the length of the longer diagonal? (Solve by using only the Law of Cosines.)

14–9 THE LAW OF TANGENTS

A disadvantage in the use of the Law of Cosines to solve a triangle in which two sides and the included angle are known is that this method does not lend itself well to logarithmic computation. Hence if the numbers involved have more than three significant figures, the method is inefficient. On the other hand, the formulas to be developed here are particularly well adapted for use with logarithms.

Starting with the Law of Sines in the form

$$\frac{a}{b} = \frac{\sin A}{\sin B}, \tag{10}$$

we subtract 1 from each member, and have

$$\frac{a}{b} - 1 = \frac{\sin A}{\sin B} - 1,$$

so that

$$\frac{a - b}{b} = \frac{\sin A - \sin B}{\sin B}. \tag{11}$$

Similarly, by adding 1 to each member of (10), we obtain

$$\frac{a + b}{b} = \frac{\sin A + \sin B}{\sin B}. \tag{12}$$

Division of the members of (11) by the corresponding members of (12) gives

$$\frac{a - b}{a + b} = \frac{\sin A - \sin B}{\sin A + \sin B}.$$

Application of the factor formulas of Section 10–9 to the numerator and denominator of the right member yields

$$\frac{a - b}{a + b} = \frac{2 \sin \frac{1}{2}(A - B) \cos \frac{1}{2}(A + B)}{2 \sin \frac{1}{2}(A + B) \cos \frac{1}{2}(A - B)},$$

which becomes, upon dividing numerator and denominator of the fraction on the right by $\cos \frac{1}{2}(A - B) \cos \frac{1}{2}(A + B)$,

$$\boxed{\frac{a - b}{a + b} = \frac{\tan \frac{1}{2}(A - B)}{\tan \frac{1}{2}(A + B)}.} \tag{13}$$

Formula (13) is known as the *Law of Tangents.* Similar formulas can immediately be written involving a and c, or b and c.

In solving Case C by the Law of Tangents, formula (13) is used in the form involving the two known sides, let us say a and b. Then, since angle C is given, the sum $A + B$ can be found as $180° - C$, and (13) enables us to find $A - B$. Then with the sum and difference of A and B known, the angles A and B themselves can be found. With the angles known, the third side can be found by the Law of Sines.

Example 1. Solve the triangle ABC if

$$a = 18.32, \qquad b = 27.09, \qquad C = 58° \, 42'.$$

Solution. Since $a < b$, it is convenient to use the Law of Tangents in the form

$$\frac{b - a}{b + a} = \frac{\tan \frac{1}{2}(B - A)}{\tan \frac{1}{2}(B + A)}. \tag{14}$$

We have $B + A = 180° - C = 121° \, 18'$, and hence

$$\tfrac{1}{2}(B + A) = 60° \, 39'. \tag{15}$$

Furthermore, $b - a = 8.77$, $b + a = 45.41$. Solving (14) for $\tan \frac{1}{2}(B - A)$, and substituting the known values, we find

$$\tan \tfrac{1}{2}(B - A) = \frac{8.77 \tan 60° \, 39'}{45.41},$$

which yields the logarithmic equation

$$\log \tan \tfrac{1}{2}(B - A) = \log 8.77 + \log \tan 60° \, 39' - \log 45.41.$$

The logarithmic computation follows:

$$\begin{aligned}
\log 8.77 &= 0.9430 \\
\log \tan 60° \, 39' &= 0.2500 \qquad (+) \\
\log (\text{Num}) &= 11.1930 - 10 \\
\log 45.41 &= 1.6572 \qquad (-) \\
\log \tan \tfrac{1}{2}(B - A) &= 9.5358 - 10 \\
\tfrac{1}{2}(B - A) &= 18° \, 57'.
\end{aligned} \tag{16}$$

Addition of (15) and (16) then gives $B = 79° \, 36'$, and subtraction of (16) from (15) gives $A = 41° \, 42'$. Side c may now be found by the Law of Sines as $c = 23.53$.

EXERCISE GROUP 14-5

In each of Exercises 1-20, solve the triangle ABC with the given parts.

1. $b = 32.41, \quad c = 43.25, \quad A = 37° \, 26'$
2. $a = 431.2, \quad b = 542.3, \quad C = 113° \, 25'$
3. $b = 134.8, \quad c = 246.5, \quad A = 63° \, 19'$
4. $a = 329.6, \quad b = 834.9, \quad C = 22° \, 14'$
5. $a = 0.01763, \quad b = 0.04273, \quad C = 133° \, 47'$
6. $c = 0.4532, \quad a = 0.6324, \quad B = 121° \, 34'$

7. $c = 34820$, $a = 193200$, $B = 98° 16'$
8. $b = 92.23$, $c = 86.31$, $A = 134° 51'$
9. $b = 0.4137$, $a = 0.3241$, $C = 87° 34'$
10. $c = 349800$, $b = 163500$, $A = 65° 19'$
11. $c = 8.379$, $a = 0.7246$, $B = 131° 21'$
12. $a = 0.008217$, $c = 0.03146$, $B = 85° 54'$
13. $B = 39° 18'$, $c = 517.8$, $a = 613.2$
14. $A = 38° 17'$, $b = 83.11$, $c = 76.12$
15. $A = 47° 37'$, $b = 2.501$, $c = 2.811$
16. $C = 63° 52'$, $a = 489.3$, $b = 470.7$
17. $C = 6° 49'$, $a = 0.8191$, $b = 0.6432$
18. $B = 65° 06'$, $a = 0.03138$, $c = 0.3221$
19. $B = 95° 17'$, $c = 0.2913$, $a = 2.153$
20. $A = 43° 29'$, $b = 0.3176$, $c = 0.01243$
21. A pilot must fly from A to B, which is a distance of 300 mi in the direction $S\ 23° 31'\ E$. The wind is blowing from the west at 20 mph. Find the heading and the average air-speed the pilot must maintain to complete the trip in exactly 2 hr.
22. Find the resultant F_3 of two forces F_1 and F_2, if the magnitude of F_1 is 175.8 lb and its direction is horizontal, while the magnitude of F_2 is 217.3 lb and its direction makes an angle of 24° 31′ with the direction of F_1.
23. A force F_1 has a magnitude of 216.2 lb and is directed vertically. A second force F_2 has a magnitude of 163.8 lb and its direction makes an angle of 94° 34′ with the direction of F_1. Find the magnitude and direction of the resultant F_3 of the two forces F_1 and F_2.
24. An aircraft carrier is steaming at 25 knots on a course of 119° 28′ and continues on this course at the given speed. An airplane takes off and flies on a course of 349° 31′ at a speed of 300 nautical miles per hour. How far is the plane from the carrier after 2 hr, and what is the direction of the carrier relative to the plane?
25. It is desired to find the distance between two points A and B as accurately as possible. The two points are on opposite sides of a small body of water. A third point C is located so that angle ACB is 78° 12′, and the distances AC and BC are measured and found to be 492.3 ft and 348.6 ft, respectively. Compute the distance AB as accurately as the data justify.
26. Two airplanes take off from the same airport at the same time. One flies on a course of 343° 12′ at an average speed of 456.8 mph, while the other flies on a course of 38° 19′ at an average speed of 286.7 mph. How far apart are the planes at the end of 3 hr, and what is the direction of the second relative to the first plane?
27. An observer at point C, which is 50 ft above the level of point B, notes that the angle of depression of B is 29°, and the angle of depression of a second point A is 27°. It is known that the point A is 10 ft above the level of B, and the observer finds that the vertical plane through the points A and C makes an angle of 63° with the vertical plane through the points B and C. Compute the distance AB.

14–10 THE HALF-ANGLE FORMULAS AND CASE D

Formulas may be derived from the Law of Cosines which can be used to solve logarithmically a triangle in which the three sides are given (Case D). These formulas are expressed in terms of the *semiperimeter* s of the triangle; thus, we have

$$2s = a + b + c.$$

The following relations will be needed, and are easily verified:

$$b + c - a = 2(s - a), \qquad a - b + c = 2(s - b), \qquad a + b - c = 2(s - c). \tag{17}$$

We shall use the half-angle formulas (Section 10–8),

$$\sin\frac{A}{2} = \sqrt{\frac{1 - \cos A}{2}}, \qquad \cos\frac{A}{2} = \sqrt{\frac{1 + \cos A}{2}}, \tag{18}$$

with the positive values of the square roots taken since $A/2 < 90°$. From the Law of Cosines, we have (see the example in Section 14–8)

$$\cos A = \frac{b^2 + c^2 - a^2}{2bc}.$$

Hence we find

$$1 - \cos A = 1 - \frac{b^2 + c^2 - a^2}{2bc} = \frac{a^2 - b^2 + 2bc - c^2}{2bc}$$
$$= \frac{a^2 - (b - c)^2}{2bc} = \frac{(a - b + c)(a + b - c)}{2bc}.$$

Applying (17) here, we obtain

$$1 - \cos A = \frac{2(s - b) \cdot 2(s - c)}{2bc},$$

which, with (18), gives

$$\sin\frac{A}{2} = \sqrt{\frac{(s - b)(s - c)}{bc}}. \tag{19}$$

An entirely similar procedure gives

$$\cos\frac{A}{2} = \sqrt{\frac{s(s - a)}{bc}}. \tag{20}$$

Division of $\sin(A/2)$ by $\cos(A/2)$ then yields

$$\tan\frac{A}{2} = \sqrt{\frac{(s - b)(s - c)}{s(s - a)}},$$

which can be expressed in the form

$$\tan\frac{A}{2} = \frac{1}{s-a}\sqrt{\frac{(s-a)(s-b)(s-c)}{s}}. \tag{21}$$

Formulas (19), (20), and (21), together with the corresponding ones for angles B and C, are the *half-angle formulas* for a triangle. Let r be the radius of the circle inscribed in triangle ABC. It can be shown (see Exercise 28 in Exercise Group 14–6) that

$$\boxed{r = \sqrt{\frac{(s-a)(s-b)(s-c)}{s}}.} \tag{22}$$

The half-angle formulas for the tangent may now be written in the form

$$\boxed{\tan\frac{A}{2} = \frac{r}{s-a}, \quad \tan\frac{B}{2} = \frac{r}{s-b}, \quad \tan\frac{C}{2} = \frac{r}{s-c}.} \tag{23}$$

Whenever three sides of a triangle are known, the half-angle formulas may be used to find any or all angles. Formulas (23), in conjunction with (22), will generally be found to be the most useful for this purpose.

Example. Solve the triangle ABC if

$$a = 103.2, \qquad b = 97.40, \qquad c = 158.8.$$

Solution. The semiperimeter of the triangle is

$$s = \tfrac{1}{2}(a + b + c) = 179.7.$$

From (22) we obtain, with the appropriate numbers,

$$\log r = \tfrac{1}{2}(\log 76.5 + \log 82.3 + \log 20.9 - \log 179.7).$$

To compute $\log r$ we have

$$\begin{aligned} \log 76.5 &= 1.8837 \\ \log 82.3 &= 1.9154 \quad (+) \\ \log 20.9 &= \underline{1.3201} \\ & 5.1192 \\ \log 179.7 &= \underline{2.2546} \quad (-) \\ \log r^2 &= 2.8646 \\ \log r &= 1.4323. \quad (\div 2) \end{aligned}$$

The value of r itself is not required. From (23) we find

$$\log\tan\frac{A}{2} = \log r - \log(s - a),$$

and similar equations involving $B/2$ and $C/2$. The computation follows:

$$\begin{aligned} \log r &= 1.4323 \\ \log 76.5 &= \underline{1.8837} \quad (-) \\ \log \tan (A/2) &= 9.5486 - 10 \\ A/2 &= 19^\circ\, 29' \\ A &= 38^\circ\, 58' \end{aligned} \qquad \begin{aligned} \log r &= 1.4323 \\ \log 82.3 &= \underline{1.9154} \quad (-) \\ \log \tan (B/2) &= 9.5169 - 10 \\ B/2 &= 18^\circ\, 12' \\ B &= 36^\circ\, 24' \end{aligned}$$

$$\begin{aligned} \log r &= 1.4323 \\ \log 20.9 &= \underline{1.3201} \quad (-) \\ \log \tan (C/2) &= 0.1122 \\ C/2 &= 52^\circ\, 19' \\ C &= 104^\circ\, 38' \end{aligned}$$

Note that we can find the third angle very simply after we have found two angles. However, very little additional work is required to obtain the third angle as was done above, and a check is provided for the computation by verifying that $A + B + C = 180^\circ$.

EXERCISE GROUP 14-6

Solve the triangles having the given parts in each of Exercises 1–20.

1. $a = 2431$, $b = 4213$, $c = 3234$
2. $a = 2134$, $b = 5312$, $c = 4123$
3. $a = 424.3$, $b = 234.1$, $c = 531.4$
4. $a = 23.41$, $b = 34.12$, $c = 43.16$
5. $a = 0.02316$, $b = 0.04172$, $c = 0.05743$
6. $a = 0.04347$, $b = 0.06518$, $c = 0.03075$
7. $a = 0.4263$, $b = 0.5347$, $c = 0.3523$
8. $a = 0.5376$, $b = 0.6835$, $c = 0.2786$
9. $a = 4.639$, $b = 2.863$, $c = 3.526$
10. $a = 5.837$, $b = 6.034$, $c = 5.035$
11. $a = 34.26$, $b = 45.25$, $c = 52.38$
12. $a = 89.36$, $b = 68.73$, $c = 71.35$
13. $a = 3.456$, $b = 4.567$, $c = 5.678$
14. $a = 27.34$, $b = 35.19$, $c = 17.28$
15. $a = 0.4234$, $b = 0.3456$, $c = 0.6520$
16. $a = 0.004213$, $b = 0.006435$, $c = 0.002526$
17. $a = 654.3$, $b = 765.4$, $c = 876.5$
18. $a = 4372$, $b = 9153$, $c = 8271$
19. $a = 8.329$, $b = 24.15$, $c = 17.84$
20. $a = 98.23$, $b = 52.14$, $c = 71.87$
21. Two forces F_1 and F_2 are applied at the same point and have magnitudes of 523 lb and 216 lb, respectively. Their resultant has a magnitude of 417 lb. Find the directions of the force F_2 and the resultant with respect to F_1.
22. A triangular park which is bounded by three streets has frontages of 697 ft, 493 ft, and 562 ft. Find the angles at which the three streets intersect.
23. The airspeed of a plane is 276 mph on a heading of 217°, and its groundspeed is 283 mph. The wind velocity is 21 mph. Find the direction of the wind and the course flown by the plane, getting results as accurately as the data justify.

24. B is 1392 mi directly east of A, and C is north of the line joining A and B. The distance from A to C is 895.5 mi, and the distance from B to C is 756 mi. Find the direction from A to C, and also from B to C.

25. An airplane maintains an airspeed of 300 mph and a course of 180°. There is a northwesterly wind of 25 mph, and the plane has an average groundspeed of 317 mph. What heading does the plane fly, and what is the exact direction of the wind?

26. An airplane takes off from an airfield A and flies in a northeasterly direction with an average groundspeed of 176.4 mph. At the same instant a second plane takes off from an airfield B, which is 300 mi due east of A, and flies in a northwesterly direction with an average groundspeed of 217.3 mph. If they meet one hour and ten minutes after taking off, find the course each was flying.

27. Three friends A, B, and C have their own airplanes and plan to meet at a point equidistant from all three. A lives 1200 mi due east of B; C lives north of the line joining A and B, and is 800 mi from A and 1000 mi from B. What is the direction each must fly to reach the point agreed upon?

28. In Fig. 14–6,

$$\tan (A/2) = r/AD,$$

where r is the radius of the inscribed circle. Show that $AD = s - a$. Then use formula (21) to derive the expression for r in formula (22).

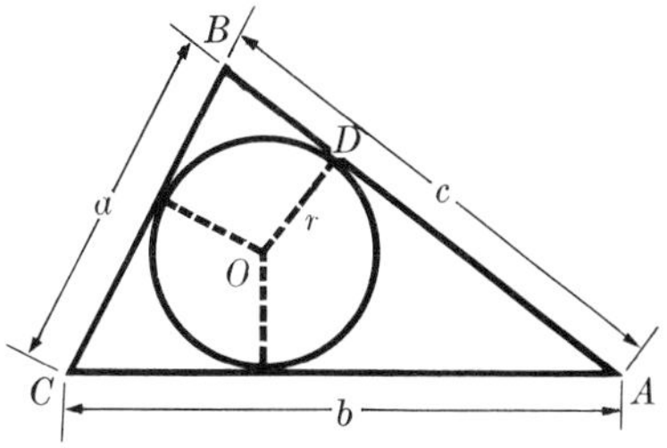

FIGURE 14–6

14–11 AREA OF A TRIANGLE

The basic theorem from plane geometry on the area of a triangle states: *The area of a triangle is equal to one-half the product of any side of the triangle and the altitude drawn to that side.* With this result several different formulas may be obtained for the area of a triangle, each being particularly suited to one of the cases of the oblique triangle. We shall use the letter K to denote the area.

Referring to Fig. 14–1 of Section 14–2, we see that in either triangle the length of the altitude h is given by $h = c \sin A$. Hence, since $K = \frac{1}{2}bh$, we have

$$\boxed{K = \tfrac{1}{2}bc \sin A.} \tag{24}$$

Similar formulas involving the other angles of the triangle may be written at once. In words, the formula becomes: *The area of a triangle is equal to one-half the product of any two sides and the sine of the included angle.* This statement indicates the applicability of formula (24) to Case C.

We may derive a second formula for K as follows. By the Law of Sines we have

$$\frac{b}{c} = \frac{\sin B}{\sin C} \quad \text{and} \quad b = \frac{c \sin B}{\sin C}.$$

Substitution of the latter in (24) gives the formula

$$\boxed{K = \frac{1}{2}\frac{c^2 \sin A \sin B}{\sin C}.} \tag{25}$$

Whenever two angles of a triangle are known, the third angle can be found directly. Hence formula (25), or one of the two other similar forms, applies to Case A.

Finally, we obtain a formula for K in terms of the sides a, b, c. In Fig. 14–6, in which r is the radius of the inscribed circle, the area of triangle BOC is $\frac{1}{2}ra$, the area of AOC is $\frac{1}{2}rb$, and the area of AOB is $\frac{1}{2}rc$. Hence, the area K of triangle ABC is

$$K = \tfrac{1}{2}ra + \tfrac{1}{2}rb + \tfrac{1}{2}rc = r[\tfrac{1}{2}(a + b + c)],$$

or

$$\boxed{K = rs,} \tag{26}$$

where s is the semiperimeter, and the value of r is given by (22).

Example 1. Find the area of triangle ABC if $A = 23° 09'$, $B = 108° 43'$, $c = 123.2$.

Solution. We find $C = 48° 08'$. Then by formula (25) we have

$$K = \frac{1}{2}\frac{(123.2)^2 \sin 23^\circ 09' \sin 108^\circ 43'}{\sin 48° 08'}.$$

Logarithmic computation is well suited to this expression, and gives the value $K = 15180$.

Example 2. Find the area of the triangle ABC if $a = 4$, $b = 6$, $C = 120°$.

Solution. The area of the triangle is found from the formula

$$K = \tfrac{1}{2}ab \sin C$$

to be

$$K = \tfrac{1}{2}(4)(6) \sin 120^\circ = \tfrac{1}{2}(4)(6)\left(\frac{\sqrt{3}}{2}\right) = 6\sqrt{3}.$$

Example 3. Find the area of the triangle ABC if $a = 103.2$, $b = 97.40$, $c = 158.8$.

Solution. This is the triangle in the example of Section 14–10, where the values of $\log r$ and $\log s$ were found to be

$$\log r = 1.4323, \qquad \log s = 2.2546.$$

From (26) we obtain the relation

$$\log K = \log r + \log s.$$

We then find

$$\log K = 1.4323 + 2.2546 = 3.6869, \qquad K = 4863.$$

EXERCISE GROUP 14–7

In each of Exercises 1–16, find the area of the triangle having the given parts.

1. $A = 62° 13'$, $C = 34° 16'$, $b = 43.21$
2. $C = 123° 12'$, $B = 42° 18'$, $a = 0.02357$
3. $A = 83° 17'$, $B = 79° 14'$, $c = 13.67$
4. $B = 32° 15'$, $A = 95° 53'$, $c = 0.4198$
5. $c = 0.3176$, $a = 2.364$, $A = 46° 43'$
6. $a = 623$, $b = 913$, $A = 34°$
7. $b = 0.08933$, $c = 0.07341$, $B = 86° 15'$
8. $c = 813.2$, $b = 651.3$, $C = 79° 42'$
9. $a = 3.692$, $b = 8.293$, $C = 24° 21'$
10. $c = 0.6534$, $a = 0.4623$, $B = 132° 15'$
11. $b = 0.3842$, $c = 0.9328$, $A = 103° 18'$
12. $c = 7.318$, $b = 37.19$, $A = 14° 31'$
13. $a = 0.9318$, $b = 0.7165$, $c = 0.3252$
14. $a = 3.567$, $b = 4.892$, $c = 5.837$
15. $a = 38.42$, $b = 47.96$, $c = 58.17$
16. $a = 57.96$, $b = 126.3$, $c = 137.2$
17. Two sides of a parallelogram are 2.143 in. and 4.261 in., and the longer diagonal is 5.316 in. Find the area of the parallelogram.
18. A triangular lot has frontages of 87 ft and 147 ft on two streets which intersect at an angle of 96°. Find the area of the lot.
19. A triangular park has frontages of 697 ft, 493 ft, and 562 ft on the three streets which bound it. Find the area of the park.
20. Find the area of a regular pentagon (five equal sides and five equal angles), the length of a side being 43.26 ft.
21. Three points A, B, and C are located so that the distance AB is 30 ft, angle CAB is 70°, and angle ABC is 80°. Find the area of triangle ABC.
22. Find the area of a regular hexagon (six equal sides and six equal angles), which is inscribed in a circle of radius 21.43 in.
23. A triangular field has an area of 10 acres (435,600 ft^2). The longest side runs along a river and needs no fence. How much fence will be required for the other two sides if the angles at the vertices of the field are 31°, 68°, and 81°?
24. A quadrangular plot of ground has two sides of 62.83 ft and 132.8 ft which are perpendicular to each other. The other sides have lengths of 83.72 ft and 139.5 ft. Find the area of the plot.

CHAPTER 15

Complex Numbers

15–1 INTRODUCTION

Complex numbers were introduced in Section 1–9 as pairs of real numbers (a, b), subject to certain definitions. In the present chapter the development of complex numbers will be extended, and in order to make this treatment more nearly self-contained, we shall repeat the necessary material from the earlier chapter.

The need for complex numbers arises when the attempt is made, in the study of algebra, to solve certain quadratic equations, such as the equation

$$x^2 + x + 1 = 0.$$

When a solution is attempted, it becomes evident that the system of real numbers is inadequate. An extension of the real number system, by the addition of complex numbers as defined below, then provides a system of numbers sufficient for the purposes of algebra. Complex numbers, as they will be defined, include the real numbers, and the definitions of addition, subtraction, multiplication, and division for complex numbers will be such that they will generalize the corresponding ones for real numbers.

***Definition* 15–1.** *A complex number is a number pair (a, b), where a and b are real numbers, and subject to the following conditions:*

$$(a, b) = (c, d) \text{ if and only if } a = c \text{ and } b = d,$$
$$(a, b) + (c, d) = (a + c, b + d),$$
$$(a, b) \cdot (c, d) = (ac - bd, ad + bc).$$

The number a is called the real part of the complex number and b is called the imaginary part.

The *zero complex number* may be taken as $(0, 0)$, and the *unit complex number* as $(1, 0)$. On the basis of these definitions the further properties of complex numbers may be obtained. It was seen in Section 1–9 that the subset of the number system consisting of complex numbers of the form $(a, 0)$, with a real, behaves in all respects like the real number system, if the complex number $(a, 0)$ is identified with the real number a.

It was also shown that the complex number (a, b) may be identified with a number written in the form $a + bi$, where a and b are, of course, real, and i has the property that $i^2 = -1$. In this notation, the definition of equality of two complex numbers becomes

$$a + bi = c + di$$

if and only if

$$a = c \qquad \text{and} \qquad b = d.$$

The statement of the definitions of addition and subtraction will appear in later sections.

Moreover, the system of complex numbers is closed under addition, subtraction, multiplication, and division except by zero. It possesses the commutative and associative properties of addition and multiplication, the distributive property of multiplication with respect to addition, and satisfies the cancellation laws for addition and multiplication. For completeness it may be stated that any polynomial equation with complex coefficients can be solved completely within the complex number system. (See Section 8–4.)

Example 1. Find the values of x and y if

$$(x + 3y - 1) + (2x - y)i = 0.$$

Solution. By Definition 15–1 and the definition of zero, we must have

$$x + 3y - 1 = 0, \qquad 2x - y = 0.$$

The solution of this pair of simultaneous linear equations gives the desired values $x = \frac{1}{7}$, $y = \frac{2}{7}$.

Example 2. Solve for x and y if

$$(x^2 - y) + (2x - y)i = (y - x) + i.$$

Solution. By Definition 15–1, we must have

$$x^2 - y = y - x, \qquad 2x - y = 1.$$

Substitution in the first equation of the value $y = 2x - 1$, as obtained from the second equation, yields the quadratic equation

$$x^2 - 3x + 2 = 0.$$

The solution of this equation gives $x = 1$ or 2; the corresponding values of y may be obtained from the second of the above pair of equations as $y = 1$ when $x = 1$, and $y = 3$ when $x = 2$. The two solutions are then $x = 1, y = 1$, and $x = 2, y = 3$.

15–2 GRAPHICAL REPRESENTATION OF COMPLEX NUMBERS

The points of a rectangular Cartesian coordinate system may be used to represent graphically any concept defined by a pair of real numbers. In particular, a complex number in the form (a, b) or $a + bi$ depends on two real numbers a and b, and may be represented in this manner. Accordingly, *we shall represent the complex number $a + bi$ by the point P with abscissa a and ordinate b.* It follows at once that a real number is represented by a point on the x-axis, and a pure imaginary number by a point on the y-axis. It is helpful and instructive to represent the number $a + bi$ at times also by the vector $\overline{OP}$ (see Fig. 15–1), directed from the origin to the point (a, b). We shall use both the *vector and point representations* of a complex number as thus defined.

***Definition* 15–2.** *The conjugate of the complex number $a + bi$ is defined as the complex number $a - bi$.*

It is clear that the conjugate of $a - bi$ is then $a - (-b)i = a + bi$. Hence two conjugate complex numbers differ only in the signs of their imaginary parts. Since the imaginary part of a complex number is the y-coordinate of its point representation, two conjugate complex numbers are the images of each other in the x-axis. For example, $-1 + 2i$ and $-1 - 2i$ are conjugate complex numbers; each is the image of the other in the x-axis, with the first point in Q_2 and the second point in Q_3.

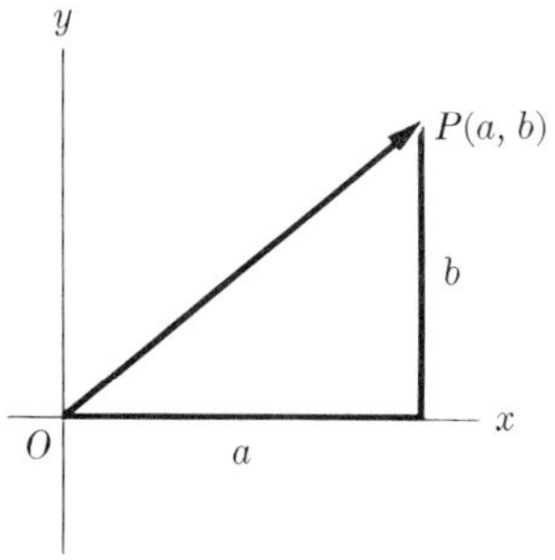

FIGURE 15–1

***Definition* 15–3.** *The absolute value or modulus of the complex number $a + bi$ is the length of the vector $\overline{OP}$ in Fig.* 15–1, *or the polar distance of P.*

We shall denote the modulus of $a + bi$ by $|a + bi|$ or by r. It is then clear from the figure, with the use of the Pythagorean Theorem, that

$$\boxed{r = |a + bi| = \sqrt{a^2 + b^2},} \tag{1}$$

for any complex number. It follows from (1) that *the modulus of a complex number is always positive, or zero.*

***Definition* 15–4.** *The amplitude or argument of the complex number $a + bi$ is the angle that $\overline{OP}$ in Fig.* 15–1 *makes with the positive x-axis.*

We shall denote the argument of $a + bi$ by $\arg(a + bi)$, and usually by θ. It follows that

$$\boxed{\theta = \arg(a + bi) = \arctan b/a = \arcsin b/r,} \tag{2}$$

the two latter expressions being given in order to specify the correct quadrant for the angle θ.

Example. Find the modulus and argument of the complex number $1 - \sqrt{3}\,i$.

Solution. By (1) we have, for the modulus,

$$r = |1 - \sqrt{3}\,i| = \sqrt{1 + (-\sqrt{3})^2} = \sqrt{1 + 3} = 2,$$

and by (2) the argument is

$$\theta = \arg(1 - \sqrt{3}\,i) = \arctan(-\sqrt{3}) = \arcsin(-\sqrt{3}/2).$$

Since $\tan\theta < 0$ and $\sin\theta < 0$, the argument θ must be an angle in Q_4, and one value is 300°. Another possible value is $-60°$.

It follows from Definition 15–4 that the argument of a complex number is infinitely many-valued; in fact, *the difference between any two arguments of the same complex number is a multiple of* 360° *or of* 2π.

EXERCISE GROUP 15–1

In each of Exercises 1–16, plot the point that represents the complex number, and the point that represents its conjugate. Draw the vectors that represent the number and its conjugate.

1. $3 + 4i$
2. $12 + 5i$
3. $7 - 24i$
4. $-4 + 3i$
5. $-5 - 12i$
6. $24 - 7i$
7. $5i$
8. 7
9. $-6i$
10. -9
11. $-8 + 6i$
12. $-10 - 24i$
13. $\sqrt{3} - i$
14. $-1 - i\sqrt{3}$
15. $\frac{3}{2}(-\sqrt{3} - i)$
16. $\frac{1}{5}(6 + 8i)$

Find the modulus and the argument of the complex number, and also of its conjugate, in each of Exercises 17–36.

17. $1 + i\sqrt{3}$
18. $1 + i$
19. $\sqrt{3} - i$
20. $-1 - \sqrt{3}\,i$
21. $-1 + i$
22. 5
23. $6i$
24. $-7i$
25. $3 - 3i$
26. $-\sqrt{3} + 3i$
27. $2\sqrt{3} - 6i$
28. $-\sqrt{11} + 5i$
29. $\sqrt{13} - 6i$
30. $7 + \sqrt{15}\,i$
31. $\frac{1}{2}\sqrt{3} - 0.5i$
32. $0.5 + 1.2i$
33. $2(\cos 215° + i \sin 215°)$
34. $3(\sin 30° + i \sin 30°)$
35. $2.4 - 0.7i$
36. $5[\cos(-17°) + i \sin(-17°)]$

In each of Exercises 37–46, determine the real values of x and y for which the statements are true.

37. $5 - 3i = 2x + 3 + yi$
38. $xi - 4y = 8 + 3i$
39. $3x + 5 = (2y - 6)i$
40. $3 + 2ax = 8bi + 2yi$
41. $(a + y) - (b - x)i = 0$
42. $5a + by = (3d - bx)i$
43. $5a - 3di = bxi - by$
44. $4a - 3x = (5b - 4y)i$
45. $3xi + 2 = (y - 3)i - y$
46. $3ax - bi = (y - x)i + 3$

47. Prove that the absolute values of conjugate complex numbers are equal.

15-3 ADDITION AND SUBTRACTION OF COMPLEX NUMBERS

Algebraic addition of complex numbers was defined in Definition 15-1. If complex numbers are written in the form involving i, this definition becomes

***Definition* 15-5.** $(a + bi) \pm (c + di) = (a \pm c) + (b \pm d)i$, *where the upper signs are taken together, as are the lower signs.*

Thus the real part of the sum is equal to the sum of the real parts of the numbers, and the imaginary part of the sum is equal to the sum of the imaginary parts of the numbers. Moreover, if the numbers are real, so that $b = d = 0$, the sum is $a + c$ and the difference is $a - c$.

Example 1. Determine the sum and difference of the complex numbers $3 + 2i$ and $5 + i$.

Solution. From the above definition we have

for the sum: $(3 + 2i) + (5 + i) = (3 + 5) + (2 + 1)i = 8 + 3i$;

for the difference: $(3 + 2i) - (5 + i) = (3 - 5) + (2 - 1)i = -2 + i$.

In the graphical representation of complex numbers, as defined in Section 15-2, an interesting interpretation of addition and subtraction arises. By Definition 15-5, the real part of the sum of $a + bi$ and $c + di$ is $a + c$, while the imaginary part is $b + d$. On the other hand, if $\overline{OC}$ is the diagonal of the parallelogram $OACB$ in Fig. 15-2, it follows that $a + c$ is the abscissa of C and $b + d$ is the ordinate. Since $\overline{OC}$ is the sum of the vectors $\overline{OA}$ and $\overline{OB}$, we conclude that *the sum of the complex numbers $a + bi$ and $c + di$ can be represented by the vector sum of the vectors $a + bi$ and $c + di$ as defined in Section* 5-7.

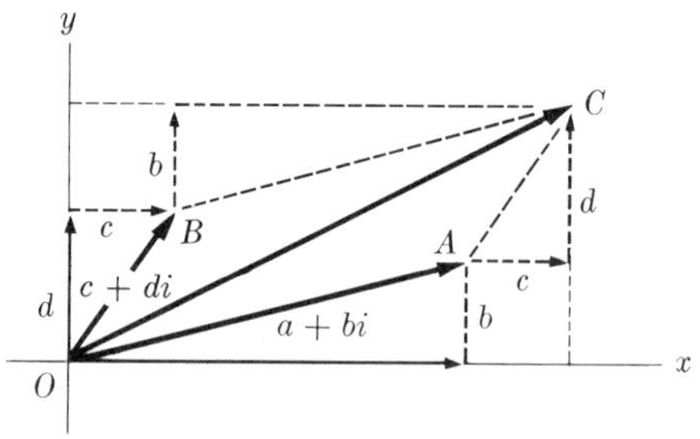

FIGURE 15-2

The negative of a vector is given by a vector with the same length and opposite direction. *The difference of two complex numbers is then given graphically by the sum of the first vector and the negative of the second vector.*

Example 2. Find the sum and difference of the numbers $3 + 2i$ and $5 + i$ graphically.

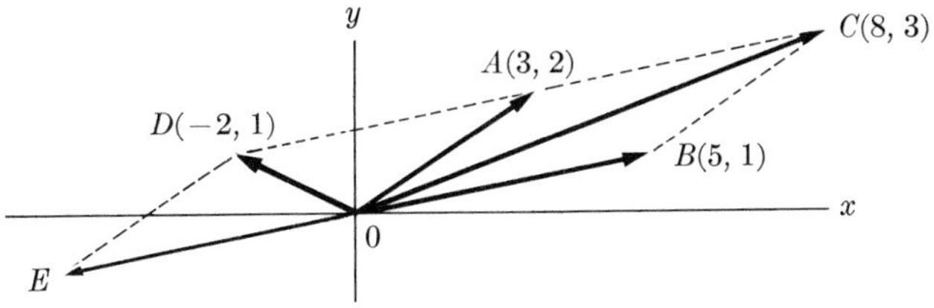

FIGURE 15–3

Solution. In Fig. 15–3 the vector $\overline{OA}$ represents the number $3 + 2i$, and $\overline{OB}$ represents $5 + i$. The sum of these vectors is given by $\overline{OC}$, which is seen to be the complex number $8 + 3i$.

The difference $(3 + 2i) - (5 + i)$ is given by

$$\overline{OA} + (-\overline{OB}) = \overline{OA} + \overline{OE},$$

which is the vector $\overline{OD}$, or $-2 + i$.

EXERCISE GROUP 15–2

In each of Exercises 1–20, find the complex number which is equal to the sum of the given complex numbers, and find the complex number which is the first given number minus the second. Work each exercise both graphically and algebraically.

1. $7 + 5i$, $5 + 8i$
2. $5 - 7i$, $-5 + 8i$
3. $-7i$, $-10 - 3i$
4. -15, $13 - 9i$
5. $(2 - 3i) + (4 + 2i)$, $6 + i$
6. $-5 - 3i$, $-2 + 5i$
7. $4 + 5i + (-7 - 3i)$, $3 + 2i$
8. $5 - 4i$, $(2 - 3i) - (6 + 2i)$
9. $3 + 4i$, $(7 + 8i) + (3 - 12i)$
10. $(3 + 2i) + 5$, $7i - (9 + 9i)$
11. $(6 + 7i) + (6 - 7i)$, $5 - 4i$
12. $(7 + 2i) - (7 - 2i)$, $5 - 4i$
13. $(5 - 2i) + (2 + 2i)$, $4 - 5i$
14. $3 - 4i$, $(6 - 7i) - (5 + 6i)$
15. $2(\cos 30° + i \sin 30°)$, $6(\cos 120° + i \sin 120°)$
16. $3[\cos (\pi/2) + i \sin (\pi/2)] - 4(\cos \pi + i \sin \pi)$, $5\sqrt{2}[\cos (5\pi/4) + i \sin (5\pi/4)]$
17. $3 \cos (3\pi/2) + 4i \sin (3\pi/2)$, $5 \cos 60° + 5i \sin 60°$
18. $5(\cos 240° + i \sin 240°)$, $7[\cos (-240°) + i \sin (-240°)]$
19. $r(\cos \theta + i \sin \theta)$, $r(\cos \theta - i \sin \theta)$
20. $r_1(\cos \theta_1 + i \sin \theta_1)$, $r_2(\cos \theta_2 + i \sin \theta_2)$
21. Prove that the sum of two conjugate complex numbers is real, and that the difference is a pure imaginary.
22. Prove that the conjugate of the sum of two complex numbers is equal to the sum of the conjugates of the numbers.

15–4 TRIGONOMETRIC FORM OF COMPLEX NUMBERS

From Fig. 15–4, and similar ones with θ in different quadrants, or simply from the definitions of $\cos\theta$ and $\sin\theta$ as given in Section 3–6, we find

$$a = r\cos\theta,$$
$$b = r\sin\theta,$$

where r is the absolute value and θ is the argument of $a + bi$. Hence for the complex number $a + bi$ we have

$$a + bi = r\cos\theta + (r\sin\theta)i = r(\cos\theta + i\sin\theta).$$

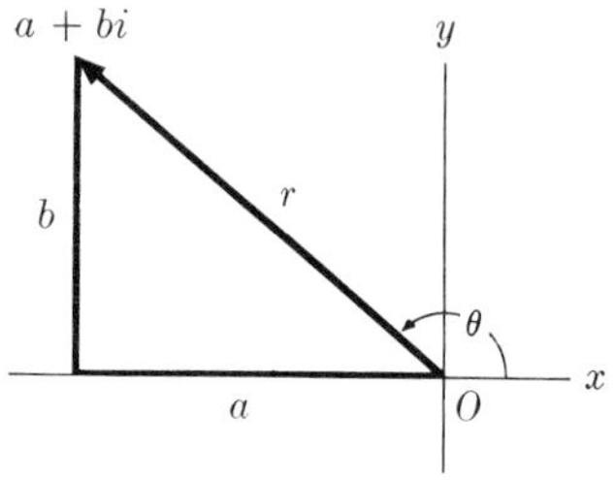

FIGURE 15–4

***Definition* 15–6.** *The expression $r(\cos\theta + i\sin\theta)$, where r is the absolute value and θ is the amplitude of a complex number, is called the trigonometric form of that number.*

Thus, any complex number can be written in trigonometric form, and in this form the angle θ is of course subject to the multiple-valuedness of the amplitude. At times a particular choice of θ may be more convenient than others, but any choice may be used in writing the trigonometric form.

Example 1. Write the number $1 - \sqrt{3}\,i$ in trigonometric form.

Solution. In the example of Section 15–2 we found for the given number that $r = 2$, $\theta = 300°$. One trigonometric form of the number is then

$$1 - \sqrt{3}\,i = 2(\cos 300° + i\sin 300°).$$

Note that the trigonometric form of a complex number is essentially in the form $a + bi$. Thus in the example, the real part is $a = 2\cos 300° = 1$, and the imaginary part is $b = 2\sin 300° = -\sqrt{3}$.

Example 2. Express the number $2(\cos 10° + i\sin 20°)$ in trigonometric form.

Solution. The number as given is not in trigonometric form because different angles appear. From the table of trigonometric ratios we find

$$2(\cos 10° + i\sin 20°) = 2(0.9848 + 0.3420i) = 1.9696 + 0.6840i.$$

To find r we use Eq. (1) and have

$$r = \sqrt{(1.9696)^2 + (0.6840)^2} = \sqrt{4.3472} = 2.0850.$$

For the amplitude θ we have

$$\theta = \arctan\frac{0.6840}{1.9696} = \arctan 0.3473 = 19°\,09',$$

so that the trigonometric form of the number is actually

$$2.0850(\cos 19^\circ\, 09' + i \sin 19^\circ\, 09').$$

Example 3. Express the number $3(\cos 120^\circ - i \sin 120^\circ)$ in trigonometric form.

Solution. The given number is not in trigonometric form because of the minus sign. The real part is $3 \cos 120^\circ$ and the imaginary part is $-3 \sin 120^\circ$.

The modulus is then

$$r = \sqrt{9 \cos^2 120^\circ + 9 \sin^2 120^\circ} = 3,$$

and for the amplitude θ we have

$$\theta = \arctan\left(\frac{-3 \sin 120^\circ}{3 \cos 120^\circ}\right) = \arctan\,(-\tan 120^\circ) = 240^\circ,$$

since an angle in Q_3 is required. The desired form is then

$$3(\cos 120^\circ - i \sin 120^\circ) = 3(\cos 240^\circ + i \sin 240^\circ).$$

Since the trigonometric form of a complex number is determined by the modulus r and the amplitude θ, we may represent the complex number in the notation of a number pair (r, θ). The real part of the complex number is $a = r \cos \theta$ and the imaginary part is $b = r \sin \theta$. The point in the coordinate plane whose coordinates are a and b is then also represented by the new coordinates r and θ, with the meanings given above. This representation of a point in the coordinate plane is called the *polar-coordinate* representation, or *polar form.* In polar form the number in Example 3 becomes $(3, 240^\circ)$.

It is clear that if a pair of polar coordinates is given there is one and only one corresponding point in the plane, whereas if a point is given there are many representations in polar coordinates. Specifically, any integral multiple of 360° or 2π radians may be added to the angle.

EXERCISE GROUP 15-3

In each of Exercises 1–12, express the given complex number in trigonometric form.

1. $1 + i$	2. $1 + \sqrt{3}\, i$	3. $1 - i$	4. $\sqrt{3} - i$
5. $-1 + i$	6. $-3 + \sqrt{3}\, i$	7. $-2 - 2i$	8. $-\sqrt{3} + i$
9. 2	10. $-5i$	11. $1.2 + 0.5i$	12. $3 + 4i$

In each of Exercises 13–20, express the given complex number in polar form.

13. $\cos 182^\circ + i \sin 358^\circ$	14. $10(\cos 293^\circ\, 40' - i \sin 293^\circ\, 40')$
15. $5(-\cos 25^\circ\, 35' + i \sin 25^\circ\, 35')$	16. $0.7 - 2.4i$
17. $-1.2 + 0.5i$	18. $5 - 12i$
19. $-24 + 7i$	20. $-7 - i\sqrt{15}$

15-5 MULTIPLICATION AND DIVISION OF COMPLEX NUMBERS

Multiplication of complex numbers was defined in Definition 15-1. If complex numbers are written in the form $a + bi$, this definition becomes

$$(a + bi)(c + di) = (ac - bd) + (bc + ad)i.$$

The value of the product given in this definition is equal to the direct product of the complex numbers $a + bi$ and $c + di$ by the rules for real numbers, with simplification of the result by use of the relation $i^2 = -1$. This statement indicates the procedure usually used for multiplying complex numbers.

Example 1. Determine the product $(2 + 3i)(3 + 5i)$.

Solution. Direct multiplication gives

$$6 + 9i + 10i + 15i^2 = 6 + 19i - 15 = -9 + 19i,$$

which is also in accord with the definition.

The quotient $(a + bi) \div (c + di)$ *of two complex numbers, with* c *and* d *not both zero, is defined as that complex number* K *such that*

$$a + bi = K \cdot (c + di).$$

By the previous properties of complex numbers this leads to the relation

$$\frac{a + bi}{c + bi} = \frac{(ac + bd) + (bc - ad)i}{c^2 + d^2}.$$

This relation may also be obtained by formally multiplying numerator and denominator of the fraction on the left by $c - di$, and simplifying the result.

Example 2. Reduce the quotient $(2 + 3i) \div (3 + 5i)$ to a complex number of the form $a + bi$.

Solution. Writing the quotient as a fraction, and multiplying numerator and denominator of the fraction by $3 - 5i$, which is the conjugate of the denominator, we have

$$\frac{2 + 3i}{3 + 5i} = \frac{2 + 3i}{3 + 5i} \cdot \frac{3 - 5i}{3 - 5i} = \frac{6 + 9i - 10i - 15i^2}{9 + 25}$$
$$= \frac{21 - i}{34} = \frac{21}{34} + \frac{-1}{34} i.$$

Multiplication and division of complex numbers become very simple for numbers in trigonometric form. In fact, this simplicity accounts for much of the advantage in using the trigonometric form. Thus, we have for the product of two complex numbers in trigonometric form,

$$r_1(\cos \theta_1 + i \sin \theta_1) \cdot r_2(\cos \theta_2 + i \sin \theta_2)$$
$$= r_1 r_2[(\cos \theta_1 \cos \theta_2 - \sin \theta_1 \sin \theta_2) + i(\sin \theta_1 \cos \theta_2 + \cos \theta_1 \sin \theta_2)].$$

We may apply the addition formulas (17) and (16) of Section 10–5 to the quantities in parentheses, and obtain

$$r_1(\cos\theta_1 + i\sin\theta_1)\cdot r_2(\cos\theta_2 + i\sin\theta_2) = r_1r_2[\cos(\theta_1+\theta_2) + i\sin(\theta_1+\theta_2)]. \tag{3}$$

Hence, *the product of two complex numbers is a complex number whose absolute value is the product of the two absolute values, and for which an amplitude is the sum of the two amplitudes.*

Similarly, we have for the division of two complex numbers in trigonometric form

$$\frac{r_1(\cos\theta_1 + i\sin\theta_1)}{r_2(\cos\theta_2 + i\sin\theta_2)} = \frac{r_1(\cos\theta_1 + i\sin\theta_1)}{r_2(\cos\theta_2 + i\sin\theta_2)}\cdot\frac{(\cos\theta_2 - i\sin\theta_2)}{(\cos\theta_2 - i\sin\theta_2)}$$
$$= \frac{r_1}{r_2}\cdot\frac{(\cos\theta_1\cos\theta_2 + \sin\theta_1\sin\theta_2) + i(\sin\theta_1\cos\theta_2 - \cos\theta_1\sin\theta_2)}{\cos^2\theta_2 + \sin^2\theta_2}.$$

If we apply to this expression the appropriate addition formulas of Section 10–5 and the squares identity (7) of Section 10–1, we obtain

$$\frac{r_1(\cos\theta_1 + i\sin\theta_1)}{r_2(\cos\theta_2 + i\sin\theta_2)} = \frac{r_1}{r_2}[\cos(\theta_1-\theta_2) + i\sin(\theta_1-\theta_2)].$$

Thus, *the quotient of one complex number by another is a complex number whose absolute value is the quotient of the two absolute values in the same order, and for which an amplitude is the amplitude of the dividend minus the amplitude of the divisor.*

Example 3. Use the trigonometric form in finding the product of the numbers $1 - \sqrt{3}i$ and $1 + i$, and the quotient of the first by the second.

Solution. The trigonometric forms of these numbers are found to be $1 - \sqrt{3}\,i = 2(\cos 300° + i\sin 300°)$, $1 + i = \sqrt{2}(\cos 45° + i\sin 45°)$. The above rules then give

$$\begin{aligned}(1-\sqrt{3}\,i)(1+i) &= 2(\cos 300° + i\sin 300°)\cdot\sqrt{2}(\cos 45° + i\sin 45°)\\ &= 2\sqrt{2}(\cos 345° + i\sin 345°);\\ \frac{1-\sqrt{3}\,i}{1+i} &= \frac{2(\cos 300° + i\sin 300°)}{\sqrt{2}(\cos 45° + i\sin 45°)}\\ &= \sqrt{2}(\cos 255° + i\sin 255°).\end{aligned}$$

These results can, if necessary, be continued further by substituting the values of the trigonometric ratios which appear.

If complex numbers are written in polar form, the formulas for multiplication and division become particularly simple, and are

$$(r_1, \theta_1) \cdot (r_2, \theta_2) = (r_1 r_2, \theta_1 + \theta_2), \qquad (r_1, \theta_1)/(r_2, \theta_2) = (r_1/r_2, \theta_1 - \theta_2).$$

In this notation the solution of Example 3 becomes

$$(1 - \sqrt{3}\,i)(1 + i) = (2, 300°)(\sqrt{2}, 45°) = (2\sqrt{2}, 345°),$$
$$(1 - \sqrt{3}\,i)/(1 + i) = (2, 300°)/(\sqrt{2}, 45°) = (\sqrt{2}, 255°).$$

EXERCISE GROUP 15-4

Perform the indicated operations in Exercises 1–10.

1. $(3 + 4i)(5 - 12i)$
2. $(i - 1)(3 + 7i)$
3. $i^2(6 - 8i)(i^7 + i^8)$
4. $i^3(-8i^3 + 6i^2)$
5. $(i - 2)^2(1 + 3i)$
6. $(2 + 3i)^2(3 - 2i)^2$
7. $\dfrac{2 + 5i}{5 - 3i}$
8. $\dfrac{5i + 8}{9i + 7}$
9. $\dfrac{(2 + 3i)(1 - i)}{1 + i - i^2}$
10. $\dfrac{12 - 9i}{(2 + 3i)(4 - 5i)}$

Express each of the complex numbers in Exercises 11–28 in trigonometric or polar form, and then perform the indicated operations. Give the answer in polar form.

11. $(2 - 2i\sqrt{3})(-5 - 5i)$
12. $(\sqrt{3} - i)(i - 1)$
13. $(\sqrt{3} + i)(1 - i)$
14. $(3 - 3i)(3 - \sqrt{3}\,i)$
15. $\dfrac{1 - i\sqrt{3}}{1 + i}$
16. $\dfrac{4 - 4i}{\sqrt{3} - 3i}$
17. $\dfrac{(24 - 7i)(3 + 4i)}{(15i - 8)(5 - 12i)}$
18. $\dfrac{i(12 - 4i\sqrt{3})}{2(7i - 7)}$
19. $\dfrac{2\sqrt{5} + \sqrt{5}\,i}{-i(\sqrt{7} - 3i)}$
20. $\dfrac{3i(i - \sqrt{3})}{5(-4 + 4i)}$
21. $\dfrac{(\sqrt{3} - i)(1 + i)}{(-\sqrt{3} - 3i)(7 + 24i)}$
22. $\dfrac{7(\sqrt{3} - \sqrt{22}\,i)}{25(3i^2 + \sqrt{3}\,i)}$
23. $\dfrac{(2.4 + 0.7i)(0.5 - 1.2i)}{(1.5 - 0.8i)(3 + 4i)}$
24. $\dfrac{(7 - \sqrt{15}\,i)(-\sqrt{11} + 5i)}{(-\sqrt{13} - 6i)(2 - 2\sqrt{3}\,i)}$
25. $(\cos 10° + i \sin 15°)(\cos 15° - i \sin 10°)$
26. $(\cos 143° - i \sin 37°)(-\sin 43° + i \cos 317°)$
27. $\dfrac{10(\cos 293°\,40' - i \sin 293°\,40')3(\cos 182° - i \sin 358°)}{5(-\cos 25°\,35' + i \sin 25°\,35')}$
28. $\dfrac{(\cos 157° - i \sin 743°)(\cos 317° - i \sin 223°)}{\cos 30° - i \sin 210°}$
29. Prove that the product of two conjugate complex numbers is real.
30. Prove that the conjugate of the product of two complex numbers is equal to the product of their conjugates.

31. Prove that the conjugate of the quotient of two complex numbers is equal to the quotient of their conjugates.
32. Prove that the quotient of two complex numbers is unique.

15–6 DE MOIVRE'S THEOREM

The rule of the preceding section for the multiplication of complex numbers in trigonometric form can be used in the derivation of an important theorem for the raising of complex numbers to powers.

Let us set $r_1 = r_2 = r$ and $\theta_1 = \theta_2 = \theta$ in Eq. (3) of Section 15–5; we obtain the relation

$$[r(\cos\theta + i\sin\theta)]^2 = r^2(\cos 2\theta + i\sin 2\theta). \tag{4}$$

If we now multiply each member of this equation by $r(\cos\theta + i\sin\theta)$, we have

$$[r(\cos\theta + i\sin\theta)]^3 = r^3(\cos 2\theta + i\sin 2\theta)\cdot(\cos\theta + i\sin\theta).$$

When Eq. (3) is applied to the right member, this equation becomes

$$[r(\cos\theta + i\sin\theta)]^3 = r^3(\cos 3\theta + i\sin 3\theta).$$

On the basis of the formulas obtained, it would seem reasonable to expect that a similar formula holds for any positive integral exponent. Such is indeed the case, and in fact a more general theorem holds, for any rational exponent. The statement of this theorem follows.

De Moivre's Theorem. *The relation*

$$\boxed{[r(\cos\theta + i\sin\theta)]^n = r^n(\cos n\theta + i\sin n\theta)} \tag{5}$$

holds if n is any integer. If n is a rational number p/q in lowest terms, with q > 1, the right member of (5) *gives one of the q values of the left member.*

Proof. The theorem has been proved for $n = 2$ in the derivation of Eq. (4). The extension of the proof to all positive integers, by the method of mathematical induction, is left to the reader (see Exercise 22 of Exercise Group 11–1).

If n is a negative integer, so that $n = -p$ where $p > 0$, we have

$$[r(\cos\theta + i\sin\theta)]^{-p} = \frac{1}{[r(\cos\theta + i\sin\theta)]^p} = \frac{1}{r^p(\cos p\theta + i\sin p\theta)}$$

[by the theorem for positive integers]

$$= r^{-p}[\cos(-p\theta) + i\sin(-p\theta)]$$

[by the rule for quotients],

and the theorem is proved for negative integers.

If $n = 1/q$, the theorem states that $r^{1/q}[\cos(\theta/q) + i\sin(\theta/q)]$ is one qth root of $r(\cos\theta + i\sin\theta)$. To prove this statement it is sufficient to show that

$$[r^{1/q}(\cos(\theta/q) + i\sin(\theta/q))]^q = r(\cos\theta + i\sin\theta);$$

this follows at once from the theorem for positive integers. The theorem is now proved for any exponent of the form $n = 1/q$ with q a positive integer.

Finally, if $n = p/q$ is a rational number in lowest terms, with $q > 1$, the theorem follows by a combination of the proofs for integers and for exponents of the form $1/q$. Thus we have

$$\begin{aligned}[r(\cos\theta + i\sin\theta)]^{p/q} &= \{[r(\cos\theta + i\sin\theta)]^p\}^{1/q} \\ &= [r^p(\cos p\theta + i\sin p\theta)]^{1/q} \\ &\qquad\text{[by the theorem for integers]} \\ &= r^{p/q}\left(\cos\frac{p}{q}\theta + i\sin\frac{p}{q}\theta\right) \\ &\qquad\text{[by the theorem for } n = 1/q\text{]},\end{aligned}$$

and the theorem is proved for rational exponents.

Example. Evaluate the quantity $(1 - i)^7$.

Solution. By using De Moivre's Theorem, we have

$$\begin{aligned}(1 - i)^7 &= [2^{1/2}(\cos 315° + i\sin 315°)]^7 = 2^{7/2}(\cos 2205° + i\sin 2205°) \\ &= 2^{7/2}(\cos 45° + i\sin 45°) = 2^{7/2}\left(\frac{\sqrt{2}}{2} + \frac{\sqrt{2}}{2}i\right) = 8 + 8i.\end{aligned}$$

In polar form De Moivre's Theorem becomes

$$(r, \theta)^n = (r^n, n\theta).$$

Then the Example may be written as

$$\begin{aligned}(1 - i)^7 &= (2^{1/2}, 315°)^7 = (2^{7/2}, 2205°) \\ &= (2^{7/2}, 45°) = 8 + 8i.\end{aligned}$$

15–7 ROOTS OF COMPLEX NUMBERS

In Section 8–4 it was stated that any polynomial equation of degree n has exactly n roots. Applying this statement to the particular equation

$$x^n - A = 0,$$

where A is any complex number and n is a positive integer, we see that *any complex number has exactly n nth roots.* De Moivre's Theorem may be used to find all of them, that is, to find the n values of $A^{1/n}$.

If θ is an argument of A, then $\theta + 2k\pi$, where k is any integer, is also an argument of A, since the argument of any complex number may be increased by any multiple of 2π. We may then write A in trigonometric form as

$$A = r[\cos(\theta + 2k\pi) + i \sin(\theta + 2k\pi)],$$

or, in polar form, as

$$A = (r, \theta + 2k\pi),$$

where r is the modulus of A. Applying De Moivre's Theorem with exponent $1/n$ to this expression, we obtain

$$(r, \theta + 2k\pi)^{1/n} = \left(r^{1/n}, \frac{\theta + 2k\pi}{n}\right),$$

where k is any integer. The n distinct roots of A may be obtained by letting $k = 0, 1, 2, \ldots, n - 1$ in turn. Any other integral value of k will differ from one of these by a multiple of n, so that the corresponding values of $(\theta + 2k\pi)/n$ will differ by a multiple of 2π, and the same nth root will result. We shall state explicitly the result that has been proved.

Theorem 15–1. *The n nth roots of the number $r(\cos\theta + i\sin\theta)$, where n is a positive integer, are given by*

$$[r(\cos\theta + i\sin\theta)]^{1/n} = r^{1/n}\left[\cos\frac{\theta + 2k\pi}{n} + i\sin\frac{\theta + 2k\pi}{n}\right],$$
$$k = 0, 1, 2, \ldots, n - 1.$$

Example 1. Find the cube roots of $\sqrt{3} + i$.

Solution. The absolute value of $\sqrt{3} + i$ is 2, and one argument is $\pi/6$. We then have

$$\sqrt{3} + i = 2\left(\cos\frac{\pi}{6} + i\sin\frac{\pi}{6}\right),$$

and by Theorem 15–1 we obtain

$$\begin{aligned}
(\sqrt{3} + i)^{1/3} &= \left[2\left(\cos\frac{\pi}{6} + i\sin\frac{\pi}{6}\right)\right]^{1/3} \\
&= 2^{1/3}\left[\cos\frac{1}{3}\left(\frac{\pi}{6} + 2k\pi\right) + i\sin\frac{1}{3}\left(\frac{\pi}{6} + 2k\pi\right)\right] \\
&= 2^{1/3}\left[\cos\left(\frac{\pi}{18} + \frac{2k\pi}{3}\right) + i\sin\left(\frac{\pi}{18} + \frac{2k\pi}{3}\right)\right] \\
&= 2^{1/3}\left(\cos\frac{\pi}{18} + i\sin\frac{\pi}{18}\right) \quad \text{for } k = 0, \\
&= 2^{1/3}\left(\cos\frac{13\pi}{18} + i\sin\frac{13\pi}{18}\right) \quad \text{for } k = 1, \\
&= 2^{1/3}\left(\cos\frac{25\pi}{18} + i\sin\frac{25\pi}{18}\right) \quad \text{for } k = 2.
\end{aligned}$$

If $k = 3$, the argument $\pi/18 + 2k\pi/3$ becomes $\pi/18 + 2\pi$, which gives the same root as for $k = 0$.

This method of finding roots of complex numbers applies equally well to finding the nth roots of real numbers.

Example 2. Find the fourth roots of -16.

Solution. One argument of -16 is π radians. Hence, applying Theorem 15–1 in the same manner as above, we have

$$\begin{aligned}
(-16)^{1/4} &= [16(\cos\pi + i\sin\pi)]^{1/4} \\
&= 2[\cos\tfrac{1}{4}(\pi + 2k\pi) + i\sin\tfrac{1}{4}(\pi + 2k\pi)] \\
&= 2\left[\cos\left(\frac{\pi}{4} + \frac{k\pi}{2}\right) + i\sin\left(\frac{\pi}{4} + \frac{k\pi}{2}\right)\right] \\
&= 2\left(\cos\frac{\pi}{4} + i\sin\frac{\pi}{4}\right) = \sqrt{2} + i\sqrt{2} \qquad \text{for } k = 0, \\
&= 2\left(\cos\frac{3\pi}{4} + i\sin\frac{3\pi}{4}\right) = -\sqrt{2} + i\sqrt{2} \qquad \text{for } k = 1, \\
&= 2\left(\cos\frac{5\pi}{4} + i\sin\frac{5\pi}{4}\right) = -\sqrt{2} - i\sqrt{2} \qquad \text{for } k = 2, \\
&= 2\left(\cos\frac{7\pi}{4} + i\sin\frac{7\pi}{4}\right) = \sqrt{2} - i\sqrt{2} \qquad \text{for } k = 3.
\end{aligned}$$

It is easy to see that, in general, successive nth roots of a complex number differ in argument by $2\pi/n$, but have the same absolute value. We may then state the following result.

Theorem 15–2. *The n nth roots of the complex number with absolute value r and argument θ lie equally spaced on the circumference of a circle with center at the origin and radius $r^{1/n}$, one of them having the argument θ/n.*

EXERCISE GROUP 15–5

Perform the indicated operations in Exercises 1–16.

1. $(3 - \sqrt{3}\,i)^4$
2. $(-2 - 2i)^5$
3. $(i - \sqrt{3})^6$
4. $(1 - i\sqrt{3})^{10}$
5. $(-i)^{15}$
6. $\left[\dfrac{-1 + i\sqrt{3}}{2}\right]^{-9}$
7. $\left[\dfrac{1 - i}{\sqrt{2}}\right]^{-11}$
8. $\dfrac{(-i)^7(-\sqrt{3} + i)^6}{64}$
9. $(1 - i)^5(-1 + \sqrt{3}\,i)^{-7}$
10. $\left[\dfrac{1 - i}{\sqrt{2}}\right]^8\left[\dfrac{-\sqrt{3} - i}{2}\right]^7$
11. $\dfrac{(3i - \sqrt{3})^5(-i)^9}{(3i - 3)^7}$
12. $\dfrac{(3 + 4i)^5(5 - 12i)^4}{(-\sqrt{11} + 5i)^7}$

13. $\dfrac{(7 + \sqrt{15}\,i)^3(-\sqrt{13} - 6i)^6}{(5 - 12i)^8}$

14. $\dfrac{(-8 + 15i)^7}{(7 - 24i)^4(12 + 4i\sqrt{3})^6}$

15. $(\sin 210° + i \sin 300°)^4$

16. $(\cos 132° - i \sin 132°)^5$

Find all of the indicated roots in Exercises 17–28.

17. The cube roots of 8

18. The fourth roots of 16

19. The fifth roots of -32

20. The fourth roots of -16

21. The cube roots of $-i$

22. The fifth roots of $-i$

23. The fifth roots of $\dfrac{-1 - i\sqrt{3}}{2}$

24. The sixth roots of $1 - i$

25. The square roots of $3 - \sqrt{3}\,i$

23. The cube roots of $3 + 4i$

27. The fifth roots of $24 - 7i$

28. The fourth roots of $-5 - 12i$

Find all of the roots of each equation in Exercises 29–34.

29. $x^3 + 8i = 0$

30. $32x^5 + 1 = 0$

31. $16x^4 + 81 = 0$

32. $3x^7 - 729x^2 = 0$

33. $2x^6 + (1 + i\sqrt{3}) = 0$

34. $\sqrt{2}\,x^9 - 1 - i = 0$

SUPPLEMENTARY EXERCISES FOR CHAPTER 15

In Exercises 1–8, perform the indicated operations by the methods of Examples 1 and 2 of Section 15–5, and express the result in the form $a + bi$.

1. $(2 + 3i)(3 - 4i)$

2. $(4 - 5i)(3 + 7i)$

3. $(32 + i)(4 - i)$

4. $(1 - i)(3i + 7)$

5. $(2 - 3i)/(5 - 4i)$

6. $(3i - 7)/(5 + 6i)$

7. $(4 - 3i)/(4 + 5i)$

8. $(3 - 4i)/(3 + 7i)$

In Exercises 9–14, express each of the complex numbers in trigonometric form, and then perform the indicated operations.

9. $\dfrac{(0.3 - 0.4i)(-2.4 + 0.7i)}{(1.2i - 0.5)i}$

10. $\dfrac{(\sqrt{13} - \sqrt{3}\,i)(i - 1)}{\sqrt{7} + 3i}$

11. $\dfrac{(\sqrt{17} + 2\sqrt{2}\,i)(-3\sqrt{2} + \sqrt{7}\,i)}{(\sqrt{31} - \sqrt{5}\,i)(-\sqrt{26} - \sqrt{10}\,i)}$

12. $\dfrac{i^2(\sqrt{19} - \sqrt{6}\,i)}{(i - 2)(1 + 3i)}$

13. $\dfrac{i(6 - 8i)(i\sqrt{2} + 7\sqrt{2})}{(-i - 4\sqrt{3})(1 - 4\sqrt{5}\,i)}$

14. $\dfrac{i^3(-8i^3 + 6i^2)}{(4\sqrt{5} - 2\sqrt{5}\,i)(2\sqrt{5} - 4\sqrt{5}\,i)}$

In Exercises 15–20, find the indicated roots.

15. The fifth roots of 32

16. The cube roots of -8

17. The seventh roots of 7

18. The eighth roots of -32

19. The cube roots of $-6 - 6i$

20. The fourth roots of $2 + 2i$

21. Express the formula in Theorem 15–1 in polar form.

CHAPTER 16

Determinants

16–1 LINEAR SYSTEMS. DETERMINANTS OF ORDERS TWO AND THREE

In Chapter 12, we solved a system of two linear equations in two unknowns. In this chapter we shall extend the methods and introduce new symbols which will facilitate the solution of a system of n linear equations in n unknowns if a solution of the system exists.

Consider the two equations

$$\begin{aligned} a_1x + b_1y &= c_1, \\ a_2x + b_2y &= c_2, \end{aligned} \tag{1}$$

where the coefficients a_1, b_1, c_1, a_2, b_2, c_2 are constants. In accordance with the method of Chapter 12, we multiply the members of the first equation by b_2, the members of the second equation by $-b_1$, and add corresponding members of the resulting equations. This gives the equation

$$(a_1b_2 - a_2b_1)x = c_1b_2 - c_2b_1.$$

If $a_1b_2 - a_2b_1 \neq 0$, then

$$x = \frac{c_1b_2 - c_2b_1}{a_1b_2 - a_2b_1}.$$

If we introduce the symbol $\begin{vmatrix} p_1 & p_2 \\ q_1 & q_2 \end{vmatrix}$, defined by the equation

$$\boxed{\begin{vmatrix} p_1 & p_2 \\ q_1 & q_2 \end{vmatrix} = p_1q_2 - p_2q_1,} \tag{2}$$

the value of x above can be written as

$$x = \frac{\begin{vmatrix} c_1 & b_1 \\ c_2 & b_2 \end{vmatrix}}{\begin{vmatrix} a_1 & b_1 \\ a_2 & b_2 \end{vmatrix}}. \tag{3}$$

The quantity defined in (2) is called a *second-order determinant.*

To solve (1) for y we multiply the members of the first equation by a_2, those of the second equation by $-a_1$, and add corresponding members of the resulting equations. The new equation can be solved for y, and gives, similarly,

$$y = \frac{a_1c_2 - a_2c_1}{a_1b_2 - b_1a_2} = \frac{\begin{vmatrix} a_1 & c_1 \\ a_2 & c_2 \end{vmatrix}}{\begin{vmatrix} a_1 & b_1 \\ a_2 & b_2 \end{vmatrix}}. \tag{4}$$

Let us now consider the following system of three equations in three unknowns:

$$\begin{aligned} a_1x + b_1y + c_1z &= d_1, \\ a_2x + b_2y + c_2z &= d_2, \\ a_3x + b_3y + c_3z &= d_3, \end{aligned} \tag{5}$$

where the coefficients of x, y, and z are constants. If we multiply the members of the second equation of (5) by c_3 and those of the third equation by $-c_2$ and add corresponding members of the two resulting equations, we obtain

$$\begin{vmatrix} a_2 & c_2 \\ a_3 & c_3 \end{vmatrix} x + \begin{vmatrix} b_2 & c_2 \\ b_3 & c_3 \end{vmatrix} y = \begin{vmatrix} d_2 & c_2 \\ d_3 & c_3 \end{vmatrix}. \tag{6}$$

In a similar manner the multiplication of the members of the first equation of (5) by c_3 and those of the third equation by $-c_1$ gives two equations. By adding corresponding members of these equations, we find

$$\begin{vmatrix} a_1 & c_1 \\ a_3 & c_3 \end{vmatrix} x + \begin{vmatrix} b_1 & c_1 \\ b_3 & c_3 \end{vmatrix} y = \begin{vmatrix} d_1 & c_1 \\ d_3 & c_3 \end{vmatrix}. \tag{7}$$

Finally, if we eliminate z similarly from the first two equations of (5), we obtain

$$\begin{vmatrix} a_1 & c_1 \\ a_2 & c_2 \end{vmatrix} x + \begin{vmatrix} b_1 & c_1 \\ b_2 & c_2 \end{vmatrix} y = \begin{vmatrix} d_1 & c_1 \\ d_2 & c_2 \end{vmatrix}. \tag{8}$$

Let us now multiply the members of (6) by a_1, those of (7) by $-a_2$, and those of

(8) by a_3, and add corresponding members of the resulting equations; we obtain

$$\left[a_1\begin{vmatrix} b_2 & c_2 \\ b_3 & c_3 \end{vmatrix} - a_2\begin{vmatrix} b_1 & c_1 \\ b_3 & c_3 \end{vmatrix} + a_3\begin{vmatrix} b_1 & c_1 \\ b_2 & c_2 \end{vmatrix}\right] y = a_1\begin{vmatrix} d_2 & c_2 \\ d_3 & c_3 \end{vmatrix} - a_2\begin{vmatrix} d_1 & c_1 \\ d_3 & c_3 \end{vmatrix} + a_3\begin{vmatrix} d_1 & c_1 \\ d_2 & c_2 \end{vmatrix} \tag{9}$$

since, as can be verified by multiplying out and simplifying,

$$a_1\begin{vmatrix} a_2 & c_2 \\ a_3 & c_3 \end{vmatrix} - a_2\begin{vmatrix} a_1 & c_1 \\ a_3 & c_3 \end{vmatrix} + a_3\begin{vmatrix} a_1 & c_1 \\ a_2 & c_2 \end{vmatrix} = 0. \tag{10}$$

If the coefficient of y in Eq. (9) is not zero, we have

$$y = \frac{a_1\begin{vmatrix} d_2 & c_2 \\ d_3 & c_3 \end{vmatrix} - a_2\begin{vmatrix} d_1 & c_1 \\ d_3 & c_3 \end{vmatrix} + a_3\begin{vmatrix} d_1 & c_1 \\ d_2 & c_2 \end{vmatrix}}{a_1\begin{vmatrix} b_2 & c_2 \\ b_3 & c_3 \end{vmatrix} - a_2\begin{vmatrix} b_1 & c_1 \\ b_3 & c_3 \end{vmatrix} + a_3\begin{vmatrix} b_1 & c_1 \\ b_2 & c_2 \end{vmatrix}}. \tag{11}$$

Let the following equation define the quantity which appears in its left member:

$$\begin{vmatrix} p_1 & p_2 & p_3 \\ q_1 & q_2 & q_3 \\ r_1 & r_2 & r_3 \end{vmatrix} = p_1\begin{vmatrix} q_2 & q_3 \\ r_2 & r_3 \end{vmatrix} - q_1\begin{vmatrix} p_2 & p_3 \\ r_2 & r_3 \end{vmatrix} + r_1\begin{vmatrix} p_2 & p_3 \\ q_2 & q_3 \end{vmatrix}. \tag{12}$$

The symbol thus defined is called a *third-order determinant.* With use of this new symbol, the value of y in (11) can now be written as

$$y = \frac{\begin{vmatrix} a_1 & d_1 & c_1 \\ a_2 & d_2 & c_2 \\ a_3 & d_3 & c_3 \end{vmatrix}}{\begin{vmatrix} a_1 & b_1 & c_1 \\ a_2 & b_2 & c_2 \\ a_3 & b_3 & c_3 \end{vmatrix}}.$$

In a similar manner, the elimination of x and y from (5) leads to z, and the elimination of y and z gives x, thus:

$$z = \frac{\begin{vmatrix} a_1 & b_1 & d_1 \\ a_2 & b_2 & d_2 \\ a_3 & b_3 & d_3 \end{vmatrix}}{\begin{vmatrix} a_1 & b_1 & c_1 \\ a_2 & b_2 & c_2 \\ a_3 & b_3 & c_3 \end{vmatrix}}, \qquad x = \frac{\begin{vmatrix} d_1 & b_1 & c_1 \\ d_2 & b_2 & c_2 \\ d_3 & b_3 & c_3 \end{vmatrix}}{\begin{vmatrix} a_1 & b_1 & c_1 \\ a_2 & b_2 & c_2 \\ a_3 & b_3 & c_3 \end{vmatrix}}. \tag{13}$$

The above results can be summarized, and also extended to a system of n equations in n unknowns when determinants of order more than 3 are defined, as follows:

1. *Arrange the equations to be solved so that the unknowns x, y, z, etc., appear in the same order in each equation; if any unknown is missing from an equation it is considered as having a coefficient of zero in that equation.*
2. *All terms which do not involve the unknowns are placed in the right member of each equation.*
3. *Designate by D the determinant of the coefficients of the unknowns written in the same order as they appear in the equations. Designate by D_i the determinant obtained by replacing the elements of the* ith *column of D by the terms in the right members of the equations.*
4. *Then, if $D \neq 0$, the values of the unknowns x, y, z, etc., are given by the equations*

$$x = \frac{D_1}{D}, \qquad y = \frac{D_2}{D}, \qquad z = \frac{D_3}{D}, \qquad \textit{etc.}$$

This method of expressing the values of the unknowns in terms of the coefficients is known as *Cramer's Rule*, after the Swiss mathematician Gabriel Cramer (1704–1752), who first stated it.

Example 1. Solve the following pair of equations by determinants:

$$2x + 3y = 7,$$
$$3x - 5y = 9.$$

Solution. By the above result, we have

$$x = \frac{\begin{vmatrix} 7 & 3 \\ 9 & -5 \end{vmatrix}}{\begin{vmatrix} 2 & 3 \\ 3 & -5 \end{vmatrix}} = \frac{-35 - 27}{-10 - 9} = \frac{-62}{-19} = \frac{62}{19},$$

$$y = \frac{\begin{vmatrix} 2 & 7 \\ 3 & 9 \end{vmatrix}}{\begin{vmatrix} 2 & 3 \\ 3 & -5 \end{vmatrix}} = \frac{18 - 21}{-10 - 9} = \frac{-3}{-19} = \frac{3}{19}.$$

Example 2. Solve the following system of equations by determinants:

$$5x - y + 4z = 5,$$
$$2x + 3y + 5z = 2,$$
$$7x - 2y + 6z = 5.$$

Solution.

$$x = \frac{\begin{vmatrix} 5 & -1 & 4 \\ 2 & 3 & 5 \\ 5 & -2 & 6 \end{vmatrix}}{\begin{vmatrix} 5 & -1 & 4 \\ 2 & 3 & 5 \\ 7 & -2 & 6 \end{vmatrix}} = \frac{5\begin{vmatrix} 3 & 5 \\ -2 & 6 \end{vmatrix} - 2\begin{vmatrix} -1 & 4 \\ -2 & 6 \end{vmatrix} + 5\begin{vmatrix} -1 & 4 \\ 3 & 5 \end{vmatrix}}{5\begin{vmatrix} 3 & 5 \\ -2 & 6 \end{vmatrix} - 2\begin{vmatrix} -1 & 4 \\ -2 & 6 \end{vmatrix} + 7\begin{vmatrix} -1 & 4 \\ 3 & 5 \end{vmatrix}}$$

$$= \frac{5(18 + 10) - 2(-6 + 8) + 5(-5 - 12)}{5(18 + 10) - 2(-6 + 8) + 7(-5 - 12)}$$

$$= \frac{5(28) - 2(2) + 5(-17)}{5(28) - 2(2) + 7(-17)} = \frac{140 - 4 - 85}{140 - 4 - 119} = \frac{51}{17} = 3.$$

$$y = \frac{\begin{vmatrix} 5 & 5 & 4 \\ 2 & 2 & 5 \\ 7 & 5 & 6 \end{vmatrix}}{17} = \frac{5\begin{vmatrix} 2 & 5 \\ 5 & 6 \end{vmatrix} - 2\begin{vmatrix} 5 & 4 \\ 5 & 6 \end{vmatrix} + 7\begin{vmatrix} 5 & 4 \\ 2 & 5 \end{vmatrix}}{17}$$

$$= \frac{5(-13) - 2(10) + 7(17)}{17} = \frac{34}{17} = 2.$$

$$z = \frac{\begin{vmatrix} 5 & -1 & 5 \\ 2 & 3 & 2 \\ 7 & -2 & 5 \end{vmatrix}}{17}.$$

The reader should evaluate z and show that $z = -2$.

EXERCISE GROUP 16–1

In the following exercises, use determinants to solve for x and y in each pair of equations, and for x, y, and z in each system of three equations.

1. $2x + 3y = -7$
   $8x - y = 15$
2. $3x + 5y = 9$
   $5x - 2y = -16$
3. $3x + 2y = -15$
   $2x - y = -3$
4. $5x - 2y = 0$
   $-3x + 3y = 9/4$
5. $2x + 3y = -1$
   $4x + 5y = 71$
6. $2x + y = 2a$
   $4x + 3y = 5a - 2$
7. $3x - 2y = 6a + 2b$
   $4x + 5y = 8a - 5b$
8. $6x + 3y - 8u = 0$
   $15x - 9y + 13u = 0$
9. $7x - 3y + u = 0$
   $11x + 5y - 13u = 0$
10. $6x - 5y + 4z = -1$
    $4x - y - 6z = 11$
    $10x + 7y - 4z = 9$
11. $x + 2y - z = 1$
    $-3x - 5y + 2z = -5$
    $2x + 6y + 3z = -2$
12. $x + 2y + z = 4$
    $3y - z = 3$
    $2y + 3z = 13$
13. $3x - 5y + 2z = -1$
    $2x - y - 3z = 11$
    $5x + 7y - 2z = 9$

14. $x + y + z = 0$
$2x - y + 2z = 7$
$-3x + 2y + 7z = 5$

15. $3x + 6y + 5z = 0$
$-5x + 7y + 2z = 1$
$x - 4y - 4z = 1$

16. $3x + 2y - z = 2$
$-3x + 5y - z = 2$
$x + y + z = 0$

17. $2x + 2y + z = 5a$
$3x - y - 2z = 4b$
$x + y + z = 3a$

18. $3x + 2y + 8z + u = 0$
$4x - 3y + 2z + 9u = 0$
$7x + 5y + 20z + 6u = 0$

19. $7x + 9y + 5z - 15u = 0$
$-2x + y + z + 5u = 0$
$9x + 8y + 14z + 5u = 0$

16–2 DETERMINANTS OF ANY ORDER

We now wish to define the general determinant of order n, which may be designated as the square array

$$\begin{vmatrix} a_{11} & a_{12} & a_{13} \dots a_{1n} \\ a_{21} & a_{22} & a_{23} \dots a_{2n} \\ \vdots & & \vdots \\ a_{n1} & a_{n2} & a_{n3} \dots a_{nn} \end{vmatrix} \tag{14}$$

with n *rows* and n *columns*, hence n^2 *elements*. The *element* a_{ij} is the quantity in the ith row and jth column. If the ith row and jth column are removed from the determinant, the resulting determinant, of order $n - 1$, is designated by A_{ij} and is called the *minor* of a_{ij}.

Example 1. Consider the fifth-order determinant

$$D = \begin{vmatrix} 2 & 3 & 1 & 4 & 5 \\ 1 & 2 & 5 & -3 & 6 \\ 3 & 5 & 2 & 1 & 4 \\ 5 & 1 & 3 & 2 & 7 \\ 5 & 6 & 1 & 3 & 4 \end{vmatrix}.$$

The element -3 is in the second row and fourth column and is therefore a_{24}; its minor A_{24} is the determinant, of order 4:

$$A_{24} = \begin{vmatrix} 2 & 3 & 1 & 5 \\ 3 & 5 & 2 & 4 \\ 5 & 1 & 3 & 7 \\ 5 & 6 & 1 & 4 \end{vmatrix}.$$

The nth-*order determinant may now be defined by the following relation:*

$$\begin{vmatrix} a_{11} & a_{12} & a_{13} \dots a_{1n} \\ a_{21} & a_{22} & a_{23} \dots a_{2n} \\ \vdots & & \vdots \\ a_{n1} & a_{n2} & a_{n3} \dots a_{nn} \end{vmatrix} = a_{11}A_{11} - a_{21}A_{21} + \cdots + (-1)^{n+1}a_{n1}A_{n1}, \tag{15}$$

which is also called the *expansion of the determinant of order n in terms of the elements of the first column.* It is seen that (15) is an extension of the definition of the determinant of order 3 given in Eq. (12). The determinants A_{j1} $(j = 1, 2, \ldots, n)$ in Eq. (15) are of order $n - 1$.

To understand how Eq. (15) actually defines a determinant of any order n, the student should recall that a determinant of order 3 was defined in Eq. (12). This means that if $n = 4$ in (15) above, the third-order determinants on the right have been defined; hence the fourth-order determinant on the left is defined. Now that fourth-order determinants are defined, Eq. (15) defines a fifth-order determinant in the same manner. A continuation of this process then defines determinants of any order n.

Example 2. The fifth-order determinant of Example 1 becomes, by virtue of (15),

$$\begin{vmatrix} 2 & 3 & 1 & 4 & 5 \\ 1 & 2 & 5 & -3 & 6 \\ 3 & 5 & 2 & 1 & 4 \\ 5 & 1 & 3 & 2 & 7 \\ 5 & 6 & 1 & 3 & 4 \end{vmatrix} = 2\begin{vmatrix} 2 & 5 & -3 & 6 \\ 5 & 2 & 1 & 4 \\ 1 & 3 & 2 & 7 \\ 6 & 1 & 3 & 4 \end{vmatrix} - 1\begin{vmatrix} 3 & 1 & 4 & 5 \\ 5 & 2 & 1 & 4 \\ 1 & 3 & 2 & 7 \\ 6 & 1 & 3 & 4 \end{vmatrix}$$

$$+ 3\begin{vmatrix} 3 & 1 & 4 & 5 \\ 2 & 5 & -3 & 6 \\ 1 & 3 & 2 & 7 \\ 6 & 1 & 3 & 4 \end{vmatrix} - 5\begin{vmatrix} 3 & 1 & 4 & 5 \\ 2 & 5 & -3 & 6 \\ 5 & 2 & 1 & 4 \\ 6 & 1 & 3 & 4 \end{vmatrix} + 5\begin{vmatrix} 3 & 1 & 4 & 5 \\ 2 & 5 & -3 & 6 \\ 5 & 2 & 1 & 4 \\ 1 & 3 & 2 & 7 \end{vmatrix}$$

where each of the fourth-order determinants on the right can now be expressed in terms of four third-order determinants, etc.

In the definition of determinants given in (12) and (15) above, the elements of the first column and their minors were used. In the case of the third-order determinant it can readily be shown, by evaluating the minors A_{11}, A_{12}, etc., which are determinants of order 2, and substituting these values, that the elements of any column can be used if the proper sign is placed before each term, thus:

$$\begin{aligned} a_{11}A_{11} - a_{21}A_{21} + a_{31}A_{31} &= -a_{12}A_{12} + a_{22}A_{22} - a_{32}A_{32} \\ &= a_{13}A_{13} - a_{23}A_{23} + a_{33}A_{33}. \end{aligned}$$

More generally, it can be shown that *in the expansion of a determinant of order n the elements of any row or column together with their minors may be used, with the proper sign attached to each product.* The product $a_{ij}A_{ij}$ has the sign of $(-1)^{i+j}$ assigned to it. For example, if the product $a_{13}A_{13}$ appears in an expansion it will be preceded by a plus sign, since $(-1)^{1+3} = (-1)^4 = +1$; the product $a_{23}A_{23}$ will be preceded by a minus sign, since $(-1)^{2+3} = (-1)^5 = -1$. The minor A_{ij} together with the proper sign is called the *cofactor* of a_{ij} and will be designated by C_{ij}; thus, $C_{ij} = (-1)^{i+j}A_{ij}$.

Example 3. In the fourth-order determinant

$$\begin{vmatrix} a_{11} & a_{12} & a_{13} & a_{14} \\ a_{21} & a_{22} & a_{23} & a_{24} \\ a_{31} & a_{32} & a_{33} & a_{34} \\ a_{41} & a_{42} & a_{43} & a_{44} \end{vmatrix},$$

the cofactor of a_{43} is $C_{43} = -A_{43}$; also $C_{13} = +A_{13}$.

This general result is contained in the following theorem, stated without proof.

Theorem. *The value of a determinant of any order is given by the sum of the products of the elements of any column (or row) by their respective cofactors.*

Example 4. Use the theorem to evaluate the determinant

$$\begin{vmatrix} 2 & 3 & 4 & 5 \\ 6 & 8 & 10 & 12 \\ -3 & -1 & 1 & 3 \\ 4 & 7 & 10 & 13 \end{vmatrix}.$$

Solution. Using the elements of the third row, we have

$$\begin{vmatrix} 2 & 3 & 4 & 5 \\ 6 & 8 & 10 & 12 \\ -3 & -1 & 1 & 3 \\ 4 & 7 & 10 & 13 \end{vmatrix} = -3\begin{vmatrix} 3 & 4 & 5 \\ 8 & 10 & 12 \\ 7 & 10 & 13 \end{vmatrix} - (-1)\begin{vmatrix} 2 & 4 & 5 \\ 6 & 10 & 12 \\ 4 & 10 & 13 \end{vmatrix}$$

$$+ 1\begin{vmatrix} 2 & 3 & 5 \\ 6 & 8 & 12 \\ 4 & 7 & 13 \end{vmatrix} - 3\begin{vmatrix} 2 & 3 & 4 \\ 6 & 8 & 10 \\ 4 & 7 & 10 \end{vmatrix}$$

$$= -3\left[3\begin{vmatrix} 10 & 12 \\ 10 & 13 \end{vmatrix} - 8\begin{vmatrix} 4 & 5 \\ 10 & 13 \end{vmatrix} + 7\begin{vmatrix} 4 & 5 \\ 10 & 12 \end{vmatrix}\right]$$

$$+ 1\left[2\begin{vmatrix} 10 & 12 \\ 10 & 13 \end{vmatrix} - 6\begin{vmatrix} 4 & 5 \\ 10 & 13 \end{vmatrix} + 4\begin{vmatrix} 4 & 5 \\ 10 & 12 \end{vmatrix}\right]$$

$$+ 1\left[2\begin{vmatrix} 8 & 12 \\ 7 & 13 \end{vmatrix} - 6\begin{vmatrix} 3 & 5 \\ 7 & 13 \end{vmatrix} + 4\begin{vmatrix} 3 & 5 \\ 8 & 12 \end{vmatrix}\right]$$

$$- 3\left[2\begin{vmatrix} 8 & 10 \\ 7 & 10 \end{vmatrix} - 6\begin{vmatrix} 3 & 4 \\ 7 & 10 \end{vmatrix} + 4\begin{vmatrix} 3 & 4 \\ 8 & 10 \end{vmatrix}\right]$$

$$= -3[3(130 - 120) - 8(52 - 50) + 7(48 - 50)]$$
$$+ 1[2(130 - 120) - 6(52 - 50) + 4(48 - 50)]$$
$$+ 1[2(104 - 84) - 6(39 - 35) + 4(36 - 40)]$$
$$- 3[2(80 - 70) - 6(30 - 28) + 4(30 - 32)]$$
$$= -3[30 - 16 - 14] + [20 - 12 - 8]$$
$$+ [40 - 24 - 16] - 3[20 - 12 - 8]$$
$$= 3(0) + (0) + (0) - 3(0) = 0.$$

EXERCISE GROUP 16–2

Evaluate the determinant in each of Exercises 1–14 by use of the theorem of Section 16–2.

1. $\begin{vmatrix} 3 & -2 & 4 & 1 \\ 2 & -3 & 1 & 1 \\ 5 & 1 & 0 & 2 \\ -1 & 3 & 1 & 5 \end{vmatrix}$
2. $\begin{vmatrix} 1 & 3 & 2 & -1 \\ 4 & 1 & 2 & 2 \\ -4 & 2 & 1 & 4 \\ 3 & 1 & 2 & 2 \end{vmatrix}$
3. $\begin{vmatrix} 1 & -3 & 4 & -2 \\ 1 & 0 & 2 & 3 \\ 0 & -1 & -3 & 2 \\ 1 & -2 & 1 & 1 \end{vmatrix}$

4. $\begin{vmatrix} 6 & -3 & 4 & -2 \\ 9 & 0 & -2 & 3 \\ 1 & 1 & -3 & 2 \\ 10 & -2 & 1 & 1 \end{vmatrix}$
5. $\begin{vmatrix} 1 & 1 & 0 & 0 \\ 2 & -3 & 4 & 1 \\ 3 & 0 & 5 & 2 \\ 1 & 1 & 1 & 1 \end{vmatrix}$
6. $\begin{vmatrix} 3 & 1 & 1 & 2 \\ 1 & 5 & 0 & 3 \\ 2 & -2 & 1 & 6 \\ 0 & 4 & -5 & 3 \end{vmatrix}$

7. $\begin{vmatrix} 2 & -1 & -3 & 1 \\ 1 & 2 & 1 & -1 \\ 3 & -3 & -1 & 2 \\ -2 & -1 & 2 & -3 \end{vmatrix}$
8. $\begin{vmatrix} 1 & x & 1 \\ 1 & x+1 & -2 \\ 1 & x+2 & 4 \end{vmatrix}$
9. $\begin{vmatrix} x^2 & x & 1 \\ x & 1 & 0 \\ 1 & x & x^2 \end{vmatrix}$

10. $\begin{vmatrix} x & y & 1 \\ 1 & -2 & 1 \\ -3 & 4 & 1 \end{vmatrix}$
11. $\begin{vmatrix} 0 & -a & -b \\ a & 0 & -c \\ b & c & 0 \end{vmatrix}$
12. $\begin{vmatrix} (x+1)^2 & (x-1)^2 & x \\ 2(x+1) & 2(x-1) & 1 \\ 1 & 1 & 0 \end{vmatrix}$

13. $\begin{vmatrix} x & x^2 & x^2+3x \\ 1 & 2x & 2x+3 \\ 0 & 1 & 1 \end{vmatrix}$
14. $\begin{vmatrix} 0 & 1 & 0 \\ \sin x & \tan x & \cos x \\ -\cos x & \cot x & \sin x \end{vmatrix}$

Verify each of the identities in Exercises 15–18.

15. $\begin{vmatrix} \cos x & \sin x \\ \sin y & \cos y \end{vmatrix} = \cos (x + y)$
16. $\begin{vmatrix} \sin x & \cos x \\ \sin y & \cos y \end{vmatrix} = \sin (x - y)$

17. $\begin{vmatrix} \cos x & \sin x \\ \sin x & \cos x \end{vmatrix} = \cos 2x$

18. $\begin{vmatrix} 1 & 1 & 1 \\ \sin x & \sin y & \sin z \\ \cos x & \cos y & \cos z \end{vmatrix} = \sin (y - z) + \sin (z - x) + \sin (x - y)$

In each of the following, replace each element by its cofactor and evaluate the resulting determinant.

19. $\begin{vmatrix} 1 & 2 & 3 \\ 2 & 1 & 1 \\ 3 & 2 & 1 \end{vmatrix}$
20. $\begin{vmatrix} 8 & 2 & -3 \\ 1 & -1 & 4 \\ 2 & -2 & 1 \end{vmatrix}$
21. $\begin{vmatrix} 20 & 2 & -7 \\ 4 & 5 & -1 \\ -4 & -3 & 2 \end{vmatrix}$

22. $\begin{vmatrix} 3 & 5 & 1 \\ 1 & -4 & -2 \\ 7 & -5 & -4 \end{vmatrix}$
23. $\begin{vmatrix} 1 & 1 & 1 \\ 0 & 0 & 1 \\ 3 & 4 & -3 \end{vmatrix}$
24. $\begin{vmatrix} 0 & 0 & 2 \\ 0 & 2 & 5 \\ 1 & 2 & 2 \end{vmatrix}$

25. $\begin{vmatrix} \sin x & \cos x & \cot x \\ 0 & 0 & 1 \\ -\cos x & \sin x & \tan x \end{vmatrix}$
26. $\begin{vmatrix} \sec x & 0 & \tan x \\ 0 & 1 & 0 \\ \tan x & \cot x & \sec x \end{vmatrix}$

16–3 SOME PROPERTIES OF DETERMINANTS

The labor involved in evaluating the fourth-order determinant of Example 4 in the preceding section indicates the need for simpler methods if the use of determinants is to be of help in solving systems of equations. Fortunately, there are properties of determinants which simplify considerably the work of evaluating a determinant.

I. *The value of a determinant is unchanged if all correspondingly numbered rows and columns are interchanged.*

The proof of this property will not be attempted but the student should verify the statement for third-order determinants by showing that

$$\begin{vmatrix} a_{11} & a_{12} & a_{13} \\ a_{21} & a_{22} & a_{23} \\ a_{31} & a_{32} & a_{33} \end{vmatrix} = \begin{vmatrix} a_{11} & a_{21} & a_{31} \\ a_{12} & a_{22} & a_{32} \\ a_{13} & a_{23} & a_{33} \end{vmatrix}.$$

As a consequence of Property I the words *row* and *column* can always be interchanged in a statement of a property of determinants.

II. *If all the elements of a column (or row) are multiplied by the same number k, the value of the determinant is multiplied by k.*

Let the elements of the jth column be multiplied by k. If

$$D = \begin{vmatrix} a_{11} & a_{12} \ldots a_{1j} \ldots a_{1n} \\ a_{21} & a_{22} \ldots a_{2j} \ldots a_{2n} \\ \vdots & \qquad\qquad\quad \vdots \\ a_{n1} & a_{n2} \ldots a_{nj} \ldots a_{nn} \end{vmatrix}, \qquad D' = \begin{vmatrix} a_{11} & a_{12} \ldots ka_{1j} \ldots a_{1n} \\ a_{21} & a_{22} \ldots ka_{2j} \ldots a_{2n} \\ \vdots & \qquad\qquad\quad \vdots \\ a_{n1} & a_{n2} \ldots ka_{nj} \ldots a_{nn} \end{vmatrix},$$

then by the theorem of Section 16–2, D' can be expanded as

$$\begin{aligned} D' &= (ka_{1j})C_{1j} + (ka_{2j})C_{2j} + \cdots + (ka_{nj})C_{nj} \\ &= k(a_{1j}C_{1j} + a_{2j}C_{2j} + \cdots + a_{nj}C_{nj}) \\ &= kD. \end{aligned}$$

III. *If two columns (or rows) of a determinant are identical, the value of the determinant is zero.*

This property follows from Property IV, and will be proved after that property.

IV. *If two columns (or rows) of a determinant are interchanged, the value of the determinant is merely changed in sign.*

This property is easily seen for a second-order determinant, on verifying the relation

$$\begin{vmatrix} a_1 & a_2 \\ b_1 & b_2 \end{vmatrix} = -\begin{vmatrix} a_2 & a_1 \\ b_2 & b_1 \end{vmatrix}.$$

Now let D and D' be two nth-order determinants, differing only in that two columns, say the ith and jth, are interchanged. By the theorem of Section 16–2 let us express each of D and D' as the sum of the products of the elements of the same column, other than the ith and jth, and their cofactors. This will express D and D' as a sum of determinants of order $n - 1$, the sums differing only in that corresponding determinants have two columns interchanged. Each of these can be expressed in terms of the cofactors of the elements of a column other than the two interchanged ones. Now D and D' are represented as sums of $n(n - 1)$ determinants of order $n - 2$, differing again only in that corresponding determinants have two columns interchanged. By repeating this process we shall eventually have D and D' as a sum of $n(n - 1)(n - 2) \cdots 4 \cdot 3$ second-order determinants, with the columns interchanged in corresponding determinants. According to the first statement of this paragraph, each second-order determinant in D is the negative of the corresponding determinant in D', and it follows that $D = -D'$. This completes the proof of Property IV.

The proof of Property III now proceeds easily. Let D be an nth-order determinant in which two columns are identical. The determinant with the two identical columns interchanged is equal to $-D$ by Property IV, but is also equal to D since the determinant is actually the same. Hence $D = -D$, or $2D = 0$, and we conclude that $D = 0$. Property III has thus been proved.

V. *The value of a determinant is unchanged if the elements of any column (or row) are multiplied by any number k and the resulting numbers are added to the corresponding elements of another column (or row).*

To prove this property, consider the determinants

$$D = \begin{vmatrix} a_{11} & a_{12} \ldots a_{1j} \ldots a_{1n} \\ a_{21} & a_{22} \ldots a_{2j} \ldots a_{2n} \\ \vdots & \vdots \\ a_{n1} & a_{n2} \ldots a_{nj} \ldots a_{nn} \end{vmatrix}, \qquad D' = \begin{vmatrix} a_{11} & a_{12} \ldots (a_{1j} + ka_{1r}) \ldots a_{1n} \\ a_{21} & a_{22} \ldots (a_{2j} + ka_{2r}) \ldots a_{2n} \\ \vdots & \vdots \\ a_{n1} & a_{n2} \ldots (a_{nj} + ka_{nr}) \ldots a_{nn} \end{vmatrix}.$$

Let us expand D' using the elements of the jth column and their cofactors, thus:

$$\begin{aligned} D' &= (a_{1j} + ka_{1r})C_{1j} + (a_{2j} + ka_{2r})C_{2j} + \cdots + (a_{nj} + ka_{nr})C_{nj} \\ &= (a_{1j}C_{1j} + a_{2j}C_{2j} + \cdots + a_{nj}C_{nj}) + k(a_{1r}C_{1j} + a_{2r}C_{2j} + \cdots + a_{nr}C_{nj}). \end{aligned}$$

The quantity $a_{1j}C_{1j} + a_{2j}C_{2j} + \cdots + a_{nj}C_{nj}$ is the expansion of D in terms of the cofactors and elements of the jth column. The sum $a_{1r}C_{1j} + a_{2r}C_{2j} + \cdots +$

$a_{nr}C_{nj}$ is the expansion of a determinant which differs from D only in that the jth column consists of $a_{1r}, a_{2r}, \ldots, a_{nr}$, making this column identical with the rth column; the value of this determinant is therefore zero by Property III. Hence $D = D'$, regardless of the value of k.

Example 1.

$$D = \begin{vmatrix} 3 & 2 & 1 & 5 \\ 4 & -1 & 6 & 2 \\ 5 & 3 & 7 & -2 \\ -3 & 4 & -1 & 7 \end{vmatrix} = \begin{vmatrix} 3 & 2+(-2)\cdot 1 & 1 & 5 \\ 4 & -1+(-2)\cdot 6 & 6 & 2 \\ 5 & 3+(-2)\cdot 7 & 7 & -2 \\ -3 & 4+(-2)(-1) & -1 & 7 \end{vmatrix}$$

$$= \begin{vmatrix} 3 & 0 & 1 & 5 \\ 4 & -13 & 6 & 2 \\ 5 & -11 & 7 & -2 \\ -3 & 6 & -1 & 7 \end{vmatrix} = \begin{vmatrix} 0 & 0 & 1 & 0 \\ -14 & -13 & 6 & -28 \\ -16 & -11 & 7 & -37 \\ 0 & 6 & -1 & 12 \end{vmatrix}.$$

Property V was used to obtain a zero as the first element of the second column and then, in turn, zeros as the first elements in the first and fourth columns. If the resulting determinant, which is still equal to the given one, is expanded in terms of the elements of the first row and their cofactors, it is seen that three of the four products are zero, so that what remains is the third-order determinant

$$\begin{vmatrix} -14 & -13 & -28 \\ -16 & -11 & -37 \\ 0 & 6 & 12 \end{vmatrix} = (-2)\cdot\begin{vmatrix} 7 & -13 & -28 \\ 8 & -11 & -37 \\ 0 & 6 & 12 \end{vmatrix} \quad \text{(by Property II).}$$

In the last determinant the elements of the first row can be subtracted from those of the second row by virtue of Property V to give

$$D = (-2)\cdot\begin{vmatrix} 7 & -13 & -28 \\ 1 & 2 & -9 \\ 0 & 6 & 12 \end{vmatrix}.$$

We can obtain a zero as the element in the first row and first column by multiplying the elements of the second row by -7 and adding them to the elements of the first row; thus

$$D = (-2)\begin{vmatrix} 0 & -27 & 35 \\ 1 & 2 & -9 \\ 0 & 6 & 12 \end{vmatrix},$$

and by expanding in terms of elements of the first column and their cofactors:

$$D = -2(-1)\begin{vmatrix} -27 & 35 \\ 6 & 12 \end{vmatrix}$$
$$= 2[(-27)(12) - (6)(35)] = -1068.$$

It is thus seen that the use of the foregoing properties can greatly reduce the labor of evaluating determinants. There is no fixed procedure for applying them. At each stage in the simplification of a determinant the situation must be studied in order to find the most effective use of these properties.

EXERCISE GROUP 16-3

Evaluate the determinants in Exercises 1–5 by using the properties of determinants.

1. $\begin{vmatrix} 1 & 1 & 1 & 1 \\ 1 & 2 & 3 & 4 \\ 1 & 3 & 6 & 10 \\ 1 & 4 & 10 & 20 \end{vmatrix}$ 2. $\begin{vmatrix} 3 & 2 & 2 & 2 \\ 2 & 3 & 2 & 2 \\ 2 & 2 & 3 & 2 \\ 2 & 2 & 2 & 3 \end{vmatrix}$ 3. $\begin{vmatrix} 1 & 15 & 14 & 4 \\ 12 & 6 & 7 & 9 \\ 8 & 10 & 11 & 5 \\ 13 & 3 & 2 & 16 \end{vmatrix}$

4. $\begin{vmatrix} \sin^2 x & \cos^2 x & 1 \\ \sin^2 y & \cos^2 y & 1 \\ \sin^2 z & \cos^2 z & 1 \end{vmatrix}$ 5. $\begin{vmatrix} \cos x & \sin x \cos x & \cos x(\sin y + \sin z) \\ \cos y & \sin y \cos y & \cos y(\sin x + \sin z) \\ \cos z & \sin z \cos z & \cos z(\sin x + \sin y) \end{vmatrix}$

Show, by use of the properties of determinants, that each of the relations in Exercises 6–14 is true.

6. $\begin{vmatrix} 6 & 1 & -7 \\ 5 & -10 & 5 \\ 4 & 3 & -7 \end{vmatrix} = 0$ 7. $\begin{vmatrix} 0 & 1 & 2 \\ a - 1 & a & a + 1 \\ a^2 - 1 & a^2 & a^2 + 1 \end{vmatrix} = 0$

8. $\begin{vmatrix} 4 & 4 & 2 \\ 1 & 8 & -3 \\ 4 & -2 & 5 \end{vmatrix} = 0$ 9. $\begin{vmatrix} 2 & 1 & 0 \\ a + 1 & a & a - 1 \\ b + 1 & b & b - 1 \end{vmatrix} = 0$

10. $\begin{vmatrix} b + c & c & b \\ c & c + a & a \\ b & a & a + b \end{vmatrix} = 4abc$ 11. $\begin{vmatrix} 1 & 1 & 1 & 1 \\ 1 & 1 + a & 1 & 1 \\ 1 & 1 & 1 + b & 1 \\ 1 & 1 & 1 & 1 + c \end{vmatrix} = abc$

12. $\begin{vmatrix} 1 & 1 & 1 \\ x & y & z \\ x^2 & y^2 & z^2 \end{vmatrix} = (x - y)(y - z)(z - x)$

13. $\begin{vmatrix} \sin x & \sin 2x & \sin 3x \\ \sin^2 x & \sin^2 2x & \sin^2 3x \\ \sin 2x & \sin 4x & \sin 6x \end{vmatrix} = 2 \sin x \sin 2x \sin 3x(\sin 2x - 2 \sin x)$

14. $\begin{vmatrix} 1 & \sin x & \sin^2 x \\ 1 & \sin y & \sin^2 y \\ 1 & \sin z & \sin^2 z \end{vmatrix} = (\sin x - \sin y)(\sin y - \sin z)(\sin z - \sin x)$

In Exercises 15–17, use determinants to solve for x, y, and z and use the properties of determinants in evaluating each of the determinants involved.

15. $3x - 5y + 2z = -1$
$2x - y - 3x = 11$
$5x + 7y - 2z = 9$

16. $3x + 2y + 8z + u = 0$
$4x - 3y + 2z + 9u = 0$
$7x + 5y + 20z + 6u = 0$

17. $7x + 9y + 5z - 15u = 0$
$-2x + y + z + 5u = 0$
$9x + 8y + 14z + 5u = 0$

Solve for x, y, z, and w in each system of equations in Exercises 18–20.

18. $y - 2z + 3w = 20$
    $5x - 4y - z + 2w = -2$
    $-5y - 2z + w = 0$
    $y + 2z + w = 0$

19. $2x - y + 3z - 2w = 1$
    $3x + 2y - 4z + 2w = 3$
    $-2x + 3y + 2z - 3w = -2$
    $5x - 3y - 5z + 6w = 8$

20. $2x + 3y + 3z + 2w = 1$
    $x - y + z - w = 1$
    $5x + 3y - 4z + 7w = 3$
    $-x + 2y - 5z + 6w = 3$

CHAPTER 17

Permutations, Combinations, and Probability

17–1 FUNDAMENTAL PRINCIPLE

Let us consider the following question. How many numbers of two *different* digits can be formed with the digits 6, 7, 8, 9? One method of solution is to write down all such two-digit numbers. Thus we have the twelve numbers

$$67, 68, 69; \qquad 76, 78, 79; \qquad 86, 87, 89; \qquad 96, 97, 98.$$

How can we be certain that all of the desired numbers are accounted for? There are four choices for the first digit, that is, 6, 7, 8, or 9, and after the first digit has been chosen there are three choices for the second digit. For example, if the first digit is 7 the second may be 6 or 8 or 9, and the second group of three numbers above is obtained. With four choices for the first digit and three for the second, by the very meaning of multiplication there are then $4 \cdot 3 = 12$ of the desired numbers possible.

Suppose, now, that with the same four digits, the number of two-digit numbers is required, but repetition is permitted. The same kind of analysis as above shows that there are four choices for the first digit and also four choices for the second digit, hence $4 \cdot 4 = 16$ two-digit numbers. The four numbers in addition to the twelve above are 66, 77, 88, 99.

The principle used in these analyses is the basis of the present topic and will be stated explicitly.

Fundamental Principle. *If an act can be performed in u distinct ways and if after its performance a second act can be performed in v distinct ways, then the two acts can be performed in $u \cdot v$ distinct ways.*

As a corollary, it follows that if a third act can then be performed in w ways, the three acts can be performed in uvw ways.

Example. In the above problem, twelve numbers of two different digits were formed with 6, 7, 8, 9. If numbers of three different digits are to be formed, the first two digits can thus be formed in twelve ways and the third digit can be found in two ways, so that in all there are $12 \cdot 2 = 24$ numbers of three different digits from the digits 6, 7, 8, 9. For example, by adding 8 or 9 as a third digit to the number 67, the two numbers 678 and 679 are obtained. In the same way, the three-digit numbers starting with 68 are 687 and 689. The other three-digit numbers can be found in a similar manner.

17–2 PERMUTATIONS

Any *ordered* set of objects is called a *permutation* of the objects. Thus 6, 7 and 7, 6 are different permutations of the same digits. In many problems it is necessary to know the *number of permutations of n different objects taken r at a time*. This number is evidently a function of n and r, and will be denoted by $P(n, r)$. The symbol ${}_nP_r$ is also frequently used for this function.

A formula for $P(n, r)$ can be developed by use of the fundamental principle. There are n choices for the first position, but only $n - 1$ choices for the second position, hence the first two positions can be chosen in $n(n - 1)$ ways. For the third position, $n - 2$ choices are available, so that the first three positions can be chosen in $n(n - 1)(n - 2)$ ways. We continue in this manner. The rth position can be chosen in $n - r + 1$ ways, and we obtain the formula

$$P(n, r) = n(n - 1)(n - 2) \cdots (n - r + 1). \tag{1}$$

Note that the product on the right contains r factors.

Let us recall here the factorial symbol defined in Section 11–5. Thus

$$n! = n(n - 1)(n - 2) \cdots 3 \cdot 2 \cdot 1 \text{ if } n \text{ is a positive integer,}$$
$$0! = 1.$$

An alternative form of formula (1) can be obtained by multiplying the right member of (1) by

$$\frac{(n - r)!}{(n - r)!}.$$

This gives

$$P(n, r) = \frac{n(n - 1)(n - 2) \cdots (n - r + 1) \cdot (n - r)!}{(n - r)!}$$

or

$$P(n, r) = \frac{n!}{(n - r)!}. \tag{2}$$

If we set $r = n$ in (1), we have

$$\boxed{P(n, n) = n!,} \tag{3}$$

which is the formula for the *number of permutations of n different objects taken all at a time.*

Formula (3) applies when all the objects are different. Clearly, a modification is required if some are alike. Of the n objects, let n_1 be alike, n_2 others alike, . . . , n_k others alike, with

$$n_1 + n_2 + \cdots + n_k = n.$$

Some or all of the n_p may equal one. We shall designate by $P(n; n_1, \ldots, n_k)$ *the number of permutations of the n objects taken all together.* To find the value of this function, let us temporarily replace all the like objects of each group by different ones which are also different from those of the other groups (all n objects are then different). By the fundamental principle, the total number of permutations of the n different objects is then $P(n; n_1, \ldots, n_k) \cdot n_1! \cdots n_k!$. But by formula (3) this number is also $P(n, n) = n!$. Hence

$$P(n; n_1, \ldots, n_k) \cdot n_1! \cdots n_k! = n!$$

and the desired *formula for the number of permutations of n objects taken all at a time of which n_1 are alike, n_2 are alike, and so on,* is

$$\boxed{P(n; n_1, \ldots, n_k) = \frac{n!}{n_1!\, n_2! \cdots n_k!}.} \tag{4}$$

Example 1. How many telephone numbers of four different digits each can be made from the digits 0, 1, 2, 3, 4, 5, 6, 7, 8, 9?

Solution. There are ten digits to choose from and four different ones are to be chosen at a time. Hence $n = 10$, $r = 4$, and the desired number is

$$P(10, 4) = 10 \cdot 9 \cdot 8 \cdot 7 = 5040.$$

Example 2. Five tires on a car (one as spare) are to be rotated so that all will be used equally. How many different ways are there of putting the five tires on the car without removing the tires from the wheels?

Solution. We have a permutation of five things taken all at a time, hence the desired number is

$$P(5, 5) = 5! = 5 \cdot 4 \cdot 3 \cdot 2 \cdot 1 = 120 \text{ ways.}$$

Example 3. How many different arrangements are there of the letters in the word *Mississippi*, taken all together?

Solution. These arrangements are permutations of 11 things, with some alike. There are 4 *s*'s, 4 *i*'s, and 2*p*'s. Hence by formula (4),

$$P(11; 4, 4, 2, 1) = \frac{11!}{4!4!2!} = \frac{11 \cdot 10 \cdot 9 \cdot 8 \cdot 7 \cdot 6 \cdot 5}{4 \cdot 3 \cdot 2 \cdot 1 \cdot 2 \cdot 1} = 34{,}650 \text{ arrangements.}$$

EXERCISE GROUP 17–1

1. Evaluate $P(11, 4)$, $P(19, 5)$, and $P(6, 6)$.
2. Evaluate $P(10, 7)$, $P(28, 3)$, and $P(5, 5)$.
3. Evaluate $P(5; 2, 1, 2)$ and $P(5; 1, 1, 3)$.
4. Evaluate $P(8; 4, 4)$ and $P(8; 2, 2, 2, 2)$.
5. Find the value of n such that $P(n, 6) = 3P(n, 5)$.
6. Find the value of n such that $P(n, 6) = 5P(n, 5)$.
7. Find the value of n for which $P(10, n) = 2P(9, n)$.
8. Find the value of n for which $P(n, 4) = 20P(n, 2)$.
9. (a) How many numbers of four different digits can be formed from the digits 1, 2, 3, 4, 5, 6, 7, 8, 9?
   (b) How many of the numbers formed in part (a) are less than 5000?
   (c) How many of the numbers formed in part (a) are even?
10. (a) How many numbers of not more than three different digits can be formed from the digits 2, 4, 5, 7, 8, 9?
    (b) How many of the numbers formed in part (a) are less than 200?
    (c) How many of the numbers formed in part (a) are odd?
11. In how many ways may 4 boys and 3 girls be seated in a row of 7 chairs, if boys and girls alternate?
12. In how many ways may 4 boys and 4 girls be seated in a row of 8 chairs if boys and girls alternate?
13. How many different signals can be made from 5 different flags if each signal consists of 5 flags placed one above the other on a flagpole?
14. How many different signals can be made from 7 flags, of which 4 are red and 3 are white, if each signal consists of 7 flags placed one above the other?
15. A railway signal has 3 arms and each arm can be put into 2 positions besides its position of rest. How many signals can be formed if every position of the arms, except the one in which they are all at rest, forms a signal?
16. In how many ways may 3 books be chosen from 7, and arranged in a row?
17. In how many ways may 3 books be chosen from 7, and arranged in a row, if a certain 2 of the books may not be simultaneously chosen?
18. In how many ways can the positions of president, vice president, secretary, and treasurer be filled in a club of 12 members if no member may hold more than one position?
19. An automobile manufacturer offers 5 choices of body design, 11 color combinations, and 3 different engines. How many different automobiles are required for a complete display?

20. In how many ways may 4 people be seated in a row of 5 chairs?
21. In how many ways may 4 people be seated in a row of 6 chairs, if the 2 empty chairs are adjacent to each other?
22. How many permutations are there of the letters in the word *syzygy?*
23. How many permutations are there of the letters in the word *Corregidor?*

17-3 COMBINATIONS

Whereas a permutation is an ordered set of objects, *a combination is a set of objects which have no particular order.* For example, in terms of combinations, *abd* and *dab* are the same.

We shall denote by $C(n, r)$ *the number of combinations of n things taken r at a time.* Another symbol which is sometimes used for this number is $\binom{n}{r}$. To derive a formula for $C(n, r)$, let us compute $P(n, r)$ in the following way. First we select a group of r objects and then we obtain all the arrangements of each such group. The selection can be made in $C(n, r)$ ways and each combination of r objects can then be arranged in $r!$ ways. This gives all the possible permutations and, by the fundamental principle, can be done in $r! \cdot C(n, r)$ ways. Hence

$$r! \cdot C(n, r) = P(n, r), \qquad C(n, r) = \frac{P(n, r)}{r!},$$

and by use of (1) we have the desired formula:

$$\boxed{C(n, r) = \frac{n(n-1)(n-2)\cdots(n-r+1)}{r!}.} \tag{5}$$

An alternative form can be obtained by using (2); thus

$$\boxed{C(n, r) = \frac{n!}{r!(n-r)!}.} \tag{6}$$

An important relation involving the combination symbol is the following:

$$\boxed{C(n, n-r) = C(n, r).} \tag{7}$$

One method of proof makes use of (6), and is left to the reader.

The relation (7) may also be seen as follows. We have

$$(a + b)^n = (a + b)(a + b)\cdots(a + b), \qquad n \text{ factors}$$

We obtain a term $a^{n-r}b^r$ in the product by choosing a from $n-r$ factors, and this choice of $n - r$ factors from the n factors may be made in $C(n, n - r)$ ways. We may, instead, choose b from r factors, and this choice may be made in $C(n, r)$ ways. The relation (7) then follows, since the coefficient of $a^{n-r}b^r$ may be either $C(n, n - r)$ or $C(n, r)$.

It is seen that the binomial expansion (Section 11–4) may now also be written as

$$(a + b)^n = \sum_{r=0}^{n} C(n, r)a^{n-r}b^r, \qquad C(n, 0) = 1,$$

with $C(n, r)$ given by (5) or (6). Hence $C(n, r)$ is the binomial coefficient of the $(r + 1)$-term in the expansion of $(a + b)^n$.

In the solution of a problem the important thing is to analyze the problem and break it down into various elements, rather than to try to apply one of the permutation or combination formulas directly. The formulas may then apply to the various elements, or the fundamental principle itself may often be used directly.

Example 1. How many committees of 5 people can be chosen from a group of 10 people?

Solution. There is no question of order in a committee; hence the required number of committees is the number of combinations of 10 things taken 5 at a time and is

$$C(10, 5) = \frac{10 \cdot 9 \cdot 8 \cdot 7 \cdot 6}{5 \cdot 4 \cdot 3 \cdot 2 \cdot 1} = 252.$$

Example 2. How many ways are there of getting exactly 3 heads in a toss of 5 coins?

Solution. If there are 3 heads the other 2 coins must of course be tails. It is enough merely to choose the 3 coins which are to be heads; hence there are

$$C(5, 3) = \frac{5 \cdot 4 \cdot 3}{3 \cdot 2 \cdot 1} = 10 \text{ ways},$$

(out of a total of $2^5 = 32$ ways in which 5 coins may fall).

If in Example 2 at least 3 heads are wanted, we may say that there are either exactly 3 heads, or exactly 4 heads, or exactly 5 heads, and the number of ways is

$$C(5, 3) + C(5, 4) + C(5, 5) = 10 + 5 + 1 = 16$$

EXERCISE GROUP 17–2

1. Evaluate $C(7, 4)$, $C(8, 3)$.
2. Evaluate $C(8, 7)$, $C(9, 4)$.
3. Use (7) to evaluate $C(500, 497)$.
4. Given $P(n, 4) = 3024$. (a) Determine $C(n, 4)$. (b) Find n.
5. Determine the values of n for which $3\, C(n, 4) = 5\, C(n - 1, 5)$.
6. Show that $C(n, r) + C(n, r - 1) = C(n + 1, r)$.
7. Find the smallest value of n for which $C(n, 3) \geqq 35$.

8. Use the binomial theorem to prove

   (a) $\binom{n}{0} + \binom{n}{1} + \cdots + \binom{n}{n} = 2^n$,

   (b) $\binom{n}{0} - \binom{n}{1} + \cdots + (-1)^n\binom{n}{n} = 0$.

   [*Hint:* Choose suitable values of a and b in the expansion of $(a + b)^n$.]

9. A set contains 4 elements. How many subsets are there of (a) 4 elements each? (b) 3 elements each? (c) 2 elements each? (d) 1 element each? (e) no elements (this empty set is considered to be a subset of every set)? (f) How many subsets are there in all?

10. How many subsets are there of a set of 10 elements? [See Exercises 9 and 8(a)].

11. A bag contains 4 green marbles and 3 white marbles. In how many ways can we select (a) 2 green marbles? (b) 2 marbles of the same color? (c) 1 marble of each color?

12. A bag contains 7 black, 6 blue, and 3 green marbles. In how many ways can we select (a) 3 black marbles? (b) 2 marbles of each color? (c) 3 marbles of each color?

13. (a) In how many ways may 3 coins be tossed? (b) How many of these will have exactly 2 heads? (c) How many will have at least 2 heads?

14. (a) In how many ways may 4 coins be tossed? (b) How many of these will have exactly 3 heads? (c) How many will have exactly 3 heads if we know that the first one is heads?

15. A signal consists of 3 white flags and 2 blue flags, arranged vertically. How many such signals can be made if 5 different white flags and 4 different blue flags are available?

16. In how many ways can a committee of 4 Democrats and 3 Republicans be selected from a group of 6 Democrats and 7 Republicans?

17. In the preceding exercise, how many committees of 7 can be chosen if there are at least 3 Republicans?

18. In how many ways can 6 books be distributed to John and Mary, if John gets 4 books and Mary 2?

19. In how many ways can 8 books be distributed if John gets 4, Mary gets 2, and 2 are retained?

20. In how many ways may a student select a program of 4 courses if 9 courses are available?

21. In how many ways may 4 courses be selected from 9 available ones if a certain 2 courses may not be taken together?

17–4 PERMUTATIONS AS FUNCTIONS

It is instructive to examine the various kinds of permutation discussed in Section 17–2 in terms of functions with domains consisting of a finite number of elements.

To begin with an illustration, let us consider the permutations of 4 objects, 2 of which are alike, such as a, b, c, c. Any permutation of these 4 objects may be obtained by labeling the integers 1, 2, 3, and 4 as a or b or c, or by associating with 1, 2, 3, and 4 the letters a, b, and c, *with c being used twice.* Thus, the pairs $(1, a)$, $(2, c)$, $(3, b)$, $(4, c)$ describe the permutation $acbc$. The set of these pairs also defines a function with domain $(1, 2, 3, 4)$ and range (a, b, c), in which c must appear twice as a functional value. Any other permutation of a, b, c, c may be thought of as a function of this type, so that the *number of permutations* of 4 objects of which 2 are alike is the *number of functions* with domain $(1, 2, 3, 4)$ and range (a, b, c) in which c is used twice.

More generally, if we have n objects of which n_1 are alike, say c_1, n_2 are $c_2, \ldots,$ n_k are c_k, with

$$n_1 + n_2 + \cdots + n_k = n, \tag{8}$$

any permutation of these n objects may be considered as defining a function with domain $(1, 2, 3, \ldots, n)$, and range $(c_1, c_2, \ldots, c_k)$, where c_i is used n_i times. The number of such functions is $P(n; n_1, \ldots, n_k)$, and is given by (4). Again, we may think of any of these permutations as a labeling of $1, 2, \ldots, n$ with the labels $c_1, c_2, \ldots, c_k$, each label being used n_i times. Of course, some of the n_i may be 1, provided (8) holds.

The case $k = n$, in which all n objects are different, is included in the above, since in this case $n_i = 1$ for each i. We then have

$$P(n; 1, 1, \ldots, 1) = P(n, n) = n!.$$

Moreover, the formula for the number of permutations of n different things taken r at a time is also included. We need merely use the labels $1, 2, \ldots, r$, "excluded" (the word "excluded" being one of the labels). We have

$$P(n, r) = P(n; \underbrace{1, 1, \ldots, 1}_{r \text{ of these}}, n - r) = \frac{n!}{1! \cdots 1!(n - r)!} = \frac{n!}{(n - r)!},$$

which is in agreement with (2).

Example 1. How many functions are there with domain $(1, 2, 3, 4)$ and range (a, b) if a is used 3 times as a functional value, and b is used once?

Solution. By the above, the number of such functions is

$$P(4; 3, 1) = \frac{4!}{3!1!} = 4.$$

Another illustration of these ideas is provided by the following example.

Example 2. In how many ways may 9 toys be distributed to 3 children if John gets 3 toys, Mary gets 2 toys, and Jim gets 4 toys?

Solution. Each toy may be considered to be labeled as either John or Mary or Jim. The number of ways in which they may be distributed is then

$$P(9; 3, 2, 4) = \frac{9!}{3!2!4!} = 1860.$$

The number of combinations of n objects taken r at a time may also be considered as the number of ways of labeling n objects, with r of them labeled as "included" and $n - r$ of them labeled as "excluded." With this interpretation we have

$$C(n, r) = P(n; r, n - r),$$

which, with use of (4), again yields (6). In this vein we may consider $C(n, r)$ as the number of functions with domain $(1, 2, \ldots, n)$, and range (a, b), with a used r times, and b used $n - r$ times as functional values. It follows at once [see (7)] that

$$C(n, n - r) = C(n, r).$$

EXERCISE GROUP 17–3

1. How many functions are there with domain (1, 2, 3, 4, 5) and range (a, b)
   (a) if a is used 3 times and b twice?
   (b) if a is used once and b 4 times?
   (c) if a is used 5 times and b not at all?
2. How many functions are there with domain (1, 2, 3, 4, 5, 6) and range (a, b, c)
   (a) if each letter is used twice?
   (b) if a is used 3 times, b twice, and c once?
   (c) if a and b are used once and c is used 4 times?
3. How many functions are there with domain (1, 2, 3) and range (a, b) if one considers all possible numbers of ways of using a and b?
4. In how many ways may a student select 3 elective courses from 7 that are available?
5. In how many ways may 9 books be distributed evenly among 3 people?
6. In how many ways may 5 books be distributed among 3 people, if each person receives at least 1 book?
7. In how many ways may 5 books be distributed among 4 people, if each person receives at least 1 book?
8. In how many ways may 15 marbles be placed in 3 bags, if 5 go into the first bag, 4 into the second, and 6 into the third?
9. In how many ways may 16 persons be distributed among 4 bridge tables of 4 persons each?
10. Write down the four functions as specified in Example 1.
11. In how many ways may 15 students be assigned to advisers A, B, and C
    (a) if 6 are assigned to A, 4 to B, and 5 to C?
    (b) if 5 are assigned to each?
    (c) if 10 are assigned to A, 2 to B, and 3 to C?
12. Work Exercise 11 by first choosing the students assigned to A, then those assigned to B, and finally those assigned to C.
13. Prove that $P(n; n_1, n_2, n_3) = C(n, n_1) \cdot C(n - n_1, n_2) \cdot C(n - n_1 - n_2, n_3)$, where $n_1 + n_2 + n_3 = n$.

17–5 THE MULTINOMIAL EXPANSION

Consider the expansion of $(a_1 + a_2 + a_3)^n$. Any term will be of the form

$$a_1^{n_1}a_2^{n_2}a_3^{n_3}, \qquad \text{where} \qquad n_1 + n_2 + n_3 = n. \tag{9}$$

Since we are expanding a product of n factors $a_1 + a_2 + a_3$, the coefficient of (9) in the expansion will be the number of ways in which a_1 may be chosen from n_1 factors, a_2 from n_2 factors, and a_3 from the remaining n_3 factors. By Section 17–4 this coefficient must be $P(n; n_1, n_2, n_3)$, and we have

$$(a_1 + a_2 + a_3)^n = \sum_{n_1+n_2+n_3=n} P(n; n_1, n_2, n_3)a_1^{n_1}a_2^{n_2}a_3^{n_3}, \tag{10}$$

where the expression on the right means the sum of all terms of the indicated form for which $n_1 + n_2 + n_3 = n$.

Using precisely the same kind of proof, we may derive the *multinomial expansion*, which may be written as

$$(a_1 + a_2 + \cdots + a_k)^n = \sum_{n_1+\cdots+n_k=n} P(n; n_1, n_2, \ldots, n_k)a_1^{n_1}a_2^{n_2} \ldots a_k^{n_k}, \tag{11}$$

where $P(n; n_1, n_2, \ldots, n_k)$ is given by (4). The multinomial expansion is a generalization of the binomial expansion (Section 11–4), and reduces to it if $k = 2$.

Example 1. Find the coefficient of $a_1^2a_2a_3$ in the expansion of $(a_1 + a_2 + a_3)^4$.

Solution. By (10) the coefficient is

$$P(4; 2, 1, 1) = \frac{4!}{2!1!1!} = 12.$$

Example 2. Find the term involving x^3yz^2 in the expansion of $(x + 2y - 3z)^6$.

Solution. The desired term is

$$P(6; 3, 1, 2)\, x^3(2y)(-3z)^2 = 1080\, x^3yz^2.$$

A further result relating to the multinomial expansion will now be stated without proof. *The number of terms in the expansion* (11) *is given by the binomial coefficient*

$$\binom{n + k - 1}{n}. \tag{12}$$

Example 3. Find the number of terms in the expansion of $(a_1 + a_2 + a_3)^4$.

Solution. We use (12) with $n = 4$, $k = 3$, and the desired number is

$$\binom{6}{4} = 15.$$

An interesting application of (12) may be given. A term in (11) is determined by any ordered set of integers $n_1, n_2, \ldots, n_k$, with

$$n_1 + n_2 + \cdots + n_k = n,$$

where some of the n_i may be zero. Thus, if $n = 5$, we may have (1, 1, 1, 1, 1) or (2, 0, 2, 1, 0) or (0, 2, 2, 1, 0), and so on. Since any such set of integers corresponds to a term of (11), the number of such sets is given by (12). We may then say that $\binom{n+k-1}{n}$ *also represents the number of ways in which an ordered set of k nonnegative integers may add up to n.*

Example 4. In how many ways may 7 indistinguishable marbles be placed in 4 numbered bags?

Solution. This is precisely the number of ways in which 4 nonnegative integers may add up to 7, and, by (12), is given by

$$\binom{7+4-1}{7} = \binom{10}{7} = \binom{10}{3} = \frac{10 \cdot 9 \cdot 8}{6} = 120.$$

The reader should note the inherent distinction between this example and Example 2 of Section 17–4. In the latter the number of objects was specified for each recipient. In the present example the number of recipients is specified, but not the number of objects given to each.

EXERCISE GROUP 17–4

In each of Exercises 1–10, find the number of terms in the indicated expansion, and also the coefficient of the specified term.

1. $(x + y - z)^3$; term in xy^2
2. $(2x + y - z - 2w)^4$; term in x^2yz
3. $(x^2 + y + z)^3$; term in x^4z
4. $(2a - b^2 - c^2)^5$; term in ab^6c^2
5. $(u^2 + v^2 + w^2)^4$; term in $u^4v^2w^2$
6. $(x^2 - 2y + z)^6$; term in x^6yz^2
7. $\left(x + 1 + \frac{1}{x}\right)^4$; term in x^3
8. $\left(x^2 - 2 + \frac{1}{x}\right)^5$; term in x^{-1}
9. $(a + b + c + d + e)^5$; term in $abcde$
10. $(a + b + c + d)^8$; term in $a^3b^3d^2$

In each of Exercises 11–16, find the number of ordered sets as described.

11. 2 nonnegative integers whose sum is 15
12. 5 nonnegative integers whose sum is 3
13. 3 nonnegative integers whose sum is 5
14. 4 nonnegative integers whose sum is 4
15. 3 nonnegative integers whose sum is 8
16. 10 nonnegative integers whose sum is 4
17. In how many ways may 8 indistinguishable apples be distributed to 3 children?
18. In how many ways may 4 indistinguishable apples be distributed to 7 children?
19. In how many ways may 4 indistinguishable books be distributed to 3 persons, if each person receives at least 1 book?
20. Sixteen indistinguishable marbles are placed in 3 bags. In how many ways may this be done?

17–6 PROBABILITY

The study of probability was begun in the early sixteenth century when attempts were made to analyze games of chance. It has continued ever since to interest mathematicians, with the result that the theory of probability is now an important branch of mathematics. It is the foundation of a body of material, often called mathematical statistics, which has many applications in such diverse fields as agriculture, biology, industry, and insurance. However, most of these interesting applications involve mathematics beyond the scope of this book. Here we can discuss only the rudiments of the subject.

In the study of probability we wish to determine the chances that an event will occur in a certain specified way, relative to a more general type of occurrence. Let p denote the specified type of occurrence. We shall use the notation $Pr(p)$ for the probability of p, that is, for the probability that the specified event occurs.

To help make the ideas more precise, we designate as a *trial* any occurrence of the general type permitted. Then an occurrence of the specified type may be called a *success*, and a permitted occurrence of any other type, a *failure*.

In the discussion of mathematical probability, we do not carry out trials experimentally. Rather, for the trials we consider the set of *logical possibilities* under which an act can occur, and for the successes we consider the subset of these logical possibilities for which the specified requirement holds, or for which the given statement is true. In general, we assume that there is no bias in our choice, or that each logical possibility is equally likely.

Example 1. Suppose that we draw 3 cards from a deck of playing cards, and we are interested in the chances of getting 3 red ones. All ways of drawing 3 cards from 52 cards are logical possibilities, and we have $C(52, 3)$ logical possibilities, or trials. The type of occurrence p, whose chances we are considering, is the drawing of 3 red cards. Since there are 26 red cards, this requirement can be achieved in $C(26, 3)$ ways, which is then the number of successes.

***Definition* 17–1.** *Let N denote the number of ways in which an event can occur. If s denotes the number of successes for an occurrence p, and f the number of failures, so that $N = s + f$, the probability of the occurrence p is given by*

$$\boxed{Pr(p) = \frac{s}{N} = \frac{s}{s+f}.}$$

If p' designates the nonoccurrence of p, it follows that the probability of p' is given by

$$Pr(p') = \frac{f}{N} = \frac{f}{s+f}.$$

From the above it is clear that

$$0 \leqq Pr(p) \leqq 1, \qquad 0 \leqq Pr(p') \leqq 1, \qquad Pr(p) + Pr(p') = 1.$$

When a specified event p is certain, $s = N$ and $Pr(p) = 1$. If p cannot occur, that is, if p' is certain, then $Pr(p) = 0$.

In the definition, $s + f$ is the number of ways the event can take place, and is usually computed as a sum. The formulas in Sections 17–2 and 17–3 for the number of permutations and combinations are often precisely what is required to obtain s, f, and $s + f$ to be applied in the definition.

Example 2. Let p again be the drawing of 3 red cards when 3 cards are drawn from a deck of playing cards. By Example 1, we have

$$N = s + f = C(52, 3) = 22{,}100,$$
$$s = C(26, 3) = 2600.$$

Hence by Definition 17–1,

$$Pr(p) = \frac{2600}{22{,}100} = \frac{2}{17}.$$

In a more abstract development of mathematical probability, each logical possibility is assigned a certain measure, which then defines a measure for each subset of logical possibilities. The probability of a given occurrence p is then the ratio of the measure of the subset for which p holds to the measure of the total set of logical possibilities.

The meaning of probability. Suppose that a certain probability is $\frac{1}{4}$ and that 3 trials have produced 3 failures. Must the fourth trial result in a success? Definitely not! There is no way of predicting the result of an individual trial. A probability of $\frac{1}{4}$ means simply that in a large number of trials the number of successes will be approximately $\frac{1}{4}$ the total number of trials, and that the larger the number of trials the closer the approximation.

EXERCISE GROUP 17–5

1. If 2 marbles are drawn from a bag containing 8 black, 3 blue, and 4 green marbles, what is the probability that (a) both will be green? (b) both will be black?
2. If 3 cards are drawn from a deck of playing cards, what is the probability that (a) 2 will be queens and the other a king? (b) all will be hearts?
3. If 10 people are seated at random in a row of 10 seats, what is the probability that a certain 2 will occupy adjacent seats?
4. If a 4-digit number is formed with different digits from the digits 2, 3, 4, 5, 6, 7, 8, what is the probability that it is an odd number?
5. What is the probability that the number formed in Exercise 4 is less than 6000?
6. What is the probability of throwing a 4 with a single die?
7. What is the probability of throwing a total of 5 with one throw of 2 dice?
8. What is the probability of throwing a total of 15 with a single throw of 3 dice?
9. A radio set has 9 tubes, of which a group of 4 are interchangeable; a second group of 3 are also interchangeable. If the tubes are removed and placed in a box with no

attempt to keep them in order, what is the probability that when they are replaced each will be in the same socket from which it was taken?

10. If 10 people are seated at random at a round table with 10 places, what is the probability that 2 particular people will be in adjacent chairs?
11. A box contains 60 tickets which are numbered from 1 to 60. If 2 tickets are drawn at random, what is the probability that the sum of the numbers on them is odd?
12. A box contains 100 blank tickets and 50 that are numbered from 1 to 50. If 3 tickets are drawn at random, what is the probability that 2 are blank?
13. A subcommittee of 7 people is to be chosen from the 25 members of a committee. What is the probability of a particular member of the committee being chosen to serve on the subcommittee?
14. If a group of 5 couples (husbands and wives) are seated at random in a row of chairs, what is the probability that each couple (husband and wife) will be seated in adjacent chairs?
15. What is the probability that a bridge hand will contain all the aces, kings, and queens?
16. If 6 books are distributed to John and Mary, what is the probability that John gets 4 and Mary 2?
17. If 3 books are distributed to 3 people, what is the probability that each person gets 1 book?

17–7 THE PROBABILITY OF THE OCCURRENCE OF TWO OR MORE EVENTS

There are problems in probability which involve a consideration of more than one event. On the one hand, the problem may involve these events together in some way, either *simultaneously* or *consecutively;* on the other hand, the events may be involved in such a way that they are considered separately.

Let p_1 and p_2 be two events. Whether p_1 and p_2 are simultaneous or consecutive, they are said to be *independent* if neither affects the other, and *dependent* if one does affect the other. In either case we use the symbol $p_1 \wedge p_2$ to denote the occurrence of *both* p_1 *and* p_2.

Example 1. A coin is tossed twice. Define p_1 and p_2 as follows:

$$p_1\text{: the first toss is heads,}$$

$$p_2\text{: the second toss is tails.}$$

Then p_1 and p_2 are independent, and $p_1 \wedge p_2$ is the statement that the first toss is heads *and* the second toss is tails.

An illustration of dependent occurrences will appear in Example 3.

The laws governing the probability of occurrence of the event $p_1 \wedge p_2$ are similar, and are given in the following theorem, which is stated for the case of two events. The extension to more than two events will be clear.

Theorem 17–1. *If p_1 and p_2 are independent events, the probability of $p_1 \wedge p_2$ is given by*

$$\boxed{Pr(p_1 \wedge p_2) = Pr(p_1) \cdot Pr(p_2).}$$

If p_2 depends on p_1, let $Pr(p_2|p_1)$ denote the probability of the occurrence of p_2 after the occurrence of p_1. Then

$$\boxed{Pr(p_1 \wedge p_2) = Pr(p_1) \cdot Pr(p_2|p_1).}$$

Proof. The first part of the theorem is a special case of the second part, since in the case of independent events,

$$Pr(p_2|p_1) = Pr(p_2).$$

It is necessary, therefore, to prove only the second part.

Let s_i and f_i be the respective numbers of successes and failures for p_i, where s_2 and f_2 are the numbers after p_1 occurs. According to the fundamental principle, the number of possibilities for $p_1 \wedge p_2$ is $s_1 \cdot s_2$, and the total number of possibilities is $(s_1 + f_1) \cdot (s_2 + f_2)$. Hence

$$Pr(p_1 \wedge p_2) = \frac{s_1 s_2}{(s_1 + f_1)(s_2 + f_2)} = \frac{s_1}{s_1 + f_1} \cdot \frac{s_2}{s_2 + f_2} = Pr(p_1) \cdot Pr(p_2|p_1),$$

where the third equality results from the definitions of $Pr(p_1)$ and $Pr(p_2|p_1)$, and the proof is complete.

Example 2. A bag contains 4 black and 5 blue marbles. A marble is drawn and then replaced, after which a second marble is drawn. What is the probability that the first is black and second blue?

Solution. Let p_1 be the occurrence that the first marble is black, and p_2 that the second marble is blue. Then p_1 and p_2 are independent, and

$$Pr(p_1 \wedge p_2) = Pr(p_1) \cdot Pr(p_2) = \tfrac{4}{9} \cdot \tfrac{5}{9} = \tfrac{20}{81}.$$

Example 3. If, in Example 2, the first marble drawn is not replaced before the second is drawn, what is the probability that the first is black and the second blue?

Solution. If p_1 and p_2 are defined as in Example 2, they are now dependent. We still have $Pr(p_1) = \frac{4}{9}$. To find $Pr(p_2|p_1)$ we must assume a success in the first draw, which leaves 3 black and 5 blue marbles. Hence $Pr(p_2|p_1) = \frac{5}{8}$, and the probability that the first marble is black and the second is blue is

$$Pr(p_1 \wedge p_2) = Pr(p_1) \cdot Pr(p_2|p_1) = \tfrac{4}{9} \cdot \tfrac{5}{8} = \tfrac{5}{18}.$$

If p_1 and p_2 are two events, we may consider the event which consists of the occurrence of p_1 *or* of p_2, denoted by $p_1 \vee p_2$. If the events are such that the occurrence of one of them prevents the occurrence of the other, the events are said to be *mutually exclusive*, and the set of possibilities for $p_1 \wedge p_2$ is empty. If $s(p_i)$ denotes the number of successes for p_i, then $s(p_1 \wedge p_2) = 0$ in this case, and we have

$$s(p_1 \vee p_2) = s(p_1) + s(p_2).$$

On the other hand, if $s(p_1 \wedge p_2) \neq 0$ then p_1 and p_2 may occur simultaneously. In this case we understand $p_1 \vee p_2$ to mean that either p_1 occurs alone or p_2 occurs alone or both p_1 and p_2 occur, and we have

$$s(p_1 \vee p_2) = s(p_1) + s(p_2) - s(p_1 \wedge p_2), \tag{13}$$

where $s(p_1 \wedge p_2)$ is subtracted, since this number is included twice in $s(p_1) + s(p_2)$. If we now divide both members of (13) by N, the total number of logical possibilities, we obtain the following result.

Theorem 17–2. *For any two events p_1 and p_2,*

$$\boxed{Pr(p_1 \vee p_2) = Pr(p_1) + Pr(p_2) - Pr(p_1 \wedge p_2).}$$

If p_1 and p_2 are mutually exclusive, then

$$\boxed{Pr(p_1 \vee p_2) = Pr(p_1) + Pr(p_2).}$$

Example 4. Determine the probability of getting 6 or 7 in a toss of two dice.

Solution. Define p_1 and p_2 as:

p_1: 6 is obtained in the toss,
p_2: 7 is obtained in the toss.

Since p_1 and p_2 are mutually exclusive, we have $Pr(p_1 \wedge p_2) = 0$. Also $Pr(p_1) = \frac{5}{36}$ and $Pr(p_2) = \frac{1}{6}$. Hence

$$Pr(p_1 \vee p_2) = \tfrac{5}{36} + \tfrac{1}{6} = \tfrac{11}{36}.$$

More complex events may often be analyzed in terms of combined events and alternative events. A verbal clue to combined events is frequently the word "and," and to alternative events the word "or."

Example 5. What is the probability that the two marbles drawn in Example 2 above are (a) of the same color, (b) of different colors?

Solution. (a) To be of the same color the marbles must either both be black *or* both be blue, which are mutually exclusive. We define the following occurrences:

p: both marbles are of the same color,
p_1: the first marble is black,
p_2: the second marble is black,
p_3: the first marble is blue,
p_4: the second marble is blue.

Then $Pr(p_1) = Pr(p_2) = \frac{4}{9}$, $Pr(p_3) = Pr(p_4) = \frac{5}{9}$, and

$$\begin{aligned} Pr(p) &= Pr(p_1) \cdot Pr(p_2) + Pr(p_3) \cdot Pr(p_4) \\ &= \tfrac{4}{9} \cdot \tfrac{4}{9} + \tfrac{5}{9} \cdot \tfrac{5}{9} = \tfrac{41}{81}. \end{aligned}$$

(b) The only alternatives are that the two marbles are either of the same color or of different colors, so that if P is the probability of obtaining different colors, we must have

$$P + \tfrac{41}{81} = 1 \qquad \text{or} \qquad P = 1 - \tfrac{41}{81} = \tfrac{40}{81}.$$

A second analysis shows that we may also have the first marble blue and the second black, or the reverse; this gives

$$P = \tfrac{5}{9} \cdot \tfrac{4}{9} + \tfrac{4}{9} \cdot \tfrac{5}{9} = \tfrac{40}{81}.$$

Another illustration of the methods of this section is given in the following example.

Example 6. The probability that A wins a certain game is $\frac{2}{3}$. If A plays 5 games, what is the probability that A will win (a) exactly 3 games? (b) at least 3 games?

Solution. (a) The probability that A loses a game is $\frac{1}{3}$. For A to win a certain 3 games only, he must also lose the other 2; hence the probability is

$$\tfrac{2}{3} \cdot \tfrac{2}{3} \cdot \tfrac{2}{3} \cdot \tfrac{1}{3} \cdot \tfrac{1}{3} = \tfrac{8}{243}.$$

But A may win any 3 games, and these may be chosen in $C(5, 3) = 10$ ways. Hence the probability of winning exactly 3 games is

$$10 \cdot \tfrac{8}{243} = \tfrac{80}{243}.$$

(b) To win at least 3 games A must win either exactly 3 or exactly 4 or all 5 games. Applying Theorem 17-2 and the method of part (a), we have

$$\begin{aligned} P &= C(5, 3) \cdot (\tfrac{2}{3})^3 \cdot (\tfrac{1}{3})^2 + C(5, 4) \cdot (\tfrac{2}{3})^4 \cdot (\tfrac{1}{3}) + C(5, 5) \cdot (\tfrac{2}{3})^5 \\ &= 10 \cdot \tfrac{8}{243} + 5 \cdot \tfrac{16}{243} + 1 \cdot \tfrac{32}{243} = \tfrac{192}{243} = \tfrac{64}{81}. \end{aligned}$$

EXERCISE GROUP 17-6

1. (a) If 2 marbles are drawn from a bag containing 6 white, 4 blue, and 2 green marbles, what is the probability that both are of the same color? (b) If 3 marbles are drawn from the above bag, what is the probability that they will all be of the same color?
2. If 4 marbles are drawn from the bag in Exercise 1, what is the probability that (a) exactly 2 are white? (b) 2 are white and the other 2 are of the same color?
3. If 2 coins are tossed together, what is the probability that one will be heads and the other one tails?
4. If 3 coins are tossed together what is the probability (a) that 2 will be heads and the other one tails? (b) that all 3 will land with the same side up?
5. The probability of A winning a certain event in a track meet is $\frac{1}{3}$, and the probability of B winning a different event in the meet is $\frac{1}{4}$. What is the probability (a) that each will win his event? (b) at least one will win his event?
6. If 5 coins are tossed, what is the probability of obtaining at most 3 heads?

7. A library has 3 copies of a certain book. If 5 people use copies of this book at different times, what is the probability that they all use the same copy?
8. Find the probability that in a bridge hand of 13 cards all will be of the same suit.
9. A committee of 4 is to be chosen at random from a group of 6 freshmen and 8 sophomores, and a chairman of the committee is then chosen by lot. What is the probability that the chairman will be a sophomore?
10. In a football game the probability that team A will kick goal after touchdown is $\frac{1}{3}$, and the probability that team B will kick goal after touchdown is $\frac{1}{2}$. If in a particular game each scores 2 touchdowns, what is the probability that the game does not end in a tie?
11. One letter is chosen at random from each of the words *fighter* and *freighter*. What is the probability that the same letter is chosen from each?
12. The probability that a certain door is locked is $\frac{1}{3}$. The key to the door is one of a group of 10 keys kept in a cabinet. If a person selects 2 keys at random from the cabinet, and takes them to the door, what is the probability that he can open the door without returning for another key?
13. In a batch of 75 light bulbs, 4% are defective. (a) If 1 bulb is chosen at random, what is the probability that it is defective? (b) If 5 bulbs are chosen at random, what is the probability that exactly 1 of the 5 is defective?
14. In a toss of 6 coins, what is the probability of getting (a) at least 3 heads? (b) at most 3 heads?
15. If a single coin is tossed repeatedly, determine the probability (a) that the second head will occur on the seventh toss, (b) that the kth head will occur on the nth toss.
16. If a pair of dice is thrown twice, find the probability (a) that the throws will yield a 6 followed by a 7, (b) that one throw will yield 6 and the other 7, (c) that the sum of the two throws will be 13.

17–8 CONDITIONAL PROBABILITY

In Section 17–7 the symbol $Pr(p_2|p_1)$ was introduced to denote the probability of p_2 after the knowledge of p_1. This value is called the *conditional probability* of p_2, given p_1, or after the knowledge of p_1, and warrants a further look. In the proof of Theorem 17–1 it was stated, in effect, that s_2 and f_2 were the numbers of successes and failures for p_2 after p_1 occurred. If the occurrence of p_1 has any effect on p_2, the total number of logical possibilities for p_2 after p_1 is smaller than for p_2 without the knowledge of p_1.

The second part of Theorem 17–1 may then be solved for $Pr(p_2|p_1)$ to give the formula for the *conditional probability* of p_2 after the knowledge of p_1 as

$$\boxed{Pr(p_2|p_1) = \frac{Pr(p_1 \wedge p_2)}{Pr(p_1)}.} \tag{14}$$

In (14) the total number of logical possibilities is the same for $p_1 \wedge p_2$ as for p_1.

Example 1. A coin is tossed 3 times. Find the probability that all 3 are heads,

(a) if it is known that the first is heads,
(b) if it is known that the first 2 are heads,
(c) if it is known that 2 of them are heads.

Solution. (a) Define

p_1: the first is heads,

p_2: the other 2 are heads.

The event $p_1 \wedge p_2$ may occur in only one way, so that $Pr(p_1 \wedge p_2) = \frac{1}{8}$; the first toss must be either heads or tails, so that $Pr(p_1) = \frac{1}{2}$. Hence by (14) we obtain the result

$$Pr(p_2|p_1) = \frac{1/8}{1/2} = \frac{1}{4}.$$

To see what happens, in detail, we note that if the first toss is heads, the logical possibilities are *HHH*, *HHT*, *HTH*, *HTT*. There is only one of these for which the second and third are heads. Hence $Pr(p_1|p_2) = \frac{1}{4}$.

(b) Define

p_1: the first 2 tosses are heads,

p_2: the third toss is heads.

Again, 3 heads may occur in only one way, so that $Pr(p_1 \wedge p_2) = \frac{1}{8}$, but now $Pr(p_1) = \frac{1}{4}$. Hence, by formula (14),

$$Pr(p_2|p_1) = \frac{1/8}{1/4} = \frac{1}{2}.$$

(c) Define

p_1: 2 of the tosses are heads,

p_2: the remaining toss is heads.

We have $Pr(p_1 \wedge p_2) = \frac{1}{8}$, $Pr(p_1) = \frac{1}{2}$. Then

$$Pr(p_2|p_1) = \frac{1/8}{1/2} = \frac{1}{4}.$$

The logical possibilities for p_1 are *HHH*, *HHT*, *HTH*, and *THH*.

Another application of (14) is the following.

Example 2. A coin is tossed 3 times, and 2 heads and 1 tail fall. What is the probability that the first toss was heads?

Solution. Define

p_1: 2 heads and 1 tail fall,

p_2: the first toss is heads.

Then $Pr(p_1) = \frac{3}{8}$, and $Pr(p_1 \wedge p_2) = \frac{1}{4}$. Hence

$$Pr(p_2|p_1) = \frac{1/4}{3/8} = \frac{2}{3}.$$

In this case there are 3 logical possibilities with 2 heads and 1 tail, *HHT*, *HTH*, *THH*; two of these (*HHT*, *HTH*) begin with *H*.

EXERCISE GROUP 17-7

1. Two coins are tossed. Find the probability that (a) both are heads if the first one is heads, (b) both are heads if at least one is heads.
2. A coin is tossed 4 times. Find the probability that (a) 3 are heads if the first one is heads, (b) 3 are heads if the first one is tails, (c) at least 2 are heads if the first one is heads, (d) at least 2 are heads if the first one is tails.
3. A total of 7 turns up in two tosses of a die. Find the probability (a) that the first toss came up 3, (b) that one of the tosses is 3.
4. Two marbles are drawn from a bag containing 7 green and 4 blue marbles. Find the probability that (a) both are green if it is known that one is green, (b) both are blue if it is known that one is blue.
5. A bag contains 3 green and 2 blue marbles. One marble is removed without replacement, then a second, and then a third. Find the probability that (a) the last one removed is green, (b) the last one removed is blue, (c) the last one removed is green if it is known that the first one was green, (d) the last one removed is green if it is known that the first one was blue.
6. A bag contains 6 blue marbles, 5 green ones, and 4 red ones. Three marbles are drawn from the bag. Find the probability (a) that all are of the same color, (b) all are of the same color if none is green.
7. A student must choose 2 elective courses from the following list: mathematics, French, German, chemistry, and economics. Find the probability that (a) mathematics is one of them, (b) mathematics is one of them if no language is included.
8. Find $Pr(p_1|q)$ if $Pr(p_1) = \frac{1}{3}$, $Pr(p_2) = \frac{2}{3}$, $Pr(q|p_1) = 0.1$, and $Pr(q|p_2) = 0.2$.
9. A bag contains 2 green marbles and 3 white ones. A marble is removed without replacement, and then a second. If both are of the same color, what is the probability (a) that the first one is white? (b) that the second one is white?

17-9 ODDS. MATHEMATICAL EXPECTATION

An additional matter of interest in connection with probability concerns the value of a given outcome. The *relative value* of an outcome may be expressed in terms of odds.

Suppose that a bag contains 4 red marbles and 2 yellow marbles. The probability of drawing a red marble is $\frac{2}{3}$ and the probability of drawing a yellow marble is $\frac{1}{3}$. There is twice as good a chance of drawing a red marble as there is of not drawing a red marble, and we say that the odds of drawing a red marble are $2:1$. If a yellow marble is added to the bag, the odds of drawing a red marble become $4:3$.

***Definition* 17-2.** *If an outcome has probability a, the odds assigned to that outcome are $a : (1 - a)$.*

An interpretation of odds concerns wagers. If a person wins 10 dollars by drawing a red marble from the bag containing 4 red marbles and 2 yellow marbles, what amount s should he pay if he loses? In a large number of draws N, he will win

$\frac{2}{3}N$ times, or $20N/3$ dollars. For a fair wager he should, in the same large number of draws N, lose the same amount. The amount he loses is $Ns/3$. Therefore

$$\tfrac{1}{3}Ns = \tfrac{20}{3}N, \qquad \text{and} \qquad s = 20.$$

He should therefore pay 20 dollars for each loss.

In general, if a person wins s_1 dollars for each success and loses s_2 dollars for each failure, in a large number of trials N, we have

$$aNs_1 = (1 - a)Ns_2,$$

where a is the probability of success, and the odds are

$$\frac{a}{1 - a} = \frac{s_1}{s_2}.$$

When monetary values are assigned to one or more possible outcomes in a trial, the value of a trial is called the *mathematical expectation*, defined as follows:

***Definition* 17–3.** *If s dollars is the value of an occurrence whose probability is a, the mathematical expectation of the occurrence is sa dollars.*

Example 1. If a person receives 3 dollars for getting a 7 in a toss of 2 dice, the mathematical expectation of the toss is $3 \times \frac{1}{6}$ dollars, or $\frac{1}{2}$ dollar.

Example 2. In a toss of 4 coins, 10 dollars will be awarded if all 4 are heads, and 5 dollars will be awarded if exactly 3 are heads. Find the mathematical expectation of a toss.

Solution. The probability of getting 4 heads is $\frac{1}{16}$, while the probability of getting exactly 3 heads is

$$C(4, 3) \cdot (\tfrac{1}{2})^3 \cdot \tfrac{1}{2} = 4 \cdot \tfrac{1}{16} = \tfrac{1}{4}.$$

The mathematical expectation per toss of the 4 coins is

$$10 \times \tfrac{1}{16} + 5 \times \tfrac{1}{4} = 1.875 \text{ (dollars).}$$

An interpretation of mathematical expectation may be based on Example 2. If a large number of tosses N are made and a person pays 1.875 dollars for each toss, he may expect to break even. For, N tosses will cost 1.875 N dollars. He may expect to receive 10 dollars for each of $N/16$ tosses, 5 dollars for each of $N/4$ tosses, and nothing for the remaining tosses, or a total of 1.875 N dollars, and his receipts will exactly equal his cost.

EXERCISE GROUP 17–8

1. Find the odds of an outcome p for each value of $Pr(p)$:

   (a) $\frac{1}{2}$ (b) $\frac{2}{5}$ (c) 0.72 (d) a

2. Find the odds of an outcome p for each value of $Pr(p')$:

   (a) 0.2 (b) $\frac{1}{3}$ (c) 0.43 (d) a

In each of Exercises 3–8, determine the odds for the indicated outcome.

3. Getting 7 in a throw of 2 dice
4. Getting 11 in a throw of 2 dice
5. Getting 6 in a throw of 3 dice
6. Getting 12 in a throw of 3 dice
7. Getting exactly 3 heads in a toss of 5 coins
8. Getting at least 3 heads in a toss of 5 coins

9. A bag contains 4 oranges, 3 apples, and 5 pears. Three pieces of fruit are drawn. Find the odds of getting (a) 3 oranges, (b) 3 of the same fruit, (c) 3 different fruits.
10. Four French books and four German books are placed on a shelf at random. Find the odds for each of the following: (a) the French and German books alternate, (b) the French books are consecutive, (c) the two end books are in the same language.
11. John draws 2 marbles from a bag containing 2 blue marbles and 3 green ones. He will receive 2 dollars if both are of the same color. What should he pay per draw?
12. A person draws 2 marbles in succession from the bag in Exercise 11, without replacement. Find the odds (a) that the second one is blue, (b) that the second one is green.
13. If weather records show that rain occurred in 70% of the years on a certain date, what are the odds that it will rain on that date?
14. The odds are 4 : 3 in favor of a certain event. How many times will that event be expected to occur in 84 trials?

17–10 EMPIRICAL PROBABILITY

The problems discussed in Sections 17–6, 17–7, and 17–8 are examples of *a priori* probabilities, that is, probabilities derived from theoretical considerations, in which it was possible to determine the number of successes and failures exactly. It is frequently impossible to determine from theoretical considerations the number of equally likely ways in which an event can happen or fail to happen. However, in such cases it may be possible to observe a large number of trials of the event and thus determine the ratio of the number of happenings of the event to the number of trials. This ratio is called the *relative frequency* of occurrence of the event, and in cases where the number of trials is large, this relative frequency is considered to be the probability of occurrence of the event. Probability determined in this manner is called *empirical* probability.

For example, let us assume that from a survey of 100,000 people it is found that 69,712 watch television on Sunday evening at seven o'clock Central Standard Time. If this sample of 100,000 is properly chosen, it is reasonable to assume that approximately the same proportion of the total population watches television at that time. In other words, the probability that a given person will be watching is 0.697.

Another example of empirical probability is furnished by the *Commissioners' Standard Ordinary (CSO) Mortality Table*, which gives the number of persons surviving at various ages, out of an initial group of 1,000,000 at age 1 year. (See Table 5 of Appendix.)

Let the symbol l_x denote the number of persons living at age x, according to the mortality table. Then, of course, l_t denotes the number of persons living at age t. Let $p(x, t)$ denote the probability that a person at age x is still living at age t; then, by the definition of empirical probability,

$$\boxed{p(x, t) = \frac{l_t}{l_x}.}$$

Example. Determine the probability that a person of age 18 will live to be 35.

Solution. From Table 5,

$$l_{18} = 955{,}942 \qquad \text{and} \qquad l_{35} = 906{,}554.$$

The desired probability is then

$$p(18, 35) = \frac{906{,}554}{955{,}942} = 0.948.$$

EXERCISE GROUP 17-9

Use the CSO Mortality Table to determine the probabilities in each of Exercises 1-6.

1. A person of age 18 living to the age of 65
2. A person of age 18 dying within 5 years
3. A person of age 18 and a second person of age 50 both living to age 65
4. A person of age 18 living to age 65, and the person of age 50 failing to live to age 65
5. A person of age 65 dying within 5 years
6. A man 30 years old and his wife 28 years old both attaining age 72
7. Find the odds that a person of age 20 will be living at age 40.
8. Find the odds that a person of age 19 or 20 will be living at age 40.
9. In 1958 there were 4,203,812 live births registered in the United States, of which 2,152,546 were boys. Compute the relative frequency of boys and girls. In Wisconsin there were 76,072 live births reported. What was the probable number of boys born in Wisconsin?
10. The United States population figures for 1959 show that there were 63,173,000 persons under 18 years of age, of whom 32,212,000 were boys. In a school system of 100,000 pupils in that age group, how many boys should there be?
11. The unemployment ratio fell from 5% to 4.6% in a period of 6 months. Find the odds that an unemployed person at the beginning of the period was employed at the end of that period.

SUPPLEMENTARY EXERCISES FOR CHAPTER 17

1. How many numbers without repeated digits and greater than 5000 can be formed with the digits 1, 2, 4, 7, 8?
2. (a) How many numbers between 3000 and 7000 can be formed from the digits 1, 2, 3, 4, 5, 6, 7, 8, 9, no digit being repeated? (b) How many of these will be even?
3. If the number of pairs of players that can be formed from the members of a club is 666, how many members are there in the club?
4. How many 8-digit numbers can be made from the digits of the number 32,625,235?
5. Out of 20 consecutive integers, (a) in how many ways can 2 be selected so that the sum is even? (b) In how many ways can 3 be selected so that the sum is even?
6. Find the probability that of the first 5 persons encountered on a given day (a) exactly 3 of them were born on Wednesday, (b) at least 3 of them were born on Wednesday.
7. If A and B stand in a line with 8 other persons, find the probability that there are exactly 3 persons between A and B.
8. In how many ways can persons A, B, C, and D choose hotels in a town where there are 9 hotels, if B and C refuse to stay at the same hotel?
9. How many committees can be formed from 5 men and 3 women if there are at least one man and one woman on each committee?
10. A committee of 5 is to be chosen from a group of 12 people and a certain 2 of the 12 refuse to serve on the same committee. If the committee is chosen by lot, what is the probability that it will have these 2 people on it?
11. A box contains 20 good screws and 4 defective screws. If 4 screws are used, what is the probability that none is defective?
12. In how many ways can 4 shoes be chosen from a group of 6 different pairs of shoes, so that the 4 contain at least one pair?
13. Six pairs of shoes are in a closet, and 4 shoes are selected at random. Find the probability that these 4 contain at least one pair.
14. How many distinct numbers can be formed with the digits 0, 1, 2, 3, with no repetition permitted?
15. A number without repeated digits is to be formed, using one or more of the digits 1, 2, 3, 4, 5. Find the probability (a) that the number is less than 10, (b) that the number is greater than 1000, (c) that the number is greater than 1400, (d) that the number is odd.
16. A card is selected at random from a deck of 52 playing cards and then replaced. If the act is performed 4 times, find the probability that cards of the 4 different suits are drawn.
17. Four people work independently at deciphering an intercepted message in code. The respective probabilities that they will solve it are $\frac{1}{5}$, $\frac{1}{4}$, $\frac{1}{3}$, and $\frac{1}{2}$. What is the probability that the message will be deciphered?
18. A portion of a radio circuit contains 7 tubes of which 4 are the same. The other 3 are also alike, but different from the 4. However, all sockets and tube bases are alike. If the 7 tubes are inserted at random in the 7 sockets, what is the probability that all the tubes are in their proper places?

19. In how many different ways can 9 different books be divided (a) between 2 people so that one person receives 4 and the other 5 books? (b) among 3 people so that each will receive 3 books? (c) among Tom, Dick, and Harry so that each will receive 3 books?

20. In how many different ways may 8 people be seated on a ferris wheel with 8 single seats? [*Hint:* Note that the people are arranged with respect to each other and not with respect to the ferris wheel.]

21. If 8 people are seated at random on the above ferris wheel, what is the probability that a certain 2 will occupy adjacent seats?

22. A postoffice keeps supplies of 10 different stamps. (a) In how many ways can a person buy 8 different stamps? (b) In how many different ways can he buy 3 stamps?

23. A and B play a game in which the probability that A wins is $\frac{3}{5}$, and the probability that B wins is $\frac{2}{5}$. (a) If 3 games are played, what is the probability that A wins all 3? that A wins exactly one game? (b) A and B play a series of games, the winner of the series to be the first one to win 4 games. If A has won 3 times and B once, find the probability that A wins the series; that B wins the series.

24. A committee of 5 is selected from 6 lawyers, 7 engineers, and 4 doctors. What is the probability that all on the committee are of the same profession?

25. From a group of 5 men and 4 women a committee of 3 is chosen by lot. (a) How many different committees can be so chosen? (b) How many will have at least one woman member?

26. One bag contains 6 oranges and 5 grapefruit, and a second bag contains 8 apples and 6 oranges. If a bag is selected and then a piece of fruit is chosen at random, find the probability that an orange will be selected.

27. (a) What is the most probable number of heads if a coin is tossed 10 times? (b) What is the probability of the most probable number of heads in 10 tosses?

28. "On the average" a student does 4 problems out of 5 correctly. If he is assigned 5 problems, find the probability that he will do at least 4 correctly.

29. Ten members of a high school graduating class, all eighteen years old, agree to meet again in 50 years to celebrate the 50th anniversary of their graduation. What is the probability that they will all be alive on the 50th anniversary?

30. If 3 dice are thrown, show that the number of ways in which the totals 3 through 18 can occur are, respectively, 1, 3, 6, 10, 15, 21, 25, 27, 27, 25, 21, 15, 10, 6, 3, 1.

Appendix A

A–1 INTRODUCTION

It has been stated that all of the properties of elementary algebra depend on the properties of real numbers. Since the student has studied these properties in previous courses, we shall present only a summary of them, which may be used for review or reference purposes. This summary will include topics in factoring, fractions, and exponents and radicals, together with some indication of their dependence on the properties of real numbers. In addition, some exercises are furnished to facilitate the review. A more detailed treatment of the manipulative aspects of these topics may be found in *Introductory Algebra and Trigonometry* or *Intermediate Algebra.**

A–2 POSITIVE INTEGRAL EXPONENTS

A positive integral exponent is associated with a number to indicate repeated multiplication by that number. We write $3 \cdot 3 = 3^2$, where the number 2, used in this manner, is called an *exponent*, and indicates that 3 is multiplied by itself; thus, $3^2 = 3 \cdot 3 = 9$. Similarly, we write

$$3^4 = 3 \cdot 3 \cdot 3 \cdot 3 = 81,$$

in which 4 is the exponent of 3^4 and indicates that 3 is used as a multiplier 4 times. In the same manner we write

$$b^2 = b \cdot b, \qquad b^3 = b \cdot b \cdot b, \qquad b^5 = b \cdot b \cdot b \cdot b \cdot b,$$

and analogously for any exponent which is a positive integer. The quantity 3^2 is called the second power, or *square* of 3, while b^3 is called the third power, or *cube* of b.

Definition A–1. *If n is a positive integer, the quantity b^n, the* nth *power of b, is defined as the product of n numbers each equal to b. In symbols, $b^n = b \cdot b \cdot b \cdots b$, where there are n numbers b in the product on the right.*

* A. Spitzbart and R. H. Bardell, *Introductory Algebra and Trigonometry*, pp. 1–85; R. H. Bardell and A. Spitzbart, *Intermediate Algebra*, pp. 1–62, 141–163. Reading, Mass.: Addison-Wesley Publishing Co., Inc.

In particular, the first power by any number b is the number itself,

$$b^1 = b.$$

The following result is easily established, with n a positive integer:

b^n is positive if b is positive,
b^n is positive if b is negative and n is even,
b^n is negative if b is negative and n is odd.

Examples. $3^4 = 81$, $(-3)^4 = 81$, $(-4)^3 = -64$, $(-b)^3 = -b^3$, $(-b)^4 = b^4$.

The distinction between $(-b)^4$ and $-b^4$ should be noted. The two quantities are not equal. In particular, we may write $-b^4 = -(b^4)$, but in practice the parentheses are omitted.

The relevant properties are:

PROPERTIES OF EXPONENTS	ILLUSTRATIONS
1. $x^p x^q = x^{p+q}$	$a^2a^3 = a^{2+3} = a^5$
2. $(x^p)^q = x^{pq}$	$(b^2)^3 = b^{2\cdot 3} = b^6$
3. $(xy)^p = x^p y^p$	$(2b)^5 = 2^5 b^5 = 32b^5$
4. $\left(\frac{x}{y}\right)^p = \frac{x^p}{y^p}$, if $y \neq 0$	$\left(\frac{a}{b}\right)^7 = \frac{a^7}{b^7}$

5. If $x \neq 0$, $$\frac{x^p}{x^q} = \begin{cases} 1 & \text{if } p = q, \\ x^{p-q} & \text{if } p \text{ is larger than } q, \\ \dfrac{1}{x^{q-p}} & \text{if } q \text{ is larger than } p. \end{cases}$$

Property 2 may be proved as follows:

$$(x^p)^q = \underbrace{x^p \cdot x^p \cdots x^p}_{q \text{ numbers } x^p} = \underbrace{\underbrace{(x \cdot x \cdots x)}_{p \text{ numbers } x} \cdots \underbrace{(x \cdot x \cdots x)}_{p \text{ numbers } x}}_{q \text{ products } (x \cdot x \cdots x)} = \underbrace{x \cdot x \cdots x}_{pq \text{ numbers } x} = x^{pq}.$$

Property 3 may be proved similarly.

The student should give the reason for each of the equals signs in the following examples.

Examples. $(a^2b^3)(a^4b^2) = (a^2a^4)(b^3b^2) = a^{2+4}b^{3+2} = a^6b^5$;
$(-2ab^2)^3 = (-2)^3a^3(b^2)^3 = -8a^3b^6$.

Proof of Property 5. If $p = q$ then $x^p = x^q$, and the quotient of two equal numbers is 1.

If $p \neq q$, we have, by Definition A-1,

$$\frac{x^p}{x^q} = \frac{\overbrace{x \cdot x \cdots x}^{p \text{ numbers } x}}{\underbrace{x \cdot x \cdots x}_{q \text{ numbers } x}}.$$

Let $x^p/x^q = Q$. Then $Q \cdot x^q = x^p$. If p is larger than q, then $p - q$ is positive and, by Property 2 of exponents,

$$x^{p-q} \cdot x^q = x^p \quad \text{and} \quad Q = x^{p-q}.$$

If q is larger than p, then $q - p$ is positive; moreover, q is larger than $q - p$. Hence by the second part of the proof,

$$\frac{x^q}{x^{q-p}} = x^{q-(q-p)} = x^p.$$

But

$$\frac{1}{x^{q-p}} \cdot x^q = \frac{x^q}{x^{q-p}}.$$

Hence this time we have $Q = 1/x^{q-p}$, and the property is proved.

Examples.

$$\frac{x^3}{x} = x^{3-1} = x^2; \qquad \frac{x^3}{x^7} = \frac{1}{x^{7-3}} = \frac{1}{x^4}.$$

EXERCISE GROUP A-1

In each of Exercises 1–21, perform the indicated operations.

1. 3^2
2. 4^3
3. 6^3
4. 3^5
5. $3^2 \cdot 3^3$
6. $10^5 \cdot 10^8$
7. $7^2 \cdot 7^9 \cdot 7^4$
8. $(2 \cdot 5)^3$
9. $(2^3 \cdot 3^2)^5$
10. $(2^5 \cdot 7^2)^3$
11. $(2^3 \cdot 3^2)^2(2^2 \cdot 3^3)^4$
12. $(2^5 \cdot 3^2 \cdot 5^3)(2^3 \cdot 5^2)^2$
13. $3x^3 \cdot x^2 \cdot x^4$
14. $(2^2a^3)^2(3^2b^4)^3$
15. $(a^2b^3)^2(a^3b^2)^3$
16. $(-2ab^2)^5(-5a^3)^4$
17. $(2a^h)^2(3a^h)^3$
18. $(a^2b)^k(ab^2)^k$
19. $(a^2b^3)^k(a^3b)^k$
20. $(3a^{2b}c^x)^d(3c^x)^d$
21. $(3a^{2h}b^k)^n(b^n)^k$

In each of Exercises 22–43, perform the indicated multiplications and collect similar terms.

22. $3x(2x - 5)$
23. $-a(2x - ay)$
24. $-3y(a - 2y)$
25. $-3xy(x^2 - y^2 - 1)$

26. $\frac{3}{2}a^2(4a^4 - 2ab - 4b^4)$

27. $-5x^4y(7xyz - 5xy^2z^2 - 2z^3)$

28. $3x(2 - 3x + 4x^2)$

29. $(x - 4)(x + 5)$

30. $(2x - 5)^2$

31. $(3x - 4y)(5x + 7y)$

32. $(x + 5)(x^2 - 5x + 25)$

33. $(2x - b)(2x + b)$

34. $(x - 2y)(x^2 + 2xy + 4y^2)$

35. $(x + 1)(x + 2)(x + 3)$

36. $(2x - 3y)(2x + 3y)$

37. $(2x - 3y)(3x - 4y)$

38. $(x^4 - 3x^3 - 4x^2 + 5x + 3)(x - 7)$

39. $(x^7 + x^3 + x + 1)(x^3 - 3x - 1)$

40. $(a + 1)(a - 1)(a^2 + 1)(a^4 + 1)(a^8 + 1)$

41. $(a^m - 3a^{m-1} + 4a^{m-2})(a^2 + a + 1)$

42. $(x^n + y^k)(x^{2n} - x^ny^k + y^{2k})$

43. $(x^3 + x^2 + x + 1)(x - 1) - (x^2 + 1)(x + 1)(x - 1)$

In each of Exercises 44–55, perform the indicated operations.

44. $\dfrac{2^7}{2^2}$

45. $\dfrac{5^3}{5^8}$

46. $\dfrac{2^7 \cdot 3^3}{2^3 \cdot 3^8}$

47. $\dfrac{10^2 \cdot 10^6}{10^7 \cdot 10^5}$

48. $\dfrac{3^4 \cdot 10^2}{3^9 \cdot 10^7}$

49. $\dfrac{2x^{10}}{6x^2}$

50. $\dfrac{2^3x^9}{6^3x^2}$

51. $\dfrac{x^3y^3}{x^8y^2}$

52. $\dfrac{2x^3y^7z^8}{3x^7yz^2}$

53. $\dfrac{5^7a^6bx^8}{10^5a^2b^7x}$

54. $\dfrac{2^3x^2y^7}{3^2x^7y^3}$

55. $\dfrac{a^7b^3c^9x}{a^5b^9cx^7}$

In each of Exercises 56–61, perform the indicated operations, assuming that the letters x, y, and z represent positive integers each less than 10, and also that x is less than y, which in turn is less than z. Obtain the answers with no negative exponents.

56. $\dfrac{2^xa^yb^z}{2^za^xb^y}$

57. $\dfrac{a^xa^zb^y}{a^yb^x}$

58. $\dfrac{2^x3^ya^7b^z}{2^y3^za^2b^x}$

59. $\dfrac{a^9a^yb^xb^{10}}{a^zb^y}$

60. $\dfrac{2^x5^xa^yb^z}{10^za^xb^y}$

61. $\dfrac{a^xa^yb^zc^{10}}{ab^{10}b^xc^z}$

In each of the following exercises, determine the quotient and remainder.

62. $(x^2 - 5x + 6) \div (x - 2)$

63. $(x^2 - 2x - 15) \div (x - 5)$

64. $(21a^2 + 13ab - 20b^2) \div (7a - 5b)$

65. $(2a^3 - 9a^2 + 11a - 3) \div (2a - 3)$

66. $(7 - 8x^2 + 4x^3 - 9x) \div (2x - 3)$

67. $(15x^4 + 9x + 7x^3 + 15x^2 + 7) \div (3x^2 + 2x + 1)$

68. $(6a^3 - 3 + 8a^4 + 6a) \div (2a - 1 + 2a^2)$

69. $(a^4 + a^2b^2 + b^4) \div (a^2 - ab + b^2)$

70. $(6x^{3n} + 5x^{2n} - 18x^n + 8) \div (3x^n - 2)$

A-3 SPECIAL PRODUCTS

The properties of real numbers as presented in Section 1-8 may be applied to algebraic expressions in which letters are used to represent real numbers. In particular, certain multiplication formulas occur so frequently as to warrant special attention. They are:

1. $u(x + y) = ux + uy,$
2. $(u + v)(u - v) = u^2 - v^2,$

3a. $(u + v)^2 = u^2 + 2uv + v^2,$

3b. $(u - v)^2 = u^2 - 2uv + v^2,$

4. $(au + b)(cu + d) = acu^2 + (ad + bc)u + bd,$

5a. $(u + v)(u^2 - uv + v^2) = u^3 + v^3,$

5b. $(u - v)(u^2 + uv + v^2) = u^3 - v^3.$

The proofs of these formulas depend on the properties discussed in Section 1-8, with particular emphasis on the distributive law of multiplication with respect to addition, the laws of signs, and the properties of exponents.

We emphasize the fact that these formulas have a quite general nature, because each letter in each of the formulas may represent any quantity whatever.

Example 1. Expand $(a + b - 2)^2$.

Solution. When we enclose $a + b$ in parentheses we may write

$$\begin{aligned}(a + b - 2)^2 &= [(a + b) - 2]^2 \\ &= (a + b)^2 - 4(a + b) + 4 && \text{(by formula type 3b)} \\ &= a^2 + 2ab + b^2 - 4a - 4b + 4 && \text{(by types 3a and 1).}\end{aligned}$$

Example 2. Expand $(x + 2y + 3)(x - 2y + 3)$.

Solution. By rearranging within the parentheses we have

$$\begin{aligned}(x + 2y + 3)(x - 2y + 3) &= [(x + 3) + 2y][(x + 3) - 2y] \\ &= (x + 3)^2 - 4y^2 && \text{(by formula type 2)} \\ &= x^2 + 6x + 9 - 4y^2 && \text{(by type 3a).}\end{aligned}$$

EXERCISE GROUP A-2

1. Prove formula 2.
2. Prove formula 3b.
3. Prove formula 5a.
4. Prove formula 5b.

Use one or more of the formulas listed in Section A-2 to perform the indicated multiplication in each of Exercises 5-20.

5. $-3xy(x^2 - y^2 - 1)$
6. $2xyz(7x^2y + 2yz^2 - 3x^2z)$
7. $b^m(1 + b^n - b^m)$
8. $(2a - 3b)(2a + 3b)$

9. $(-bu - v)(bu - v)$
10. $(x^m - y^m)(x^m + y^m)$
11. $(2a + 9b)^2$
12. $(4d^2e^2 + 3f^2)^2$
13. $[(a + b) + c]^2$
14. $(3x + 5y)(2x + 7y)$
15. $(2x^2 + 3y^3)(2x^2 + 5y^3)$
16. $[(a + b) + 2c][(a + b) - c]$
17. $[a + (x + y)][a - (x + y)]$
18. $[x + (2y + 3z)]^2$
19. $(0.3u^2 + 0.5v^2)(0.09u^4 - 0.15u^2v^2 + 0.25v^4)$
20. $(0.2x - 0.3y)(0.04x^2 + 0.06xy + 0.09y^2)$

In each of the following exercises, use parentheses to group the quantities so that the multiplication formulas may be employed, and then perform the indicated multiplication.

21. $(x + y - 2z)(x + y + 2z)$
22. $(a - 3 + b)^2$
23. $(2x + 3y - 5z)^2$
24. $(2a - 3b + 4c - 5d)^2$
25. $(2u - 3v - 5x + 7y)(7y + 3v + 2u + 5x)$
26. $(3x - 5y - 7u + 9v)^2$
27. $(x + y + u - v)(x + y - u + v)$
28. $(a + 2b + 3c - d)(a + 2b - 3c + d)$
29. $(c - a - 3b - d)(d - 3b + a + c)$

A–4 FACTORING

The formulas of Section A-3, when read from right to left, may be considered to be *factorization formulas*, that is, formulas which express various quantities in the form of products. The quantities which are multiplied together in a product are known as the *factors* of the given expression. In the factorization of algebraic expressions it is very often desirable to obtain factors such that, in some sense, none of them can be factored further. In particular, we shall mean by this a factorization in which no factor can be further broken down into expressions containing only rational numbers.

Definition A–2. *To factor completely an expression containing only rational numbers shall mean to factor it as far as possible in the rational number system (in other words, in the sense described above).*

Example 1. Factor $3x^2 + 8x - 3$.

Solution. If the given expression can be factored, it appears that formula 4 above, which factors a trinomial as a product of two binomials, must apply. Upon consideration of the relatively few possibilities, we obtain the result

$$3x^2 + 8x - 3 = (3x - 1)(x + 3).$$

Example 2. Factor $4x^2y^2 - 36x^2z^2$ completely.

Solution. Formula 1 above applies, with $u = 4x^2$. We obtain

$$4x^2y^2 - 36x^2z^2 = 4x^2(y^2 - 9z^2).$$

However, we now recognize that the factor $y^2 - 9z^2$ is a difference of two squares and can also be factored. The final result is then

$$4x^2y^2 - 36x^2z^2 = 4x^2(y + 3z)(y - 3z).$$

In Example 2 the factor 4 can be written as 2^2, but it is customary in this connection not to factor an integral factor further.

Example 3. Factor $a^4 - a^2 - 12$ completely.

Solution. Formula 4 applies, with $u = a^2$, and we obtain

$$a^4 - a^2 - 12 = (a^2 + 3)(a^2 - 4).$$

The first factor on the right does not factor further, but the second factor, $a^2 - 4$, is a difference of two squares. Completion of the factorization gives

$$a^4 - a^2 - 12 = (a^2 + 3)(a + 2)(a - 2).$$

Example 4. Factor $x^6 - 64$ completely.

Solution. A careful inspection will show that formula 2 applies with $u = x^3$, $v = 8$, and also that formula 5b, with $u = x^2$, $v = 4$, applies. When an expression may be factored either as a difference of two squares or as a difference of two cubes, it is desirable to factor as a difference of two squares. In this manner we obtain

$$x^6 - 64 = (x^3 + 8)(x^3 - 8).$$

Each resulting factor, however, factors further, as a sum and as a difference of two cubes, respectively. We get, finally, as the desired factorization,

$$x^6 - 64 = (x + 2)(x^2 - 2x + 4)(x - 2)(x^2 + 2x + 4).$$

It is of interest to see what results on factoring $x^6 - 64$ as a difference of two cubes. We get, in this case,

$$x^6 - 64 = (x^2 - 4)(x^4 + 4x^2 + 16),$$

in which $x^2 - 4$ clearly factors as $(x + 2)(x - 2)$. A comparison of the two results shows that $x^4 + 4x^2 + 16$ must be factorable as

$$x^4 + 4x^2 + 16 = (x^2 - 2x + 4)(x^2 + 2x + 4).$$

This may be verified by multiplication, but it is not easy to see directly. It is possible, however, to express $x^4 + 4x^2 + 16$ as

$$\begin{aligned} x^4 + 8x^2 + 16 - 4x^2 &= (x^2 + 4)^2 - (2x)^2 \\ &= [(x^2 + 4) + 2x][(x^2 + 4) - 2x] \quad \text{(by formula type 2)} \\ &= (x^2 + 2x + 4)(x^2 - 2x + 4). \end{aligned}$$

Obviously, treating $x^6 - 64$ as the difference of two squares is much simpler than thinking of it as the difference of two cubes.

EXERCISE GROUP A-3

Factor each of the following completely.

1. $x^4 - 9x^2$
2. $x^3 - 5x$
3. $8a^2 + 22a^2x - 6a^2x^2$
4. $9x^2y^2z^2 - 9x^2y^2$
5. $2x^2 - 7x - 15$
6. $6 - 3x^2 - 7x$
7. $27b - 64a^3b$
8. $-72k^2 + 2$
9. $x^2y + 9xy + 14y$
10. $(a + 5)(x - y) + (b - 3)(x - y)$
11. $x^2(a + b) + 4x(a + b) + 4(a + b)$
12. $48xy - 8x^3y - 20x^2y$
13. $2(a + b)^2 + 11(a + b) + 5$
14. $x^2(x - 3) - 4(x - 3)$
15. $2m^3n^3 - n^6 - m^6$
16. $(x^2 - 3x)^2 - 8(x^2 - 3x) - 20$
17. $12x^n + 36x^{2n} + 1$
18. $3x^{2n} - x^n - 2x^{3n}$
19. $x^6 - 5x^3 + 4$
20. $a^6 - 1$
21. $729a^8b^2 - a^2b^8$
22. $a^9 + x^9$
23. $a^{12} - 5a^6 + 4$
24. $98x^4y^2 - 56x^3y^3 + 8x^2y^4$
25. $4a^6 - 52a^4 + 144a^2$
26. $36x^2 - (5x + 6)^2$
27. $28x^4 - 19x^2y^2 - 99y^4$
28. $6x^{k+4}y^3 - x^{k+2}y^5 - 35x^ky^7$
29. $64a^6 - (b + c)^6$
30. $(a^2 + 2ab)^2 - 2b^2(a^2 + 2ab) - 3b^4$
31. $x^{n+2}y^n(a + b) - x^ny^{n+2}(a + b)$

Factoring by grouping of terms. There are many problems in factoring which do not conform directly to the above formula types but can be made to do so by properly grouping the terms. This is usually accomplished through the use of parentheses or other grouping symbols. We seek a grouping of some of the terms in such a way that the group which is formed can be factored while at the same time the new form of the expression conforms to one of the standard formula types.

We will illustrate the procedure by some examples. The reference numbers employed to identify the formula types involved are used in accordance with the listing of forms in Section A-3.

Example 5. Factor $ax + by + ay + bx$ completely.

Solution. The first and last terms have the factor x in common, while the second and third terms have the factor y in common. Hence we may rewrite the expression, and we have

$$\begin{aligned} ax + bx + ay + by &= x(a + b) + y(a + b) \\ &= (a + b)(x + y) \qquad \text{(by 1 with } u = a + b). \end{aligned}$$

Example 6. Factor $2ax - 3by - 2ay + 3bx$ completely.

Solution. As in Example 5, x is a common factor of the first and last terms while y is a common factor of the second and third terms. Upon rewriting we obtain

$$\begin{aligned} 2ax + 3bx - 2ay - 3by &= x(2a + 3b) - y(2a + 3b) \\ &= (2a + 3b)(x - y). \end{aligned}$$

The same result may be obtained by noting that $2a$ is a common factor of the first and third terms, and that $3b$ is a common factor of the second and last terms. Hence a different grouping gives

$$\begin{aligned} 2ax - 2ay + 3bx - 3by &= 2a(x - y) + 3b(x - y) \\ &= (x - y)(2a + 3b). \end{aligned}$$

Example 7. Factor $xy - 3y + y^2 - 3x$ completely.

Solution. $xy - 3y + y^2 - 3x = (xy + y^2) - (3x + 3y)$

$$= y(x + y) - 3(x + y) = (x + y)(y - 3).$$

Example 8. Factor $x^2 + 2xy + y^2 - 9$ completely.

Solution. The appearance of the trinomial $x^2 + 2xy + y^2$, which is the square of the binomial $(x + y)$, suggests the grouping. We obtain

$$\begin{aligned} (x^2 + 2xy + y^2) - 9 &= (x + y)^2 - 9 && \text{(by 3a)} \\ &= [(x + y) + 3][(x + y) - 3] && \text{(by 2)} \\ &= (x + y + 3)(x + y - 3). \end{aligned}$$

Example 9. Factor $a^2 - 2ab + b^2 - x^2 - 2xy - y^2$ completely.

Solution. Familiarity with formula types 3a and 3b suggests the following grouping:

$$\begin{aligned} (a^2 - 2ab + b^2) - (x^2 + 2xy + y^2) &= (a - b)^2 - (x + y)^2 \\ &= [(a - b) + (x + y)][(a - b) - (x + y)] \\ &= (a - b + x + y)(a - b - x - y). \end{aligned}$$

EXERCISE GROUP A-4

By inserting parentheses (rearranging terms where necessary), reduce each of the following expressions to a known form and then factor completely.

1. $x - y - 3z(x - y)$
2. $ax - by - bx + ay$
3. $3ax - 5bx + 6ay - 10by$
4. $bu + bv + 2hu + 2hv$
5. $3cw - 3cx - 4kw + 4kx$
6. $-2ax - 2ah - abx - abh$
7. $(a^3 - 2a^2) - a + 2$
8. $u^3 + 2u^2 + u + 2$
9. $u^2 - (2x - y)^2$
10. $xm + ym + xn + yn$
11. $2y^4 - y^3 + 16y - 8$
12. $x^2 + mxy - 4xy - 4my^2$
13. $ax + by + az + bx + ay + bz$
14. $x^2 - y^2 - x + y$
15. $16a^2 + 8ab + b^2 - 25c^2$
16. $x^2 + 2xy - 16z^2 + y^2$

17. $u^2 - 4b^2 + 2uv + v^2$
18. $(a + 3) + 3a^2 + a^3$
19. $bx^2 + x^3 - by^2 - xy^2$
20. $4x^2 - 12xy + 9y^2 - 2x + 3y$
21. $4u^2 - 12uv + 9v^2 - 2ab - a^2 - b^2$
22. $a^4 - 2a^2b^2 + b^4 - 25x^4 - 40x^2y^2 - 16y^4$
23. $3x^2 - 6xy + 3y^2 - 10x + 10y + 3$
24. $x^2 - 6xy + 9y^2 - 7x + 21y + 12$
25. $x^4 + 2x^3 - 7x^2 - 8x + 12$
26. $9x^4 + 30x^3 + 25x^2 - 4$
27. $6x(x - 2)^2(2x^2 + 1)^2 + 2(2x^2 + 1)(2 - x)^3$
28. $2a^2 - 7ab - 22b^2 - 5a + 35b - 3$
29. $a^2 - ab - 6b^2 + 4ac + 13bc - 5c^2$
30. $(x^2 + 4x - 6)^2 - 14x(x^2 + 4x - 6) + 45x^2$

A–5 FRACTIONS

Division of the real number a by the real number b is always possible if $b \neq 0$. The *quotient* Q is unique and may be written as

$$\frac{a}{b} \quad \text{or} \quad a/b \quad \text{or} \quad a \div b.$$

In the division a is called the *dividend* and b the *divisor*. Any such indicated quotient of two real numbers is called a *fraction*, the dividend being the *numerator*, and the divisor the *denominator* of the fraction.

Because of the manner in which real numbers can be defined by using rational numbers, the formal properties of fractions are identical with those of rational numbers, but involve more advanced concepts which it is not feasible to introduce here. The proofs of these properties follow from the properties of real numbers as stated in Section 1–8.

PROPERTY I. $a/b = c/d$ if and only if $ad = bc$.

Proof. If $a/b = Q_1$ and $c/d = Q_2$, then $a = bQ_1$ and $c = dQ_2$. It follows that $ad = bdQ_1$ and $bc = bdQ_2$. If $Q_1 = Q_2$ then, at once, $ad = bc$.

On the other hand, if $ad = bc$, then $bdQ_1 = bdQ_2$. Since $bd \neq 0$, the cancellation property of multiplication gives $Q_1 = Q_2$, and the proof is complete.

Property I leads directly to a most useful property, stated as follows.

Fundamental Principle. *The value of a fraction is unaltered if both numerator and denominator are multiplied or divided by the same nonzero number.*

Proof. Both parts of the principle are verified if we prove that

$$\frac{ac}{bc} = \frac{a}{b}, \qquad c \neq 0.$$

By Property I we must then show that $(ac)b = (bc)a$, which holds since each product is equal to abc, so that the fundamental principle is established.

There are three signs associated with a fraction: the sign of the numerator, the sign of the denominator, and the sign preceding the fraction. It is easily shown that

$$\frac{-a}{b} = \frac{a}{-b} = -\frac{a}{b},$$

so that we have

PROPERTY II. Any two of the three signs of a fraction may be changed without changing the value of the fraction.

By the Fundamental Principle, a fraction in which the numerator and denominator have a factor in common may be simplified, or reduced, by dividing out that factor.

For a fraction to be in *simplest form* or *lowest terms* the numerator and denominator may have no common factor other than $+1$ and -1. *One may eliminate any common factors by*

1. *factoring both numerator and denominator completely,*
2. *dividing out all common factors.*

The following examples illustrate the reduction of a fraction to simplest form.

Example 1. $$\frac{-36}{20} = \frac{(-1)\cdot 2^2\cdot 3^2}{2^2\cdot 5} = \frac{(-1)\cdot 3^2}{5} = -\frac{9}{5}.$$

Example 2. $$\frac{a^4x^2y^3}{a^7xy^2} = \frac{a^4xy^2(xy)}{a^4xy^2(a^3)} = \frac{xy}{a^3}.$$

Example 3. $$\frac{a^2+5ab}{a^2+3ab} = \frac{a(a+5b)}{a(a+3b)} = \frac{a+5b}{a+3b}.$$

Example 4. $$\frac{b^2-9}{b^2-6b+9} = \frac{(b+3)(b-3)}{(b-3)(b-3)} = \frac{b+3}{b-3}.$$

Example 5. $$\frac{ax-by+bx-ay}{3ax-5by+5bx-3ay} = \frac{x(a+b)-y(a+b)}{x(3a+5b)-y(3a+5b)}$$

$$= \frac{(a+b)(x-y)}{(3a+5b)(x-y)} = \frac{a+b}{3a+5b}.$$

In order to simplify a fraction it is not actually necessary to factor both numerator and denominator completely. If, for example, the numerator has been factored completely, it is sufficient to test whether each factor obtained is or is not a factor of the denominator.

Example 6. Simplify $\dfrac{84}{4551}$.

Solution. We factor 84 as $84 = 2^2 \cdot 3 \cdot 7$. Of these factors only 3 is a factor of 4551. Thus we have

$$\frac{84}{4551} = \frac{2^2 \cdot 3 \cdot 7}{3 \cdot 1517} = \frac{28}{1517},$$

and no further simplification is possible.

EXERCISE GROUP A–5

Reduce each of the following fractions to simplest form.

1. $\dfrac{63}{135}$
2. $\dfrac{57x^3y^2}{95xy^3}$
3. $\dfrac{3a^2 + ab}{b^2 + 3ab}$
4. $\dfrac{a^2 - 4}{3a - 6}$
5. $\dfrac{a^2(x + y)^2}{ax^2 - ay^2}$
6. $\dfrac{ax^2 - ay^2}{a^2x + a^2y}$
7. $\dfrac{x^2 - y^2}{a(y - x)}$
8. $\dfrac{x^2 - x - 6}{x^2 + x - 12}$
9. $\dfrac{3x^2 - 17x + 20}{6x^2 - 7x - 5}$
10. $\dfrac{6x^2 - 19x + 15}{9x^2 - 21x + 10}$
11. $\dfrac{x^2 + ax - ab - bx}{(x + a)(b - x)}$
12. $\dfrac{cx^2 - dy^2 - cy^2 + dx^2}{dx + cy + dy + cx}$
13. $\dfrac{ax - by + bx - ay}{3ax - 5by + 5bx - 3ay}$
14. $\dfrac{a^2x^2 + x^3 - a^2y^2 - xy^2}{ax - ay + by - bx}$
15. $\dfrac{a^2c - a^2d + b^2d - b^2c}{c^2a - c^2b + d^2b - d^2a}$
16. $\dfrac{x^4 - y^4 + 2xy(x^2 - y^2)}{x^4 - y^4}$
17. $\dfrac{a^3 - b^3}{a^2 - b^2}$
18. $\dfrac{(x - y)^2}{y^2 - xy}$
19. $\dfrac{8x^3 - 27b^3}{9b^2 + 4x^2 - 12bx}$
20. $\dfrac{x^4 - 6x^3 + 13x^2 - 12x - 21}{x^4 + 2x^3 - 5x^2 + 26x + 21}$
21. $\dfrac{3a^3 - 13a^2 + 23a - 21}{9a^2 - 36a + 35}$
22. $\dfrac{4x^4 - 12x^3 + 7x^2 + 3x - 2}{4x^4 - 4x^3 - 25x^2 + x + 6}$

Addition of fractions. This is accomplished by the relation

$$\frac{a}{b} + \frac{c}{d} = \frac{ad + bc}{bd}, \tag{1}$$

which is, formally, merely the definition of addition of rational numbers. If both denominators are equal, we may write

$$\frac{a}{c} + \frac{b}{c} = \frac{a + b}{c}, \tag{2}$$

which may be stated as:

To add or subtract two or more fractions with the same denominator, form the corresponding sum or difference of the numerators as the numerator of the resulting fraction with the common denominator as denominator.

Addition of fractions with different denominators, which is covered by (1), is facilitated by using the Fundamental Principle to reduce each fraction to an equivalent fraction, in such a way that all the new fractions have the same denominator. This common denominator is usually the *lowest common denominator*, or LCD, defined as the product of all the different prime factors which appear in the given denominators, each with an exponent which is the largest exponent of that prime factor in any denominator. The fractions with common denominators are then added by use of (2).

Example 7. Reduce to a single fraction in lowest terms

$$\frac{3}{x^2 - 1} + \frac{4x}{2x^2 + x - 3} - \frac{3x + 2}{2x^2 + 5x + 3}.$$

Solution. The denominators factor as

$$x^2 - 1 = (x + 1)(x - 1), \qquad 2x^2 + x - 3 = (2x + 3)(x - 1),$$
$$2x^2 + 5x + 3 = (2x + 3)(x + 1).$$

Hence, LCD $= (x + 1)(x - 1)(2x + 3)$. Changing each fraction to an equivalent fraction with the LCD as the denominator, we get

$$\frac{3(2x + 3)}{(x + 1)(x - 1)(2x + 3)}$$
$$+ \frac{4x(x + 1)}{(x + 1)(x - 1)(2x + 3)} - \frac{(3x + 2)(x - 1)}{(x + 1)(x - 1)(2x + 3)}$$
$$= \frac{6x + 9 + 4x^2 + 4x - 3x^2 + x + 2}{(x + 1)(x - 1)(2x + 3)} = \frac{x^2 + 11x + 11}{(x + 1)(x - 1)(2x + 3)}.$$

Since $x^2 + 11x + 11$ cannot be factored, the last fraction is in simplest form, and hence is the answer.

Example 8. Express as a single fraction in simplest form

$$\frac{2 - x}{x^2 - 1} + \frac{8}{1 - x^2} - \frac{5 + x}{1 - x^2}.$$

Solution. Since $1 - x^2 = -(x^2 - 1)$, the LCD may be taken as $x^2 - 1$. The sum can then be written as

$$\frac{(2 - x) + 8(-1) - (5 + x)(-1)}{x^2 - 1} = \frac{-1}{x^2 - 1} = \frac{1}{1 - x^2}.$$

Note that the LCD may also be taken as $1 - x^2$.

EXERCISE GROUP A–6

In each of the following exercises, reduce the given expression to a single fraction in simplest form.

1. $2 - \frac{3}{5} + \frac{2}{3}$

2. $\frac{4}{5} - 3 + \frac{3}{7}$

3. $\frac{3x}{2a} - \frac{5y}{3b}$

4. $\frac{3a}{b} - \frac{a + 2b}{a}$

5. $\frac{x}{bx - bc} - \frac{b}{cx - x^2}$

6. $\frac{3x - 2}{x - 1} - \frac{3}{1 - x} + \frac{x}{1 - x}$

7. $\frac{a}{3 + a} - \frac{a}{3 - a} - \frac{a^2}{a^2 - 9}$

8. $\frac{3}{2a - 3} - \frac{2}{3 - 2a} + \frac{15}{9 - 4a^2}$

9. $\frac{x^2 + 1}{x - 1} - x + 1 - \frac{x^2 - 1}{1 - x} + \frac{x^3}{x^2 - 1}$

10. $a^2 + a + 1 + \frac{a^3}{1 - a} - \frac{3}{a - 1}$

11. $2a + 1 - \frac{6a^3 + a^2 - 1}{2a - 1}$

12. $\frac{1}{1 - 2a} - \frac{8a^3 - 8a^2 + 1}{(2a - 1)^2}$

13. $\frac{6}{1 - 3x} - \frac{1}{2x - 1} + \frac{3}{x} + \frac{x}{5x - 6x^2 - 1}$

14. $\frac{1}{x + 2} - \frac{2x + 9}{6 + x - x^2} - \frac{2x}{x^2 - 2x - 3}$

15. $\frac{2x + 3}{6x^2 - 7x - 5} - \frac{x - 5}{3x^2 + x - 10} - \frac{53x + 100}{2x^2 + 5x + 2}$

16. $\frac{x + 3}{x^2 + 5x + 6} + \frac{x + 2}{x^2 + 8x + 12} - \frac{3}{x + 6}$

17. $\frac{2x - 1}{4x^2 + 4x + 1} - \frac{2x + 1}{4x^2 - 4x + 1} - \frac{16x^4 + 3}{16x^4 - 8x^2 + 1}$

18. $\frac{5 - 4a}{7 - 2a} - \frac{8a^2 - 8a + 2}{4a^2 - 16a + 7} + 1$

19. $\dfrac{3(3x+2)}{6x^2-x-1}+\dfrac{28(x+3)}{3x^2+7x+2}+\dfrac{7(x-2)}{2x^2+3x-2}$

20. $\dfrac{50(x+1)}{x^2-x-6}-\dfrac{36(x-4)}{x^2-4x+3}+\dfrac{15(x+4)}{x^2+x-2}$

Multiplication and division of fractions. It can be shown from the definitions that

$$\frac{a}{b}\cdot\frac{c}{d}=\frac{ac}{bd}, \qquad b\neq 0,\ d\neq 0,$$

so that we may state the following:

The product of two or more fractions is a fraction whose numerator is the product of all the numerators, and whose denominator is the product of all the denominators.

The *quotient of two fractions* is given by the relation

$$\frac{a}{b}\div\frac{c}{d}=\frac{a}{b}\cdot\frac{d}{c}=\frac{ad}{bc}, \qquad b\neq 0,\ c\neq 0,\ d\neq 0.$$

In carrying out multiplications and divisions of fractions it is customary to simplify any fractions which result.

Example 9. Perform the multiplication and simplify:

$$\frac{9y^2-1}{y^2-16}\cdot\frac{y^2+4y}{6y+2}.$$

Solution. Factor each numerator and denominator to obtain,

$$\frac{9y^2-1}{y^2-16}\cdot\frac{y^2+4y}{6y+2}=\frac{(3y+1)(3y-1)}{(y+4)(y-4)}\cdot\frac{y(y+4)}{2(3y+1)}$$

$$=\frac{3y-1}{y-4}\cdot\frac{y}{2}=\frac{y(3y-1)}{2(y-4)}.$$

Example 10.

$$\frac{\dfrac{3x-1}{9x^2-1}}{4x+5}=\frac{3x-1}{1}\cdot\frac{4x+5}{9x^2-1}=\frac{(3x-1)(4x+5)}{(3x+1)(3x-1)}=\frac{4x+5}{3x+1}.$$

Example 11. Simplify the expression

$$\frac{x^2+14x-15}{x^2+4x-5}\div\frac{x^2+12x-45}{x^2+6x-27}.$$

Solution. Inverting the second fraction, we obtain

$$\frac{x^2+14x-15}{x^2+4x-5}\cdot\frac{x^2+6x-27}{x^2+12x-45}=\frac{(x+15)(x-1)}{(x+5)(x-1)}\cdot\frac{(x+9)(x-3)}{(x+15)(x-3)}$$

$$=\frac{x+9}{x+5}.$$

EXERCISE GROUP A–7

In each of the following exercises, perform the indicated operations and express the result in simplest form.

1. $\dfrac{au - av}{3x + 6y} \cdot \dfrac{2y + x}{v - u}$

2. $\dfrac{y^2 - x^2}{(x + y)^2} \div \dfrac{(x - y)^2}{y^2 - x^2}$

3. $(a^2 - b^2) \cdot \dfrac{xy}{zb - za}$

4. $\dfrac{xy^2 + y^3}{x^3 - x^2y} \div \dfrac{x^2 - xy - 2y^2}{x^2 - 2xy + y^2}$

5. $\dfrac{x^2 - 11x + 18}{x^2 - 9x + 8} \div \dfrac{x^2 - 7x + 10}{x^2 - 6x - 16}$

6. $\dfrac{(x - y)^2}{x^4 - y^4} \cdot \dfrac{x^2 + xy}{x - y} \cdot \dfrac{x^2 + y^2}{x^2}$

7. $\dfrac{u^4 - v^4}{u^2 - 2uv + v^2} \div \dfrac{u^2 + v^2}{u^2 - uv}$

8. $\left(\dfrac{y^2}{1 - y^2} \div \dfrac{2y}{1 - y}\right) \div \dfrac{1 - y}{y + 1}$

9. $\dfrac{(x - y)^2}{x^4 - y^4} \cdot \dfrac{x^2 - 4x - 21}{x^2 - 3x - 10} \cdot \dfrac{x^2 - 6x - 16}{x^2 - 9x + 14}$

10. $\dfrac{5a + 5}{16a + 4} \cdot \dfrac{6a - 6}{a^2 - 1} \cdot \dfrac{4a^2 - 3a - 1}{a^2 - 2a + 1}$

11. $(a + b) \div \left(\dfrac{a^2 - b^2}{1 + c} \div \dfrac{b - a}{y^2 - 1}\right)$

12. $\dfrac{7 + 6a - a^2}{3a - 2} \cdot \dfrac{2a - 3}{a^2 - 8a + 7} \div \dfrac{1 - a^2}{a^2 - 2a + 1}$

13. $\dfrac{a^2 - 5a}{a - 1} \div \left(\dfrac{a^2 - 25}{a^2 + a - 20} \div \dfrac{a^2 + a - 2}{a^2 - 2a - 8}\right)$

14. $\dfrac{4x^2 - 9}{2x^2 - 13x + 15} \div \left(\dfrac{2x + 1}{2x - 1} \div \dfrac{x - 5}{2x - 1}\right)$

15. $\dfrac{3x - y}{y^2 - 4x^2} \cdot \dfrac{y^2 - 3xy + 2x^2}{y - 3x} \div \dfrac{y - x}{(2x - y)^2}$

16. $\left(\dfrac{a^2 - ab}{a^2 + ab} \div \dfrac{a - b}{a^3 + a^2b + ab^2}\right) \cdot \dfrac{a + b}{a^2 + ab + b^2}$

17. $\left[3x - 2 - \dfrac{8(2x + 3)}{x + 3}\right] \div \left[3(x + 2) - \dfrac{2(x^2 - 4)}{x - 3}\right]$

18. $\left(9a + \dfrac{17a^3 + 9a^2b}{b^2 - ab - 2a^2}\right) \div \left(3 + \dfrac{5a}{b - 2a}\right)$

19. $\left(a + \dfrac{2a^2b}{6a^2 - ab - b^2}\right) \cdot \left(1 - \dfrac{2ab}{6a^2 + ab - b^2}\right)$

20. $\left[x - 2 + \dfrac{2(47x - 144)}{x^2 - 7x - 144}\right] \div \left(x + 17 + \dfrac{267x - 816}{x^2 - 19x + 48}\right)$

Complex fractions. A *complex fraction* is any fraction in which the numerator or denominator or both contain fractions. (Of course, an expression such as $a - b$ can be considered as a fraction with denominator equal to 1.) Two methods are given for simplifying a complex fraction.

I. *Multiply numerator and denominator of the principal fraction by the* LCD *of all the secondary fractions.*

II. *Express the principal numerator as a single fraction, and also the principal denominator.*

Example 12. Simplify

$$\frac{1 + \frac{2}{3}}{3 - \frac{2}{5}}.$$

Solution I. If we multiply numerator and denominator by $3 \cdot 5 = 15$, we obtain

$$\frac{1 + \frac{2}{3}}{3 - \frac{2}{5}} \cdot \frac{15}{15} = \frac{15 + 10}{45 - 6} = \frac{25}{39}.$$

Solution II. $\dfrac{1 + \frac{2}{3}}{3 - \frac{2}{5}} = \dfrac{\frac{5}{3}}{\frac{13}{5}} = \dfrac{5}{3} \cdot \dfrac{5}{13} = \dfrac{25}{39}.$

Example 13. Simplify

$$\frac{3 - \dfrac{2a}{5a - 1}}{4a - \dfrac{a}{1 + 2a}}.$$

Solution I. Multiplying numerator and denominator by $(5a - 1)(1 + 2a)$, we obtain

$$\begin{aligned}\frac{3 - \dfrac{2a}{5a - 1}}{4a - \dfrac{a}{1 + 2a}} \cdot \frac{(5a - 1)(1 + 2a)}{(5a - 1)(1 + 2a)} &= \frac{3(5a - 1)(1 + 2a) - 2a(1 + 2a)}{4a(5a - 1)(1 + 2a) - a(5a - 1)} \\ &= \frac{(1 + 2a)(15a - 3 - 2a)}{a(5a - 1)(4 + 8a - 1)} \\ &= \frac{(1 + 2a)(13a - 3)}{a(5a - 1)(8a + 3)}.\end{aligned}$$

Solution II.

$$\frac{3 - \dfrac{2a}{5a - 1}}{4a - \dfrac{a}{1 + 2a}} = \frac{\dfrac{15a - 3 - 2a}{5a - 1}}{\dfrac{4a + 8a^2 - a}{1 + 2a}} = \frac{13a - 3}{5a - 1} \cdot \frac{1 + 2a}{a(8a + 3)} = \frac{(13a - 3)(1 + 2a)}{a(5a - 1)(8a + 3)}.$$

EXERCISE GROUP A–8

In each of the following exercises, reduce the given complex fraction to a fraction in simplest form.

1. $\dfrac{\frac{5}{8} - 7}{\frac{9}{16} + \frac{2}{7}}$

2. $\dfrac{15 - \frac{3}{11}}{\frac{7}{13} + 5}$

3. $\dfrac{5\frac{3}{7} - 2\frac{2}{3}}{3\frac{7}{9} + 5\frac{3}{7}}$

4. $\dfrac{4}{4 + \dfrac{3}{3 + \frac{2}{3}}}$

5. $\dfrac{5}{\frac{3}{8} - \dfrac{1}{\frac{2}{3} + \dfrac{6}{1 - \frac{3}{7}}}}$

6. $\dfrac{a + 1 - \dfrac{6}{a}}{a + 5 + \dfrac{6}{a}}$

7. $\dfrac{\dfrac{2a + b}{a + b} + 1}{\dfrac{2a + b}{a + b} - 1}$

8. $\dfrac{1 + \dfrac{2}{x^2} + \dfrac{1}{x^4}}{1 + \dfrac{2}{x} + \dfrac{1}{x^2}}$

9. $\dfrac{4 - \dfrac{1}{1 - x}}{16 + \dfrac{7}{x^2 - 1}}$

10. $\dfrac{1 + \dfrac{2}{x - 1}}{\dfrac{x^2 + x}{x^2 + x - 2}}$

11. $\dfrac{1 - \dfrac{1}{x + 2}}{2x - 2 - \dfrac{12}{x - 2}}$

12. $\dfrac{a^2 - \dfrac{1}{a}}{a + \dfrac{1}{a} + 1}$

13. $\dfrac{\dfrac{1}{x + 1} - \dfrac{1}{x - 1}}{\dfrac{1}{x - 1} + \dfrac{1}{x + 1}}$

14. $\dfrac{\dfrac{a}{b} - \dfrac{b}{a}}{\dfrac{a}{b} + \dfrac{b}{a} + 2}$

15. $\dfrac{\dfrac{a + 1}{a - 1} - \dfrac{a - 1}{a + 1}}{\dfrac{a + 1}{a - 1} + \dfrac{a - 1}{a + 1}}$

16. $\dfrac{\dfrac{1}{x - 2} - \dfrac{1}{x - 3}}{1 + \dfrac{1}{x^2 - 5x + 6}}$

17. $\dfrac{\left[x - \dfrac{y(x - y)}{x + y}\right]\left[x - \dfrac{y^2(x - y)}{x^2 + y^2}\right]}{1 - \dfrac{xy - y^2}{x^2}}$

18. $\dfrac{\dfrac{1 - x^2}{1 + y}\left(\dfrac{x}{1 + x} - 1\right)}{1 - \left(\dfrac{1}{1 - y} - \dfrac{x^2 + y^2 - x + y}{1 - y^2}\right)}$

19. $\dfrac{\left(\dfrac{x + y}{x - y} - \dfrac{x - y}{x + y} + \dfrac{4y^2}{y^2 - x^2}\right)\dfrac{x + y}{2y}}{\dfrac{x^2 - y^2}{x^2 + xy - 2y^2} \div \dfrac{x + y}{x - y}}$

20. $1 - \dfrac{\dfrac{x^2}{y^2} - \dfrac{27y}{x}}{\dfrac{x}{y} + 3 + \dfrac{9y}{x}}$

21. $\dfrac{\dfrac{2xy}{x^2 - xy + y^2} + 1}{\dfrac{x^3 - y^3}{x^3 + y^3}\left(\dfrac{2y}{x - y} + 1\right)}$

22. $$\frac{1 + \dfrac{r^2 - n^2}{m^2 - r^2}}{1 - \dfrac{2m(n + r)}{m^2 + mn + mr + nr}}$$

23. $$\frac{\dfrac{1}{x} + \dfrac{1}{y + z}}{\dfrac{1}{x} - \dfrac{1}{y + z}}\left(1 + \frac{y^2 + z^2 - x^2}{2yz}\right)$$

24. $$\frac{\dfrac{2(2 - 3x)}{5 - 4x} - \dfrac{2(7 - x)}{2 - x}}{\dfrac{22x - 29}{4x^2 - 13x + 10}}$$

25. $$\frac{\left(\dfrac{a^2 + b^2}{b} - a\right) \div \left(\dfrac{1}{b} - \dfrac{1}{a}\right)}{\left(\dfrac{1}{a^3} + \dfrac{1}{b^3}\right) \div \left(\dfrac{1}{b^2} - \dfrac{1}{a^2}\right)}$$

26. $$\frac{\dfrac{c^3 - d^3}{c^3 + d^3}\left(1 + \dfrac{2d}{c - d}\right)}{1 + \dfrac{2cd}{c^2 - cd + d^2}}$$

27. $$\frac{x - \dfrac{1}{x^2}}{x + \dfrac{1}{x} - 2} \div \frac{\left(x + \dfrac{1}{x}\right)^2 - 1}{\left(1 - \dfrac{1}{x}\right)\left(x - 1 + \dfrac{1}{x}\right)}$$

28. $$\frac{\dfrac{x + 3}{x - 1} - \dfrac{x - 1}{x + 3}}{(x + 3)^2}$$

29. $$\frac{\dfrac{a - x}{x} - \dfrac{x - 1}{x - a}}{x(x - a)}$$

30. $$\frac{2}{2 - \dfrac{3}{3 - \dfrac{4}{4 - \dfrac{5}{5 - x}}}}$$

31. $$\frac{1}{1 + \dfrac{2}{2 + \dfrac{3}{3 + \dfrac{4}{4 + x}}}}$$

32. $$\frac{a}{a - \dfrac{b}{b - \dfrac{c}{1 - \dfrac{d}{d - x}}}}$$

33. $$\frac{x}{x + \dfrac{y}{y + \dfrac{z}{1 - \dfrac{1}{1 - u}}}}$$

A-6 EXPONENTS EXTENDED

The power x^n, where the exponent n is a positive integer, or natural number, was defined and elaborated in Section A-2. One of the laws of exponents given there,

$$\frac{x^p}{x^q} = x^{p-q}, \qquad x \neq 0, \tag{3}$$

is thus valid only when p is larger than q. To make (3) valid for all integral exponents, we give the following:

Definition A-3. *If $x \neq 0$, then $x^0 = 1$.*

Definition A-4. *If n is a positive integer and $x \neq 0$, then $x^{-n} = 1/x^n$.*

With the addition of these definitions, (3) becomes valid for all integral values of p and q. In fact, all the previous properties of exponents remain valid.

We now wish to extend the idea of exponents to include all *rational exponents.* The symbol $x^{1/3}$, for example, has no meaning under previous definitions. We may then define it as we like, which we do with the goal of preserving the previous properties of exponents. Thus if Property 2 of Section A-2 is to hold, we must have

$$(x^{1/3})^3 = x^{(1/3)\cdot 3} = x,$$

so that $x^{1/3}$ must be a number, if it exists, such that its third power equals x. This will be the definition of $x^{1/3}$. In general, we have

Definition A-5. *If there exists a number y such that $y^p = x$, where p is a positive integer greater than 1, then y is called a* p*th root of x.*

The number (or numbers) y just defined can be shown to exist if x is any complex number. However, such generality is not needed here. We shall adopt the convention that *in what follows all letters represent real positive numbers.* Then x has a positive pth root; henceforth *the symbols $x^{1/p}$ and $\sqrt[p]{x}$ will be used to designate the positive* p*th root of x if x is positive.*

Definition A-6. *If p is any integer and q is a positive integer, then*

$$x^{p/q} = x^{(1/q)p} = (\sqrt[q]{x})^p;$$

also

$$x^{p/q} = (x^p)^{1/q} = \sqrt[q]{x^p}.$$

It can be shown that the two parts of the definition are consistent, and that the laws of exponents hold for rational exponents.

A negative number may be raised to a power with a rational exponent p/q if q is odd. The value will be negative if p is odd, and positive if p is even. Definition A-6 still applies.

Example 1. Write $5x^{-3}y^0$ without zero or negative exponents.

Solution. $y^0 = 1$ and $x^{-3} = 1/x^3$. Therefore

$$5x^{-3}y^0 = 5 \cdot \frac{1}{x^3} \cdot 1 = \frac{5}{x^3} \cdot$$

Example 2. Use the properties of exponents, given in Section A-2, to perform the indicated operations in

$$(2^3x^45^2y^7)^5.$$

Solution. Application of Property 3 gives

$$(2^3x^45^2y^7)^5 = (2^3)^5(x^4)^5(5^2)^5(y^7)^5.$$

If we now apply Property 2 to each power of the right member, we obtain

$$(2^3x^45^2y^7)^5 = (2^3)^5(x^4)^5(5^2)^5(y^7)^5 = 2^{15}x^{20}5^{10}y^{35}.$$

Example 3. Perform the indicated operations:

$$(7 \cdot 10^5)^3 \cdot (3 \cdot 10^{-3})^4.$$

Solution.
$$\begin{aligned}(7 \cdot 10^5)^3 \cdot (3 \cdot 10^{-3})^4 &= (7^3 10^{15}) \cdot (3^4 10^{-12}) && \text{(by Property 3 and 2)}\\ &= 3^4 \cdot 7^3 \cdot 10^{15} \cdot 10^{-12}\\ &= 3^4 \cdot 7^3 \cdot 10^3 && \text{(by Property 1).}\end{aligned}$$

Example 4. Perform the indicated operations and simplify:

$$\left(\frac{-5b^y}{3^2x^5}\right)^3\left(\frac{3x^7}{5b^y}\right)^2.$$

Solution.
$$\begin{aligned}\left(\frac{-5b^y}{3^2x^5}\right)^3\left(\frac{3x^7}{5b^y}\right)^2 &= \frac{(-5b^y)^3}{(3^2x^5)^3} \cdot \frac{(3x^7)^2}{(5b^y)^2} && \text{(by Property 4)}\\ &= \frac{(-5)^3(b^y)^3}{(3^2)^3(x^5)^3} \cdot \frac{3^2(x^7)^2}{5^2(b^y)^2} && \text{(by Property 3)}\\ &= \frac{-5^3b^{3y}}{3^6x^{15}} \cdot \frac{3^2x^{14}}{5^2b^{2y}} && \text{(by Property 2)}\\ &= \frac{-5b^y}{3^4x} = -\frac{5b^y}{81x}. && \text{(by Property 5)}\end{aligned}$$

Example 5. Express $\left(\dfrac{3x^{-1} - y^{-2}}{x^{-2} + 2y^{-1}}\right)^{-2}$ without negative exponents.

Solution.
$$\begin{aligned}\frac{3x^{-1} - y^{-2}}{x^{-2} + 2y^{-1}} &= \frac{\dfrac{3}{x} - \dfrac{1}{y^2}}{\dfrac{1}{x^2} + \dfrac{2}{y}} = \frac{\dfrac{3y^2 - x}{xy^2}}{\dfrac{y + 2x^2}{x^2y}}\\ &= \frac{3y^2 - x}{xy^2} \cdot \frac{x^2y}{y + 2x^2}\\ &= \frac{x(3y^2 - x)}{y(y + 2x^2)}.\end{aligned}$$

Therefore

$$\left(\frac{3x^{-1} - y^{-2}}{x^{-2} + 2y^{-1}}\right)^{-2} = \left[\frac{x(3y^2 - x)}{y(y + 2x^2)}\right]^{-2} = \frac{1}{\left[\frac{x(3y^2 - x)}{y(y + 2x^2)}\right]^2} = \frac{y^2(y + 2x^2)^2}{x^2(3y^2 - x)^2}.$$

Example 6. $(x^6)^{2/3} = x^{6(2/3)} = x^4$.

Example 7. $27^{-2/3} = (27^{1/3})^{-2} = 3^{-2} = \frac{1}{3^2} = \frac{1}{9}$.

Example 8. $x^{3/7} \cdot x^{5/2} = x^{(3/7)+(5/2)}$ (Property 1) $= x^{41/14}$.

Example 9. $x^{3/5} \div x^{2/3} = x^{(3/5)-(2/3)}$ (Property 5) $= x^{-1/15} = \frac{1}{x^{1/15}}$.

Example 10. Determine the value of $(0.0081)^{-3/4}$.

Solution. $(0.0081)^{-3/4} = [(0.3)^4]^{-3/4} = (0.3)^{-3} = \frac{1}{(0.3)^3} = \frac{1}{0.027} = \frac{1000}{27}$.

Example 11. Determine the value of

$$\frac{5^{3/4}5^{2/3}5^{-5/2}5^{5/3}}{5^{1/3}5^{-5/2}5^{7/4}}.$$

Solution. By Property 1 of Section A-2 we have

$$\frac{5^{(9+8-30+20)/12}}{5^{(4-30+21)/12}} = \frac{5^{7/12}}{5^{-5/12}}.$$

Now applying Property 5, we obtain

$$5^{(7/12)-(-5/12)} = 5^{12/12} = 5.$$

Example 12. Perform the indicated operations in the following expression and write the final result without negative or zero exponents:

$$\left(\frac{64a^{-3}b^{4/3}}{27a^{-9}b^{-14/3}}\right)^{-2/3}.$$

Solution. Applying Properties 4 and 3 in that order we have

$$\frac{(64)^{-2/3}a^2b^{-8/9}}{(27)^{-2/3}a^6b^{28/9}} = \frac{(4^3)^{-2/3}}{(3^3)^{-2/3}a^4b^{36/9}} = \frac{4^{-2}}{3^{-2}a^4b^4} = \frac{\frac{1}{16}}{\frac{1}{9}a^4b^4} = \frac{9}{16a^4b^4}.$$

Example 13. Determine the value of

$$\frac{(25^{-3/2} + 7x^0 + 8^{2/3})^{-1}}{[5y^0 + 0.5(-2.5)^{-1} + 3(81)^{-0.75}]^{-1}}.$$

Solution. Using Definitions A-3 and A-4, together with the five properties of exponents, we have

$$(25^{-3/2} + 7x^0 + 8^{2/3})^{-1} = \left(\frac{1}{125} + 7 + 4\right)^{-1} = \left(\frac{1 + 1375}{125}\right)^{-1} = \frac{125}{1376},$$

and

$$\begin{aligned}[5y^0 + 0.5(-2.5)^{-1} + 3(81)^{-0.75}]^{-1} &= [5 - 0.2 + 3(\tfrac{1}{27})]^{-1}\\ &= (5 - \tfrac{1}{5} + \tfrac{1}{9})^{-1}\\ &= \left(\frac{225 - 9 + 5}{45}\right)^{-1} = \frac{45}{221}.\end{aligned}$$

Therefore

$$\frac{(25^{-3/2} + 7x^0 + 8^{2/3})^{-1}}{[5y^0 + 0.5(-2.5)^{-1} + 3(81)^{-0.75}]^{-1}} = \frac{125}{1376} \div \frac{45}{221} = \frac{125}{1376} \cdot \frac{221}{45} = \frac{5525}{12384}.$$

Example 14.

$$\begin{aligned}(-8)^{1/3} &= -2;\\ (-32)^{2/5} &= [(-32)^{1/5}]^2 = (-2)^2 = 4;\\ (-32)^{3/5} &= [(-32)^{1/5}]^3 = (-2)^3 = -8.\end{aligned}$$

EXERCISE GROUP A–9

In each of Exercises 1–72, use the properties of exponents to perform the indicated operations and then simplify the result by expressing without zero or negative exponents.

1. a^3a^5	2. x^4x^7	3. $y^{2x}y^x$	4. $b^{3a}b^{2a}$
5. $c^{2b}c^{5b}$	6. $d^xd^{2x}d^{3x}$	7. x^7x^{-3}	8. y^ay^{-b}
9. z^xz^{3-x}	10. b^2b^{-3x}	11. $5^25^35^{-4}$	12. $3^73^{-2}3^5$
13. 5^x5^{2-x}	14. $3^2x^3x^y$	15. $(x^5)^4$	16. $(y^3)^7$
17. $(a^6)^3$	18. $(b^7)^5$	19. $(x^{2a})^3$	20. $(5^{2x})^3$
21. $(x^{3a})^{2b}$	22. $(x^2y^3)^7$	23. $(a^5b^3)^6$	24. $(c^3z^5)^7$
25. $(2^33^2)^5$	26. $(3^45^3)^x$	27. $(a^{2bc})^{5c}$	28. $(a^{3x}b^{4y})^z$
29. $(2^xa^23^yb^3)^z$	30. $(3^ab^35^cc^2)^5$	31. $(2^3a^{2x}3^2b^{3y})^c$	32. $\left(\frac{x}{y}\right)^5$
33. $\left(\frac{a}{b}\right)^7$	34. $\left(\frac{2a}{3y}\right)^4$	35. $\left(\frac{a^2}{b^3}\right)^6$	36. $\left(\frac{x^3}{y^2}\right)^7$
37. $\left(\frac{2x^2}{3y^4}\right)^5$	38. $\left(\frac{2^3a^4}{3^2b^3}\right)^7$	39. $\left(\frac{-2a}{3b^2}\right)^5$	40. $\left(\frac{-3x^2}{5y^a}\right)^6$
41. $\left(\frac{-1}{3b^2}\right)^a$	42. $\left(\frac{-a^3}{b^2c^7}\right)^b$	43. $\frac{a^2b^3}{a^3b^2}$	44. $\frac{x^7y^8}{x^{10}y^3}$

45. $\dfrac{2^5a^7}{2^3a}$

46. $\dfrac{5^7x^8}{5^3x^2}$

47. $\dfrac{10^2 10^7}{10^5}$

48. $\dfrac{(4\cdot 10^7)(3\cdot 10^{12})}{6\cdot 10^8}$

49. $\dfrac{(2\cdot 10^3)^2(3\cdot 10^5)}{5\cdot 10^7}$

50. $(2\cdot 10^7)^2(3\cdot 10^4)^3(2\cdot 10^5)$

51. $\left(\dfrac{3x^2}{4y^3}\right)^2\left(\dfrac{2y}{9x}\right)^5$

52. $\left(\dfrac{-2a^3}{3b^2}\right)^7\left(\dfrac{-a^2}{5b^4}\right)^3$

53. $\left(\dfrac{-3b^2}{2c^3}\right)^4\left(\dfrac{-2b^3}{c^2}\right)^6$

54. $\left(\dfrac{-2x}{5y^2}\right)^3\left(\dfrac{3y}{4x}\right)^5$

55. $\left(\dfrac{-2a^7}{3b^3}\right)^4\left(\dfrac{3b^5}{2a^4}\right)^3$

56. $\left(\dfrac{a^xb^y}{x^ay^b}\right)^2\left(\dfrac{x^{2a}y^{3b}}{a^{3x}b^{2y}}\right)^3$

57. $(3a^{-5} - 4a^{-4} + 5a^{-3})(2a^{-2} - a^{-1})$

58. $(2x^2 - 3x^{-1} + 2x - 3)(2x - 1)$

59. $(x^{-m} + x^m + 1)(x^{-m} + x^m - 1)$

60. $(a^m - 2 + a^{-m} - a^{-2m})(a^m + a^{-m} + 1)$

61. $\left(\dfrac{x^{-1} - y^{-1}}{x^{-1} + y^{-1}}\right)^{-1}$

62. $\left(\dfrac{2x^{-1} - y^{-2}}{x^{-2} - 2y^{-1}}\right)^{-2}$

63. $\left(\dfrac{2x^{-1}y^{-2}}{x + 2y^{-1}}\right)^{-2}$

64. $\left(\dfrac{3xy^{-5}}{2x^{-1} - y}\right)^{-2}$

65. $\dfrac{2^{a+1}}{(2^a)^{a+1}} \div \dfrac{4^{a-1}}{(2^{a-1})^a}$

66. $\dfrac{9^2\cdot 3^{3n}}{9^n\cdot 3^n(9 - 27^n)}$

67. $\left(\dfrac{a^{-2}b^{-3}c^{-4}}{a^2b^4c^{-3}}\right)^{-5}$

68. $\left(\dfrac{2x^3}{3z^2y^k} \div \dfrac{x^k}{z^k}\right)^3 \div \left(\dfrac{z^{k-2}}{x^{k-1}y^k}\right)^2$

69. $\dfrac{(b^{k+3})^k\cdot b^{k+5}}{(b^{k+2})^4}$

70. $\dfrac{(x^{3a+b})^c(x^{2a-c})^b}{(x^{2c+3b})^b}$

71. $\dfrac{3a^{-5} + 4a^{-4} - 5a^{-3}}{(2a^{-2} - a^{-1})^{-1}}$

72. $\dfrac{2x^{-1} + 3x^{-2} - 4x^{-3}}{5x^{-4} + 6x^{-5}}$

Simplify each of the following by performing the indicated operations and removing negative and zero exponents. (In each case express *without* radicals.)

73. $(9a^{-2}b^6)^{1/2}$

74. $\left(\dfrac{9x^{-2}}{4y^4}\right)^{1/2}$

75. $(2x^{1/3}y^{5/6})^6$

76. $(8a^{-9}b^6)^{1/3}$

77. $(2a^{-3}b^2)^{-5}$

78. $(8x^6y^{-3})^{2/3}$

79. $\left(\dfrac{27a^{-3}}{64b^{-3}}\right)^{-1/3}$

80. $\left(\dfrac{2a^{1/2}b^{1/3}}{3a^{1/6}b^{1/2}}\right)^6$

81. $\left(\dfrac{a^2b}{3a^4x^2}\right)^{3/2}$

82. $\left(\dfrac{4a^3b^5}{25a^{-1}b}\right)^{1/2}$

83. $\left\{\dfrac{[a^{3/5}(a^{3/5})^{1/3}]^5}{a^2}\right\}^{5/2}$

84. $\left\{x^{2/3}\left[\left(\dfrac{x^{2/3}}{x^{1/4}}\right)^6\right]^{1/3}\right\}^2$

85. $\left(\dfrac{8y^2z^5}{27x^6y^{-4}z^{-1}}\right)^{1/3}$ 86. $\left(\dfrac{9a^0b^{-5}c^3}{16b^3c^{-7}}\right)^{-1/2}$ 87. $\dfrac{10^{1/2}\cdot 10^{5/2}\cdot 10^{-3}}{10^{2/3}\cdot 10^{1/3}}$

88. $\left(\dfrac{9a^{-5}b^3}{25ab^{-7}}\right)^{3/2}$ 89. $\left(\dfrac{81x^{-8}y^6}{25a^4b^{-10}}\right)^{-3/2}$ 90. $\left(\dfrac{24b^{3/4}a^{3/2}}{16a^{3/4}b^{5/2}}\right)^{4/3}$

91. $(a^{1/3}b^{1/3} - a^{1/2}b^{1/2})(a^{1/3}b^{1/3} + a^{1/2}b^{1/2})$

92. $(a^{1/5}b^{1/7} - a^{2/5}b^{3/7})(a^{1/5}b^{1/7} + a^{2/5}b^{3/7})$

93. $(a^{1/3} - b^{1/5}c^{1/7})^2$ 94. $(a^{2/3} + 2a^{1/3}b^{1/3} + b^{2/3})^{1/2}$

95. $\sqrt[3]{a}\cdot\sqrt[4]{a}$ 96. $\sqrt[3]{a^2}\cdot\sqrt[4]{a^3}$ 97. $\dfrac{\sqrt[4]{a}}{\sqrt[3]{a}}$ 98. $\dfrac{16}{\sqrt[3]{16}}$

99. $\dfrac{\sqrt[4]{3}}{\sqrt[8]{81}}$ 100. $\dfrac{\sqrt{x^4\sqrt[4]{x^2}}}{\sqrt[3]{x}\cdot x^{3/4}}$ 101. $\sqrt[5]{x^2y}\cdot\sqrt[5]{x^3y^4}$ 102. $\dfrac{(\sqrt[3]{a^2b})^8}{\sqrt[3]{ab^2}}$

103. $\sqrt{16\sqrt[3]{a^6b^{12}}}$ 104. $\sqrt[3]{\sqrt{a^{-12}b^0}}$ 105. $\left[\dfrac{27^{-2/3} + (5a)^0}{3(a^2)^0 + 9^{3/2}}\right]^{-1/3}$

106. $8^{-2/3} + 5(25)^{-1/2} + 16^{1/2}(16)^0$

107. $(16)^{-3/4} + 5x^0 - (25^{-1})^{-1/2} - (-8)^{5/3}$

108. $\dfrac{0.0016^{-0.75} - 4^{-0.5}}{25^{-0.5} - 8^{-1/3}}$ 109. $\dfrac{(0.25)^{-2/3} - (0.008)^{-3/2}}{(0.00032)^{-0.6} - 6x^0}$

110. $(a^2 - x^2)^{1/2} - x[\frac{1}{2}(a^2 - x^2)^{-1/2}(-2x)]$

111. $\dfrac{(a^2 - x^2)^{1/3} - x[\frac{1}{3}(a^2 - x^2)^{-2/3}(-2x)]}{(a^2 - x^2)^{2/3}}$

112. $\dfrac{(a^3 - x^3)^{1/3}(\frac{1}{2}x^{-1/2}) - x^{1/2}[\frac{1}{3}(a^3 - x^3)^{-2/3}(-3x^2)]}{(a^3 - x^3)^{2/3}}$

113. $\dfrac{(a^5 + y^5)^{2/5}(\frac{1}{4}y^{-3/4}) - y^{1/4}[\frac{2}{5}(a^5 + y^5)^{-3/5}(5y^4)]}{(a^5 + y^5)^{4/5}}$

A-7 RADICALS AND THEIR PROPERTIES

A pth root of x, where p is an integer greater than 1, has been defined as any value of y for which $y^p = x$. It is clear that if $y^2 = x$ there are two values of y, namely,

$$y_1 = \sqrt{x} \quad\text{and}\quad y_2 = -\sqrt{x}.$$

There are four values of y for which $y^4 = x$. In general, there are p pth roots* of x, that is, p numbers y such that $y^p = x$. To avoid confusion, one of the pth roots

* See Crystal, *College Algebra*, p. 238. London: A. & C. Black, Ltd. (1926).

of x is designated as the *principal* pth *root* and is defined as follows:

***Definition** A-7. If x is a positive real number, the principal pth root of x is the real positive pth root of x. If p is an odd integer and x is a positive real number, the principal pth root of $(-x)$ is the negative real pth root of $(-x)$.*

Example. The principal square root of 25 is $+5$, and will be written as $\sqrt{25} = 5$. If the other root is desired, it will be designated as $-\sqrt{25} = -5$. The principal cube root of -27 is $\sqrt[3]{-27} = -3$.

The *radical* $\sqrt[p]{x}$ will be used to designate the principal pth root of x. The number x is called the *radicand* and the number p the *index of the radical.* It is customary to omit the index 2 in the case of a square root, so that $\sqrt[2]{x}$ is usually written $\sqrt{x}$.

Since, as we have seen, radicals can be expressed in terms of fractional exponents, the rules stated in Section A-2 yield rules for working with radicals. To avoid any difficulties which might arise from roots of negative numbers, we assume here and throughout the remainder of this review that all literal radicands represent real numbers and, in the case of radicals with even index, are also positive. The *laws* for radicals are then as follows:

1. $(\sqrt[n]{x})^n = x$ (by definition).

2. $\sqrt[n]{x} \cdot \sqrt[n]{y} = x^{1/n} \cdot y^{1/n} = (xy)^{1/n} = \sqrt[n]{xy}.$

3. $\dfrac{\sqrt[n]{x}}{\sqrt[n]{y}} = \dfrac{x^{1/n}}{y^{1/n}} = \left(\dfrac{x}{y}\right)^{1/n} = \sqrt[n]{\dfrac{x}{y}}.$

4. $\sqrt[p]{\sqrt[n]{x}} = (x^{1/n})^{1/p} = x^{1/np} = \sqrt[np]{x}.$

5. $\sqrt[p]{x^n} = (\sqrt[p]{x})^n = x^{n/p}$ (by definition).

Some applications of these laws can be seen in the following illustrations:

Example 1. $\sqrt{27} = \sqrt{9 \cdot 3} = \sqrt{9} \cdot \sqrt{3} = 3\sqrt{3}$ (Law 2).

Example 2. $\dfrac{\sqrt[3]{32}}{\sqrt[3]{4}} = \sqrt[3]{\dfrac{32}{4}} = \sqrt[3]{8} = 2$ (Law 3).

Example 3. $\sqrt[3]{\sqrt{27}} = \sqrt[6]{27} = \sqrt{\sqrt[3]{27}} = \sqrt{3}$ (Law 4).

We shall now adopt the following criterion for a *standard form of a radical.*

A radical is in standard form *if the following conditions are satisfied:*

(1) *the radicand contains no fractions,*

(2) *the radicand contains no factors which are perfect* nth *powers, where n is the index of the radical,*

(3) *the index of the radical is as low as possible.*

The method by which these conditions are brought about when they are not present is to apply the laws for radicals. The manner in which they are applied for this purpose is perhaps mainly a matter of experience with such procedures. It is suggested that the reader supply the reasons for the steps in the following examples.

Example 4. $\sqrt[6]{\frac{4}{9}} = \sqrt[6]{(\frac{2}{3})^2} = \sqrt[3]{\frac{2}{3}} = \frac{1}{3}\sqrt[3]{18}.$

Example 5. $\sqrt{\sqrt[3]{128x^5}} = \sqrt[6]{128x^5} = 2\sqrt[6]{2x^5}.$

Example 6.

$$\sqrt[4]{1 + \frac{4}{x^2} + \frac{4}{x^4}} = \sqrt[4]{\frac{x^4 + 4x^2 + 4}{x^4}}$$

$$= \sqrt[4]{\frac{(x^2 + 2)^2}{x^4}} = \frac{1}{x}\sqrt[4]{(x^2 + 2)^2} = \frac{1}{x}\sqrt{x^2 + 2}.$$

Example 7.

$$\sqrt[4]{16\left(\frac{9x^2}{4y^2} + 2 + \frac{4y^2}{9x^2}\right)}$$

$$= \sqrt[4]{\frac{4(81x^4 + 72x^2y^2 + 16y^4)}{9x^2y^2}} = \sqrt[4]{\left[\frac{2(9x^2 + 4y^2)}{3xy}\right]^2}$$

$$= \sqrt{\frac{2(9x^2 + 4y^2)}{3xy}} = \frac{1}{3xy}\sqrt{6xy(9x^2 + 4y^2)}.$$

It should be stated that there is an element of arbitrariness in the above criterion for the standard form of a radical. To illustrate this, we use the following example:

$$\sqrt{\frac{1}{3}} = \frac{1}{\sqrt{3}} \quad \text{(by Law 3)}$$

$$= \frac{\sqrt{3}}{3} \quad \text{(by the above criterion).}$$

The question arises as to whether $\sqrt{3}/3$ is simpler than $1/\sqrt{3}$. Good reasons can be presented for the contention that the latter form is simpler. In the last analysis, however, the determination of what is simpler is governed by the use to which the result is to be put. Whatever criterion is established, the principles employed in achieving a certain form are essentially the same. The above criterion should be considered in this light.

Addition and subtraction of radicals involve no new principle. Radicals with the same index and radicand, which are called *similar*, may be combined into a single term by use of the distributive law. We have, as an illustration,

$$3\sqrt{2} - \sqrt{2} + 5\sqrt{3} = (3 - 1)\sqrt{2} + 5\sqrt{3} = 2\sqrt{2} + 5\sqrt{3}.$$

Thus, to simplify an algebraic sum of terms involving radicals, we usually reduce each radical to standard form and combine similar terms.

Example 8. $\sqrt[3]{16} - \sqrt[3]{54} + \sqrt[3]{250} = 2\sqrt[3]{2} - 3\sqrt[3]{2} + 5\sqrt[3]{2} = 4\sqrt[3]{2}.$

Example 9. $\sqrt{12} + \sqrt{75} - \sqrt{18} = 2\sqrt{3} + 5\sqrt{3} - 3\sqrt{2} = 7\sqrt{3} - 3\sqrt{2}.$

Example 10. $\sqrt{3\tfrac{3}{5}} - \sqrt{6\tfrac{2}{5}} + \sqrt{19\tfrac{3}{5}} = \sqrt{\frac{18}{5}} - \sqrt{\frac{32}{5}} + \sqrt{\frac{98}{5}}$

$$= 3\sqrt{\frac{2}{5}} - 4\sqrt{\frac{2}{5}} + 7\sqrt{\frac{2}{5}}$$

$$= \frac{3\sqrt{10}}{5} - \frac{4\sqrt{10}}{5} + \frac{7\sqrt{10}}{5} = \frac{6\sqrt{10}}{5}.$$

Example 11. $\sqrt{\frac{a-b}{a+b}} - \sqrt{\frac{a+b}{a-b}} = \frac{\sqrt{a^2-b^2}}{a+b} - \frac{\sqrt{a^2-b^2}}{a-b}$

$$= \sqrt{a^2-b^2}\left[\frac{a-b-(a+b)}{a^2-b^2}\right]$$

$$= -\frac{2b\sqrt{a^2-b^2}}{a^2-b^2}.$$

Multiplication and division of radicals of the same index are accomplished by applying Laws 2 and 3 for radicals and simplifying the result, perhaps by reducing it to standard form.

Example 12. $\sqrt[3]{3ab^2} \cdot \sqrt[3]{18a^3b} = \sqrt[3]{54a^4b^3} = \sqrt[3]{27a^3b^3 \cdot 2a} = 3ab\sqrt[3]{2a}.$

Example 13. Multiply $(2\sqrt{3} + 3\sqrt{2})$ by $(3\sqrt{3} - 2\sqrt{2})$.

Solution. By formula type (4) of the special products in Section A-3, we have

$$(2\sqrt{3} + 3\sqrt{2})(3\sqrt{3} - 2\sqrt{2}) = 6(\sqrt{3})^2 + 5\sqrt{2}\sqrt{3} - 6(\sqrt{2})^2$$
$$= 18 + 5\sqrt{6} - 12 = 6 + 5\sqrt{6}.$$

Example 14. $\frac{\sqrt{5}}{\sqrt{3}} = \sqrt{\frac{5}{3}} = \sqrt{\frac{5}{3}\cdot\frac{3}{3}} = \frac{\sqrt{15}}{3}.$

Multiplication and division of radicals with different indices usually involve the introduction of equivalent powers with rational exponents, as illustrated in the following examples.

Example 15. $\sqrt[3]{4}\sqrt[4]{8} = 4^{1/3}8^{1/4} = 4^{4/12}8^{3/12} = (4^4 8^3)^{1/12} = \sqrt[12]{4^4 8^3}$
$= \sqrt[12]{(2^2)^4(2^3)^3} = \sqrt[12]{2^8 2^9} = \sqrt[12]{2^{17}} = 2\sqrt[12]{2^5} = 2\sqrt[12]{32}.$

Example 16. $\sqrt[5]{8a^3}\sqrt{2ab^2} = (2^3a^3)^{1/5}(2ab^2)^{1/2} = (2^3a^3)^{2/10}(2ab^2)^{5/10}$
$= (2^6a^6 2^5a^5b^{10})^{1/10} = \sqrt[10]{2^{11}a^{11}b^{10}} = 2ab\sqrt[10]{2a}.$

Example 17. $\dfrac{\sqrt[4]{8}}{\sqrt[3]{4}} = \dfrac{\sqrt[4]{8}}{\sqrt[3]{4}}\cdot\dfrac{\sqrt[3]{2}}{\sqrt[3]{2}} = \dfrac{(2^3)^{1/4}\cdot 2^{1/3}}{2} = \dfrac{2^{13/12}}{2} = 2^{1/12} = \sqrt[12]{2}.$

EXERCISE GROUP A–10

Reduce each of the radicals in Exercises 1–24 to standard form.

1. $\sqrt{\frac{2}{3}}$
2. $\sqrt{\frac{3}{4}}$
3. $\sqrt[3]{\frac{2}{3}}$
4. $\sqrt[3]{\frac{3}{4}}$
5. $\sqrt{\dfrac{uv^2}{wz^2}}$
6. $\sqrt[3]{\dfrac{54x^7}{25yz^4}}$
7. $\sqrt[10]{\dfrac{x^{15}y^{25}}{z^5}}$
8. $\dfrac{x}{y}\sqrt[n]{\dfrac{x^{n+1}}{y^{n-1}}}$
9. $\sqrt{\dfrac{xy^2}{x+y}}$
10. $\sqrt{\dfrac{1}{u^2}+\dfrac{1}{v^2}}$
11. $\sqrt{\dfrac{(x-y)^2}{y}-\dfrac{(x-y)^2}{x}}$
12. $\sqrt[4]{\dfrac{2x^2}{3y^2}-2+\dfrac{3y^2}{2x^2}}$
13. $\sqrt[3]{\dfrac{27}{8x^3}+\dfrac{27}{64y^4}}$
14. $\sqrt{\sqrt[3]{16x^4}}$
15. $\sqrt[3]{\sqrt[4]{64(a+b)^6}}$
16. $\sqrt[5]{\sqrt[4]{\sqrt[3]{32x^{10}y^{15}}}}$
17. $\sqrt[6]{(a^3+b^3)^2}$
18. $\sqrt[6]{(a^3+b^3)^2(a+b)^4}$
19. $\sqrt{32x^3+48x^2y^2}$
20. $\sqrt{x+\dfrac{2y}{x}+\dfrac{y^2}{x^3}}$
21. $\sqrt[4]{9+\dfrac{18y}{x^2}+\dfrac{9y^2}{x^4}}$
22. $\sqrt[4]{(x-y)^2\sqrt[3]{(a+b)^6}}$
23. $\sqrt[3]{\dfrac{32a^4b^{6k}}{81c^2}}$
24. $\sqrt{\dfrac{32a^3}{3b}-\dfrac{64a^2b}{c}}$

In each of Exercises 25–42, perform the indicated operations and reduce the result to standard form.

25. $2\sqrt{5}+3\sqrt{5}$
26. $3\sqrt{2}+\sqrt{8}$
27. $\sqrt{\frac{1}{2}}-\sqrt{\frac{9}{2}}+\sqrt{50}$
28. $\sqrt{75}-\sqrt{\frac{4}{3}}+\sqrt{\frac{50}{6}}$

29. $\sqrt[3]{3} - \sqrt[3]{-375} + \sqrt[3]{-81}$

30. $2\sqrt[3]{-16} + 3\sqrt[3]{250} - 4\sqrt[3]{128}$

31. $\sqrt[3]{\frac{32}{9}} - \frac{2}{3}\sqrt[3]{\frac{250}{18}} + \frac{3}{5}\sqrt[3]{\frac{1280}{45}}$

32. $\sqrt{49ax^3} - \sqrt{16a^3x}$

33. $\sqrt{18a} + \sqrt{72ab^2}$

34. $\sqrt[3]{54a^3b} - \sqrt[3]{16ab^4}$

35. $\sqrt{\frac{a^4c}{b^3}} + \sqrt{\frac{a^2c^2}{bx^2}} + \sqrt{\frac{a^2cx^2}{by^2}}$

36. $\sqrt[4]{81a^5} + 2\sqrt[4]{16a^5} - \sqrt[4]{256a^9}$

37. $\sqrt{xy^3z^3} + \frac{\sqrt{x^3y^5z^7}}{xyz^2} - \sqrt{x^3y^7z^5}$

38. $\sqrt{\frac{x+y}{x-y}} - \sqrt{\frac{x-y}{x+y}}$

39. $2\sqrt{\frac{3}{5a}} + 3\sqrt{\frac{5}{3a}}$

40. $\frac{-10 - \sqrt{100 - 4 \cdot 5 \cdot 3}}{10}$

41. $\frac{-3b - \sqrt{9b^2 - 4(2)(-9b)}}{4}$

42. $\frac{-q + \sqrt{q^2 - 4pr}}{2r} + \frac{-q - \sqrt{q^2 - 4pr}}{2r}$

In each of Exercises 43–64, perform the indicated operations and reduce the result to standard radical form.

43. $\sqrt{3}\sqrt{5}$

44. $\sqrt{15}\sqrt{5}$

45. $\sqrt{27}\sqrt{18}$

46. $\sqrt[3]{-18}\sqrt[3]{-12}$

47. $\sqrt[3]{25}\sqrt[3]{40}$

48. $\sqrt[3]{16}\sqrt[3]{36}$

49. $\sqrt{3ax^3}\sqrt{2a^3x}$

50. $\sqrt[3]{4a^2b}\sqrt[3]{6a^2b^5}$

51. $\sqrt{x}\sqrt{2x}\sqrt{6x^3}$

52. $(2x\sqrt[3]{3x^2})^3$

53. $(\sqrt{a^2 + b^2})^2$

54. $\sqrt{3}(\sqrt{6} - \sqrt{30})$

55. $(2\sqrt{7} - \sqrt{3})^2$

56. $(\sqrt{5} - \sqrt{3})(\sqrt{5} + \sqrt{3})$

57. $(2\sqrt{x} - 5\sqrt{x+1})(3\sqrt{x} - \sqrt{x+1})$

58. $\left(\frac{-5 + \sqrt{7}}{3}\right)\left(\frac{-5 - \sqrt{7}}{3}\right)$

59. $\left(\frac{-2 + 3\sqrt{5}}{7}\right)\left(\frac{-2 - 3\sqrt{5}}{7}\right)$

60. $\left(\frac{-3 + \sqrt{3}}{3}\right)\left(\frac{-3 - \sqrt{3}}{3}\right)$

61. $\left(\frac{-q + \sqrt{q^2 - 4pr}}{2r}\right)\left(\frac{-q - \sqrt{q^2 - 4pr}}{2r}\right)$

62. $\sqrt[6]{(x-y)^3} + y\sqrt[6]{x^2 - 2xy + y^2} - (x-y)\sqrt[3]{x-y}$

63. $(\sqrt{x} + \sqrt{3-x})^2$

64. $\sqrt{2}\sqrt[3]{3}$

Determine the value in each of Exercises 65–70.

65. $3x^2 + 2x - 3$, when $x = -1 + \sqrt{10}$

66. $x^2 + 2x - 5$, when $x = -1 + \sqrt{6}$

67. $x^2 - x - 3$, when $x = \frac{1}{2}(1 - \sqrt{13})$

68. $2x^2 - x - 5$, when $x = \frac{1}{4}(1 + \sqrt{41})$

69. $3x^2 + 2x - 5$, when $x = \frac{1}{3}(-1 + \sqrt{14})$

70. $3x^2 - 2xy - 4y^2$, when $x = 2 - \sqrt{3}$ and $y = 2 + \sqrt{3}$

In each of the following exercises, rationalize the denominator and reduce the result to standard radical form.

71. $\dfrac{\sqrt{5}}{\sqrt{3}}$ 72. $\dfrac{3\sqrt{7}}{\sqrt{2}}$ 73. $\dfrac{\sqrt{15}}{\sqrt{3x}}$ 74. $\dfrac{\sqrt{12x^3}}{\sqrt{3x^5}}$

75. $\dfrac{3x\sqrt{2x}}{\sqrt{5x}}$ 76. $\dfrac{3\sqrt{5x}}{\sqrt{2x^3}}$ 77. $\dfrac{2\sqrt[3]{6x}}{\sqrt[3]{3x^2}}$ 78. $\dfrac{\sqrt{2x^3}}{\sqrt{9x}}$

79. $\dfrac{\sqrt[3]{3x}}{\sqrt{2x^3}}$ 80. $\dfrac{\sqrt{6}}{4 - 2\sqrt{3}}$ 81. $\dfrac{9\sqrt{10}}{4 + 2\sqrt{5}}$ 82. $\dfrac{3\sqrt{7} - 5\sqrt{3}}{5\sqrt{7} + 3\sqrt{3}}$

83. $\dfrac{2\sqrt{5} - 7\sqrt{2}}{7\sqrt{2} - 3\sqrt{7}}$ 84. $\dfrac{x\sqrt{y} - y\sqrt{x}}{a\sqrt{x} + y\sqrt{y}}$ 85. $\dfrac{x - \sqrt{x^2 - 1}}{x + \sqrt{x^2 - 1}}$

86. $\dfrac{\sqrt{8}}{\sqrt[3]{4}}$ 87. $\dfrac{\sqrt[4]{6}}{\sqrt[3]{4}}$ 88. $\dfrac{\sqrt[3]{x^2}}{\sqrt{3xy}}$

Appendix B

TABLE 1

Powers and Roots

No.	Sq.	Sq. Root	Cube	Cube Root	No.	Sq.	Sq. Root	Cube	Cube Root
1	1	1.000	1	1.000	51	2,601	7.141	132,651	3.708
2	4	1.414	8	1.260	52	2,704	7.211	140,608	3.733
3	9	1.732	27	1.442	53	2,809	7.280	148,877	3.756
4	16	2.000	64	1.587	54	2,916	7.348	157,464	3.780
5	25	2.236	125	1.710	55	3,025	7.416	166,375	3.803
6	36	2.449	216	1.817	56	3,136	7.483	175,616	3.826
7	49	2.646	343	1.913	57	3,249	7.550	185,193	3.849
8	64	2.828	512	2.000	58	3,364	7.616	195,112	3.871
9	81	3.000	729	2.080	59	3,481	7.681	205,379	3.893
10	100	3.162	1,000	2.154	60	3,600	7.746	216,000	3.915
11	121	3.317	1,331	2.224	61	3,721	7.810	226,981	3.936
12	144	3.464	1,728	2.289	62	3,844	7.874	238,328	3.958
13	169	3.606	2,197	2.351	63	3,969	7.937	250,047	3.979
14	196	3.742	2,744	2.410	64	4,096	8.000	262,144	4.000
15	225	3.873	3,375	2.466	65	4,225	8.062	274,625	4.021
16	256	4.000	4,096	2.520	66	4,356	8.124	287,496	4.041
17	289	4.123	4,913	2.571	67	4,489	8.185	300,763	4.062
18	324	4.243	5,832	2.621	68	4,624	8.246	314,432	4.082
19	361	4.359	6,859	2.668	69	4,761	8.307	328,509	4.102
20	400	4.472	8,000	2.714	70	4,900	8.367	343,000	4.121
21	441	4.583	9,261	2.759	71	5,041	8.426	357,911	4.141
22	484	4.690	10,648	2.802	72	5,184	8.485	373,248	4.160
23	529	4.796	12,167	2.844	73	5,329	8.544	389,017	4.179
24	576	4.899	13,824	2.884	74	5,476	8.602	405,224	4.198
25	625	5.000	15,625	2.924	75	5,625	8.660	421,875	4.217
26	676	5.099	17,576	2.962	76	5,776	8.718	438,976	4.236
27	729	5.196	19,683	3.000	77	5,929	8.775	456,533	4.254
28	784	5.292	21,952	3.037	78	6,084	8.832	474,552	4.273
29	841	5.385	24,389	3.072	79	6,241	8.888	493,039	4.291
30	900	5.477	27,000	3.107	80	6,400	8.944	512,000	4.309
31	961	5.568	29,791	3.141	81	6,561	9.000	531,441	4.327
32	1,024	5.657	32,768	3.175	82	6,724	9.055	551,368	4.344
33	1,089	5.745	35,937	3.208	83	6,889	9.110	571,787	4.362
34	1,156	5.831	39,304	3.240	84	7,056	9.165	592,704	4.380
35	1,225	5.916	42,875	3.271	85	7,225	9.220	614,125	4.397
36	1,296	6.000	46,656	3.302	86	7,396	9.274	636,056	4.414
37	1,369	6.083	50,653	3.332	87	7,569	9.327	658,503	4.431
38	1,444	6.164	54,872	3.362	88	7,744	9.381	681,472	4.448
39	1,521	6.245	59,319	3.391	89	7,921	9.434	704,969	4.465
40	1,600	6.325	64,000	3.420	90	8,100	9.487	729,000	4.481
41	1,681	6.403	68,921	3.448	91	8,281	9.539	753,571	4.498
42	1,764	6.481	74,088	3.476	92	8,464	9.592	778,688	4.514
43	1,849	6.557	79,507	3.503	93	8,649	9.644	804,357	4.531
44	1,936	6.633	85,184	3.530	94	8,836	9.695	830,584	4.547
45	2,025	6.708	91,125	3.557	95	9,025	9.747	857,375	4.563
46	2,116	6.782	97,336	3.583	96	9,216	9.798	884,736	4.579
47	2,209	6.856	103,823	3.609	97	9,409	9.849	912,673	4.595
48	2,304	6.928	110,592	3.634	98	9,604	9.899	941,192	4.610
49	2,401	7.000	117,649	3.659	99	9,801	9.950	970,299	4.626
50	2,500	7.071	125,000	3.684	100	10,000	10.000	1,000,000	4.642

TABLE 2

Four-Place Values of Trigonometric Ratios and Radians

Degrees	Radians	Sin	Cos	Tan	Cot	Sec	Csc		
0° 00′	.0000	.0000	1.0000	.0000	——	1.000	——	1.5708	**90° 00′**
10	029	029	000	029	343.8	000	343.8	679	50
20	058	058	000	058	171.9	000	171.9	650	40
30	.0087	.0087	1.0000	.0087	114.6	1.000	114.6	1.5621	30
40	116	116	.9999	116	85.94	000	85.95	592	20
50	145	145	999	145	68.75	000	68.76	563	10
1° 00′	.0175	.0175	.9998	.0175	57.29	1.000	57.30	1.5533	**89° 00′**
10	204	204	998	204	49.10	000	49.11	504	50
20	233	233	997	233	42.96	000	42.98	475	40
30	.0262	.0262	.9997	.0262	38.19	1.000	38.20	1.5446	30
40	291	291	996	291	34.37	000	34.38	417	20
50	320	320	995	320	31.24	001	31.26	388	10
2° 00′	.0349	.0349	.9994	.0349	28.64	1.001	28.65	1.5359	**88° 00′**
10	378	378	993	378	26.43	001	26.45	330	50
20	407	407	992	407	24.54	001	24.56	301	40
30	.0436	.0436	.9990	.0437	22.90	1.001	22.93	1.5272	30
40	465	465	989	466	21.47	001	21.49	243	20
50	495	494	988	495	20.21	001	20.23	213	10
3° 00′	.0524	.0523	.9986	.0524	19.08	1.001	19.11	1.5184	**87° 00′**
10	553	552	985	553	18.07	002	18.10	155	50
20	582	581	983	582	17.17	002	17.20	126	40
30	.0611	.0610	.9981	.0612	16.35	1.002	16.38	1.5097	30
40	640	640	980	641	15.60	002	15.64	068	20
50	669	669	978	670	14.92	002	14.96	039	10
4° 00′	.0698	.0698	.9976	.0699	14.30	1.002	14.34	1.5010	**86° 00′**
10	727	727	974	729	13.73	003	13.76	981	50
20	756	756	971	758	13.20	003	13.23	952	40
30	.0785	.0785	.9969	.0787	12.71	1.003	12.75	1.4923	30
40	814	814	967	816	12.25	003	12.29	893	20
50	844	843	964	846	11.83	004	11.87	864	10
5° 00′	.0873	.0872	.9962	.0875	11.43	1.004	11.47	1.4835	**85° 00′**
10	902	901	959	904	11.06	004	11.10	806	50
20	931	929	957	934	10.71	004	10.76	777	40
30	.0960	.0958	.9954	.0963	10.39	1.005	10.43	1.4748	30
40	989	987	951	992	10.08	005	10.13	719	20
50	.1018	.1016	948	.1022	9.788	005	9.839	690	10
6° 00′	.1047	.1045	.9945	.1051	9.514	1.006	9.567	1.4661	**84° 00′**
10	076	074	942	080	9.255	006	9.309	632	50
20	105	103	939	110	9.010	006	9.065	603	40
30	.1134	.1132	.9936	.1139	8.777	1.006	8.834	1.4573	30
40	164	161	932	169	8.556	007	8.614	544	20
50	193	190	929	198	8.345	007	8.405	515	10
7° 00′	.1222	.1219	.9925	.1228	8.144	1.008	8.206	1.4486	**83° 00′**
10	251	248	922	257	7.953	008	8.016	457	50
20	280	276	918	287	7.770	008	7.834	428	40
30	.1309	.1305	.9914	.1317	7.596	1.009	7.661	1.4399	30
40	338	334	911	346	7.429	009	7.496	370	20
50	367	363	907	376	7.269	009	7.337	341	10
8° 00′	.1396	.1392	.9903	.1405	7.115	1.010	7.185	1.4312	**82° 00′**
10	425	421	899	435	6.968	010	7.040	283	50
20	454	449	894	465	6.827	011	6.900	254	40
30	.1484	.1478	.9890	.1495	6.691	1.011	6.765	1.4224	30
40	513	507	886	524	6.561	012	6.636	195	20
50	542	536	881	554	6.435	012	6.512	166	10
9° 00′	.1571	.1564	.9877	.1584	6.314	1.012	6.392	1.4137	**81° 00′**
		Cos	Sin	Cot	Tan	Csc	Sec	Radians	Degrees

TABLE 2

Four-Place Values of Trigonometric Ratios and Radians

Degrees	Radians	Sin	Cos	Tan	Cot	Sec	Csc		
9° 00′	.1571	.1564	.9877	.1584	6.314	1.012	6.392	1.4137	**81° 00′**
10	600	593	872	614	197	013	277	108	50
20	629	622	868	644	084	013	166	079	40
30	.1658	.1650	.9863	.1673	5.976	1.014	6.059	1.4050	30
40	687	679	858	703	871	014	5.955	1.4021	20
50	716	708	853	733	769	015	855	992	10
10° 00′	.1745	.1736	.9848	.1763	5.671	1.015	5.759	1.3963	**80° 00′**
10	774	765	843	793	576	016	665	934	50
20	804	794	838	823	485	016	575	904	40
30	.1833	.1822	.9833	.1853	5.396	1.017	5.487	1.3875	30
40	862	851	827	883	309	018	403	846	20
50	891	880	822	914	226	018	320	817	10
11° 00′	.1920	.1908	.9816	.1944	5.145	1.019	5.241	1.3788	**79° 00′**
10	949	937	811	974	066	019	164	759	50
20	978	965	805	.2004	4.989	020	089	730	40
30	.2007	.1994	.9799	.2035	4.915	1.020	5.016	1.3701	30
40	036	.2022	793	065	843	021	4.945	672	20
50	065	051	787	095	773	022	876	643	10
12° 00′	.2094	.2079	.9781	.2126	4.705	1.022	4.810	1.3614	**78° 00′**
10	123	108	775	156	638	023	745	584	50
20	153	136	769	186	574	024	682	555	40
30	.2182	.2164	.9763	.2217	4.511	1.024	4.620	1.3526	30
40	211	193	757	247	449	025	560	497	20
50	240	221	750	278	390	026	502	468	10
13° 00′	.2269	.2250	.9744	.2309	4.331	1.026	4.445	1.3439	**77° 00′**
10	298	278	737	339	275	027	390	410	50
20	327	306	730	370	219	028	336	381	40
30	.2356	.2334	.9724	.2401	4.165	1.028	4.284	1.3352	30
40	385	363	717	432	113	029	232	323	20
50	414	391	710	462	061	030	182	294	10
14° 00′	.2443	.2419	.9703	.2493	4.011	1.031	4.134	1.3265	**76° 00′**
10	473	447	696	524	3.962	031	086	235	50
20	502	476	689	555	914	032	039	206	40
30	.2531	.2504	.9681	.2586	3.867	1.033	3.994	1.3177	30
40	560	532	674	617	821	034	950	148	20
50	589	560	667	648	776	034	906	119	10
15° 00′	.2618	.2588	.9659	.2679	3.732	1.035	3.864	1.3090	**75° 00′**
10	647	616	652	711	689	036	822	061	50
20	676	644	644	742	647	037	782	032	40
30	.2705	.2672	.9636	.2773	3.606	1.038	3.742	1.3003	30
40	734	700	628	805	566	039	703	974	20
50	763	728	621	836	526	039	665	945	10
16° 00′	.2793	.2756	.9613	.2867	3.487	1.040	3.628	1.2915	**74° 00′**
10	822	784	605	899	450	041	592	886	50
20	851	812	596	931	412	042	556	857	40
30	.2880	.2840	.9588	.2962	3.376	1.043	3.521	1.2828	30
40	909	868	580	994	340	044	487	799	20
50	938	896	572	.3026	305	045	453	770	10
17° 00′	.2967	.2924	.9563	.3057	3.271	1.046	3.420	1.2741	**73° 00′**
10	996	952	555	089	237	047	388	712	50
20	.3025	979	546	121	204	048	356	683	40
30	.3054	.3007	.9537	.3153	3.172	1.049	3.326	1.2654	30
40	083	035	528	185	140	049	295	625	20
50	113	062	520	217	108	050	265	595	10
18° 00′	.3142	.3090	.9511	.3249	3.078	1.051	3.236	1.2566	**72° 00′**
		Cos	Sin	Cot	Tan	Csc	Sec	Radians	Degrees

TABLE 2

Four-Place Values of Trigonometric Ratios and Radians

Degrees	Radians	Sin	Cos	Tan	Cot	Sec	Csc		
18° 00′	.3142	.3090	.9511	.3249	3.078	1.051	3.236	1.2566	**72° 00′**
10	171	118	502	281	047	052	207	537	50
20	200	145	492	314	018	053	179	508	40
30	.3229	.3173	.9483	.3346	2.989	1.054	3.152	1.2479	30
40	258	201	474	378	960	056	124	450	20
50	287	228	465	411	932	057	098	421	10
19° 00′	.3316	.3256	.9455	.3443	2.904	1.058	3.072	1.2392	**71° 00′**
10	345	283	446	476	877	059	046	363	50
20	374	311	436	508	850	060	021	334	40
30	.3403	.3338	.9426	.3541	2.824	1.061	2.996	1.2305	30
40	432	365	417	574	798	062	971	275	20
50	462	393	407	607	773	063	947	246	10
20° 00′	.3491	.3420	.9397	.3640	2.747	1.064	2.924	1.2217	**70° 00′**
10	520	448	387	673	723	065	901	188	50
20	549	475	377	706	699	066	878	159	40
30	.3578	.3502	.9367	.3739	2.675	1.068	2.855	1.2130	30
40	607	529	356	772	651	069	833	101	20
50	636	557	346	805	628	070	812	072	10
21° 00′	.3665	.3584	.9336	.3839	2.605	1.071	2.790	1.2043	**69° 00′**
10	694	611	325	872	583	072	769	1.2014	50
20	723	638	315	906	560	074	749	985	40
30	.3752	.3665	.9304	.3939	2.539	1.075	2.729	1.1956	30
40	782	692	293	973	517	076	709	926	20
50	811	719	283	.4006	496	077	689	897	10
22° 00′	.3840	.3746	.9272	.4040	2.475	1.079	2.669	1.1868	**68° 00′**
10	869	773	261	074	455	080	650	839	50
20	898	800	250	108	434	081	632	810	40
30	.3927	.3827	.9239	.4142	2.414	1.082	2.613	1.1781	30
40	956	854	228	176	394	084	595	752	20
50	985	881	216	210	375	085	577	723	10
23° 00′	.4014	.3907	.9205	.4245	2.356	1.086	2.559	1.1694	**67° 00′**
10	043	934	194	279	337	088	542	665	50
20	072	961	182	314	318	089	525	636	40
30	.4102	.3987	.9171	.4348	2.300	1.090	2.508	1.1606	30
40	131	.4014	159	383	282	092	491	577	20
50	160	041	147	417	264	093	475	548	10
24° 00′	.4189	.4067	.9135	.4452	2.246	1.095	2.459	1.1519	**66° 00′**
10	218	094	124	487	229	096	443	490	50
20	247	120	112	522	211	097	427	461	40
30	.4276	.4147	.9100	.4557	2.194	1.099	2.411	1.1432	30
40	305	173	088	592	177	100	396	403	20
50	334	200	075	628	161	102	381	374	10
25° 00′	.4363	.4226	.9063	.4663	2.145	1.103	2.366	1.1345	**65° 00′**
10	392	253	051	699	128	105	352	316	50
20	422	279	038	734	112	106	337	286	40
30	.4451	.4305	.9026	.4770	2.097	1.108	2.323	1.1257	30
40	480	331	013	806	081	109	309	228	20
50	509	358	001	841	066	111	295	199	10
26° 00′	.4538	.4384	.8988	.4877	2.050	1.113	2.281	1.1170	**64° 00′**
10	567	410	975	913	035	114	268	141	50
20	596	436	962	950	020	116	254	112	40
30	.4625	.4462	.8949	.4986	2.006	1.117	2.241	1.1083	30
40	654	488	936	.5022	1.991	119	228	054	20
50	683	514	923	059	977	121	215	1.1025	10
27° 00′	.4712	.4540	.8910	.5095	1.963	1.122	2.203	1.0996	**63° 00′**
		Cos	Sin	Cot	Tan	Csc	Sec	Radians	Degrees

TABLE 2

Four-Place Values of Trigonometric Ratios and Radians

Degrees	Radians	Sin	Cos	Tan	Cot	Sec	Csc		
27° 00′	.4712	.4540	.8910	.5095	1.963	1.122	2.203	1.0996	**63° 00′**
10	741	566	897	132	949	124	190	966	50
20	771	592	884	169	935	126	178	937	40
30	.4800	.4617	.8870	.5206	1.921	1.127	2.166	1.0908	30
40	829	643	857	243	907	129	154	879	20
50	858	669	843	280	894	131	142	850	10
28° 00′	.4887	.4695	.8829	.5317	1.881	1.133	2.130	1.0821	**62° 00′**
10	916	720	816	354	868	134	118	792	50
20	945	746	802	392	855	136	107	763	40
30	.4974	.4772	.8788	.5430	1.842	1.138	2.096	1.0734	30
40	.5003	797	774	467	829	140	085	705	20
50	032	823	760	505	816	142	074	676	10
29° 00′	.5061	.4848	.8746	.5543	1.804	1.143	2.063	1.0647	**61° 00′**
10	091	874	732	581	792	145	052	617	50
20	120	899	718	619	780	147	041	588	40
30	.5149	.4924	.8704	.5658	1.767	1.149	2.031	1.0559	30
40	178	950	689	696	756	151	020	530	20
50	207	975	675	735	744	153	010	501	10
30° 00′	.5236	.5000	.8660	.5774	1.732	1.155	2.000	1.0472	**60° 00′**
10	265	025	646	812	720	157	1.990	443	50
20	294	050	631	851	709	159	980	414	40
30	.5323	.5075	.8616	.5890	1.698	1.161	1.970	1.0385	30
40	352	100	601	930	686	163	961	356	20
50	381	125	587	969	675	165	951	327	10
31° 00′	.5411	.5150	.8572	.6009	1.664	1.167	1.942	1.0297	**59° 00′**
10	440	175	557	048	653	169	932	268	50
20	469	200	542	088	643	171	923	239	40
30	.5498	.5225	.8526	.6128	1.632	1.173	1.914	1.0210	30
40	527	250	511	168	621	175	905	181	20
50	556	275	496	208	611	177	896	152	10
32° 00′	.5585	.5299	.8480	.6249	1.600	1.179	1.887	1.0123	**58° 00′**
10	614	324	465	289	590	181	878	094	50
20	643	348	450	330	580	184	870	065	40
30	.5672	.5373	.8434	.6371	1.570	1.186	1.861	1.0036	30
40	701	398	418	412	560	188	853	1.0007	20
50	730	422	403	453	550	190	844	977	10
33° 00′	.5760	.5446	.8387	.6494	1.540	1.192	1.836	.9948	**57° 00′**
10	789	471	371	536	530	195	828	919	50
20	818	495	355	577	520	197	820	890	40
30	.5847	.5519	.8339	.6619	1.511	1.199	1.812	.9861	30
40	876	544	323	661	501	202	804	832	20
50	905	568	307	703	1.492	204	796	803	10
34° 00′	.5934	.5592	.8290	.6745	1.483	1.206	1.788	.9774	**56° 00′**
10	963	616	274	787	473	209	781	745	50
20	992	640	258	830	464	211	773	716	40
30	.6021	.5664	.8241	.6873	1.455	1.213	1.766	.9687	30
40	050	688	225	916	446	216	758	657	20
50	080	712	208	959	437	218	751	628	10
35° 00′	.6109	.5736	.8192	.7002	1.428	1.221	1.743	.9599	**55° 00′**
10	138	760	175	046	419	223	736	570	50
20	167	783	158	089	411	226	729	541	40
30	.6196	.5807	.8141	.7133	1.402	1.228	1.722	.9512	30
40	225	831	124	177	393	231	715	483	20
50	254	854	107	221	385	233	708	454	10
36° 00′	.6283	.5878	.8090	.7265	1.376	1.236	1.701	.9425	**54° 00′**
		Cos	Sin	Cot	Tan	Csc	Sec	Radians	Degrees

TABLE 2

Four-Place Values of Trigonometric Ratios and Radians

Degrees	Radians	Sin	Cos	Tan	Cot	Sec	Csc		
36° 00′	.6283	.5878	.8090	.7265	1.376	1.236	1.701	.9425	**54° 00′**
10	312	901	073	310	368	239	695	396	50
20	341	925	056	355	360	241	688	367	40
30	.6370	.5948	.8039	.7400	1.351	1.244	1.681	.9338	30
40	400	972	021	445	343	247	675	308	20
50	429	995	004	490	335	249	668	279	10
37° 00′	.6458	.6018	.7986	.7536	1.327	1.252	1.662	.9250	**53° 00′**
10	487	041	969	581	319	255	655	221	50
20	516	065	951	627	311	258	649	192	40
30	.6545	.6088	.7934	.7673	1.303	1.260	1.643	.9163	30
40	574	111	916	720	295	263	636	134	20
50	603	134	898	766	288	266	630	105	10
38° 00′	.6632	.6157	.7880	.7813	1.280	1.269	1.624	.9076	**52° 00′**
10	661	180	862	860	272	272	618	047	50
20	690	202	844	907	265	275	612	.9018	40
30	.6720	.6225	.7826	.7954	1.257	1.278	1.606	.8988	30
40	749	248	808	.8002	250	281	601	959	20
50	778	271	790	050	242	284	595	930	10
39° 00′	.6807	.6293	.7771	.8098	1.235	1.287	1.589	.8901	**51° 00′**
10	836	316	753	146	228	290	583	872	50
20	865	338	735	195	220	293	578	843	40
30	.6894	.6361	.7716	.8243	1.213	1.296	1.572	.8814	30
40	923	383	698	292	206	299	567	785	20
50	952	406	679	342	199	302	561	756	10
40° 00′	.6981	.6428	.7660	.8391	1.192	1.305	1.556	.8727	**50° 00′**
10	.7010	450	642	441	185	309	550	698	50
20	039	472	623	491	178	312	545	668	40
30	.7069	.6494	.7604	.8541	1.171	1.315	1.540	.8639	30
40	098	517	585	591	164	318	535	610	20
50	127	539	566	642	157	322	529	581	10
41° 00′	.7156	.6561	.7547	.8693	1.150	1.325	1.524	.8552	**49° 00′**
10	185	583	528	744	144	328	519	523	50
20	214	604	509	796	137	332	514	494	40
30	.7243	.6626	.7490	.8847	1.130	1.335	1.509	.8465	30
40	272	648	470	899	124	339	504	436	20
50	301	670	451	952	117	342	499	407	10
42° 00′	.7330	.6691	.7431	.9004	1.111	1.346	1.494	.8378	**48° 00′**
10	359	713	412	057	104	349	490	348	50
20	389	734	392	110	098	353	485	319	40
30	.7418	.6756	.7373	.9163	1.091	1.356	1.480	.8290	30
40	447	777	353	217	085	360	476	261	20
50	476	799	333	271	079	364	471	232	10
43° 00′	.7505	.6820	.7314	.9325	1.072	1.367	1.466	.8203	**47° 00′**
10	534	841	294	380	066	371	462	174	50
20	563	862	274	435	060	375	457	145	40
30	.7592	.6884	.7254	.9490	1.054	1.379	1.453	.8116	30
40	621	905	234	545	048	382	448	087	20
50	650	926	214	601	042	386	444	058	10
44° 00′	.7679	.6947	.7193	.9657	1.036	1.390	1.440	.8029	**46° 00′**
10	709	967	173	713	030	394	435	999	50
20	738	988	153	770	024	398	431	970	40
30	.7767	.7009	.7133	.9827	1.018	1.402	1.427	.7941	30
40	796	030	112	884	012	406	423	912	20
50	825	050	092	942	006	410	418	883	10
45° 00′	.7854	.7071	.7071	1.000	1.000	1.414	1.414	.7854	**45° 00′**
		Cos	Sin	Cot	Tan	Csc	Sec	Radians	Degrees

TABLE 3

Four-Place Logarithms of Numbers

N	0	1	2	3	4	5	6	7	8	9
10	0000	0043	0086	0128	0170	0212	0253	0294	0334	0374
11	0414	0453	0492	0531	0569	0607	0645	0682	0719	0755
12	0792	0828	0864	0899	0934	0969	1004	1038	1072	1106
13	1139	1173	1206	1239	1271	1303	1335	1367	1399	1430
14	1461	1492	1523	1553	1584	1614	1644	1673	1703	1732
15	1761	1790	1818	1847	1875	1903	1931	1959	1987	2014
16	2041	2068	2095	2122	2148	2175	2201	2227	2253	2279
17	2304	2330	2355	2380	2405	2430	2455	2480	2504	2529
18	2553	2577	2601	2625	2648	2672	2695	2718	2742	2765
19	2788	2810	2833	2856	2878	2900	2923	2945	2967	2989
20	3010	3032	3054	3075	3096	3118	3139	3160	3181	3201
21	3222	3243	3263	3284	3304	3324	3345	3365	3385	3404
22	3424	3444	3464	3483	3502	3522	3541	3560	3579	3598
23	3617	3636	3655	3674	3692	3711	3729	3747	3766	3784
24	3802	3820	3838	3856	3874	3892	3909	3927	3945	3962
25	3979	3997	4014	4031	4048	4065	4082	4099	4116	4133
26	4150	4166	4183	4200	4216	4232	4249	4265	4281	4298
27	4314	4330	4346	4362	4378	4393	4409	4425	4440	4456
28	4472	4487	4502	4518	4533	4548	4564	4579	4594	4609
29	4624	4639	4654	4669	4683	4698	4713	4728	4742	4757
30	4771	4786	4800	4814	4829	4843	4857	4871	4886	4900
31	4914	4928	4942	4955	4969	4983	4997	5011	5024	5038
32	5051	5065	5079	5092	5105	5119	5132	5145	5159	5172
33	5185	5198	5211	5224	5237	5250	5263	5276	5289	5302
34	5315	5328	5340	5353	5366	5378	5391	5403	5416	5428
35	5441	5453	5465	5478	5490	5502	5514	5527	5539	5551
36	5563	5575	5587	5599	5611	5623	5635	5647	5658	5670
37	5682	5694	5705	5717	5729	5740	5752	5763	5775	5786
38	5798	5809	5821	5832	5843	5855	5866	5877	5888	5899
39	5911	5922	5933	5944	5955	5966	5977	5988	5999	6010
40	6021	6031	6042	6053	6064	6075	6085	6096	6107	6117
41	6128	6138	6149	6160	6170	6180	6191	6201	6212	6222
42	6232	6243	6253	6263	6274	6284	6294	6304	6314	6325
43	6335	6345	6355	6365	6375	6385	6395	6405	6415	6425
44	6435	6444	6454	6464	6474	6484	6493	6503	6513	6522
45	6532	6542	6551	6561	6571	6580	6590	6599	6609	6618
46	6628	6637	6646	6656	6665	6675	6684	6693	6702	6712
47	6721	6730	6739	6749	6758	6767	6776	6785	6794	6803
48	6812	6821	6830	6839	6848	6857	6866	6875	6884	6893
49	6902	6911	6920	6928	6937	6946	6955	6964	6972	6981
50	6990	6998	7007	7016	7024	7033	7042	7050	7059	7067
51	7076	7084	7093	7101	7110	7118	7126	7135	7143	7152
52	7160	7168	7177	7185	7193	7202	7210	7218	7226	7235
53	7243	7251	7259	7267	7275	7284	7292	7300	7308	7316
54	7324	7332	7340	7348	7356	7364	7372	7380	7388	7396

TABLE 3

Four-Place Logarithms of Numbers

N	0	1	2	3	4	5	6	7	8	9
55	7404	7412	7419	7427	7435	7443	7451	7459	7466	7474
56	7482	7490	7497	7505	7513	7520	7528	7536	7543	7551
57	7559	7566	7574	7582	7589	7597	7604	7612	7619	7627
58	7634	7642	7649	7657	7664	7672	7679	7686	7694	7701
59	7709	7716	7723	7731	7738	7745	7752	7760	7767	7774
60	7782	7789	7796	7803	7810	7818	7825	7832	7839	7846
61	7853	7860	7868	7875	7882	7889	7896	7903	7910	7917
62	7924	7931	7938	7945	7952	7959	7966	7973	7980	7987
63	7993	8000	8007	8014	8021	8028	8035	8041	8048	8055
64	8062	8069	8075	8082	8089	8096	8102	8109	8116	8122
65	8129	8136	8142	8149	8156	8162	8169	8176	8182	8189
66	8195	8202	8209	8215	8222	8228	8235	8241	8248	8254
67	8261	8267	8274	8280	8287	8293	8299	8306	8312	8319
68	8325	8331	8338	8344	8351	8357	8363	8370	8376	8382
69	8388	8395	8401	8407	8414	8420	8426	8432	8439	8445
70	8451	8457	8463	8470	8476	8482	8488	8494	8500	8506
71	8513	8519	8525	8531	8537	8543	8549	8555	8561	8567
72	8573	8579	8585	8591	8597	8603	8609	8615	8621	8627
73	8633	8639	8645	8651	8657	8663	8669	8675	8681	8686
74	8692	8698	8704	8710	8716	8722	8727	8733	8739	8745
75	8751	8756	8762	8768	8774	8779	8785	8791	8797	8802
76	8808	8814	8820	8825	8831	8837	8842	8848	8854	8859
77	8865	8871	8876	8882	8887	8893	8899	8904	8910	8915
78	8921	8927	8932	8938	8943	8949	8954	8960	8965	8971
79	8976	8982	8987	8993	8998	9004	9009	9015	9020	9025
80	9031	9036	9042	9047	9053	9058	9063	9069	9074	9079
81	9085	9090	9096	9101	9106	9112	9117	9122	9128	9133
82	9138	9143	9149	9154	9159	9165	9170	9175	9180	9186
83	9191	9196	9201	9206	9212	9217	9222	9227	9232	9238
84	9243	9248	9253	9258	9263	9269	9274	9279	9284	9289
85	9294	9299	9304	9309	9315	9320	9325	9330	9335	9340
86	9345	9350	9355	9360	9365	9370	9375	9380	9385	9390
87	9395	9400	9405	9410	9415	9420	9425	9430	9435	9440
88	9445	9450	9455	9460	9465	9469	9474	9479	9484	9489
89	9494	9499	9504	9509	9513	9518	9523	9528	9533	9538
90	9542	9547	9552	9557	9652	9566	9571	9576	9581	9586
91	9590	9595	9600	9605	9609	9614	9619	9624	9628	9633
92	9638	9643	9647	9652	9657	9661	9666	9671	9675	9680
93	9685	9689	9694	9699	9703	9708	9713	9717	9722	9727
94	9731	9736	9741	9745	9750	9754	9759	9763	9768	9773
95	9777	9782	9786	9791	9795	9800	9805	9809	9814	9818
96	9823	9827	9832	9836	9841	9845	9850	9854	9859	9863
97	9868	9872	9877	9881	9886	9890	9894	9899	9903	9908
98	9912	9917	9921	9926	9930	9934	9939	9943	9948	9952
99	9956	9961	9965	9969	9974	9978	9983	9987	9991	9996

TABLE 4

Logarithms of Trigonometric Ratios

Degrees	$\log_{10}$ Sine	$\log_{10}$ Tangent	$\log_{10}$ Cotangent	$\log_{10}$ Cosine	
0° 00′					**90° 00′**
10′	.4637—3	.4637—3	2.5363	.0000	50′
20′	.7648—3	.7648—3	2.2352	.0000	40′
30′	.9408—3	.9409—3	2.0591	.0000	30′
40′	.0658—2	.0658—2	1.9342	.0000	20′
50′	.1627—2	.1627—2	1.8373	.0000	10′
1° 00′	.2419—2	.2419—2	1.7581	.9999—1	**89° 00′**
10′	.3088—2	.3089—2	1.6911	.9999—1	50′
20′	.3668—2	.3669—2	1.6331	.9999—1	40′
30′	.4179—2	.4181—2	1.5819	.9999—1	30′
40′	.4637—2	.4638—2	1.5362	.9998—1	20′
50′	.5050—2	.5053—2	1.4947	.9998—1	10′
2° 00′	.5428—2	.5431—2	1.4569	.9997—1	**88° 00′**
10′	.5776—2	.5779—2	1.4221	.9997—1	50′
20′	.6097—2	.6101—2	1.3899	.9996—1	40′
30′	.6397—2	.6401—2	1.3599	.9996—1	30′
40′	.6677—2	.6682—2	1.3318	.9995—1	20′
50′	.6940—2	.6945—2	1.3055	.9995—1	10′
3° 00′	.7188—2	.7194—2	1.2806	.9994—1	**87° 00′**
10′	.7423—2	.7429—2	1.2571	.9993—1	50′
20′	.7645—2	.7652—2	1.2348	.9993—1	40′
30′	.7857—2	.7865—2	1.2135	.9992—1	30′
40′	.8059—2	.8067—2	1.1933	.9991—1	20′
50′	.8251—2	.8261—2	1.1739	.9990—1	10′
4° 00′	.8436—2	.8446—2	1.1554	.9989—1	**86° 00′**
10′	.8613—2	.8624—2	1.1376	.9989—1	50′
20′	.8783—2	.8795—2	1.1205	.9988—1	40′
30′	.8946—2	.8960—2	1.1040	.9987—1	30′
40′	.9104—2	.9118—2	1.0882	.9986—1	20′
50′	.9256—2	.9272—2	1.0728	.9985—1	10′
5° 00′	.9403—2	.9420—2	1.0580	.9983—1	**85° 00′**
10′	.9545—2	.9563—2	1.0437	.9982—1	50′
20′	.9682—2	.9701—2	1.0299	.9981—1	40′
30′	.9816—2	.9836—2	1.0164	.9980—1	30′
40′	.9945—2	.9966—2	1.0034	.9979—1	20′
50′	.0070—1	.0093—1	.9907	.9977—1	10′
6° 00′	.0192—1	.0216—1	.9784	.9976—1	**84° 00′**
10′	.0311—1	.0336—1	.9664	.9975—1	50′
20′	.0426—1	.0453—1	.9547	.9973—1	40′
30′	.0539—1	.0567—1	.9433	.9972—1	30′
40′	.0648—1	.0678—1	.9322	.9971—1	20′
50′	.0755—1	.0786—1	.9214	.9969—1	10′
7° 00′	.0859—1	.0891—1	.9109	.9968—1	**83° 00′**
10′	.0961—1	.0995—1	.9005	.9966—1	50′
20′	.1060—1	.1096—1	.8904	.9964—1	40′
30′	.1157—1	.1194—1	.8806	.9963—1	30′
40′	.1252—1	.1291—1	.8709	.9961—1	20′
50′	.1345—1	.1385—1	.8615	.9959—1	10′
8° 00′	.1436—1	.1478—1	.8522	.9958—1	**82° 00′**
10′	.1525—1	.1569—1	.8431	.9956—1	50′
20′	.1612—1	.1658—1	.8342	.9954—1	40′
30′	.1697—1	.1745—1	.8255	.9952—1	30′
40′	.1781—1	.1831—1	.8169	.9950—1	20′
50′	.1863—1	.1915—1	.8085	.9948—1	10′
9° 00′	.1943—1	.1997—1	.8003	.9946—1	**81° 00′**
	$\log_{10}$ Cosine	$\log_{10}$ Cotangent	$\log_{10}$ Tangent	$\log_{10}$ Sine	Degrees

TABLE 4

Logarithms of Trigonometric Ratios

Degrees	Log₁₀ Sine	Log₁₀ Tangent	Log₁₀ Cotangent	Log₁₀ Cosine	
9° 00′	.1943—1	.1997—1	.8003	.9946—1	**81° 00′**
10′	.2022—1	.2078—1	.7922	.9944—1	50′
20′	.2100—1	.2158—1	.7842	.9942—1	40′
30′	.2176—1	.2236—1	.7764	.9940—1	30′
40′	.2251—1	.2313—1	.7687	.9938—1	20′
50′	.2324—1	.2389—1	.7611	.9936—1	10′
10° 00′	.2397—1	.2463—1	.7537	.9934—1	**80° 00′**
10′	.2468—1	.2536—1	.7464	.9931—1	50′
20′	.2538—1	.2609—1	.7391	.9929—1	40′
30′	.2606—1	.2680—1	.7320	.9927—1	30′
40′	.2674—1	.2750—1	.7250	.9924—1	20′
50′	.2740—1	.2819—1	.7181	.9922—1	10′
11° 00′	.2806—1	.2887—1	.7113	.9919—1	**79° 00′**
10′	.2870—1	.2953—1	.7047	.9917—1	50′
20′	.2934—1	.3020—1	.6980	.9914—1	40′
30′	.2997—1	.3085—1	.6915	.9912—1	30′
40′	.3058—1	.3149—1	.6851	.9909—1	20′
50′	.3119—1	.3212—1	.6788	.9907—1	10′
12° 00′	.3179—1	.3275—1	.6725	.9904—1	**78° 00′**
10′	.3238—1	.3336—1	.6664	.9901—1	50′
20′	.3296—1	.3397—1	.6603	.9899—1	40′
30′	.3353—1	.3458—1	.6542	.9896—1	30′
40′	.3410—1	.3517—1	.6483	.9893—1	20′
50′	.3466—1	.3576—1	.6424	.9890—1	10′
13° 00′	.3521—1	.3634—1	.6366	.9887—1	**77° 00′**
10′	.3575—1	.3691—1	.6309	.9884—1	50′
20′	.3629—1	.3748—1	.6252	.9881—1	40′
30′	.3682—1	.3804—1	.6196	.9878—1	30′
40′	.3734—1	.3859—1	.6141	.9875—1	20′
50′	.3786—1	.3914—1	.6086	.9872—1	10′
14° 00′	.3837—1	.3968—1	.6032	.9869—1	**76° 00′**
10′	.3887—1	.4021—1	.5979	.9866—1	50′
20′	.3937—1	.4074—1	.5926	.9863—1	40′
30′	.3986—1	.4127—1	.5873	.9859—1	30′
40′	.4035—1	.4178—1	.5822	.9856—1	20′
50′	.4083—1	.4230—1	.5770	.9853—1	10′
15° 00′	.4130—1	.4281—1	.5719	.9849—1	**75° 00′**
10′	.4177—1	.4331—1	.5669	.9846—1	50′
20′	.4223—1	.4381—1	.5619	.9843—1	40′
30′	.4269—1	.4430—1	.5570	.9839—1	30′
40′	.4314—1	.4479—1	.5521	.9836—1	20′
50′	.4359—1	.4527—1	.5473	.9832—1	10′
16° 00′	.4403—1	.4575—1	.5425	.9828—1	**74° 00′**
10′	.4447—1	.4622—1	.5378	.9825—1	50′
20′	.4491—1	.4669—1	.5331	.9821—1	40′
30′	.4533—1	.4716—1	.5284	.9817—1	30′
40′	.4576—1	.4762—1	.5238	.9814—1	20′
50′	.4618—1	.4808—1	.5192	.9810—1	10′
17° 00′	.4659—1	.4853—1	.5147	.9806—1	**73° 00′**
10′	.4700—1	.4898—1	.5102	.9802—1	50′
20′	.4741—1	.4943—1	.5057	.9798—1	40′
30′	.4781—1	.4987—1	.5013	.9794—1	30′
40′	.4821—1	.5031—1	.4969	.9790—1	20′
50′	.4861—1	.5075—1	.4925	.9786—1	10′
18° 00′	.4900—1	.5118—1	.4882	.9782—1	**72° 00′**
	Log₁₀ Cosine	Log₁₀ Cotangent	Log₁₀ Tangent	Log₁₀ Sine	Degrees

TABLE 4

Logarithms of Trigonometric Ratios

Degrees	Log$_{10}$ Sine	Log$_{10}$ Tangent	Log$_{10}$ Cotangent	Log$_{10}$ Cosine	
18° 00′	.4900—1	.5118—1	.4882	.9782—1	**72° 00′**
10′	.4939—1	.5161—1	.4839	.9778—1	50′
20′	.4977—1	.5203—1	.4797	.9774—1	40′
30′	.5015—1	.5245—1	.4755	.9770—1	30′
40′	.5052—1	.5287—1	.4713	.9765—1	20′
50′	.5090—1	.5329—1	.4671	.9761—1	10′
19° 00′	.5126—1	.5370—1	.4630	.9757—1	**71° 00′**
10′	.5163—1	.5411—1	.4589	.9752—1	50′
20′	.5199—1	.5451—1	.4549	.9748—1	40′
30′	.5235—1	.5491—1	.4509	.9743—1	30′
40′	.5270—1	.5531—1	.4469	.9739—1	20′
50′	.5306—1	.5571—1	.4429	.9734—1	10′
20° 00′	.5341—1	.5611—1	.4389	.9730—1	**70° 00′**
10′	.5375—1	.5650—1	.4350	.9725—1	50′
20′	.5409—1	.5689—1	.4311	.9721—1	40′
30′	.5443—1	.5727—1	.4273	.9716—1	30′
40′	.5477—1	.5766—1	.4234	.9711—1	20′
50′	.5510—1	.5804—1	.4196	.9706—1	10′
21° 00′	.5543—1	.5842—1	.4158	.9702—1	**69° 00′**
10′	.5576—1	.5879—1	.4121	.9697—1	50′
20′	.5609—1	.5917—1	.4083	.9692—1	40′
30′	.5641—1	.5954—1	.4046	.9687—1	30′
40′	.5673—1	.5991—1	.4009	.9682—1	20′
50′	.5704—1	.6028—1	.3972	.9677—1	10′
22° 00′	.5736—1	.6064—1	.3936	.9672—1	**68° 00′**
10′	.5767—1	.6100—1	.3900	.9667—1	50′
20′	.5798—1	.6136—1	.3864	.9661—1	40′
30′	.5828—1	.6172—1	.3828	.9656—1	30′
40′	.5859—1	.6208—1	.3792	.9651—1	20′
50′	.5889—1	.6243—1	.3757	.9646—1	10′
23° 00′	.5919—1	.6279—1	.3721	.9640—1	**67° 00′**
10′	.5948—1	.6314—1	.3686	.9635—1	50′
20′	.5978—1	.6348—1	.3652	.9629—1	40′
30′	.6007—1	.6383—1	.3617	.9624—1	30′
40′	.6036—1	.6417—1	.3583	.9618—1	20′
50′	.6065—1	.6452—1	.3548	.9613—1	10′
24° 00′	.6093—1	.6486—1	.3514	.9607—1	**66° 00′**
10′	.6121—1	.6520—1	.3480	.9602—1	50′
20′	.6149—1	.6553—1	.3447	.9596—1	40′
30′	.6177—1	.6587—1	.3413	.9590—1	30′
40′	.6205—1	.6620—1	.3380	.9584—1	20′
50′	.6232—1	.6654—1	.3346	.9579—1	10′
25° 00′	.6259—1	.6687—1	.3313	.9573—1	**65° 00′**
10′	.6286—1	.6720—1	.3280	.9567—1	50′
20′	.6313—1	.6752—1	.3248	.9561—1	40′
30′	.6340—1	.6785—1	.3215	.9555—1	30′
40′	.6366—1	.6817—1	.3183	.9549—1	20′
50′	.6392—1	.6850—1	.3150	.9543—1	10′
26° 00′	.6418—1	.6882—1	.3118	.9537—1	**64° 00′**
10′	.6444—1	.6914—1	.3086	.9530—1	50′
20′	.6470—1	.6946—1	.3054	.9524—1	40′
30′	.6495—1	.6977—1	.3023	.9518—1	30′
40′	.6521—1	.7009—1	.2991	.9512—1	20′
50′	.6546—1	.7040—1	.2960	.9505—1	10′
27° 00′	.6570—1	.7072—1	.2928	.9499—1	**63° 00′**
	Log$_{10}$ Cosine	Log$_{10}$ Cotangent	Log$_{10}$ Tangent	Log$_{10}$ Sine	Degrees

TABLE 4

Logarithms of Trigonometric Ratios

Degrees	Log$_{10}$ Sine	Log$_{10}$ Tangent	Log$_{10}$ Cotangent	Log$_{10}$ Cosine	
27° 00′	.6570—1	.7072—1	.2928	.9499—1	**63° 00′**
10′	.6595—1	.7103—1	.2897	.9492—1	50′
20′	.6620—1	.7134—1	.2866	.9486—1	40′
30′	.6644—1	.7165—1	.2835	.9479—1	30′
40′	.6668—1	.7196—1	.2804	.9473—1	20′
50′	.6692—1	.7226—1	.2774	.9466—1	10′
28° 00′	.6716—1	.7257—1	.2743	.9459—1	**62° 00′**
10′	.6740—1	.7287—1	.2713	.9453—1	50′
20′	.6763—1	7317—1	.2683	.9446—1	40′
30′	.6787—1	.7348—1	.2652	.9439—1	30′
40′	.6810—1	.7378—1	.2622	.9432—1	20′
50′	.6833—1	.7408—1	.2592	.9425—1	10′
29° 00′	.6856—1	.7438—1	.2562	.9418—1	**61° 00′**
10′	.6878—1	.7467—1	.2533	.9411—1	50′
20′	.6901—1	.7497—1	.2503	.9404—1	40′
30′	.6923—1	.7526—1	.2474	.9397—1	30′
40′	.6946—1	.7556—1	.2444	.9390—1	20′
50′	.6968—1	.7585—1	.2415	.9383—1	10′
30° 00′	.6990—1	.7614—1	.2386	.9375—1	**60° 00′**
10′	.7012—1	.7644—1	.2356	.9368—1	50′
20′	.7033—1	.7673—1	.2327	.9361—1	40′
30′	.7055—1	.7701—1	.2299	.9353—1	30′
40′	.7076—1	.7730—1	.2270	.9346—1	20′
50′	.7097—1	.7759—1	.2241	.9338—1	10′
31° 00′	.7118—1	.7788—1	.2212	.9331—1	**59° 00′**
10′	.7139—1	.7816—1	.2184	.9323—1	50′
20′	.7160—1	.7845—1	.2155	.9315—1	40′
30′	.7181—1	.7873—1	.2127	.9308—1	30′
40′	.7201—1	.7902—1	.2098	.9300—1	20′
50′	.7222—1	.7930—1	.2070	.9292—1	10′
32° 00′	.7242—1	.7958—1	.2042	.9284—1	**58° 00′**
10′	.7262—1	.7986—1	.2014	.9276—1	50′
20′	.7282—1	.8014—1	.1986	.9268—1	40′
30′	.7302—1	.8042—1	.1958	.9260—1	30′
40′	.7322—1	.8070—1	.1930	.9252—1	20′
50′	.7342—1	.8097—1	.1903	.9244—1	10′
33° 00′	.7361—1	.8125—1	.1875	.9236—1	**57° 00′**
10′	.7380—1	.8153—1	.1847	.9228—1	50′
20′	.7400—1	.8180—1	.1820	.9219—1	40′
30′	.7419—1	.8208—1	.1792	.9211—1	30′
40′	.7438—1	.8235—1	.1765	.9203—1	20′
50′	.7457—1	.8263—1	.1737	.9194—1	10′
34° 00′	.7476—1	.8290—1	.1710	.9186—1	**56° 00′**
10′	.7494—1	.8317—1	.1683	.9177—1	50′
20′	.7513—1	.8344—1	.1656	.9169—1	40′
30′	.7531—1	.8371—1	.1629	.9160—1	30′
40′	.7550—1	.8398—1	.1602	.9151—1	20′
50′	.7568—1	.8425—1	.1575	.9142—1	10′
35° 00′	.7586—1	.8452—1	.1548	.9134—1	**55° 00′**
10′	.7604—1	.8479—1	.1521	.9125—1	50′
20′	.7622—1	.8506—1	.1494	.9116—1	40′
30′	.7640—1	.8533—1	.1467	.9107—1	30′
40′	.7657—1	.8559—1	.1441	.9098—1	20′
50′	.7675—1	.8586—1	.1414	.9089—1	10′
36° 00′	.7692—1	.8613—1	.1387	.9080—1	**54° 00′**
	Log$_{10}$ Cosine	Log$_{10}$ Cotangent	Log$_{10}$ Tangent	Log$_{10}$ Sine	Degrees

TABLE 4

Logarithms of Trigonometric Ratios

Degrees	Log_{10} Sine	Log_{10} Tangent	Log_{10} Cotangent	Log_{10} Cosine	
36° 00′	.7692—1	.8613—1	.1387	.9080—1	**54° 00′**
10′	.7710—1	.8639—1	.1361	.9070—1	50′
20′	.7727—1	.8666—1	.1334	.9061—1	40′
30′	.7744—1	.8692—1	.1308	.9052—1	30′
40′	.7761—1	.8718—1	.1282	.9042—1	20′
50′	.7778—1	.8745—1	.1255	.9033—1	10′
37° 00′	.7795—1	.8771—1	.1229	.9023—1	**53° 00′**
10′	.7811—1	.8797—1	.1203	.9014—1	50′
20′	.7828—1	.8824—1	.1176	.9004—1	40′
30′	.7844—1	.8850—1	.1150	.8995—1	30′
40′	.7861—1	.8876—1	.1124	.8985—1	20′
50′	.7877—1	.8902—1	.1098	.8975—1	10′
38° 00′	.7893—1	.8928—1	.1072	.8965—1	**52° 00′**
10′	.7910—1	.8954—1	.1046	.8955—1	50′
20′	.7926—1	.8980—1	.1020	.8945—1	40′
30′	.7941—1	.9006—1	.0994	.8935—1	30′
40′	.7957—1	.9032—1	.0968	.8925—1	20′
50′	.7973—1	.9058—1	.0942	.8915—1	10′
39° 00′	.7989—1	.9084—1	.0916	.8905—1	**51° 00′**
10′	.8004—1	.9110—1	.0890	.8895—1	50′
20′	.8020—1	.9135—1	.0865	.8884—1	40′
30′	.8035—1	.9161—1	.0839	.8874—1	30′
40′	.8050—1	.9187—1	.0813	.8864—1	20′
50′	.8066—1	.9212—1	.0788	.8853—1	10′
40° 00′	.8081—1	.9238—1	.0762	.8843—1	**50° 00′**
10′	.8096—1	.9264—1	.0736	.8832—1	50′
20′	.8111—1	.9289—1	.0711	.8821—1	40′
30′	.8125—1	.9315—1	.0685	.8810—1	30′
40′	.8140—1	.9341—1	.0659	.8800—1	20′
50′	.8155—1	.9366—1	.0634	.8789—1	10′
41° 00′	.8169—1	.9392—1	.0608	.8778—1	**49° 00′**
10′	.8184—1	.9417—1	.0583	.8767—1	50′
20′	.8198—1	.9443—1	.0557	.8756—1	40′
30′	.8213—1	.9468—1	.0532	.8745—1	30′
40′	.8227—1	.9494—1	.0506	.8733—1	20′
50′	.8241—1	.9519—1	.0481	.8722—1	10′
42° 00′	.8255—1	.9544—1	.0456	.8711—1	**48° 00′**
10′	.8269—1	.9570—1	.0430	.8699—1	50′
20′	.8283—1	.9595—1	.0405	.8688—1	40′
30′	.8297—1	.9621—1	.0379	.8676—1	30′
40′	.8311—1	.9646—1	.0354	.8665—1	20′
50′	.8324—1	.9671—1	.0329	.8653—1	10′
43° 00′	.8338—1	.9697—1	.0303	.8641—1	**47° 00′**
10′	.8351—1	.9722—1	.0278	.8629—1	50′
20′	.8365—1	.9747—1	.0253	.8618—1	40′
30′	.8378—1	.9772—1	.0228	.8606—1	30′
40′	.8391—1	.9798—1	.0202	.8594—1	20′
50′	.8405—1	.9823—1	.0177	.8582—1	10′
44° 00′	.8418—1	.9848—1	.0152	.8569—1	**46° 00′**
10′	.8431—1	.9874—1	.0126	.8557—1	50′
20′	.8444—1	.9899—1	.0101	.8545—1	40′
30′	.8457—1	.9924—1	.0076	.8532—1	30′
40′	.8469—1	.9949—1	.0051	.8520—1	20′
50′	.8482—1	.9975—1	.0025	.8507—1	10′
45° 00′	.8495—1	.0000	.0000	.8495—1	**45° 00′**
	Log_{10} Cosine	Log_{10} Cotangent	Log_{10} Tangent	Log_{10} Sine	Degrees

TABLE 5

Commissioners 1941 Standard Ordinary (CSO) Mortality Table

Age	Number Living	Number Dying	Age	Number Living	Number Dying	Age	Number Living	Number Dying
1	1,000,000	5,770	36	902,393	4,386	71	427,593	27,481
2	994,230	4,116	37	898,007	4,625	72	400,112	27,872
3	990,114	3,347	38	893,382	4,878	73	372,240	28,104
4	986,767	2,950	39	888,504	5,162	74	344,136	28,154
5	983,817	2,715	40	883,342	5,459	75	315,982	28,009
6	981,102	2,561	41	877,883	5,785	76	287,973	27,651
7	978,541	2,417	42	872,098	6,131	77	260,322	27,071
8	976,124	2,255	43	865,967	6,503	78	233,251	26,262
9	973,869	2,065	44	859,464	6,910	79	206,989	25,224
10	971,804	1,914	45	852,554	7,340	80	181,765	23,966
11	969,890	1,852	46	845,214	7,801	81	157,799	22,502
12	968,038	1,859	47	837,413	8,299	82	135,297	20,857
13	966,179	1,913	48	829,114	8,822	83	114,440	19,062
14	964,266	1,996	49	820,292	9,392	84	95,378	17,157
15	962,270	2,069	50	810,900	9,990	85	78,221	15,185
16	960,201	2,103	51	800,910	10,628	86	63,036	13,198
17	958,098	2,156	52	790,282	11,301	87	49,838	11,245
18	955,942	2,199	53	778,981	12,020	88	38,593	9,378
19	953,743	2,260	54	766,961	12,770	89	29,215	7,638
20	951,483	2,312	55	754,191	13,560	90	21,577	6,063
21	949,171	2,382	56	740,631	14,390	91	15,514	4,681
22	946,789	2,452	57	726,241	15,251	92	10,833	3,506
23	944,337	2,531	58	710,990	16,147	93	7,327	2,540
24	941,806	2,609	59	694,843	17,072	94	4,787	1,776
25	939,197	2,705	60	677,771	18,022	95	3,011	1,193
26	936,492	2,800	61	659,749	18,988	96	1,818	813
27	933,692	2,904	62	640,761	19,979	97	1,005	551
28	930,788	3,025	63	620,782	20,958	98	454	329
29	927,763	3,154	64	599,824	21,942	99	125	125
30	924,609	3,292	65	577,882	22,907			
31	921,317	3,437	66	554,975	23,842			
32	917,880	3,598	67	531,133	24,730			
33	914,282	3,767	68	506,403	25,553			
34	910,515	3,961	69	480,850	26,302			
35	906,554	4,161	70	454,548	26,955			

Answers to Odd-Numbered Exercises

Exercise Group 1–1

19. $2(3 + 5)$
21. $(2 \cdot 4) + (5 \cdot 6)$
23. $(2 \cdot 4 + 5)6$
25. $[(2 + 3)4 + 2]3$
27. $(a + b) + (c + d)$
31. (c)
33. (a)
35. (c)
37. (c)

Exercise Group 1–2

3. (2, 1) is the only positive integer

Exercise Group 1–3

1. 2
3. 1
5. 0
7. -3
9. 15
11. 63
13. 84
15. 168
17. -756
19. 1944
21. 193,545
23. -19
25. 5
27. 1
29. -9
31. -61

Exercise Group 1–4

1. Not equal
3. Equal
5. Equal
7. Equal
9. Not equal

Exercise Group 1–5

1. $12 + i$
3. $8 + 10i$
5. $(a + b + e) + (c + d)i$
7. $22 + 7i$
9. $-32 - 76i$
11. $-(ad + bc) + (ac - bd)i$
13. 0
17. $(-a, -b)$

Exercise Group 2–1

5. (a) On a straight line 3 units to the left of the y-axis
   (b) On a straight line 2 units above the x-axis
7. 9
9. -13
11. On a straight line $1\frac{1}{2}$ units above the x-axis
13. $(\frac{11}{2}, 4)$, $(\frac{11}{2}, -4)$
15. One solution, (5, 2)
17. $(1, 8)$, $(1, -2)$, $(6, 8)$, $(6, -2)$

Exercise Group 2–2

1. $(-1, -\frac{5}{2})$, $\sqrt{145}$
3. $(2, \frac{15}{2})$, $5\sqrt{5}$
5. $(-\frac{11}{2}, \frac{1}{2})$, $\sqrt{314}$
7. $\left(\frac{a+c}{2}, \frac{b+d}{2}\right)$, $\sqrt{(a-c)^2 + (b-d)^2}$
9. $\left(\frac{a-c}{2}, \frac{a-c}{2}\right)$, $(a + c)\sqrt{2}$

Exercise Group 2–3

1. (a) $g(1) = 2, g(3) = 4$; (b) $x = 2$
3. (a) $f(0) = \frac{1}{2}, f(10) = 0$; (b) $u = 2$; (c) No
5. (a) (0, 3), (1, 2), (2, 9), (3, −1); (b) (0, 4), (1, 9), (2, 16), (3, 25)
7. 12, 0, 27
9. 2, 0, 12
11. $4, \frac{2}{3}, -\frac{1}{6}$
13. $14, -2, -\frac{29}{4}$
15. 5
17. $a^2 + a - 1$
19. (a) $x^2 - x$, (b) $(x + h)^2 + (x + h)$, (c) $2x + h + 1$
21. $C = 2\pi r$
23. $A = 2w^2$
25. $F = \frac{9}{5}C + 32$
27. 0, 7, 12, 15, 16, 15, 12, 7, 0
29. $V = 300x$
31. Increase in $V = h^3 + 3ah^2 + 3a^2h$

Exercise Group 2–6

1. $y = \dfrac{2x}{5}, \dfrac{14}{5}$
3. $u = \dfrac{8}{v}, \dfrac{8}{3}$
5. $v = \dfrac{5u}{4}, \dfrac{45}{2}$
7. $S = 4\pi r^2$
9. $S = 6x^2$
11. $V = \dfrac{7A}{9}$
13. The force is four times as large.

Exercise Group 2–7

1. $y = \dfrac{x^2z}{8}, \dfrac{45}{4}$
3. $u = \dfrac{40v^2}{9w^3}, \dfrac{125}{9}$
5. $W = \dfrac{18uv^2}{t^3}, \dfrac{405}{32}$
7. $Y = -\dfrac{64xz^2}{u^3v}, -\dfrac{147}{5}$
9. $100,774
11. Reduced 90.2%
13. 3.01 in.
15. 15 hp

Supplementary Exercises for Chapter 2

1. $f(-3) = 18, f(5) = 50$
3. $f(-3) = -28, f(5) = -60$
5. $f(-1) = 16, f(0) = 15, f(3) = 0, f(-a) = 15 + 2a - a^2$
7. $\frac{16}{11}$
13. 13
15. 16
17. $(\frac{13}{2}, 4), \sqrt{965}$
19. $\left(\dfrac{a+b}{2}, \dfrac{c+d}{2}\right), \sqrt{(a-b)^2 + (d-c)^2}$
23. $\frac{1}{16}$ in.
25. 11,616,000 ft·lb
27. $V = 4x(6 - x)(8 - x)$
29. $A = 2x(10 - x)$

Exercise 3–1

1. 135°
3. 150°
5. −100°
7. 24°
9. 84°
11. 7.5°
13. −300°
15. −52°
17. 68° 45′ 18″
19. 32° 39′ 31″
21. 1° 43′ 08″
23. 286° 28′ 45″
25. −156° 25′ 05″
27. 206° 50′ 19″
29. $\dfrac{11\pi}{6}$
31. $\dfrac{7\pi}{5}$
33. $\dfrac{9\pi}{2}$
35. $\dfrac{13\pi}{5}$
37. $\dfrac{4\pi}{15}$
39. $\dfrac{13\pi}{18}$
41. 0.60
43. 2.50
45. 3.68
47. 2.09
49. −7.64
51. 1.34

Exercise Group 3–2

1. $\left(\frac{1}{2}, \frac{\sqrt{3}}{2}\right)$ 3. $\left(-\frac{\sqrt{2}}{2}, -\frac{\sqrt{2}}{2}\right)$ 5. $\left(\frac{\sqrt{3}}{2}, \frac{1}{2}\right)$ 7. $\left(\frac{1}{2}, \frac{\sqrt{3}}{2}\right)$
9. Q_3, 33° 11. Q_2, 47° 13. Q_4, 78° 30′
15. Q_2, 64° 53′ 17. $y = -3$ 19. $x = -\sqrt{17}$
21. $x = \pm\sqrt{3}$ 23. $x = 2, y = 8; x = -2, y = -8$
25. $y = 0, r = 2$ 27. Q_4 29. Q_3 31. Q_3 33. Q_2 35. Q_2
37. (a) Between 0° and 180°; (b) between 0° and 45°
39. (a) Between 0° and 180°; (b) between 0° and 240°
41. (a) Between 0° and 180°; (b) between 270° and 540°
43. Two values 45. Five values 47. Four values
49. Five values 51. Five values 53. Fifteen values

Exercise Group 3–3

In this set of answers the values of the trigonometric ratios are given in the order sin θ, cos θ, tan θ, cot θ, sec θ, csc θ.

1. $\frac{3}{5}, -\frac{4}{5}, -\frac{3}{4}, -\frac{4}{3}, -\frac{5}{4}, \frac{5}{3}$
3. $-\frac{5\sqrt{34}}{34}, -\frac{3\sqrt{34}}{34}, \frac{5}{3}, \frac{3}{5}, -\frac{\sqrt{34}}{3}, -\frac{\sqrt{34}}{5}$
5. $\frac{3}{5}, -\frac{4}{5}, -\frac{3}{4}, -\frac{4}{3}, -\frac{5}{4}, \frac{5}{3}$
7. $-\frac{2}{9}, \pm\frac{\sqrt{77}}{9}, \mp\frac{2\sqrt{77}}{77}, \mp\frac{\sqrt{77}}{2}, \pm\frac{9\sqrt{77}}{77}, -\frac{9}{2}$
9. $\frac{1}{3}, \frac{2\sqrt{2}}{3}, \frac{\sqrt{2}}{4}, 2\sqrt{2}, \frac{3\sqrt{2}}{4}, 3$
11. $\pm\frac{2\sqrt{5}}{5}, \mp\frac{\sqrt{5}}{5}, -2, -\frac{1}{2}, \mp\sqrt{5}, \pm\frac{\sqrt{5}}{2}$
13. $\frac{4}{5}, \frac{3}{5}, \frac{4}{3}, \frac{3}{4}, \frac{5}{3}, \frac{5}{4}$ 15. $\frac{\sqrt{3}}{2}, \frac{1}{2}, \sqrt{3}, \frac{\sqrt{3}}{3}, 2, \frac{2\sqrt{3}}{3}$
17. $\frac{3}{5}, -\frac{4}{5}, -\frac{3}{4}, -\frac{4}{3}, -\frac{5}{4}, \frac{5}{3}$ 19. $\frac{5}{13}, \frac{12}{13}, \frac{5}{12}, \frac{12}{5}, \frac{13}{12}, \frac{13}{5}$
21. $\pm\frac{2\sqrt{13}}{13}, \mp\frac{3\sqrt{13}}{13}, -\frac{2}{3}, -\frac{3}{2}, \mp\frac{\sqrt{13}}{3}, \pm\frac{\sqrt{13}}{2}$
23. $\frac{3}{4}, \pm\frac{\sqrt{7}}{4}, \pm\frac{3\sqrt{7}}{7}, \pm\frac{\sqrt{7}}{3}, \pm\frac{4\sqrt{7}}{7}, \frac{4}{3}$
25. $\frac{1}{2}, -\frac{\sqrt{3}}{2}, -\frac{\sqrt{3}}{3}, -\sqrt{3}, -\frac{2\sqrt{3}}{3}, 2$
27. $-\frac{2\sqrt{229}}{229}, \frac{15\sqrt{229}}{229}, -\frac{2}{15}, -\frac{15}{2}, \frac{\sqrt{229}}{15}, -\frac{\sqrt{229}}{2}$

29. $-\frac{24}{25}, -\frac{7}{25}, \frac{24}{7}, \frac{7}{24}, -\frac{25}{7}, -\frac{25}{24}$

31. $\pm\frac{\sqrt{5}}{3}, \frac{2}{3}, \pm\frac{\sqrt{5}}{2}, \pm\frac{2\sqrt{5}}{5}, \frac{3}{2}, \pm\frac{3\sqrt{5}}{5}$

33. $\pm\frac{2\sqrt{2}}{3}, -\frac{1}{3}, \mp 2\sqrt{2}, \mp\frac{\sqrt{2}}{4}, -3, \pm\frac{3\sqrt{2}}{4}$

35. $\pm\frac{\sqrt{2}}{10}, \mp\frac{7\sqrt{2}}{10}, -\frac{1}{7}, -7, \mp\frac{5\sqrt{2}}{7}, \pm 5\sqrt{2}$

Exercise Group 3–4

In this set of answers for Exercises 1–19 the values of the trigonometric ratios will be given in the order sin θ, cos θ, tan θ, cot θ, sec θ, csc θ.

1. $\frac{\sqrt{3}}{2}, \frac{1}{2}, \sqrt{3}, \frac{\sqrt{3}}{3}, 2, \frac{2\sqrt{3}}{3}$

3. $\frac{\sqrt{2}}{2}, -\frac{\sqrt{2}}{2}, -1, -1, -\sqrt{2}, \sqrt{2}$

5. $\frac{1}{2}, -\frac{\sqrt{3}}{2}, -\frac{\sqrt{3}}{3}, -\sqrt{3}, -\frac{2\sqrt{3}}{3}, 2$

7. $\frac{1}{2}, -\frac{\sqrt{3}}{2}, -\frac{\sqrt{3}}{3}, -\sqrt{3}, -\frac{2\sqrt{3}}{3}, 2$

9. 1, 0, —, 0, —, 1

11. 0, −1, 0, —, −1, —

13. 0, 1, 0, —, 1, —

15. $-\frac{\sqrt{2}}{2}, \frac{\sqrt{2}}{2}, -1, -1, \sqrt{2}, -\sqrt{2}$

17. 0, −1, 0, —, −1, —

19. $\frac{\sqrt{3}}{2}, \frac{1}{2}, \sqrt{3}, \frac{\sqrt{3}}{3}, 2, \frac{2\sqrt{3}}{3}$

37. $<$

39. $>$

41. $=$

43. $=$

Exercise Group 3–5

1. 0.3411	3. 0.7050	5. 1.258	7. 2.356	9. 0.0465
11. 1.688	13. 0.9932	15. 3.204	17. −1.836	19. −1.963
21. −0.8090	23. 1.122	25. 0.9325	27. −0.5150	29. 4.134
31. 6.314	33. −0.9929	35. −1.022	37. 71° 30′	39. 76° 40′
41. 19° 40′	43. 22° 10′	45. 63° 30′	47. 11° 30′	49. 10° 30′
51. 9° 20′	53. 89° 40′	55. 9° 40′	57. 3° 20′	59. 1°
61. 264°	63. 95° 30′	65. 102° 40′	67. 138° 20′	69. 149°
71. 220° 30′	73. cos 71° 28′	75. cot 16° 31′	77. csc 22° 02′	79. sin 51° 13′
81. tan 76° 12′	83. sec 21° 38′			

Supplementary Exercises for Chapter 3

1. $\frac{5\pi}{4}$

3. $\frac{28\pi}{15}$

5. 165°

7. 118° 01′ 47″

9. $\sin\theta = \pm\frac{\sqrt{5}}{3}$, $\tan\theta = \mp\frac{\sqrt{5}}{2}$, $\cot\theta = \mp\frac{2\sqrt{5}}{5}$, $\sec\theta = -\frac{3}{2}$,
$\csc\theta = \pm\frac{3\sqrt{5}}{5}$

11. $\sin\theta = \frac{1}{3}$, $\cos\theta = \pm\frac{2\sqrt{2}}{3}$, $\tan\theta = \pm\frac{\sqrt{2}}{4}$, $\cot\theta = \pm 2\sqrt{2}$,

$\sec\theta = \pm\frac{3\sqrt{2}}{4}$

13. $\sin\theta = \frac{\pm 1}{\sqrt{1+b^2}}$, $\cos\theta = \frac{\pm b}{\sqrt{1+b^2}}$, $\tan\theta = \frac{1}{b}$, $\sec\theta = \pm\frac{\sqrt{1+b^2}}{b}$,

$\csc\theta = \pm\sqrt{1+b^2}$

In Exercises 15–25, the values of the trigonometric ratios are given in the order $\sin\theta$, $\cos\theta$, $\tan\theta$, $\cot\theta$, $\sec\theta$, $\csc\theta$.

15. $-\frac{1}{\sqrt{2}}, \frac{1}{\sqrt{2}}, -1, -1, \sqrt{2}, -\sqrt{2}$

17. $\frac{1}{\sqrt{2}}, -\frac{1}{\sqrt{2}}, -1, -1, -\sqrt{2}, \sqrt{2}$

19. $-\frac{1}{2}, -\frac{\sqrt{3}}{2}, \frac{1}{\sqrt{3}}, \sqrt{3}, -\frac{2}{\sqrt{3}}, -2$

21. 0, −1, 0, —, −1, —

23. $\frac{1}{2}, -\frac{\sqrt{3}}{2}, -\frac{1}{\sqrt{3}}, -\sqrt{3}, -\frac{2}{\sqrt{3}}, 2$

25. $\frac{\sqrt{3}}{2}, \frac{1}{2}, \sqrt{3}, \frac{1}{\sqrt{3}}, 2, \frac{2}{\sqrt{3}}$

31. $0, -\frac{1}{2}, 0, \frac{1}{4}, 0$

33. $1, 0, -\frac{1}{9}, 0, \frac{1}{25}$

35. $-1, 1, -\frac{1}{3}, 0, -\frac{1}{5}$

37. $-4\pi, \pi, -\frac{4\pi}{9}, \frac{\pi}{4}, -\frac{4\pi}{25}$

39. 0, −1, 0, 0, 0

41. $A = bc\sin\theta$

43. $E = 0.1736(\tan\theta + \cot\theta)$; 3.147%

Exercise Group 4–1

1. 5; $-\frac{5}{2}$
3. 7; $\frac{7}{3}$
5. 5; $-\frac{5}{3}$
7. $\frac{5}{6}$
9. $\frac{8}{29}$
11. $\frac{1}{9}$
13. $-\frac{2}{37}$
15. $\frac{45}{13}$
17. $\frac{94}{15}$
19. $\frac{ab}{b-c}$, $b \neq c$
21. $y = b + c$, $b \neq c$
23. No solution
25. No solution
27. $\frac{27}{22}$
29. −3
31. $-\frac{7}{4}$
33. $\frac{(a^2+1)b}{2a^2}$
35. $0, -\frac{5}{2}$
37. 21
39. $\frac{2b}{3}$
41. $\cos x = -\frac{6}{7}$
43. $\cot x = 2$
45. $\csc x = -\frac{12}{13}$
47. $\tan x = -37$
49. $\sec x = \frac{11}{6}$
51. $C = 1.90 + 0.00105x$ (dollars)
53. (a) 10%, (b) $133\frac{1}{3}$ yr
55. $\frac{1}{6}$
57. −7
59. $\frac{5}{3}$ hr for second train
61. 587 days
63. 100 cm^3
65. $3906.25

Exercise Group 4–2

3. $(\frac{3}{4}, -\frac{41}{8})$
5. $(\frac{7}{4}, -\frac{25}{8})$
7. $(\frac{1}{2}, -\frac{7}{4})$
9. $(-\frac{1}{4}, -\frac{1}{8})$
11. (1, −3)
13. (2.5, −0.25)
15. (−5.5, −6.05)
17. $(\frac{5}{6}, \frac{71}{12})$

19. $(-0.4, 2.2)$ 21. $(1, 1)$ 23. $(\frac{1}{4}, \frac{1}{8})$ 25. $(-2, -1)$
27. 49 ft, 1.75 sec, 48 ft 29. $k = 0$
31. -16 33. 2 in. $\times$ 4 in.

Exercise Group 4–3

1. 3, 5 3. $-2, 1.5$ 5. $-\frac{5}{3}, \frac{1}{2}$ 7. 0, 5 9. $-\frac{1}{3}, \frac{2}{5}$
11. $-1, \frac{7}{5}$ 13. $\pm\frac{6}{5}$ 15. $-\frac{1}{5}, \frac{2}{3}$ 17. $-\frac{7}{5}, \frac{3}{2}$ 19. 0, 0.2
21. $-\frac{b}{a}, c$ 23. $-c, \frac{2b}{a}$ 25. $-1.5, 1$ 27. $\frac{1 \pm \sqrt{6}}{5}$ 29. $0, -\frac{5}{3}$
31. $\frac{5 \pm i\sqrt{23}}{6}$ 33. $\frac{-a \pm \sqrt{a^2 - 8b}}{4}$
35. $\frac{-b \pm \sqrt{b^2 - 4ac}}{2c}$ 37. $c \pm \sqrt{c^2 - b}$
39. $\frac{7 \pm \sqrt{29 - 20c}}{2(c + 1)}$ 41. $\frac{-(3a + b) \pm \sqrt{(3a + b)^2 - 8cd}}{4}$
43. $-3 \pm \sqrt{2}$ 45. 12, 6.5 47. $-4\sqrt{5} \pm 2\sqrt{2}$
49. $5, -\frac{23}{7}$ 51. $-\frac{13}{3}, 13$ 53. $-a, \frac{1}{a}$
55. 0.1, 3 57. $\frac{a + b}{a - b}, \frac{b - a}{b + a}$ 59. $-\frac{a}{a + 1}, \frac{a}{1 - a}$
61. $y = 0.5x \pm 2$ 63. $y = x \pm \sqrt{7 - 3x^2}$
65. $y = 2x - 0.5(1 \pm \sqrt{5})$ 67. $x = \frac{\pi}{6}, \frac{5\pi}{6}$
69. $\tan x = -\frac{1}{3}, \frac{2}{5}$ 71. $\cot x = 0.5; x = \frac{\pi}{6}, \frac{7\pi}{6}$
73. $k = 2, -4$ 75. 1 in. approx. 77. 21.5 yd
79. $300 + 200\sqrt{2} = 582.74 \text{ in}^2$ 81. 15×36

Exercise Group 4–4

1. 36; roots real, unequal, rational 3. -32; roots imaginary and unequal
5. 126; roots real, unequal, irrational 7. 49; roots real, unequal, rational
9. -3; roots imaginary and unequal 11. 0; roots real, equal, rational
13. 109; roots real, unequal, irrational 15. 0; roots real, equal, rational
17. 1.28; roots real, unequal, irrational 19. $k = \pm\sqrt{6}$ 21. $-\frac{25}{12}$
23. $-1 \pm \sqrt{3}$ 25. $-\frac{5}{3}, -2$ 27. $-\frac{3}{5}, -\frac{11}{5}$
29. $\frac{c}{a}, -\frac{d}{a}$ 31. $\frac{a}{b}, -\frac{c}{b}$ 33. $0.5i, 1$
35. $12x^2 + 7x - 10 = 0$ 37. $5x^2 + 13x - 6 = 0$
39. $3x^2 - 2x + 1 = 0$ 41. $x^2 - x + 9 - 3i = 0$
43. $x^2 - 4x - 3 = 0$ 45. $a^2x^2 - 2a\sqrt{a}\,x + 2a - c = 0$
47. $h = 0, \frac{1}{3}$ 49. $h = -1$ 51. $h = -\frac{49}{23}$
53. $h = \frac{3}{8}$ 57. (a) $acx^2 - (b^2 - 2ac)x + ac = 0$,
55. $h = \pm\sqrt{45 + c^2}$ (b) $a^4x^2 + (4a^3c - 2a^2b^2)x + b^4 - 4ab^2c = 0$

Exercise Group 4–5

1. $\pm 1, \pm 4$
3. $-1, \dfrac{1 \pm i\sqrt{3}}{2}, -3, \dfrac{3 \pm 3i\sqrt{3}}{2}$
5. $2, 3, -1 \pm i\sqrt{3}, \dfrac{3}{2}(-1 \pm i\sqrt{3})$
7. $\pm\sqrt{5}, \pm \dfrac{3\sqrt{2}}{2}$
9. $-\frac{1}{3}, \frac{1}{2}$
11. $\pm\frac{1}{3}, \pm\frac{1}{4}$
13. $\pm 1.5, \pm 1.5i, \pm 1, \pm i$
15. 16, 81
17. 25
19. $\frac{1}{4}, \frac{9}{25}$
21. 4
23. $\pm 2, \pm 3$
25. $1, -2, \dfrac{-1 \pm i\sqrt{19}}{2}$
27. $-2, -3, 4, 5$
29. $0, \pm 2, -4$
31. $-\frac{1}{3}, -\frac{3}{2}$
33. $x = 0$
35. $x = \dfrac{\pi}{6}, \dfrac{\pi}{3}, \dfrac{2\pi}{3}, \dfrac{5\pi}{6}, \dfrac{7\pi}{6}, \dfrac{4\pi}{3}, \dfrac{5\pi}{3}, \dfrac{11\pi}{6}$
37. $x = \dfrac{\pi}{6}, \dfrac{\pi}{3}, \dfrac{2\pi}{3}, \dfrac{5\pi}{6}, \dfrac{7\pi}{6}, \dfrac{4\pi}{3}, \dfrac{5\pi}{3}, \dfrac{11\pi}{6}$
39. $x = \dfrac{\pi}{6}, \dfrac{\pi}{2}, \dfrac{5\pi}{6}$
41. $x = \dfrac{\pi}{3}, \dfrac{\pi}{2}, \dfrac{4\pi}{3}, \dfrac{3\pi}{2}$

Exercise Group 4–6

1. 13
3. No solution
5. $5, -3$
7. 5, 13
9. 1
11. $5, \frac{14}{3}$
13. $-\frac{7}{19}$
15. 1
17. No solution
19. 3, 5
21. $3, \frac{55}{17}$
23. $\frac{7}{3}$
25. No solution
27. $\pm i\sqrt{3}$
29. 35
31. ± 2
33. 81
35. 14
37. $x = \dfrac{7\pi}{6}, \dfrac{11\pi}{6}$
39. $\cot x = 0.5$

Supplementary Exercises for Chapter 4

1. 74
3. $\frac{4}{3}$
5. $-\frac{11}{7}$
7. $\dfrac{1}{3a}(b \pm \sqrt{b^2 - 9a^2})$
9. $\dfrac{1}{4a}(c \pm \sqrt{c^2 - 8a^2})$
11. $\dfrac{1}{2b}(1 - c \pm \sqrt{(c-1)^2 - 4ab})$
13. $\dfrac{1}{4}(-3 \pm i\sqrt{31})$
15. $0.1(-3 \pm \sqrt{269})$
17. $0.1(3 \pm i\sqrt{131})$
19. $\dfrac{b - 3 \pm \sqrt{(b-3)^2 + 24(c-2)}}{2(c-2)}$
21. $\dfrac{b \pm \sqrt{b^2 - 4ad + 4ac}}{2a}$
23. $\dfrac{2 - b \pm \sqrt{(b-2)^2 + 4a(c+13)}}{2a}$
25. $\dfrac{7}{3}, -\dfrac{5}{2}$
27. $2, -\dfrac{4}{3}$
29. $a, -\dfrac{c}{b}$
31. $0, -12$
33. $\frac{1}{25}(-14 \pm 2\sqrt{399})$
35. $\frac{1}{2}(3 \pm 4i)$
37. Roots real, unequal, irrational; $S = -\frac{5}{3}, P = -\frac{7}{3}$
39. Roots imaginary and unequal; $S = -\frac{1}{3}, P = \frac{10}{9}$
41. Roots imaginary and unequal; $S = 5, P = 9$
43. $-2, -1, 1 \pm i\sqrt{3}, \frac{1}{2}(1 \pm i\sqrt{3})$

45. $\pm 3, \pm 5i$ 47. $\pm 1, \pm \frac{i\sqrt{21}}{3}$ 49. $\frac{11}{2}$ 51. $\frac{1}{6}$

53. 100 cc 55. 4.5% 57. $\frac{w}{4} \times \frac{w}{2}$

Exercise Group 5–1

1. $s = 6$ ft, $A = 6$ ft^2
3. $s = 8$ in., $A = 10$ in.^{2}
5. $s = \frac{21\pi}{4}$ ft, $A = \frac{147\pi}{8}$ ft^2
7. $s = 52.2$ cm, $A = 3392$ cm^2
9. $s = \frac{525\pi}{2}$ cm, $A = \frac{91875\pi}{4}$ cm^2
11. $s = 8.32$ yd, $A = 270.4$ yd^2
13. $s = 2.24$ in., $A = 0.673$ in.^{2}
15. $s = 343$ ft, $A = 53517$ ft^2
17. $s = 0.0258$ ft, $A = 0.00052$ ft^2
19. $\theta = 3$ rad $= 171°\ 53'$, $A = 54$ in.^{2}
21. $\theta = 0.6228$ rad $= 35°\ 41'$, $A = 78156$ cm^2
23. $\theta = 0.3645$ rad $= 20°\ 53'$, $A = 34.7$ ft^2
25. $\theta = 3.113$ rad $= 178°\ 21'$, $A = 17.99$ ft^2
27. $\theta = 0.7167$ rad $= 41°\ 04'$, $A = 32250$ cm^2
29. $\theta = 3.028$ rad $= 173°\ 31'$, $A = 1599$ in.^{2}
31. $\frac{572}{7}$ rad/sec
33. 3630 ft
35. 14° 29′
37. 0.00175 rad/sec
39. 2156 mi
41. 78.54 ft/sec, 75π rad/sec

Exercise Group 5–2

1. 0.2298	3. 1.586	5. 0.2720	7. 0.5898
9. 0.3776	11. 0.7432	13. 0.2742	15. −1.084
17. 1.361	19. −1.652	21. −1.032	23. 1.848
25. 89° 26′	27. 57° 54′	29. 59° 14′	31. 173° 55′
33. 138° 56′	35. 32° 35′	37. 69° 17′	39. 5° 50′
41. 59° 28′	43. 10° 53′	45. 3° 23′	47. 84° 33′

Exercise Group 5–3

1. $A = 52°\ 46'$, $a = 59.84$, $b = 45.48$
3. $B = 21°\ 21'$, $a = 72.39$, $c = 77.74$
5. $B = 53°\ 38'$, $b = 4.347$, $c = 5.400$
7. $A = 46°\ 33'$, $b = 854.7$, $c = 1243$
9. $B = 34°\ 42'$, $a = 71.02$, $b = 49.18$
11. $A = 31°\ 57'$, $B = 58°\ 03'$, $c = 4.035$
13. $A = 9°\ 13'$, $B = 80°\ 47'$, $b = 0.3769$
15. $A = 67°\ 20'$, $B = 22°\ 40'$, $a = 367.3$
17. $A = 58°\ 37'$, $a = 84.25$, $c = 98.63$
19. $A = 52°\ 36'$, $B = 37°\ 24'$, $c = 817.3$
21. $B = 46°\ 29'$, $a = 28.15$, $c = 40.87$
23. $B = 14°\ 42'$, $b = 0.2472$, $c = 0.9746$
25. $A = 47°\ 45'$, $B = 42°\ 15'$, $c = 0.3741$
27. $A = 33°\ 57'$, $a = 5.271$, $b = 7.829$
29. $A = 51°\ 29'$, $B = 38°\ 31'$, $a = 0.6544$
31. For 0° 30′, $AB = BC = CD = 0.0087$; for 2°, $AB = BC = CD = 0.0349$; for 4°, $AB = BC = 0.0698$, $CD = 0.0699$

Exercise Group 5–4

1. 23.46, 23.5
3. 0.003452, 0.00345
5. 2179000, 2180000
7. 0.9615, 0.962
9. 2.325, 2.33
11. 0.01234, 0.0123
13. ±0.05 cm
15. ±0.5 ft
17. $\pm 0.0005\ \text{ft}^3$
19. ±0.00005 yd
21. $\pm 0.5\ \text{in}^3$
23. 2.45
25. 56.6
27. 991
29. $130{,}000 = 1.3 \times 10^5$
31. 681.2
33. 9.8697
35. 30° 50′
37. 72°
39. 88° 20′
41. 55° 20′
43. 47° 10′
45. 21°
47. $B = 61°$, $a = 24$, $c = 49$
49. $B = 33°$, $b = 0.32$, $c = 0.59$
51. $A = 85°$, $B = 5°$, $c = 0.80$
53. $A = 22° 52'$, $a = 3.668$, $b = 8.696$
55. $A = 19°$, $B = 71°$, $b = 0.34$

Exercise Group 5–5

1. 65 ft
3. 280 mph
5. 58 naut mi, 241°
7. 1509 naut mi, 179°
9. 554 ft
11. 5.0 mi
13. 20.4 ft
15. 8009 ft, 1268 ft
17. 128 in.
19. 200 mi
21. 945 mi, 15°

Exercise Group 5–6

1. $H = 209.0$, $V = 137.2$
3. $H = 144.0$, $V = 274.5$
5. $H = 6.136$, $V = 51.60$
7. $H = 156.5$, $V = 313.0$
9. $H = 649.5$, $V = 375.0$
11. $R = 100$, in direction 0°
13. $R = 223.6$ in direction 33° 26′
15. $R = 49.26$, in direction 149° 43′
17. 421 mph, 215° 30′
19. 55° 50′, 334 mph
21. 183 lb
23. $F_{30} = 500\sqrt{3}$ lb, $F_{60} = 500$ lb
25. $T = 141$ lb, $C = 100$ lb
27. $T = C = 100$ lb
29. $T = 180$ lb, $C = 150$ lb

Supplementary Exercises for Chapter 5

1. $A = 67°$, $b = 14$, $c = 35$
3. $A = 45°$, $B = 45°$, $a = 2.3$
5. 90 mph
7. $H = 188$ lb, $V = 201$ lb
9. 98 ft
11. $T_1 = 500$ lb, $T_2 = 866$ lb
13. $F_\alpha = \dfrac{2000 \sin \beta}{\sin \alpha \cos \beta + \cos \alpha \sin \beta}$, $F_\beta = \dfrac{2000 \sin \alpha}{\sin \alpha \cos \beta + \cos \alpha \sin \beta}$

Exercise Group 6–1

1. (a) $x > 4$, (b) $x \leqq 4$
3. (a) $x < 3$, (b) $x \geqq 3$
5. (a) $-2 < x < 3$, (b) $x \leqq -2, x \geqq 3$
7. (a) $2 < x < 3$, (b) $x \leqq 2, x \geqq 3$
9. (a) $x < -3$, (b) $x \geqq -3$
11. (a) $-1 < x < 0.5$, (b) $x \leqq -1, x \geqq 0.5$
13. (a) $-4 < x < -2.4$, (b) $x \leqq -4, x \geqq -2.4$
15. $x < \frac{7}{3}$
17. $x > -\frac{7}{3}$
19. $x > -\frac{7}{2}$
21. $x < -6$
23. $x > -1$
25. $-4 < x < 4$
27. $x < -5, x > 5$
29. $-4 < x < 2$
31. $x < \frac{7}{4}, x > \frac{9}{4}$
33. $-1 < x < 1, 5 < x < 7$
35. $-4 < x < -2, -2 < x < 0$

Exercise Group 6–2

1. $x < -2, x > 3$
3. $x < 2, x > 3$
5. $x < \frac{3 - \sqrt{65}}{4}, x > \frac{3 + \sqrt{65}}{4}$
7. $\frac{3 - \sqrt{65}}{4} < x < \frac{3 + \sqrt{65}}{4}$
9. $\frac{5 - \sqrt{65}}{4} < x < \frac{5 + \sqrt{65}}{4}$
11. $-\frac{47}{3} < x < 24$
13. $x < \frac{3 - \sqrt{69}}{10}, x > \frac{3 + \sqrt{69}}{10}$
15. $-2 < x < \frac{1}{3}$
17. $-1 + \sqrt{3} < x < 1 + \sqrt{3}$
19. $x < \frac{-3 + \sqrt{5}}{2}, x > \frac{3 + \sqrt{5}}{2}$
21. $-\frac{1}{2} < x < \frac{1}{3}$
23. All real values of x
25. $x < \frac{1}{3}, x > \frac{3}{2}$
27. $-\frac{2}{3} < x < \frac{5}{2}$
29. $x < -\frac{2}{7}, x > \frac{7}{5}$
31. $-3 < x < -\frac{1}{3}$
33. $x < -2, x > 0$
35. $-\frac{3}{4} < x < -\frac{1}{2}$
37. $\frac{1}{4} < x < \frac{1}{2}$

Exercise Group 6–3

1. $-\frac{1}{2} < x < \frac{1}{3}$
3. $x < -\frac{3}{2}, x > 1$
5. $x < -\frac{5}{2}, x > \frac{4}{3}$
7. $-2 < x < \frac{1}{2}, x > \frac{7}{3}$
9. $x < -1, 0 < x < \frac{3}{2}$
11. $x < 0, 1 < x < 2$
13. $x < 0, 0 < x < 3$
15. $x > 2$
17. $-3 < x < -1, -1 < x < 2$
19. $x < -3, -1 < x < 1, x > 4$
21. $-\frac{5}{2} < x < -\frac{2}{3}, x > \frac{3}{7}$
23. $\frac{2}{3} < x < \frac{3}{4}, x < 0$
25. $x > \frac{5}{2}, -3 < x < -\frac{3}{2}$
27. $-3 < x < -2, -1 < x < 0$
29. $x < -1, -\frac{1}{2} < x < \frac{1}{3}, x > \frac{1}{2}$

Exercise Group 7–1

1. $0 \leqq \theta \leqq \frac{\pi}{2}, \frac{3\pi}{2} < \theta \leqq 2\pi$
3. $\frac{3\pi}{2} < \theta < 2\pi$
5. $\frac{3\pi}{2} < \theta < 2\pi$
7. $0 < \theta < \pi, \pi < \theta < 2\pi$
9. $\frac{\pi}{2}, \pi < \theta < 2\pi$
11. $\frac{\pi}{3} \leqq \theta \leqq \frac{\pi}{2}, \frac{3\pi}{2} \leqq \theta \leqq \frac{5\pi}{3}$
13. $\frac{\pi}{4} \leqq \theta < \frac{\pi}{2}, \frac{5\pi}{4} \leqq \theta < \frac{3\pi}{2}$
15. $\frac{3\pi}{4} \leqq \theta \leqq \pi, \frac{7\pi}{4} \leqq \theta \leqq 2\pi$
17. $0 \leqq \theta \leqq \frac{\pi}{4}, \frac{5\pi}{4} \leqq \theta \leqq 2\pi$
19. $-\frac{\pi}{3}$
21. 38°, −142°
23. $\frac{\pi}{3}$
25. $\frac{3\pi}{4}$
27. −153°
29. 173°, −7°
31. $-\frac{5\pi}{6}$
33. $\frac{\pi}{4}, -\frac{3\pi}{4}$
35. $-\frac{3\pi}{5}$
37. −0.4, 0.8, −1, −1
39. $\frac{4\sqrt{2}}{3}$, 2, 0, 0
41. 0.001, −0.008, 0, $(-1 + k)^3$, $(1.7 - k)^3$

Exercise Group 7–2

1. $A = 1$
7. $A = 1$
11. $A = \frac{1}{3}$
13. $A = \frac{5}{2}$
19. $A = 2$
21. $A = 1$

Exercise Group 7–3

1. $(7, -2)$ 3. $(-1, -9)$ 5. $(2, 50)$ 7. $(2, 7)$
9. (a) $3y = x + 2$, (b) $3y = x - 4$ 11. $(y + 2)^3 = (x - 1)^2$
13. $y + 4 = \cos\left(x + \frac{\pi}{3}\right)$ 15. $y - 2 = 2 \sin 3x$
17. $y = 3x^3$ 19. $y = 4 \tan x$
21. (a) $y = x^4$, (b) $y = -x^4$ 23. (a) $y = -\cos x$, (b) $y = \cos x$, (c) $y = -\cos x$
25. even, $\cos(-x) = \cos x$ 27. odd, $\cot(-x) = -\cot x$
29. odd, $\csc(-x) = -\csc x$ 31. $xy = 2$ 33. $y = -\cos\left(3x - \frac{\pi}{2}\right)$
35. Contraction in x-direction in ratio 1: 2, followed by reflection in x-axis
37. Translation of $\pi/2$ units to the right
39. Contraction in y-direction in ratio $1:\frac{1}{3}$ and in the x-direction in the ratio 1: 2, followed by a translation of π units to the right
41. Contraction in the y-direction in the ratio 1: 2 and in the x-direction in the ratio 1: 2, followed by a reflection in the y-axis, and then followed by translations of $\pi/2$ units to the right and 1 unit down
43. $P = 4\pi$, $A = 3$ 45. $P = \frac{\pi}{2}$, $A = 2$ 47. $P = 2\pi$, $A = \frac{1}{2}$
49. $P = \pi$, $A = 1$

Supplementary Exercises for Chapter 7

1. $P = \pi$ 3. $P = \frac{2\pi}{3}$, $A = \frac{1}{2}$ 5. $P = \frac{\pi}{3}$
7. $P = \pi$, $A = 3$ 9. $P = \frac{\pi}{2}$ 11. $P = 3\pi$
13. $P = 2\pi$, $A = 2$ 15. $P = \pi$, $A = \frac{1}{2}$ 17. $P = \pi$, $A = 3$
19. $P = 2\pi$, $(A = \sqrt{5})$ 21. $P = 12\pi$
27. $(y + 2)^2 = (x - 2)^2 + 2$ 29. $2x^2 + y^2 = 4$
31. $y = -\sin x$ 33. $2y = 3x \sin \frac{3x}{2}$

Exercise Group 8–1

1. 3 3. 23 5. -17 7. 3380 9. 30 11. $30a^4$
13. $\frac{209}{4}$ 15. $\frac{183}{25}$ 17. $-\frac{204}{7}$ 19. No 21. No 23. Yes
25. No 27. No 29. No 31. Yes 33. Yes 35. Yes

Exercise Group 8–2

1. $3x^3 + 4x^2 + 8x + 21, 36$ 3. $x^3 - x^2 + 5x - 5, 3$
5. $2x^2 + 4x + 4, -1$ 7. $-3x^4 + 9x^3 - 2x^2 + 6x - 3, 0$
9. $4x^2 - 6x + 5, -3$ 11. $x^3 - x^2 + 10x - 49, 281$
13. $2x^4 + 3ax^3 + 4a^2x^2 - a^3x - 2a^4, a^5$
15. $3x^4 - 3x^3 - x^2 - 10x - 20, 0$ 17. $25, -7, -70$
19. $126, 390, 26$ 21. $-4, -\frac{11}{8}, -352$ 23. $17, -13, -113$ 25. $-\frac{202}{27}, \frac{295}{8}, -34$

Exercise Group 8–3

1. $-\frac{1}{2}, 2, -\frac{5}{3}$ 3. $-\frac{2}{3}, \frac{1}{2}, \frac{5}{2}$ 5. $\frac{1}{2}, \frac{2}{3}, \frac{1 \pm 3i\sqrt{3}}{2}$
7. $-\frac{3}{5}, \pm 2i$ 9. $-3, -\frac{5}{2}, \frac{-3 \pm i\sqrt{11}}{2}$
11. $-\frac{3}{2}$ 13. $1, -\frac{3}{2}$ 15. $-\frac{3}{2}, -\frac{5}{3}, -\frac{5}{7}, \frac{-1 \pm i\sqrt{3}}{2}$
17. No rational roots 19. $-2, -\frac{3}{2}, -\frac{1}{2}, -\frac{1}{3}, 0, 1, \frac{3}{2}, 3$

Exercise Group 8–4

11. $-2.8, 1, 1.8$ 13. $-1.6, 0, 4.6$ 15. $-1.6, -0.7, 1.6$
17. $\pm 1.7, \pm 2$ 19. $0.6, 3.4$

Exercise Group 8–5

1. 0.43 3. 1.22 5. -3.87 7. 2.11 9. -1.96
11. $-0.80, 0.55, 2.25$ 13. $0.01, 0.98$ 15. $-2.50, -0.98, 0.11, 0.68$
17. $-2.646, 2.646$ 19. $-4.464, 2.464$ 21. $-3.541, 2.541$ 23. $-2.317, 4.317$

Supplementary Exercises for Chapter 8

1. $\frac{3}{2}, \frac{1 \pm i\sqrt{19}}{2}$ 5. (a) 1, (b) -2 7. (a) 3, (b) -2
9. $-1.50, 1.73, 2.78$ 11. $-3.32, -1.73, 1.73, 2.50, 3.32$

Exercise Group 9–1

1. $\frac{\pi}{3} + 2n\pi, \frac{2\pi}{3} + 2n\pi$ 3. $\frac{\pi}{3} + 2n\pi, \frac{5\pi}{3} + 2n\pi$ 5. $\frac{\pi}{4} + 2n\pi, \frac{7\pi}{4} + 2n\pi$
7. $\frac{4\pi}{3} + 2n\pi, \frac{5\pi}{3} + 2n\pi$ 9. $\frac{2\pi}{3} + n\pi$ 11. $\frac{7\pi}{6} + 2n\pi, \frac{11\pi}{6} + 2n\pi$
13. $\frac{\pi}{2} + 2n\pi$ 15. $n\pi$ 17. $x = \frac{1}{3}\arctan 2y$
19. $x = -\frac{\pi}{2} + \arccos 3y$ 21. $x = \frac{1}{2}(1 + \arccos y)$
23. $x = 3 \sin y$
25. $x = \sin\left(y + \frac{\pi}{3}\right)$
27. $x = -2 - \sin y$
37. Inverse period $= 2\pi$, no inverse amplitude
39. Inverse period $= 4\pi$, inverse amplitude $= 2$
41. Inverse period $= 6\pi$, inverse amplitude $= 2$
43. Inverse period $= 2\pi$, inverse amplitude $= 1$
45. Inverse period $= 2\pi$, inverse amplitude $= 1$
47. Inverse period $= 6\pi$, inverse amplitude $= \frac{1}{2}$

Exercise Group 9–2

1. 30° 3. 45° 5. 60° 7. 40° 24′ 9. 29° 47′
11. −45° 13. −11° 26′ 15. 97° 38′ 17. 132° 04′ 19. $\frac{\pi}{4}$

21. $\frac{2\pi}{3}$	23. $\frac{5\pi}{6}$	25. $-\frac{\pi}{2}$	27. π	29. $\frac{\pi}{2}$
31. $-\frac{\pi}{6}$	33. -0.7054	35. 2.4304	37. $\frac{3}{4}$	39. $-\sqrt{3}$
41. -1	43. $-\frac{12}{13}$	45. $-\frac{25}{7}$	47. $-\frac{\sqrt{3}}{3}$	49. $-\frac{1}{2}$
51. Undefined				

Exercise Group 9–3

1. $10^{0.7781}$	3. $10^{1.6232}$	5. $10^{-0.1761}$
7. $10^{0.1963}$	9. $10^{2.4592}$	11. $10^{3.8309}$
13. $10^{0.0333}$	15. $10^{0.2216}$	17. $10^{1.7993}$
19. $10^{2.6353}$	21. $10^{-0.3899}$	23. $10^{0.1896}$
25. $10^{3.2508}$	27. $10^{1.2596}$	29. $10^{0.9286}$
31. $10^{0.8228}$	33. $10^{0.5797}$	35. $10^{0.5325}$

Exercise Group 9–4

1. $\log_2 32 = 5$	3. $\log_4 \frac{1}{64} = -3$	5. $\log_{125} 5 = \frac{1}{3}$
7. $\log_{121} 11 = \frac{1}{2}$	9. $\log_{19} 1 = 0$	11. $\log_{1/5} 25 = -2$
13. $2^8 = 256$	15. $9^3 = 729$	17. $6^4 = 1296$
19. $81^{1.25} = 243$	21. $27^{2/3} = 9$	23. $(32)^{-0.2} = 0.5$
25. $y = 4$	27. $y = -3$	29. $y = -4$
31. $y = 4$	33. $y = \frac{5}{2}$	35. $x = 0.001$
37. $x = \frac{1}{81}$	39. $x = 5\sqrt{5}$	41. $x = \frac{1}{32}$
43. $b = 25$	45. $b = a^2$	47. $b = a^{-1/2}$
49. $b = 3^{5/4}$	51. $o = 3^{1/3}$	53. $b = x$

Exercise Group 9–6

1. 1.5185	3. 2.0212	5. 2.5522	7. 5.2894
9. 0.4149	11. 1.1604	13. 7.3736 − 10	15. 0.8764
17. 3.8364	19. 0.4971	21. 2.5110	23. 8.2871 − 10
25. 908	27. 0.0791	29. 0.997	31. 39600
33. 4230	35. 35600	37. 3.49	39. 7.17
41. 5.81	43. 1.69	51. $y = bx^a$	53. $y = b \cdot 10^{ax}$
55. $y = 10^{3x-1}$	57. $y = k^{c/a}x^{b/a}$		

Exercise Group 9–7

1. 2.6167	3. 1.8684	5. 9.9172 − 10	7. 4.9270
9. 6.9254 − 10	11. 8.6598 − 10	13. 674.3	15. 35460
17. 0.004567	19. 0.0002906	21. 0.001439	23. 0.00003235
25. 0.4843	27. 0.06683	29. 0.2997	31. 0.2353
33. 0.4196	35. 0.1815		

Exercise Group 9–8

1. 172.5
3. 1.246
5. 0.00004450
7. 8.346×10^{-10}
9. 0.1425
11. 0.0004840
13. 2.624
15. 1.929
17. 0.1591
19. 0.5020
21. 2.186×10^{-12}
23. 3.968×10^{6}
25. 0.3552
27. 3.048×10^{-9}
29. 4205

Exercise Group 9–9

1. 9.7276 − 10
3. 0.1916
5. 0.5395
7. 0.4577
9. 1.4909
11. 9.9899 − 10
13. 68° 24′
15. 30° 16′
17. 32° 04′
19. 23° 13′
21. 32° 15′
23. 39° 24′
25. $B = 46° 43'$, $b = 229.7$, $c = 315.5$
27. $A = 12° 26'$, $B = 77° 34'$, $c = 0.6466$
29. $B = 22° 15'$, $a = 83.68$, $c = 90.38$
31. $A = 42° 26'$, $b = 4.792$, $c = 6.494$
33. $A = 66° 47'$, $a = 99.60$, $c = 108.4$
35. 79.3 mph
37. 8856 lb
39. 80.70 ft
41. $H = 217.4$ lb, $V = 204.2$ lb

Exercise Group 9–11

1. 2.188
3. 0.5776
5. 25.98
7. 3591
9. 0.4306
11. 0.7731
13. 2974
15. 11.76
17. 30.07
19. $185
21. $2294
23. 4.7%

Exercise Group 9–12

1. 2.796
3. 3.533
5. −3.774
7. −0.6368
9. 27.946
11. 1.927
13. 12.744
15. 0.9608

Supplementary Exercises for Chapter 9

1. $y = 4$
3. $x = \frac{1}{5}$
5. $b = 2$
17. $y = 2(10^{3x})$
19. $y = 10^{(5x+3)/2}$
21. 0.2057
23. 2.121
25. 3.642×10^{-12}
27. 0.7761
29. 0.2507
31. 7.501
33. 0.607
35. 0.959
37. 0.039
39. $x = \dfrac{1}{2} \arccos \dfrac{y}{2}$
41. $x = \dfrac{1}{2} \sin y$
43. $x = \dfrac{1}{b} \arctan \dfrac{y}{a}$
45. $\dfrac{\pi}{6}$
47. 0.5498 rad
49. 0.7694 rad
51. $-\dfrac{5}{12}$
53. $\dfrac{3}{5}$
55. $\dfrac{2\sqrt{3}}{3}$

Exercise Group 10–1

51. $\cos \theta$
53. $\sqrt{3} \cos \theta$
55. $2 \tan \theta$
57. $5 \tan \theta$
59. $x = \arccos 0$, $x = \arccos \frac{1}{2}$
61. $x = \arccos 0$
63. $x = \arcsin (-\frac{1}{2})$, $x = \arcsin 1$
65. $x = \arccos 1$
67. $x = \arccos (-\frac{1}{2})$, $x = \arccos 1$

Exercise Group 10–2

1. (a) and (b) $-\cos 24°$, (c) $-\sin 66°$
3. (a) $-\csc 57°$, (b) and (c) $-\sec 33°$
5. (a) $\sec 69°$, (b) and (c) $\csc 21°$
7. (a) $-\cot 88°$, (b) and (c) $-\tan 2°$
9. (a) and (b) $\sin 4°$, (c) $\cos 86°$
11. (a) and (b) $\sin 38°$, (c) $\cos 52°$
13. (a) and (b) $\sin 12° 47'$, (c) $\cos 77° 13'$
15. (a) and (b) $-\sec 39° 08'$, (c) $-\csc 50° 52'$
17. (a) $-\tan 63° 13'$, (b) and (c) $-\cot 26° 47'$
19. (a) $-\sec 61° 30'$, (b) and (c) $-\csc 28° 30'$
21. (a) $-\cot 88° 17'$, (b) and (c) $-\tan 1° 43'$
41. $\cot\theta$
43. $-\cot\theta$
45. $-\cos\theta$
47. $-\tan\theta$

Exercise Group 10–3

In Exercises 1, 3, and 5 the answers are given in the order $\sin(A + B)$, $\sin(A - B)$, $\cos(A + B)$, $\cos(A - B)$, $\tan(A + B)$, and $\tan(A - B)$.

1. $-\frac{33}{65}, -\frac{63}{65}, -\frac{56}{65}, -\frac{16}{65}, \frac{33}{56}, \frac{63}{16}$
3. $\frac{117}{125}, -\frac{3}{5}, -\frac{44}{125}, -\frac{4}{5}, -\frac{117}{44}, \frac{3}{4}$
5. $\frac{56}{65}, \frac{16}{65}, -\frac{33}{65}, \frac{63}{65}, -\frac{56}{33}, \frac{16}{63}$
7. $\frac{1}{4}(\sqrt{2} + \sqrt{6})$
9. $\frac{\sqrt{3}}{2}$
11. $2 + \sqrt{3}$
13. -1
15. $2 + \sqrt{3}$
17. $\frac{\sqrt{3}}{2}$
41. 1

Exercise Group 10–4

1. $\cos 15°$
3. $-\cos A$
5. $-\cos 4A$
7. $\tan 4\theta$
9. $\cos 6\theta$
11. $\tan 3\theta$
13. $\frac{24}{25}, \frac{7}{25}, \frac{24}{7}$
15. $\frac{24}{25}, \frac{7}{25}, \frac{24}{7}$
17. $-\frac{120}{169}, \frac{119}{169}, -\frac{120}{119}$
19. $-\frac{3\sqrt{7}}{8}, -\frac{1}{8}, 3\sqrt{7}$
21. $-\frac{5\sqrt{11}}{18}, -\frac{7}{18}, \frac{5\sqrt{11}}{7}$
23. $\frac{1}{2}\sqrt{2 + \sqrt{3}} = \frac{1}{4}(\sqrt{6} + \sqrt{2}), -\frac{1}{2}\sqrt{2 - \sqrt{3}} = \frac{1}{4}(\sqrt{2} - \sqrt{6}), -(2 + \sqrt{3})$
25. 1, 0, —
27. $\frac{\sqrt{2}}{2}, -\frac{\sqrt{2}}{2}, -1$
29. $\frac{4\sqrt{17}}{17}, -\frac{\sqrt{17}}{17}, -4$
31. $-\frac{3\sqrt{13}}{13}, -\frac{2\sqrt{13}}{13}, \frac{3}{2}$
33. $\frac{4}{5}$
35. $\frac{7}{25}$
37. $2x^2 - 1$
39. $\frac{1 - \sqrt{1 - x^2}}{x}$
41. $\frac{2x}{1 + x^2}$
63. $\sin\theta = \frac{2t}{1 + t^2}, \cos\theta = \frac{1 - t^2}{1 + t^2}$

Exercise Group 10–5

1. $2 \sin 30° \cos 10°$
3. $2 \sin 61° \cos 91°$
5. $-2 \sin 20° \sin 10°$
7. $2 \sin \frac{3\theta}{2} \cos \frac{5\theta}{2}$
9. $-2 \sin 5\theta \sin 3\theta$
11. $\frac{1}{2}(\sin 80° - \sin 20°)$
13. $\frac{1}{2}(\cos 134° + \cos 46°)$
15. $\frac{1}{2}(\sin 6\theta + \sin 2\theta)$
17. $\frac{1}{2}(\cos 7\theta + \cos\theta)$
19. $\frac{1}{2}(\sin 11A - \sin A)$
21. $\frac{1}{2}(\cos 28C + \cos 2C)$

Exercise Group 10–6

1. $\theta = \frac{\pi}{3}, \frac{5\pi}{3}$ 3. $\theta = \frac{\pi}{3}, \frac{2\pi}{3}, \frac{4\pi}{3}, \frac{5\pi}{3}$ 5. $\theta = \frac{\pi}{2}, \frac{7\pi}{6}, \frac{3\pi}{2}, \frac{11\pi}{6}$

7. $\theta = 0, \pi$ 9. $\theta = \pi$ 11. $\theta = \frac{7\pi}{6}, \frac{3\pi}{2}, \frac{11\pi}{6}$

13. $\theta = \frac{\pi}{4}, \frac{3\pi}{4}, \frac{5\pi}{4}, \frac{7\pi}{4}$ 15. $\theta = 0$ 17. $\theta = \frac{\pi}{3}, \frac{5\pi}{3}$

19. $\theta = \frac{\pi}{6}, \frac{2\pi}{3}, \frac{5\pi}{6}, \frac{4\pi}{3}$ 21. $\theta = \frac{\pi}{2}, \pi$ 23. $\theta = \frac{\pi}{6}, \frac{\pi}{2}, \frac{5\pi}{6}, \frac{7\pi}{6}, \frac{3\pi}{2}, \frac{11\pi}{6}$

25. $\theta = \frac{\pi}{3}, \pi, \frac{5\pi}{3}$ 27. $\theta = 0, \frac{2\pi}{9}, \frac{2\pi}{3}, \frac{10\pi}{9}, \frac{4\pi}{3}, \frac{14\pi}{9}$

29. $\theta = \frac{\pi}{8}, \frac{3\pi}{8}, \frac{5\pi}{8}, \frac{3\pi}{4}, \frac{7\pi}{8}, \frac{9\pi}{8}, \frac{11\pi}{8}, \frac{13\pi}{8}, \frac{7\pi}{4}, \frac{15\pi}{8}$

31. $\theta = 0, \pi$ 33. $\theta = \frac{\pi}{3}, \frac{2\pi}{3}, \frac{4\pi}{3}, \frac{5\pi}{3}$ 35. $\theta = \frac{\pi}{4}, \frac{3\pi}{4}, \frac{5\pi}{4}, \frac{7\pi}{4}$

37. $\theta = 0, \frac{\pi}{6}, \frac{5\pi}{6}, \pi, \frac{7\pi}{6}, \frac{11\pi}{6},$ 39. $\theta = \frac{3\pi}{2}$ 41. $\theta = 1.9338, 3.7059$

43. $\theta = 0.3947$ 45. $\theta = 5.1065$

47. $\theta = 0, \frac{\pi}{6}, \frac{\pi}{3}, \frac{\pi}{2}, \frac{2\pi}{3}, \frac{5\pi}{6}, \pi, \frac{7\pi}{6}, \frac{4\pi}{3}, \frac{3\pi}{2}, \frac{5\pi}{3}, \frac{11\pi}{6}$ 49. $\theta = 0.1420, 3.2836$

Supplementary Exercises for Chapter 10

33. (a) $-\cos 38° 42'$, (b) $-\cos 38° 42'$

35. (a) $\tan 87°$, (b) $\cot 3°$ 37. (a) $-\sin 25°$, (b) $-\sin 25°$

39. (a) $\sin\frac{\pi}{3}$, (b) $\cos\frac{\pi}{6}$ 41. (a) $-\tan\frac{\pi}{3}$, (b) $-\cot\frac{\pi}{6}$

43. (a) $-\cos\frac{\pi}{4}$, (b) $-\cos\frac{\pi}{4}$ 45. (a) $-\tan\frac{\pi}{4}$, (b) $-\tan\frac{\pi}{4}$

47. (a) $\cos\frac{\pi}{3}$, (b) $\sin\frac{\pi}{6}$ 49. $\theta = 0, \frac{\pi}{3}, \pi, \frac{5\pi}{3}$

51. $\theta = \frac{\pi}{3}, 2.3006, 3.9826, \frac{5\pi}{3}$ 53. $\theta = 0, \frac{\pi}{4}, \frac{\pi}{2}, \frac{3\pi}{4}, \pi, \frac{5\pi}{4}, \frac{3\pi}{2}, \frac{7\pi}{4}$

55. $\theta = 0.6749, 5.6083$ 57. $\theta = 0, \frac{\pi}{4}, \pi, \frac{5\pi}{4}$

59. $\theta = \frac{\pi}{6}, \frac{7\pi}{18}, \frac{11\pi}{18}, \frac{5\pi}{6}, \frac{19\pi}{18}, \frac{23\pi}{18}, \frac{3\pi}{2}, \frac{31\pi}{18}, \frac{35\pi}{18}$

61. $\theta = \frac{5\pi}{12}, \frac{13\pi}{12}$ 63. $\theta = \frac{\pi}{4}, \frac{\pi}{2}, \frac{3\pi}{4}, \frac{5\pi}{4}, \frac{3\pi}{2}, \frac{7\pi}{4}$

Exercise Group 11–2

1. 1, 13, 78, 286, 715 3. 1, 23, 253, 1771, 8855 5. 1, 37, 666, 7770, 66045

7. 1, 53, 1378, 23426, 292825

9. $x^5 - 5x^4y + 10x^3y^2 - 10x^2y^3 + 5xy^4 - y^5$

11. $u^6 - 6u^5v + 15u^4v^2 - 20u^3v^3 + 15u^2v^4 - 6uv^5 + v^6$
13. $x^5 - 5ax^4y + 10a^2x^3y^2 - 10a^3x^2y^3 + 5a^4xy^4 - a^5y^5$
15. $x^6 + 12x^5y + 60x^4y^2 + 160x^3y^3 + 240x^2y^4 + 192xy^5 + 64y^6$
17. $32x^5 - 240x^4y + 720x^3y^2 - 1080x^2y^3 + 810xy^4 - 243y^5$
19. $\frac{1}{2187}x^7 - \frac{7}{1458}x^6y + \frac{7}{324}x^5y^2 - \frac{35}{648}x^4y^3 + \frac{35}{432}x^3y^4 - \frac{7}{96}x^2y^5 + \frac{7}{192}xy^6$
$- \frac{1}{128}y^7$
21. $x^7 + 7x^5 + 21x^3 + 35x + 35x^{-1} + 21x^{-3} + 7x^{-5} + x^{-7}$
23. $a^5x^{-5} - 5a^4bx^{-4}y^{-1} + 10a^3b^2x^{-3}y^{-2} - 10a^2b^3x^{-2}y^{-3} + 5ab^4x^{-3}y^{-4}$
$- b^5y^{-5}$
25. $x^8 - 8x^3 + 24x^{-2} - 32x^{-7} + 16x^{-12}$
27. $4(-1 + i)$
29. -1
31. $x^{-4y} + 4x^{-3y}y^{-x} + 6x^{-2y}y^{-2x} + 4x^{-y}y^{-3x} + y^{-4x}$
33. $1 + 15(0.04) + 105(0.04)^2$
35. $1 + 25(0.03) + 300(0.03)^2$
37. 1.558
39. 1.629

Exercise Group 11–3

1. $210x^4y^6$
3. $320320x^9y^6$
5. $12376a^{11}b^6x^{11/2}y^{18}$
7. $2{,}449{,}440x^4y^6$
9. 0.0008448
11. -3432
13. $-42504x^{-14}y^{19}$
15. $336xy^2$
17. 126,720
19. $96096u^{15x}$
21. $16x^4y^5$

Exercise Group 11–4

1. $1 + \frac{1}{2}y - \frac{1}{8}y^2 + \frac{1}{16}y^3$
3. $1 - x + \frac{3}{2}x^2 - \frac{5}{2}x^3$
5. $1 + \frac{2}{3}x^2 + \frac{5}{9}x^4 + \frac{40}{81}x^6$
7. $1 - 3av + 6a^2v^2 - 10a^3v^3$
9. $1 - \frac{5}{2}ax + \frac{15}{8}a^2x^2 - \frac{5}{16}a^3x^3$
11. $1 + 1 + \frac{1}{2}\left(1 - \frac{1}{x}\right) + \frac{1}{6}\left(1 - \frac{1}{x}\right)\left(1 - \frac{2}{x}\right)$
13. $-\frac{91}{3^8}x^6$
15. $2^{27}x^9$
17. Eighth
19. Seventh
21. Sixth and seventh
23. $1 - 0.45 + 0.108$
25. $2 + 0.03125 - 0.0007324$
27. $3 + 0.037037 - 0.000457$
29. $1 + \frac{1}{2}(x - 2) - \frac{1}{8}(x - 2)^2 + \frac{1}{16}(x - 2)^3$; $1 < x < 3$
31. $\frac{1}{4}\left[1 - (x - 1) + \frac{3(x - 1)^2}{4} - \frac{(x - 1)^3}{2}\right]$

Exercise Group 11–5

1. 2383
3. 301.6
5. 8.192×10^{-8}
7. 5381
9. 2.762
11. 1.948
13. -0.1715
15. 0.0280
17. 1.023
19. $r = 1.238\%$
21. 13,450,000
23. 2694 yr
25. 18.47°
27. 75.82 grams
29. 5.92%
31. 6.04%
33. The first, by $28

Supplementary Exercises for Chapter 11

1. $-320320x^6y^9$ 3. $\dfrac{116280a^7b^{14}}{x^7}$ 5. $12870x^8y^8$ 7. $-792x^9y^5$

9. $1 + \dfrac{3}{x} + \dfrac{3}{2x^2} - \dfrac{1}{2x^3}$

11. $1 + 1 + \dfrac{1}{2}\left(1 - \dfrac{x}{2}\right) + \dfrac{1}{6}\left(1 - \dfrac{x}{2}\right)(1 - x)$

13. $5 - \dfrac{1}{75} - \dfrac{1}{28125} - \dfrac{1}{6328125}$ 15. $3 + \dfrac{1}{405} - \dfrac{2}{492075} + \dfrac{2}{199{,}290{,}375}$

17. $1 + 0.55 + 0.1444 + 0.0241$ 19. $1 + 1.75 + 1.4875 + 0.818125$

25. 874 yr

Exercise Group 12–1

1. $(0, 3)$ 3. $(-\frac{24}{29}, \frac{31}{29})$ 5. $(-\frac{32}{19}, -\frac{29}{19})$ 7. $(-3, 1)$ 9. $(5, \frac{7}{3})$

11. $(-\frac{1}{3}, \frac{1}{2})$ 13. $(\frac{1}{6}, \frac{1}{5})$ 15. $(0.3, -0.5)$ 17. $(a + b, a)$

19. $(a - 3b, c - 2a)$ 21. $(1.8c^2, -2.3b^2)$ 23. $(-2, 7)$ 25. $(\frac{3}{2}, 0)$

27. $\left[\dfrac{c\cos B - d\sin B}{\sin(A - B)}, \dfrac{d\sin A - c\cos A}{\sin(A - B)}\right]$

29. $\left[\dfrac{d\cos B - c\sin B}{\cos(A + B)}, \dfrac{c\cos A - d\sin A}{\cos(A + B)}\right]$

31. 68, 22 33. 30 ft/sec, 50 ft/sec 35. $\frac{3}{5}$ 37. \$8000, 6.25%

39. 4 hr 41. 4 yd, 5 yd 43. $2x^2 + 3x - 4$

Exercise Group 12–2

1. $(1, 2, 3)$ 3. $(-2, 2, 3)$ 5. $(2, 3, -4)$ 7. $(\frac{1}{3}, \frac{1}{5}, \frac{1}{6})$

9. $(a + b, a - b, 2a)$ 11. $\left(\dfrac{a - b}{2}, \dfrac{b - c}{2}, \dfrac{c - a}{2}\right)$

13. $(4u, u, u)$ 15. $\left(2, \dfrac{1}{2}, \dfrac{1}{3}\right)$ 17. $(1, -2, 3, -4)$ 19. $1 - \dfrac{2}{x} - \dfrac{1}{x^2}$

21. $A = \frac{9}{7}, B = -\frac{2}{7}, C = -\frac{1}{7}$ 23. 2 days, 3 days, 6 days

25. 9 in., 14 in., 16 in.

Exercise Group 12–4

1. $(3, 4), (-4, -3)$ 3. $(5, -4)$ 5. $(1, 0), (-\frac{1}{2}, \sqrt{3})$

7. $(0, -5), (-10, -15)$ 9. $(-1, 0), (\frac{7}{11}, \frac{9}{11})$ 11. $(10, 3), (-3, -10)$

13. $(3, 4), (-\frac{15}{2}, \frac{1}{2})$ 15. $(-2, 2), (\frac{2}{3}, \frac{10}{9})$ 17. $(a, 0), (0, -b)$

19. Inconsistent 21. $(3, 2), (5, \frac{30}{17})$

23. (1) $k > \frac{4}{3}, k < -\frac{4}{3}$, (2) $-\frac{4}{3} < k < \frac{4}{3}$

25. (1) $\dfrac{4 - \sqrt{17}}{2} \leqq k \leqq \dfrac{4 + \sqrt{17}}{2}$, (2) $k < \dfrac{4 - \sqrt{17}}{2}, k > \dfrac{4 + \sqrt{17}}{2}$

27. $1 + i\sqrt{3}, 1 - i\sqrt{3}$ 29. 30 ft × 50 ft 31. 120 ft × 610 ft

33. 60 ft × 63 ft 35. 24 37. $m = \pm\sqrt{5}$

Exercise Group 12–5

1. $(\pm 5, \pm 2)$
3. $\left(\pm 2, \pm \frac{2\sqrt{5}}{3}\right)$
5. $(\pm\sqrt{17}, \pm\sqrt{19})$
7. $(\pm i\sqrt{3}, \pm\sqrt{7})$
9. $\left[\pm \sqrt{\frac{ac}{a^2 + b^2}}, \pm \sqrt{\frac{bc}{a^2 + b^2}}\right]$
11. $\left[\pm \frac{2\sqrt{30}}{3}, \pm \frac{4i\sqrt{3}}{3}\right]$
13. $\left(\pm \frac{\sqrt{3}}{3}, \pm \frac{\sqrt{58}}{2}\right)$
15. $(\pm i\sqrt{5}, \pm i\sqrt{3})$
17. $\left(\pm \frac{3\sqrt{4118}}{29}, \pm \frac{5\sqrt{638}}{29}\right)$
19. $\left(\pm \frac{30i\sqrt{10234}}{301}, \pm \frac{15i\sqrt{18361}}{301}\right)$
21. $\left(\pm 1, \pm \frac{\sqrt{6}}{2}\right)$
23. $[\pm(a + b), \pm(a - b)]$
25. $(-1, 6), (1, -6), (3, -2), (-3, 2), (1 + i\sqrt{2}, 2 - 2i\sqrt{2}),$ $(1 - i\sqrt{2}, 2 + 2i\sqrt{2}), (-1 + i\sqrt{2}, -2 - 2i\sqrt{2}), (-1 - i\sqrt{2}, -2 + 2i\sqrt{2})$
27. $\left(\pm \frac{i}{3}, \pm \frac{1}{5}\right)$

Exercise Group 12–6

1. $(0, \pm 2\sqrt{11}), (-4, 2), (4, -2)$
3. $(1, -1), (-1, 1), (-2, -3), (2, 3)$
5. $(1, -3), (-1, 3), (3, 1), (-3, -1)$
7. $(-1, -2), (1, 2), \left(\frac{3i\sqrt{5}}{5}, -\frac{i\sqrt{5}}{5}\right), \left(-\frac{3i\sqrt{5}}{5}, \frac{i\sqrt{5}}{5}\right)$
9. $\left(-\frac{\sqrt{2}}{2}, -\frac{3\sqrt{2}}{4}\right), \left(\frac{\sqrt{2}}{2}, \frac{3\sqrt{2}}{4}\right), (1, -1), (-1, 1)$
11. $(3, -1), (-3, 1), (1, 3), (-1, -3)$
13. $(-4, -4), (4, 4), \left(-\frac{12i\sqrt{34}}{17}, \frac{16i\sqrt{34}}{17}\right), \left(\frac{12i\sqrt{34}}{17}, -\frac{16i\sqrt{34}}{17}\right)$
15. $\left(\frac{2}{3}, 1\right), \left(-\frac{14}{19}, -\frac{21}{19}\right), \left(\frac{-5 - \sqrt{2265}}{32}, \frac{-5 - \sqrt{2265}}{160}\right),$ $\left(\frac{-5 + \sqrt{2265}}{32}, \frac{-5 + \sqrt{2265}}{160}\right)$
17. $(-\sqrt{2}, 4\sqrt{2}), (\sqrt{2}, -4\sqrt{2}), (-3, -2), (3, 2)$

Exercise Group 12–7

1. $(-1, -4), (1, 4), (2, -7), (-2, 7)$
3. $(-4, -2), (4, 2), (20, -6), (-20, 6)$
5. $(4i, i), (-4i, -i), (3, 2), (-3, -2)$
7. $(-2, -3), (2, 3), \left(\frac{i\sqrt{55}}{11}, -\frac{2i\sqrt{55}}{11}\right), \left(-\frac{i\sqrt{55}}{11}, \frac{2i\sqrt{55}}{11}\right)$
9. $\left(-\frac{\sqrt{2}}{2}, -2\sqrt{2}\right), \left(\frac{\sqrt{2}}{2}, 2\sqrt{2}\right), \left(-\frac{1}{2}, -3\right), \left(\frac{1}{2}, 3\right)$

11. $\left(\frac{1 + \sqrt{73}}{6}, \frac{-1 + \sqrt{73}}{4}\right), \left(\frac{1 - \sqrt{73}}{6}, \frac{-1 - \sqrt{73}}{4}\right),$
$\left(\frac{-1 + \sqrt{73}}{6}, \frac{1 + \sqrt{73}}{4}\right), \left(\frac{-1 - \sqrt{73}}{6}, \frac{1 - \sqrt{73}}{4}\right)$

13. $\left(\frac{3 + \sqrt{17}}{2}, \frac{-3 + \sqrt{17}}{2}\right), \left(\frac{3 - \sqrt{17}}{2}, \frac{-3 - \sqrt{17}}{2}\right),$
$\left(\frac{-3 + \sqrt{17}}{2}, \frac{3 + \sqrt{17}}{2}\right), \left(\frac{-3 - \sqrt{17}}{2}, \frac{3 - \sqrt{17}}{2}\right)$

15. $(-1, 6), (-6, 1), (2, -3), (3, -2)$

17. $(2, -3), (-2, 3), (5, -6), (-5, 6)$

19. $\frac{5}{6}, \frac{2}{3}$ or $-\frac{2}{3}, -\frac{5}{6}$

21. 7 and 9 or -7 and -9

Exercise Group 12–8

1. $r = \pm\sqrt{a^2 + b^2}, \theta = \arctan \frac{a}{b}$

3. $r = \pm \frac{ab\sqrt{a^2 - b^2}}{a^2 - b^2}, \theta = \arccos \frac{b}{a}$

5. $x = \frac{1}{2}\left[\arccos \frac{a^2 + b^2 - 2}{2} + 2 \arctan \frac{a}{b}\right],$
$y = \frac{1}{2}\left[2 \arctan \frac{a}{b} - \arccos \frac{a^2 + b^2 - 2}{2}\right]$

7. $x = \arccos \frac{1}{2}\sqrt{a^2 + b^2} + \arctan \frac{a}{b}, y = \arccos \frac{1}{2}\sqrt{a^2 + b^2} + \arctan \frac{b}{a}$

9. $x = \arccos \frac{1}{2}(a \pm \sqrt{2 + b - a^2}), y = \arccos \frac{1}{2}(a \mp \sqrt{2 + b - a^2})$

11. $(0, 0); (0, \pi); (\pi, 0); (\pi, \pi); \left(\frac{\pi}{4}, \frac{\pi}{6}\right); \left(\frac{3\pi}{4}, \frac{5\pi}{6}\right); \left(\frac{5\pi}{4}, \frac{7\pi}{6}\right); \left(\frac{7\pi}{4}, \frac{11\pi}{6}\right)$

13. $\left(\frac{\pi}{4}, \frac{7\pi}{4}\right); \left(\frac{5\pi}{4}, \frac{3\pi}{4}\right)$

15. $\left(\frac{\pi}{6}, \frac{5\pi}{6}\right); \left(\frac{5\pi}{6}, \frac{\pi}{6}\right)$

Supplementary Exercises for Chapter 12

1. $(-2, 3)$

3. $(-\frac{16}{15}, \frac{27}{25})$

5. (a, b)

7. $(1, -2, 3)$

9. (a, b, c)

11. $(1, -2, 3)$

13. $\left(\frac{a}{2}, -\frac{a}{2}, b\right)$

15. $(3, \frac{8}{5}), (-4, -\frac{6}{5})$

17. $(0, 0), (\frac{8}{3}, -\frac{16}{9})$

19. $(0, \frac{5}{3}), (\frac{5}{2}, 0)$

21. $\left(\frac{5 + \sqrt{47}}{6}, \frac{-5 + \sqrt{47}}{4}\right), \left(\frac{5 - \sqrt{47}}{6}, \frac{-5 - \sqrt{47}}{4}\right),$
$\left(\frac{-5 + \sqrt{47}}{6}, \frac{5 + \sqrt{47}}{4}\right), \left(\frac{-5 - \sqrt{47}}{6}, \frac{5 - \sqrt{47}}{4}\right)$

23. $\left(\frac{5 + i\sqrt{17}}{2}, \frac{5 - i\sqrt{17}}{4}\right), \left(\frac{5 - i\sqrt{17}}{2}, \frac{5 + i\sqrt{17}}{4}\right),$
$\left(\frac{-5 + i\sqrt{17}}{2}, \frac{-5 - i\sqrt{17}}{4}\right), \left(\frac{-5 - i\sqrt{17}}{2}, \frac{-5 + i\sqrt{17}}{4}\right)$

25. $(-1, 1), \left(\frac{7}{3}, -\frac{7}{3}\right), \left(\frac{-7 + \sqrt{14}}{5}, \frac{21 - 3\sqrt{14}}{5}\right),$
$\left(\frac{-7 - \sqrt{14}}{5}, \frac{21 + 3\sqrt{14}}{5}\right)$

27. $(0, 0), (5, \frac{10}{3}), (5, -\frac{10}{3})$

29. Airspeed 425 mph, wind velocity 25 mph

Exercise Group 13–1

1. 6, 8, 10, 12; 164
3. $\frac{1}{2}, \frac{1}{4}, \frac{1}{6}, \frac{1}{8}; \frac{1}{86}$
5. $\frac{1}{3}, \frac{3}{5}, \frac{5}{7}, \frac{7}{9}; \frac{245}{247}$
7. $1, \frac{1}{4}, \frac{1}{9}, \frac{1}{16}; \frac{1}{5041}$
9. $\frac{1}{2}, \frac{1}{4}, \frac{1}{8}, \frac{1}{16}; \frac{1}{2048}$
11. $\frac{1}{2}, \frac{\sqrt{3}}{2}, 1, \frac{\sqrt{3}}{2}; \frac{\sqrt{3}}{2}$
13. $a_n = 2n + 1$
15. $a_n = \frac{1}{n}$
17. $a_n = \frac{1}{(n + 1)^2}$
19. $a_n = \frac{n + 1}{(n + 2)(n + 3)}$
21. $a_n = \frac{n + 1}{1 \cdot 2 \cdot 3 \cdots n}$

Exercise Group 13–2

1. 7, 10, 13
3. 9, 7, 5
5. $\frac{5}{3}, \frac{1}{3}, -1$
7. $a_{23} = 193, S_{23} = 1127$
9. $a_{101} = 28, S_{101} = \frac{3131}{2}$
11. $a_{15} = 27, S_{15} = 90$
13. 18
15. $\frac{13}{12}$
17. $\frac{u + v}{2}$
19. $-5, -8, -11, -14, -17, -20$
21. $\frac{13}{4}, \frac{7}{2}, \frac{15}{4}, 4, \frac{17}{4}, \frac{9}{2}, \frac{19}{4}, 5, \frac{21}{4}, \frac{11}{2}, \frac{23}{4}, 6, \frac{25}{4}$
23. $a_1 = \frac{13}{3}, S_{35} = -\frac{140}{3}$
25. $a_{79} = -29, d = -\frac{2}{3}$
27. $d = -\frac{3}{31}, a_{63} = -8$
29. $n = 31, a_{31} = 225$
31. $n = 23, a_{23} = 71$
33. $n = 30, a_{30} = -85$
35. $n = 23, a_1 = 2$
37. $d = 3, a_{19} = 47$
39. $-\frac{155}{2}$
41. $a_{27} = 61$
43. 10,182,465
45. 16 yr
47. \$3297
49. 353.5 ft
51. $a_1 = 8, n = 59$

Exercise Group 13–3

1. 11, 33, 99
3. $\frac{3}{2}, 1, \frac{2}{3}$
5. $-5, 2, -\frac{4}{5}$
7. $a_{19} = 3 \cdot 2^{18}, S_{19} = \frac{3}{2}(2^{19} - 1)$
9. $a_{17} = \frac{5}{2^{15}}, S_{17} = \frac{5(2^{17} + 1)}{3 \cdot 2^{15}}$
11. $a_9 = -\frac{3^8}{5}, S_9 = \frac{3^9 - 1}{20}$
13. $a_n = \sin^{2n-2}\theta, S_n = \frac{1 - \sin^{2n}\theta}{\cos^2\theta}$
15. $a_n = \csc^{2n-4}\theta, S_n = \frac{1 - \csc^{2n}\theta}{\csc^2\theta - \csc^4\theta}$
17. $a_n = \sec^{2n-8}\theta, S_n = \frac{1 - \sec^{2n}\theta}{\sec^6\theta - \sec^8\theta}$
19. $\pm\frac{2}{3}, 1, \pm\frac{3}{2}$
21. $1, \frac{1}{2}, \frac{1}{4}, \frac{1}{8}, \frac{1}{16}, \frac{1}{32}$
23. $\pm 10^{9/8}, 10^{5/4}, \pm 10^{11/8}, 10^{3/2}, \pm 10^{13/8}, 10^{7/4}, \pm 10^{15/8}$
25. $2\sin^2\theta, 4\sin^4\theta\csc 2\theta, 8\sin^6\theta\csc^2 2\theta, 16\sin^8\theta\csc^3 2\theta$

27. $\pm\csc\theta\tan^2\frac{\theta}{2}$, $\csc^2\theta\tan^2\frac{\theta}{2}$, $\pm\csc^3\theta\tan^2\frac{\theta}{2}$ 29. $n = 9, S_n = 511$
31. $n = 8, S_n = \frac{18915}{128}$ 33. $a_1 = 27, n = 6$ 35. $n = 6, a_6 = \frac{125}{32}$
37. $n = 11, S_{11} = \cos^2\theta(\cot^{20}\theta + \tan^2\theta)$ 39. $r = \pm 2$
41. $r = \pm\csc\theta$ 43. 303 45. \$29,700 47. \$2558

Exercise Group 13–4

1. $\frac{18}{5}$ 3. $\frac{121}{12}$ 5. $\frac{15}{2}$ 7. 0.1026
9. $\frac{1}{\sqrt{2}-2} = -\frac{1}{2}(\sqrt{2}+2)$ 11. $\frac{1}{1+x}$, $|x| < 1$
13. $\frac{x}{1-x^2}$, $|x| < 1$ 15. $-\frac{x+3}{2x+5}$, $|x+3| < \frac{1}{2}$
17. $\frac{x-1}{x}$, $|1-x| > 1$

Exercise Group 13–5

1. $\frac{50}{33}$ 3. $\frac{8}{111}$ 5. 6 7. $\frac{79}{90}$ 9. $\frac{88}{111}$ 11. $\frac{17}{330}$ 13. $\frac{60}{37}$ 15. $\frac{5}{7}$

Supplementary Exercises for Chapter 13

5. $\frac{n}{2(1-x)}[2 + (n-3)\sqrt{x}]$ 17. 8, 12, 18 and 18, 12, 8
25. $\frac{55}{24}$ 27. $\frac{1}{11}$ 29. $3 + \frac{5}{4}\sqrt{6} = 6.06$ (sec)

Exercise Group 14–2

1. $B = 83° 23', a = 289.1, c = 183.5$ 3. $A = 106° 51', b = 23.94, c = 13.97$
5. $B = 22° 13', a = 16.46, c = 19.08$ 7. $A = 13° 49', b = 1.587, c = 1.957$
9. $C = 14° 29', a = 59.51, b = 54.41$ 11. $B = 55° 59', a = 4589, c = 2911$
13. $C = 99° 06', b = 29.88, c = 42.85$ 15. $B = 50° 52', a = 1.300, b = 1.017$
17. $A = 30° 01', a = 3.600, c = 6.116$ 19. $B = 14° 43', a = 572.2, b = 216.8$
21. Wind velocity 38 mph, groundspeed 471 mph
23. 84 ft 25. 203.0 in. 27. 1720 nautical miles
29. Airspeed 281.7 mph, wind velocity 21.42 mph

Exercise Group 14–3

1. $B = 12° 08', C = 143° 31', c = 9.102$ 3. No solution
5. $A = 102° 49', B = 40° 52', a = 38.27$; $A' = 4° 33', B' = 139° 08', a' = 3.113$ 7. No solution
9. $B = 122° 33', C = 10° 44', b = 0.4197$
11. $A = 30° 24', C = 78° 20', a = 168.3$; $A' = 7° 04', C' = 101° 40', a' = 40.92$
13. $B = 41° 51', C = 74° 20', c = 3.771$
15. $A = 40° 22', B = 45° 00', a = 12.89$
17. $A = 33° 06', C = 127° 41', c = 202.0$; $A' = 146° 54', C' = 13° 53', c' = 61.24$

19. $B = 26° 17'$, $C = 29° 27'$, $c = 3.738$
21. $A = 20° 36'$, $B = 150° 30'$, $b = 2.702$; $A' = 159° 24'$, $B' = 11° 42'$, $b' = 1.113$
23. $AB = 406$ ft
25. Average groundspeed 271.4 mph, heading 212° 06′
27. $F_3 = 4693$ lb, F_1 makes an angle of 75° 05′ with F_2.
29. Distance 162.9 mi, course 34° 11′

Exercise Group 14–4

1. $A = 34° 40'$, $B = 25° 20'$, $c = 6.1$
3. $A = 28°$, $C = 92°$, $b = 27.7$
5. $B = 41° 30'$, $C = 23° 20'$, $a = 684$
7. $A = 28° 50'$, $B = 21° 10'$, $c = 318$
9. $A = 150° 10'$, $C = 2° 50'$, $b = 0.137$
11. $A = 18°$, $B = 51°$, $C = 111°$
13. $A = 47°$, $B = 61° 20'$, $C = 71° 40'$
15. $A = 48° 10'$, $B = 58° 30'$, $C = 73° 20'$
17. $A = 23°$, $B = 54° 20'$, $C = 102° 40'$
19. $A = 34° 50'$, $B = 53° 30'$, $C = 91° 40'$
21. $AB = 201$ ft
23. 117 mi, 202° 40′
25. 33° 40′; 120°

Exercise Group 14–5

1. $B = 48° 22'$, $C = 94° 12'$, $a = 26.36$
3. $B = 32° 56'$, $C = 83° 44'$, $a = 221.6$
5. $A = 13° 02'$, $B = 33° 10'$, $c = 0.5644$
7. $A = 71° 53'$, $C = 9° 51'$, $b = 201{,}200$
9. $A = 39° 00'$, $B = 53° 26'$, $c = 0.5144$
11. $A = 3° 31'$, $C = 45° 09'$, $b = 8.874$
13. $A = 83° 38'$, $C = 57° 04'$, $b = 390.7$
15. $B = 58° 40'$, $C = 73° 44'$, $a = 2.162$
17. $A = 150° 19'$, $B = 22° 53'$, $c = 0.1963$
19. $A = 77° 10'$, $C = 7° 34'$, $b = 2.198$
21. Heading S 16° 10′ E, average airspeed 143 mph
23. 38° 47′ with F_1, magnitude 260.7 lb
25. 541.8 ft
27. $AB = 89.2$ ft

Exercise Group 14–6

1. $A = 35° 06'$, $B = 95° 02'$, $C = 49° 52'$
3. $A = 50° 50'$, $B = 25° 20'$, $C = 103° 50'$
5. $A = 20° 02'$, $B = 38° 06'$, $C = 121° 52'$
7. $A = 52° 42'$, $B = 86° 12'$, $C = 41° 06'$
9. $A = 92° 32'$, $B = 38° 04'$, $C = 49° 24'$
11. $A = 40° 16'$, $B = 58° 36'$, $C = 81° 08'$
13. $A = 37° 28'$, $B = 53° 32'$, $C = 89° 00'$
15. $A = 35° 52'$, $B = 28° 34'$, $C = 115° 34'$
17. $A = 46° 22'$, $B = 57° 50'$, $C = 75° 48'$
19. $A = 15° 04'$, $B = 131° 08'$, $C = 33° 48'$
21. F_2 makes an angle of 130° 20′ with F_1; R makes an angle of 23° 20′ with F_1.
23. Course 213°, wind from 324°; or, course 221°, wind from 110°

25. Heading 183° 20′, wind from 314° 30′
27. For A, 277° 10′; for B, 82° 50′; for C, 194° 20′

Exercise Group 14–7

1. 468.0 3. 303.4 5. 0.2972 7. 0.002049
9. 6.310 11. 0.1744 13. 0.09854 15. 916.4
17. 8.706 in^2 19. 137,300 ft^2 21. 833 ft^2 23. 1960 ft of fence

Exercise Group 15–1

17. $2, \frac{\pi}{3}; 2, -\frac{\pi}{3}$ 19. $2, -\frac{\pi}{6}; 2, \frac{\pi}{6}$ 21. $\sqrt{2}, \frac{3\pi}{4}; \sqrt{2}, -\frac{3\pi}{4}$
23. $6, \frac{\pi}{2}; 6, -\frac{\pi}{2}$ 25. $3\sqrt{2}, -\frac{\pi}{4}; 3\sqrt{2}, \frac{\pi}{4}$ 27. $4\sqrt{3}, -\frac{\pi}{3}; 4\sqrt{3}, \frac{\pi}{3}$
29. 7, −58° 59′; 7, 58° 59′ 31. $1, -\frac{\pi}{6}; 1, \frac{\pi}{6}$
33. 2, 215°; 2, −215° 35. 2.5, −16° 16′; 2.5, 16° 16′
37. $x = 1, y = -3$ 39. $x = -\frac{5}{3}, y = 3$ 41. $x = b, y = -a$
43. $x = -\frac{3d}{b}, y = -\frac{5a}{b}$ 45. $x = -\frac{5}{3}, y = -2$

Exercise Group 15–2

1. $12 + 13i, 2 - 3i$ 3. $-10 - 10i, 10 - 4i$ 5. $12, -2i$
7. $4i, -6$ 9. $13, -7 + 8i$ 11. $17 - 4i, 7 + 4i$
13. $11 - 5i, 3 + 5i$
15. $\sqrt{3} - 3 + (1 + 3\sqrt{3})i; \sqrt{3} + 3 + (1 - 3\sqrt{3})i$
17. $\frac{5}{2} + \left(\frac{5\sqrt{3}}{2} - 4\right)i, -\frac{5}{2} - \left(4 + \frac{5\sqrt{3}}{2}\right)i$ 19. $2r\cos\theta, 2ri\sin\theta$

Exercise Group 15–3

1. $\sqrt{2}(\cos 45° + i\sin 45°)$ 3. $\sqrt{2}(\cos 315° + i\sin 315°)$
5. $\sqrt{2}(\cos 135° + i\sin 135°)$ 7. $2\sqrt{2}(\cos 225° + i\sin 225°)$
9. $2(\cos 0° + i\sin 0°)$ 11. $1.3(\cos 22° 37' + i\sin 22° 37')$
13. (1, 182°) 15. (5, 154° 25′) 17. (1.3, 157° 23′) 19. (25, 163° 44′)

Exercise Group 15–4

1. $63 - 16i$ 3. $2 + 14i$ 5. $15 + 5i$ 7. $-\frac{5}{34} + \frac{31}{34}i$
9. $\frac{11}{5} - \frac{3}{5}i$ 11. $(20\sqrt{2}, 165°)$ 13. $(2\sqrt{2}, -15°)$ 15. $(\sqrt{2}, 255°)$
17. $\left(\frac{125}{221}, -13° 50'\right)$ 19. (1.25, 165° 09′) 21. $\left(\frac{\sqrt{6}}{75}, 16° 16'\right)$
23. $(\frac{13}{14}, -76° 10')$ 25. (0.9993, 4° 32′) 27. (6, 89° 55′)

Exercise Group 15–5

1. $72(1 - i\sqrt{3})$ 3. -64 5. i 7. $\frac{-\sqrt{2} + i\sqrt{2}}{2}$

9. $\left(\frac{\sqrt{2}}{32}, \frac{\pi}{12}\right) = \frac{1}{64}[\sqrt{3} + 1 + i(2\sqrt{3} - 1)]$ 11. $\left(\frac{2\sqrt{6}}{243}, 285^\circ\right)$

13. $\left(\frac{8^3 \cdot 7^6}{13^8}, 259^\circ\ 55'\right)$ 15. $-\frac{1}{2} - i\frac{\sqrt{3}}{2}$ 17. $2, -1 + i\sqrt{3}, -1 - i\sqrt{3}$

19. $\left(2, \frac{\pi}{5}\right), \left(2, \frac{3\pi}{5}\right), -2, \left(2, \frac{7\pi}{5}\right), \left(2, \frac{9\pi}{5}\right)$ 21. $i, -\frac{1}{2}(\sqrt{3} + i), \frac{1}{2}(\sqrt{3} - i)$

23. $(1, 48^\circ), -\frac{1}{2} + i\frac{\sqrt{3}}{2}, (1, 192^\circ), (1, 264^\circ), (1, 336^\circ)$

25. $(\sqrt[4]{12}, 165^\circ), (\sqrt[4]{12}, 345^\circ)$

27. $(\sqrt[5]{25}, 68^\circ\ 45'), (\sqrt[5]{25}, 140^\circ\ 45'), (\sqrt[5]{25}, 212^\circ\ 45'), (\sqrt[5]{25}, 284^\circ\ 45'),$
$(\sqrt[5]{25}, 346^\circ\ 45')$

29. $2i, -\sqrt{3} - i, \sqrt{3} - i$

31. $\frac{3\sqrt{2}}{4}(1 + i), \frac{3\sqrt{2}}{4}(-1 + i), \frac{3\sqrt{2}}{4}(-1 - i), \frac{3\sqrt{2}}{4}(1 - i)$

33. $(1, 40^\circ), (1, 100^\circ), (1, 160^\circ), (1, 220^\circ), (1, 280^\circ), (1, 340^\circ)$

Supplementary Exercises for Chapter 15

1. $18 + i$ 3. $129 - 28i$ 5. $\frac{22}{41} - \frac{7}{41}i$ 7. $\frac{1}{41} - \frac{32}{41}i$

9. $\frac{25}{26}(\cos 267^\circ\ 59' + i \sin 267^\circ\ 59')$ 11. $\frac{25}{36}(\cos 352^\circ\ 35' + i \sin 352^\circ\ 35')$

13. $\frac{100}{63}(\cos 300^\circ\ 24' + i \sin 300^\circ\ 24')$

15. $2, 2(\cos 72^\circ + i \sin 72^\circ), 2(\cos 144^\circ + i \sin 144^\circ),$
$2(\cos 216^\circ + i \sin 216^\circ), 2(\cos 288^\circ + i \sin 288^\circ)$

17. $\sqrt[7]{7}, \sqrt[7]{7}(\cos 51\frac{3}{7}^\circ + i \sin 51\frac{3}{7}^\circ), \sqrt[7]{7}(\cos 102\frac{6}{7}^\circ + i \sin 102\frac{6}{7}^\circ),$
$\sqrt[7]{7}(\cos 154\frac{2}{7}^\circ + i \sin 154\frac{2}{7}^\circ), \sqrt[7]{7}(\cos 205\frac{5}{7}^\circ + i \sin 205\frac{5}{7}^\circ),$
$\sqrt[7]{7}(\cos 257\frac{1}{7}^\circ + i \sin 257\frac{1}{7}^\circ), \sqrt[7]{7}(\cos 308\frac{4}{7}^\circ + i \sin 308\frac{4}{7}^\circ)$

19. $\sqrt[6]{72}(\cos 75^\circ + i \sin 75^\circ), \sqrt[6]{72}(\cos 195^\circ + i \sin 195^\circ),$
$\sqrt[6]{72}(\cos 315^\circ + i \sin 315^\circ) = \sqrt[3]{3}(1 - i)$

21. $(r, \theta)^{1/n} = \left(r^{1/n}, \frac{\theta + 2k\pi}{n}\right), k = 0, 1, 2, \ldots, n - 1.$

Exercise Group 16–1

1. $(\frac{19}{13}, -\frac{43}{13})$ 3. $(-3, -3)$ 5. $(109, -73)$ 7. $(2a, -b)$

9. $\left(\frac{u}{2}, \frac{3u}{2}\right)$ 11. $(5, -2, 0)$ 13. $\left(\frac{29}{27}, -\frac{8}{27}, -\frac{77}{27}\right)$

15. $\left(\frac{19}{103}, \frac{48}{103}, -\frac{69}{103}\right)$ 17. $(a + b, a - b, a)$ 19. $\left(2u, \frac{3u}{2}, -\frac{5u}{2}\right)$

Exercise Group 16–2

1. 319 3. 11 5. -6 7. -78 9. $x^2 - 1$ 11. 0

13. 0 19. 16 21. 5776 23. 1 25. -1

Exercise Group 16–3

1. 1 3. 0 5. 0 15. $(\frac{29}{27}, -\frac{8}{27}, -\frac{77}{27})$
17. $\left(2u, \frac{3u}{2}, -\frac{5u}{2}\right)$ 19. (1, 2, 3, 4)

Exercise Group 17–1

1. 7,920; 1,395, 360; 720 3. 30; 20 5. $n = 8$
7. $n = 5$ 9. (a) 3,024, (b) 1,344, (c) 1,344 11. 144
13. 120 15. 26 17. 180 19. 165 21. 120 23. 302,400

Exercise Group 17–2

1. 35; 56 3. 20, 708, 500 5. $n = 10$ 7. $n = 7$
9. (a) 1, (b) 4, (c) 6, (d) 4, (e) 1, (f) 16
11. (a) 6, (b) 9, (c) 12 13. (a) 8, (b) 3, (c) 4
15. 7,200 17. 1,583 19. 420 21. 105

Exercise Group 17–3

1. (a) 10, (b) 5, (c) 1 3. 8 5. 1,680
7. 240 9. 63,063,000 11. (a) 630,630, (b) 756,756, (c) 30,030

Exercise Group 17–4

1. 10; 3 3. 10; 3 5. 15; 12 7. 15; 4 9. 126; 120
11. 16 13. 21 15. 45 17. 45 19. 3

Exercise Group 17–5

1. (a) $\frac{2}{35}$, (b) $\frac{4}{15}$ 3. $\frac{1}{5}$ 5. $\frac{4}{7}$ 7. $\frac{1}{9}$ 9. $\frac{1}{144}$
11. $\frac{30}{59}$ 13. $\frac{7}{25}$ 15. $\frac{40}{C(52, 13)}$ 17. $\frac{2}{9}$

Exercise Group 17–6

1. (a) $\frac{1}{2}$, (b) $\frac{6}{55}$ 3. $\frac{1}{2}$ 5. (a) $\frac{1}{12}$, (b) $\frac{1}{2}$
7. $\frac{1}{81}$ 9. $\frac{4}{7}$ 11. $\frac{1}{7}$
13. (a) $\frac{1}{25}$, (b) $\frac{483}{2701}$ 15. (a) $\frac{3}{64}$, (b) $\frac{1}{2^n} C(n - 1, k - 1)$

Exercise Group 17–7

1. (a) $\frac{1}{2}$, (b) $\frac{1}{3}$ 3. (a) $\frac{1}{6}$, (b) $\frac{1}{3}$ 5. (a) $\frac{3}{5}$, (b) $\frac{2}{5}$, (c) $\frac{1}{2}$, (d) $\frac{3}{4}$
7. (a) $\frac{2}{5}$, (b) $\frac{2}{3}$ 9. (a) $\frac{3}{4}$, (b) $\frac{3}{4}$

Exercise Group 17–8

1. (a) 1:1, (b) 2:3, (c) 18:7, (d) $a:(1 - a)$ 3. 1:5 5. 5:103
7. 5:11 9. (a) 1:54, (b) 3:41, (c) 3:8 11. 80 cents 13. 7:3

Exercise Group 17–9

1. $\frac{577882}{955942}$ 3. $\frac{(577882)^2}{(955942)(810900)}$ 5. $\frac{123334}{577882}$ 7. 883342:68141

9. For boys $\frac{2152546}{4203812}$; for girls $\frac{2051266}{4203812}$; 38950 boys born in Wisconsin

11. 2:23

Supplementary Exercises for Chapter 17

1. 168 3. 37 5. (a) 90; (b) 570
7. $\frac{2}{15}$ 9. 217 11. 0.456
13. $\frac{17}{33}$ 15. (a) $\frac{1}{65}$; (b) $\frac{48}{65}$; (c) $\frac{228}{325}$; (d) $\frac{3}{5}$ 17. $\frac{4}{5}$
19. (a) 126; (b) 280; (c) 1680 21. $\frac{2}{7}$
23. (a) $\frac{27}{125}$; $\frac{36}{125}$; (b) $\frac{117}{125}$; $\frac{8}{125}$ 25. (a) 84; (b) 74 27. (a) 5; (b) $\frac{63}{256}$
29. $\left(\frac{506403}{955942}\right)^{10}$

Exercise Group A–1

1. 9 3. 216 5. 243 7. 7^{15}
9. $2^{15} \cdot 3^{10}$ 11. $2^{14} \cdot 3^{16}$ 13. $3x^9$ 15. $a^{13}b^{12}$
17. $108a^{5h}$ 19. $a^{5k}b^{4k}$ 21. $3^n a^{2hn} b^{2kn}$ 23. $-2ax + a^2y$
25. $-3x^3y + 3xy^3 + 3xy$ 27. $-35x^5y^2z + 25x^5y^3z^2 + 10x^4yz^3$
29. $x^2 + x - 20$ 31. $15x^2 + xy - 28y^2$ 33. $4x^2 - b^2$
35. $x^3 + 6x^2 + 11x + 6$ 37. $6x^2 - 17xy + 12y^2$
39. $x^{10} - 3x^8 - x^7 + x^6 - 2x^4 - 3x^2 - 4x - 1$
41. $a^{m+2} - 2a^{m+1} + 2a^m + a^{m-1} + 4a^{m-2}$
43. 0 45. $\frac{1}{3125} = \frac{1}{5^5}$ 47. $\frac{1}{10000} = \frac{1}{10^4}$ 49. $\frac{1}{3}x^8$
51. $\frac{y}{x^5}$ 53. $\frac{25a^4x^7}{32b^6}$ 55. $\frac{a^2c^8}{b^6x^6}$ 57. $a^{x-y+z}b^{y-x}$
59. $a^{9+y-z}b^{10+x-y}$ 61. $\frac{a^{x+y-1}c^{10-z}}{b^{10+x-z}}$ 63. $x + 3$, 0
65. $a^2 - 3a + 1$, 0 67. $5x^2 - x + 4$, $2x + 3$ 69. $a^2 + ab + b^2$, 0

Exercise Group A–2

5. $-3x^3y + 3xy^3 + 3xy$ 7. $b^m + b^{m+n} - b^{2m}$ 9. $v^2 - b^2u^2$
11. $4a^2 + 36ab + 81b^2$ 13. $a^2 + 2ab + b^2 + 2ac + 2bc + c^2$
15. $4x^4 + 16x^2y^3 + 15y^6$ 17. $a^2 - x^2 - 2xy - y^2$ 19. $0.027u^6 + 0.125v^6$
21. $x^2 + 2xy + y^2 - 4z^2$
23. $4x^2 + 12xy + 9y^2 - 20xz - 30yz + 25z^2$
25. $4u^2 + 28uy + 49y^2 - 9v^2 - 30vx - 25x^2$
27. $x^2 + 2xy + y^2 - u^2 + 2uv - v^2$ 29. $c^2 - 6bc + 9b^2 - a^2 - 2ad - d^2$

Exercise Group A–3

1. $x^2(x + 3)(x - 3)$
3. $2a^2(4 - x)(1 + 3x)$
5. $(2x + 3)(x - 5)$
7. $b(3 - 4a)(9 + 12a + 16a^2)$
9. $y(x + 2)(x + 7)$
11. $(a + b)(x + 2)^2$
13. $(2a + 2b + 1)(a + b + 5)$
15. $-(m - n)^2(m^2 + mn + n^2)^2$
17. $(6x^n + 1)^2$
19. $(x^3 - 4)(x - 1)(x^2 + x + 1)$
21. $a^2b^2(3a - b)(3a + b)(9a^2 + 3ab + b^2)(9a^2 - 3ab + b^2)$
23. $(a^3 + 2)(a^3 - 2)(a + 1)(a - 1)(a^2 + a + 1)(a^2 - a + 1)$
25. $4a^2(a + 3)(a - 3)(a + 2)(a - 2)$
27. $(2x + 3y)(2x - 3y)(7x^2 + 11y^2)$
29. $(2a + b + c)(2a - b - c)[4a^2 + 2a(b + c) + (b + c)^2][4a^2 - 2a(b + c) + (b + c)^2]$
31. $(a + b)(x + y)(x - y)x^ny^n$

Exercise Group A–4

1. $(x - y)(1 - 3z)$
3. $(3a - 5b)(x + 2y)$
5. $(3c - 4k)(w - x)$
7. $(a - 2)(a + 1)(a - 1)$
9. $(u + 2x - y)(u - 2x + y)$
11. $(2y - 1)(y + 2)(y^2 - 2y + 4)$
13. $(a + b)(x + y + z)$
15. $(4a + b + 5c)(4a + b - 5c)$
17. $(u + v + 2b)(u + v - 2b)$
19. $(b + x)(x + y)(x - y)$
21. $(2u - 3v + a + b)(2u - 3v - a - b)$
23. $(3x - 3y - 1)(x - y - 3)$
25. $(x + 3)(x - 2)(x + 2)(x - 1)$
27. $4(x - 2)^2(2x^2 + 1)(3x^3 + x + 1)$
29. $(a - 3b + 5c)(a + 2b - c)$

Exercise Group A–5

1. $\dfrac{7}{15}$
3. $\dfrac{a}{b}$
5. $\dfrac{a(x + y)}{x - y}$
7. $\dfrac{x + y}{-a}$
9. $\dfrac{x - 4}{2x + 1}$
11. -1
13. $\dfrac{a + b}{3a + 5b}$
15. $\dfrac{a + b}{c + d}$
17. $\dfrac{a^2 + ab + b^2}{a + b}$
19. $\dfrac{4x^2 + 6bx + 9b^2}{2x - 3b}$
21. $\dfrac{a^2 - 2a + 3}{3a - 5}$

Exercise Group A–6

1. $\dfrac{31}{15}$
3. $\dfrac{9bx - 10ay}{6ab}$
5. $\dfrac{x^2 + b^2}{bx(x - c)}$
7. $\dfrac{a^2}{a^2 - 9}$
9. $\dfrac{2x^3 + 3x^2 + x - 1}{x^2 - 1}$
11. $-3a^2$
13. $\dfrac{2x^2 - 8x + 3}{x(3x - 1)(2x - 1)}$
15. $\dfrac{-159x^2 - 19x + 511}{(2x + 1)(3x - 5)(x + 2)}$
17. $-\dfrac{16x^4 + 24x^2 + 5}{(2x - 1)^2(2x + 1)^2}$
19. $\dfrac{43}{3x + 1}$

Exercise Group A–7

1\. $-\frac{a}{3}$ 3. $\frac{(a+b)xy}{-z}$ 5. $\frac{(x-9)(x+2)}{(x-1)(x-5)}$ 7. $u(u+v)$

9\. $\frac{(x-y)(x+3)(x-8)}{(x+y)(x^2+y^2)(x-5)(x-2)}$ 11. $\frac{c+1}{1-y^2}$

13\. a 15. $-\frac{(2x-y)^2}{2x+y}$ 17. $\frac{3(x-3)}{x+3}$ 19. a

Exercise Group A–8

1\. $-\frac{714}{95}$ 3. $\frac{3}{10}$ 5. $\frac{2680}{153}$ 7. $\frac{3a+2b}{a}$

9\. $\frac{x+1}{4x+3}$ 11. $\frac{x-2}{2(x+2)(x-4)}$ 13. $-\frac{1}{x}$

15\. $\frac{2a}{a^2+1}$ 17. x^2 19. $\frac{2(x+2y)}{x-y}$

21\. 1 23. $\frac{(x+y+z)^2}{2yz}$ 25. a^2b

27\. $\frac{1}{x}$ 29. $\frac{-2x^2+(2a+1)x-a^2}{x^2(x-a)^2}$

31\. $\frac{9x+44}{15x+76}$ 33. $\frac{xuy+xuz-xz}{xuy+xuz-xz+yu}$

Exercise Group A–9

1\. a^8 3. y^{3x} 5. c^{7b} 7. x^4 9. z^3 11. 5

13\. 5^2 15. x^{20} 17. a^{18} 19. x^{6a} 21. x^{6ab} 23. a^{48}

25\. $2^{15}3^{10}$ 27. a^{10bc^2} 29. $2^{xz}a^{2z}3^{yz}b^{3z}$ 31. $2^{3c}3^{2c}a^{2cx}b^{3cy}$

33\. $\frac{a^7}{b^7}$ 35. $\frac{a^{12}}{b^{18}}$ 37. $\frac{32x^{10}}{243y^{20}}$ 39. $\frac{-32a^5}{243b^{10}}$ 41. $\frac{(-1)^a}{3^ab^{2a}}$

43\. $\frac{b}{a}$ 45. $4a^6$ 47. 10^4 49. $2^6 \cdot 3 \cdot 5^3$ 51. $\frac{2}{3^8xy}$

53\. $\frac{324b^{26}}{c^{24}}$ 55. $\frac{2a^{16}b^3}{3}$

57\. $\frac{6-11a+14a^2-5a^3}{a^7}$ 59. $\frac{1+x^{2m}+x^{4m}}{x^{2m}}$

61\. $\frac{y+x}{y-x}$ 63. $\frac{x^2y^2(xy+2)^2}{4}$

65\. 2^{3-3a}, if $1-a$ is positive 67. $a^{20}b^{35}c^5$

69\. b^{k^2-3}, if k^2-3 is positive 71. $\frac{6+5a-14a^2+5a^3}{a^7}$

73\. $\frac{3b^3}{a}$ 75. $64x^2y^5$ 77. $\frac{a^{15}}{32b^{10}}$ 79. $\frac{4a}{3b}$

81\. $\frac{b^{3/2}}{3^{3/2}a^3x^3}$ 83. a^5 85. $\frac{2y^2z^2}{3x^2}$ 87. $\frac{1}{10}$

89. $\dfrac{125a^6x^{12}}{729b^{15}y^9}$ 91. $a^{2/3}b^{2/3} - ab$ 93. $a^{2/3} - 2a^{1/3}b^{1/5}c^{1/7} + b^{2/5}c^{2/7}$

95. $a^{7/12}$ 97. $\dfrac{1}{a^{1/12}}$ 99. $\dfrac{1}{3^{1/4}}$ 101. xy

103. $4ab^2$ 105. 3 107. $\frac{257}{8}$ 109. $-\frac{1}{7}$

111. $\dfrac{3a^2 - x^2}{3(a^2 - x^2)^{4/3}}$ 113. $\dfrac{a^5 - 7y^5}{4y^{3/4}(a^5 + y^5)^{7/5}}$

Exercise Group A–10

1. $\dfrac{\sqrt{6}}{3}$ 3. $\dfrac{\sqrt[3]{18}}{3}$ 5. $\dfrac{v\sqrt{uw}}{wz}$ 7. $\dfrac{xy^2\sqrt{xyz}}{z}$

9. $\dfrac{y\sqrt{x(x + y)}}{x + y}$ 11. $\dfrac{(x - y)\sqrt{xy(x - y)}}{xy}$ 13. $\dfrac{3\sqrt[3]{y^2(8y^4 + 3)}}{4xy^2}$

15. $\sqrt{2(a + b)}$ 17. $\sqrt[3]{a^3 + b^3}$ 19. $4x\sqrt{2x + 3y^2}$ 21. $\dfrac{\sqrt{3(x^2 + y)}}{x}$

23. $\dfrac{2ab^{2k}}{9c}\sqrt[3]{36ac}$ 25. $5\sqrt{5}$ 27. $4\sqrt{2}$ 29. $\sqrt[3]{2} + 2\sqrt[3]{3}$

31. $\frac{22}{15}\sqrt[3]{12} - \frac{10}{9}\sqrt[3]{3}$ 33. $3(1 + 2b)\sqrt{2a}$

35. $\dfrac{(a^2y + abx)\sqrt{bc}}{b^2y} + \dfrac{ac\sqrt{b}}{bx}$ 37. $yz(2 - xy^2z)\sqrt{xyz}$

39. $\dfrac{7\sqrt{15a}}{5a}$ 41. $\dfrac{-3b - 3\sqrt{b^2 + 8b}}{4}$ 43. $\sqrt{15}$

45. $9\sqrt{6}$ 47. 10 49. $a^2x^2\sqrt{6}$

51. $2x^2\sqrt{3x}$ 53. $a^2 + b^2$ 55. $31 - 4\sqrt{21}$

57. $11x + 5 - 17\sqrt{x(x + 1)}$ 59. $-\dfrac{41}{49}$ 61. $\dfrac{p}{r}$

63. $3 + 2\sqrt{3x - x^2}$ 65. $28 - 4\sqrt{10}$ 67. 0

69. $-\dfrac{2}{3}$ 71. $\dfrac{\sqrt{15}}{3}$ 73. $\dfrac{\sqrt{5x}}{x}$

75. $\dfrac{3x\sqrt{10}}{5}$ 77. $\dfrac{2\sqrt[3]{2x^2}}{x}$ 79. $\dfrac{\sqrt[6]{72x^5}}{2x^2}$

81. $\dfrac{45\sqrt{2} - 18\sqrt{10}}{2}$ 83. $\dfrac{14\sqrt{10} - 98 + 6\sqrt{35} - 21\sqrt{14}}{35}$

85. $2x^2 - 2x\sqrt{x^2 - 1} - 1$ 87. $\dfrac{\sqrt[12]{3456}}{2}$

Index

SECOND EDITION

ANSWERS TO EVEN-NUMBERED EXERCISES FOR

College Algebra and Plane Trigonometry

ABRAHAM SPITZBART AND ROSS H. BARDELL

University of Wisconsin-Milwaukee

ADDISON-WESLEY PUBLISHING COMPANY, INC.
READING, MASSACHUSETTS · PALO ALTO · LONDON

CONTENTS

Answers to Even-Numbered Exercises

Exercise Group 1–1

20. $(2 \cdot 3) + 5$
22. $2 \cdot [4 + (5 \cdot 6)]$
24. $2 \cdot (4 + 5) \cdot 6$
26. $(2 + 3) \cdot (4 + 2) \cdot 3$
28. $(a \cdot b) \cdot (c \cdot d)$
30. b
32. a
34. b
36. c

Exercise Group 1–3

2. 1
4. -2
6. -11
8. 24
10. -35
12. -221
14. -315
16. 384
18. -945
20. $-174{,}933$
22. 24
24. 12
26. -15
28. 43
30. -13
32. -52

Exercise Group 1–4

2. Equal
4. Equal
6. Not equal
8. Not equal

Exercise Group 1–5

2. $-9i$
4. $9 + 9i$
6. $(a - c - f) + (b - d - e)i$
8. $121 - 23i$
10. $18 - 34i$
12. $(ab + cd) + (ad - bc)i$
14. 0
16. $(a - bi)/(a^2 + b^2)$

Exercise Group 2–1

6. (a) On a straight line a units to the right of the y-axis
   (b) On a straight line b units above the x-axis
8. 6
10. -5
12. On a straight line which is 2 units to the right of the y-axis
14. Three solutions: $(4, 1)$, $(-2, -1)$, $(-4, 5)$

Exercise Group 2–2

2. $(-\frac{1}{2}, \frac{5}{2}), \sqrt{202}$
4. $(\frac{13}{2}, 4), \sqrt{205}$
6. $(-\frac{1}{2}, -7), \sqrt{185}$
8. $\left(\frac{c + a}{2}, \frac{c - a}{2}\right), \sqrt{2(a^2 + c^2)}$
10. $2\sqrt{26}$
12. $\left(\frac{a}{2}, \frac{b}{2}\right)$

Exercise Group 2–3

2. (a) $f(2) = 2$, $f(5) = 2$; (b) $x = 2$, $x = 5$; (c) four; (d) three
4. (a) (0, 4), (1, 6), (2, 8), (3, 10); (b) (0, 1), (1, 4), (2, −1), (3, 11)
6. $f(2) = 4$, $f(0) = 0$, $f(-3) = -6$
8. $f(2) = \frac{2}{5}$, $f(0) = 0$, $f(-3) = -\frac{3}{10}$
10. $f(2) = 4$, $f(0) = 6$, $f(-3) = 24$
12. $f(2) = \frac{1}{4}$, $f(0) = \frac{3}{2}$, $f(-3) = \frac{9}{11}$
14. 0
16. $a^2 - a$
18. (a) $-x - 1$, (b) $x + h - 1$, (c) 1
20. $A = s^2$
22. $A = \dfrac{\pi d^2}{4}$
24. $y = \sqrt{5}\,x$
26. $\dfrac{16 + \pi}{8} w^2$
28. $A = \dfrac{\sqrt{3}}{4} s^2$
30. $H = \dfrac{\sqrt{3}x}{2}$

Exercise Group 2–6

2. $y = \dfrac{4x^2}{9}$; $\dfrac{16}{9}$
4. $w = \dfrac{24}{z^3}$; $\dfrac{8}{9}$
6. $v = \dfrac{3}{2u}$; $-\dfrac{21}{2}$
8. 16 ft; $16t^2$ ft
10. Intensity is four times as large.
12. $V = \dfrac{40A}{3}$
14. $p = \dfrac{15{,}000}{v}$; 75 lb/in²

Exercise Group 2–7

2. $s = \dfrac{3r^2t}{20}$; $\dfrac{45}{4}$
4. $y = -\dfrac{63x^3}{125z^2}$; $-\dfrac{56}{125}$
6. $S = \dfrac{160r^2}{v^3t}$; $\dfrac{125}{6}$
8. 4 × 4 ft
10. Unchanged
12. (a) Increased 12.5%
    (b) Reduced 62.5%
14. 1600 lb

Supplementary Exercises for Chapter 2

2. $f(-3) = -\frac{9}{11}$, $f(5) = -3$
4. $f(-3) = -\frac{28}{9}$, $f(5) = \frac{124}{25}$
6. $G(-2) = -\frac{7}{6}$, $G(0) = -\frac{5}{4}$, $G(-\frac{3}{2}) = -\frac{13}{11}$, $G(-x) = -\dfrac{x+5}{x+4}$
12. −12
14. −17
16. $(\frac{5}{2}, -6)$; $11\sqrt{5}$
18. $\left(\dfrac{p+r}{2}, \dfrac{q+s}{2}\right)$; $\sqrt{(p-r)^2 + (q-s)^2}$
22. 0.6 in.
24. 1.06 gm
26. $A = 2\pi r^2 + \dfrac{2V}{r}$
28. $V = \frac{1}{3}\pi h^2(32 - h)$

Exercise Group 3–1

2. 120°
4. 40°
6. 198°
8. 6°
10. −42°
12. 67.5°
14. 108°
16. 63°
18. 131° 46′ 51″
20. 61° 18′ 24″
22. 9° 44′ 25″

24. $83° 4' 45''$ 26. $-361° 32' 16''$ 28. $-1816° 17' 00''$

30. $\frac{3\pi}{5}$ 32. $\frac{17\pi}{6}$ 34. $\frac{\pi}{15}$ 36. $\frac{17\pi}{36}$ 38. $\frac{23\pi}{36}$ 40. $\frac{13\pi}{36}$

42. 0.99 44. 3.39 46. -3.80 48. 1.97 50. 8.96 52. 8.26

Exercise Group 3–2

2. $(-\sqrt{3}/2, \frac{1}{2})$ 4. $(-\frac{1}{2}, -\sqrt{3}/2)$ 6. $(-\sqrt{2}/2, \sqrt{2}/2)$ 8. $(\sqrt{2}/2, -\sqrt{2}/2)$
10. Q_4, 69° 12. Q_1, 77° 14. Q_3, 40° 43′ 16. Q_3, 13° 58′ 18. $r = 15$
20. $x = \pm 5\sqrt{5}$ 22. $y = \pm 2\sqrt{7}$ 24. $x = \pm\sqrt{10}/2, y = \pm 3\sqrt{10}/2$
26. $x = 7.5, r = 8.5$ 28. Q_4 30. Q_1 32. Q_1 34. Q_3
36. (a) Between 720° and 900°; (b) between 180° and 225°
38. (a) Between 180° and 360°; (b) between 270° and 540°
40. (a) Between $-90°$ and 90°; (b) between $-450°$ and $-180°$
42. Three values 44. Nine values 46. Six values
48. Three values 50. Five values 52. Six values

Exercise Group 3–3

In this set of answers the values of the trigonometric ratios are given in the order $\sin\theta$, $\cos\theta$, $\tan\theta$, $\cot\theta$, $\sec\theta$, $\csc\theta$.

2. $\frac{3\sqrt{409}}{409}, \frac{20\sqrt{409}}{409}, \frac{3}{20}, \frac{20}{3}, \frac{\sqrt{409}}{20}, \frac{\sqrt{409}}{3}$

4. $-\frac{24}{25}, -\frac{7}{25}, \frac{24}{7}, \frac{7}{24}, -\frac{25}{7}, -\frac{25}{24}$ 6. $-\frac{12}{13}, \frac{5}{13}, -\frac{12}{5}, -\frac{5}{12}, \frac{13}{5}, -\frac{13}{12}$

8. $\pm\frac{12}{13}, \frac{5}{13}, \pm\frac{12}{5}, \pm\frac{5}{12}, \frac{13}{5}, \pm\frac{13}{12}$

10. $\pm\frac{\sqrt{2}}{2}, \mp\frac{\sqrt{2}}{2}, -1, -1, \mp\sqrt{2}, \pm\sqrt{2}$ 12. $\pm\frac{4}{5}, \pm\frac{3}{5}, \frac{4}{3}, \frac{3}{4}, \pm\frac{5}{3}, \pm\frac{5}{4}$

14. $-\frac{3\sqrt{13}}{13}, -\frac{2\sqrt{13}}{13}, \frac{3}{2}, \frac{2}{3}, -\frac{\sqrt{13}}{2}, -\frac{\sqrt{13}}{3}$

16. $-\frac{24}{25}, \frac{7}{25}, -\frac{24}{7}, -\frac{7}{24}, \frac{25}{7}, -\frac{25}{24}$ 18. $-\frac{3}{5}, \frac{4}{5}, -\frac{3}{4}, -\frac{4}{3}, \frac{5}{4}, -\frac{5}{3}$

20. $-\frac{2\sqrt{2}}{3}, -\frac{1}{3}, 2\sqrt{2}, \frac{\sqrt{2}}{4}, -3, -\frac{3\sqrt{2}}{4}$

22. $\frac{24}{25}, \pm\frac{7}{25}, \pm\frac{24}{7}, \pm\frac{7}{24}, \pm\frac{25}{7}, \frac{25}{24}$

24. $\pm\frac{2\sqrt{29}}{29}, \pm\frac{5\sqrt{29}}{29}, \frac{2}{5}, \frac{5}{2}, \pm\frac{\sqrt{29}}{5}, \pm\frac{\sqrt{29}}{2}$

26. $-\frac{12}{13}, -\frac{5}{13}, \frac{12}{5}, \frac{5}{12}, -\frac{13}{5}, -\frac{13}{12}$ 28. $-\frac{24}{25}, \frac{7}{25}, -\frac{24}{7}, -\frac{7}{24}, \frac{25}{7}, -\frac{25}{24}$

30. $\frac{\sqrt{3}}{2}, -\frac{1}{2}, -\sqrt{3}, -\frac{\sqrt{3}}{3}, -2, \frac{2\sqrt{3}}{3}$

32. $\pm\frac{5\sqrt{26}}{26}, \pm\frac{\sqrt{26}}{26}, 5, \frac{1}{5}, \pm\sqrt{26}, \pm\frac{\sqrt{26}}{5}$

34. $\pm \frac{\sqrt{21}}{5}, -\frac{2}{5}, \mp \frac{\sqrt{21}}{2}, \mp \frac{2\sqrt{21}}{21}, -\frac{5}{2}, \pm \frac{5\sqrt{21}}{21}$

36. $\frac{1}{9}, \pm \frac{4\sqrt{5}}{9}, \pm \frac{\sqrt{5}}{20}, \pm 4\sqrt{5}, \pm \frac{9\sqrt{5}}{20}, 9$

Exercise Group 3–4

In this set of answers for Exercises 2–20 the values of the trigonometric ratios are given in the order $\sin\theta$, $\cos\theta$, $\tan\theta$, $\cot\theta$, $\sec\theta$, $\csc\theta$.

2. $\frac{\sqrt{2}}{2}, \frac{\sqrt{2}}{2}, 1, 1, \sqrt{2}, \sqrt{2}$

4. $-\frac{\sqrt{3}}{2}, -\frac{1}{2}, \sqrt{3}, \frac{\sqrt{3}}{3}, -2, -\frac{2\sqrt{3}}{3}$

6. $\frac{\sqrt{3}}{2}, -\frac{1}{2}, -\sqrt{3}, -\frac{\sqrt{3}}{3}, -2, \frac{2\sqrt{3}}{3}$

8. $-\frac{\sqrt{2}}{2}, -\frac{\sqrt{2}}{2}, 1, 1, -\sqrt{2}, -\sqrt{2}$

10. $-1, 0, —, 0, —, -1$

12. $\frac{\sqrt{3}}{2}, \frac{1}{2}, \sqrt{3}, \frac{\sqrt{3}}{3}, 2, \frac{2\sqrt{3}}{3}$

14. $0, 1, 0, —, 1, —$

16. $\frac{\sqrt{3}}{2}, -\frac{1}{2}, -\sqrt{3}, -\frac{\sqrt{3}}{3}, -2, \frac{2\sqrt{3}}{3}$

18. $1, 0, —, 0, —, 1$

20. $-\frac{1}{2}, \frac{\sqrt{3}}{2}, -\frac{\sqrt{3}}{3}, -\sqrt{3}, \frac{2\sqrt{3}}{3}, -2$

38. $<$ 40. $>$ 42. $=$ 44. $=$

Exercise Group 3–5

2. 0.2700	4. 12.25	6. 1.111	8. 0.7451
10. 1.091	12. 8.834	14. 0.9667	16. 0.6208
18. 1.346	20. −0.0875	22. 0.7771	24. −1.701
26. 0.4245	28. 0.8988	30. −1.239	32. 1.376
34. −0.5348	36. 1.462	38. 63° 20′	40. 82° 20′
42. 67° 40′	44. 24° 20′	46. 23° 10′	48. 80° 50′
50. 46° 30′	52. 46° 20′	54. 45° 30′	56. 45° 40′
58. 43° 30′	60. 44° 20′	62. 93° 40′	64. 102° 20′
66. 254° 30′	68. 139° 40′	70. 149°	72. 217° 10′
74. sin 46° 43′	76. tan 5° 24′	78. sec 36° 18′	80. cot 84° 07′
82. csc 40° 32′	84. cos 33° 34′		

Supplementary Exercises for Chapter 3

2. $\frac{8\pi}{15}$ 4. 3.72 6. $-228°$ 8. $-77° 55' 20''$

10. $\sin\theta = \pm \frac{5}{\sqrt{26}}$, $\cos\theta = \pm \frac{1}{\sqrt{26}}$, $\cot\theta = \frac{1}{5}$, $\sec\theta = \pm\sqrt{26}$,
$\csc\theta = \pm \frac{\sqrt{26}}{5}$

12. $\cos\theta = \pm\sqrt{1 - a^2}$, $\tan\theta = \pm\dfrac{a}{\sqrt{1 - a^2}}$, $\cot\theta = \pm\dfrac{\sqrt{1 - a^2}}{a}$,

$\sec\theta = \pm\dfrac{1}{\sqrt{1 - a^2}}$, $\csc\theta = \dfrac{1}{a}$

14. $\sin\theta = \pm\dfrac{\sqrt{c^2 - 1}}{c}$, $\cos\theta = \dfrac{1}{c}$, $\tan\theta = \pm\sqrt{c^2 - 1}$,

$\cot\theta = \pm\dfrac{1}{\sqrt{c^2 - 1}}$, $\csc\theta = \pm\dfrac{c}{\sqrt{c^2 - 1}}$

In the following six answers the values of the trigonometric ratios appear in the order $\sin\theta$, $\cos\theta$, $\tan\theta$, $\cot\theta$, $\sec\theta$, $\csc\theta$.

16. $-1, 0, —, 0, —, -1$

18. $\dfrac{\sqrt{3}}{2}, -\dfrac{1}{2}, -\sqrt{3}, -\dfrac{1}{\sqrt{3}}, -2, \dfrac{2}{\sqrt{3}}$

20. $0, -1, 0, —, -1, —$

22. $-\dfrac{1}{\sqrt{2}}, -\dfrac{1}{\sqrt{2}}, 1, 1, -\sqrt{2}, -\sqrt{2}$

24. $\dfrac{1}{\sqrt{2}}, -\dfrac{1}{\sqrt{2}}, -1, -1, -\sqrt{2}, \sqrt{2}$

26. $\dfrac{1}{\sqrt{2}}, -\dfrac{1}{\sqrt{2}}, -1, -1, -\sqrt{2}, \sqrt{2}$

32. $1, -\frac{1}{2}, \frac{1}{3}, -\frac{1}{4}, \frac{1}{5}$

34. $-\frac{4}{3}, \frac{3}{4}, -\frac{8}{15}, \frac{5}{12}, -\frac{12}{35}$

36. $0, -1, 0, 0, 0$

38. $2, 0, \frac{2}{9}, 0, \frac{2}{25}$

40. $K = \dfrac{a^2 \sin B \sin C}{2 \sin A}$

42. $L = 8000 \sin^2\theta \cos\theta$, 237.4 lb

Exercise Group 4–1

2. $-2; \frac{2}{3}$ 4. $7; \frac{7}{2}$ 6. $\frac{5}{4}$ 8. $\frac{19}{7}$ 10. $\frac{1}{4}$
12. 7 14. $\frac{1}{27}$ 16. 3 18. $(a + 7)/(5 - 2b)$ 20. $5a/(a + 2b)^2$
22. $(c + d)/(a + b)$ 24. -2 26. 0 28. 9 30. $\frac{7}{2}$
32. $a - b$, if $a^2 - b^2 \neq c$ 34. $-\frac{7}{8}$ 36. 9 38. 0 40. $\sin x = \frac{1}{2}$ 42. $\tan x = 7$
44. $\sec x = -8$ 46. $\sin x = \frac{2}{3}$ 48. $\cot x = -\frac{24}{17}$ 50. $50t + 10$
52. $25{,}000 - 500t$; time at which house is worthless 54. \$60,000 56. $\frac{12}{48}$
58. 12, 7 60. 24.1 ft 62. 7 in. 64. $\frac{28}{11}$ lb 66. 12

Exercise Group 4–2

4. $(\frac{3}{4}, \frac{23}{16})$ 6. $(1, 1)$ 8. $(\frac{3}{4}, \frac{49}{8})$ 10. $(-1, -8)$
12. $(\frac{3}{16}, -\frac{9}{128})$ 14. $(0, -6)$ 16. $(\frac{9}{4}, \frac{5}{16})$ 18. $(-\frac{3}{4}, \frac{41}{8})$
20. $(\frac{1}{4}, \frac{3}{8})$ 22. $(0, 2)$ 24. $(-\frac{1}{2}, -\frac{5}{4})$ 26. $(-\frac{1}{8}, \frac{127}{16})$
28. $\left(30 - \dfrac{x}{2}\right)(25 + x)$; \$43 30. 9 32. 1250 yd^2

Exercise Group 4–3

2. $\frac{3}{2}, -1$ 4. $-2, \frac{1}{3}$ 6. $-\frac{2}{5}, 0$ 8. $-\frac{3}{5}, \frac{2}{3}$
10. $-5, \frac{3}{2}$ 12. $\pm\frac{3}{4}$ 14. $-\frac{3}{2}, \frac{7}{5}$ 16. $\frac{2}{7}, \frac{5}{3}$

18. $-\frac{3}{7}, \frac{7}{3}$ 20. $-\frac{2}{5}, 3$ 22. $-1, -ac/b$ 24. $-b, a/c$

26. $-2, \frac{1}{2}$ 28. $\pm 3i\sqrt{5}/5$

30. $(5 \pm i\sqrt{23})/6$ 32. $(b \pm \sqrt{b^2 + 24})/2$

34. $\dfrac{-q \pm \sqrt{q^2 - 4pr}}{2p}$ 36. $\dfrac{1 \pm i\sqrt{34}}{5}$

38. $\dfrac{d \pm \sqrt{d^2 + 4ab}}{2b}$ 40. $\dfrac{3 \pm \sqrt{9 + 20a - 4a^2}}{2a}$

42. $\dfrac{1 \pm \sqrt{1 - a + ac}}{c - 1}$ 44. $\dfrac{8 \pm \sqrt{22}}{6}$

46. $-\frac{1}{10}, \frac{3}{2}$ 48. $-\frac{7}{3}, 2$ 50. $-\frac{43}{2}, 2$ 52. $a - 2b, b - 2a$

54. $2 \pm \sqrt{5}$ 56. $(13 \pm \sqrt{13})/6$ 58. $b/a, a/b$ 60. $p, 1/p$

62. $\frac{1}{2}(x \pm \sqrt{9x^2 - 16})$ 64. $\frac{1}{2}(-x - 1 \pm \sqrt{5 - 2x - 3x^2})$

66. $\dfrac{1}{2c}\left[-bx - e \pm \sqrt{(b^2 - 4ac)x^2 + 2(be - 2cd)x + e^2 - 4cf}\right]$

68. $\cos x = \frac{2}{3}$ 70. $\sec x = (-5 \pm \sqrt{113})/4$

72. $x = \pi/3, 2\pi/3, 5\pi/4, 7\pi/4$ 74. \$10 76. $\frac{3}{2}$ ft

78. $(1 \pm i\sqrt{3})/2$ 80. 7, 9, 11; −11, −9, −7 82. 25 mph

Exercise Group 4–4

2. 25; roots real, unequal, rational 4. 0; roots real, equal, rational
6. −23; roots imaginary, unequal 8. 0; roots real, equal, rational
10. 25; roots real, unequal, rational 12. −16; roots imaginary, unequal
14. −83; roots imaginary, unequal 16. $-\frac{5}{3}$; roots imaginary, unequal
18. 0; roots real, equal, irrational 20. $k = \frac{49}{12}$ 22. $k = 0, 5$
24. $k = \pm 5i/4$ 26. $\frac{3}{2}, \frac{7}{2}$ 28. $0, -\frac{9}{5}$ 30. $a/c, -7/c$ 32. $f/d, 0$
34. $x^2 - 2x - 15 = 0$ 36. $x^2 - 4x + 1 = 0$ 38. $x^2 - 4x + 13 = 0$
40. $x^2 + ax - 2a^2 = 0$ 42. $x^2 + 6x + 34 = 0$ 44. $36x^2 - 24x + 7 = 0$
46. $h = 3$ 48. $h = -1$ 50. $h = 2$ 52. $h = -\frac{5}{3}$ 54. $h = \pm 12$
58. Sum $\geqq 2$ or $\leqq -2$

Exercise Group 4–5

2. $\pm 2, \pm 3$ 4. $-2, 4, -2 \pm 2i\sqrt{3}, 1 \pm i\sqrt{3}$
6. $\pm 1, \pm 2, \pm i, \pm 2i$ 8. $\pm 3\sqrt{2}/2, \pm 4\sqrt{3}/3$ 10. $\frac{1}{5}, \frac{1}{3}$
12. $-\frac{2}{3}, 1, (-1 \pm i\sqrt{3})/2, (1 \pm i\sqrt{3})/3$ 14. $\pm 1, \pm 4$
16. 8, 64 18. $-\frac{243}{32}, 32$ 20. 7 22. $\pm 2i, \pm 3i$
24. −4, −3, 2, 3 26. $(3 \pm i\sqrt{3})/2, (3 \pm \sqrt{19})/2$ 28. −4, −2, 3, 5
30. −5, −2, −1, 2 32. $-\frac{1}{2}, 1, (1 \pm \sqrt{13})/6$ 34. $x = \pi/2, 3\pi/2$
36. $\cot x = \frac{1}{3}$ 38. $x = 0, \pi/6, 5\pi/6, \pi, 7\pi/6, 11\pi/6$
40. $x = 3\pi/4, 7\pi/4, \cot x = 2$ 42. $x = 0, \pi/3, 5\pi/3$

Exercise Group 4–6

2. $b^2 + 2$ if $b \geqq 0$ 4. $\frac{16}{9}$ 6. 5, 9 8. 3, 7 10. No solution
12. 4 14. $1, \frac{4}{3}$ 16. $\frac{1}{5}, 1$ 18. No solution 20. $\frac{5}{2}, 3$

22. No solution 24. $\frac{1}{2}, \frac{3}{4}$ 26. $x = 2$ 28. $\pm\sqrt{33}/5$ 30. $3\sqrt{2}$
32. 49 34. 6×8 36. $x = \pi/3, 5\pi/3$ 38. $\tan x = 2$

Supplementary Exercises for Chapter 4

2. 1 4. $-\frac{9}{5}$ 6. $\frac{19}{9}$ 8. $\dfrac{-q \pm \sqrt{q^2 - 4pr}}{2r}$

10. $\dfrac{1 - c \pm \sqrt{(c - 1)^2 - 4ab}}{2a}$ 12. $\dfrac{-a \pm \sqrt{a^2 - 4b + 4c}}{2}$

14. $\dfrac{-1 \pm 2\sqrt{13}}{3}$ 16. $\dfrac{5 \pm i\sqrt{31}}{4}$

18. $\dfrac{5 \pm i\sqrt{43}}{2}$ 20. $\dfrac{c - a \pm \sqrt{(c - a)^2 - 4b(d + 1)}}{2(d + 1)}$

22. $\dfrac{c - b \pm \sqrt{(b - c)^2 + 4d(a - 1)}}{2(a - 1)}$ 24. $\dfrac{a + 2b \pm \sqrt{a^2 + 4ab - 4ac}}{2}$

26. $\frac{5}{3}, \frac{7}{2}$ 28. $\dfrac{b}{a}, c$

30. $\dfrac{b}{1 - a}, -\dfrac{b}{a + 1}$ 32. $\dfrac{-1 \pm \sqrt{21}}{2}$

34. $0, \frac{8}{9}$ 36. $0, \frac{8}{7}$
38. Roots imaginary and unequal; $S = 1, P = \frac{7}{2}$
40. Roots real, unequal, irrational; $S = 11, P = 4$
42. Roots real, unequal, irrational; $S = 3, P = -2$
44. $\pm 2, \pm 4i$ 46. $\pm 1, \pm\frac{3}{2}$ 48. 2 50. 2 52. 1

54. 21%; 33.1% 56. 150 mph 58. $\dfrac{-(W + L) + \sqrt{(W + L)^2 + 4WL}}{2}$

Exercise Group 5–1

2. $s = 1.8$ ft, $A = 2.7$ ft^2 4. $s = 10.2$ in., $A = 30.6$ in^2
6. $s = 1000\pi/3$ ft, $A = 125{,}000\pi/3$ ft^2 8. $s = 50.2$ cm, $A = 627$ cm^2
10. $s = 367.5\pi$ cm, $A = 38587.5\pi$ cm^2 12. $s = 17.2$ yd, $A = 429$ yd^2
14. $s = 0.273$ in., $A = 0.00683$ in^2 16. $s = 137.5$ ft, $A = 14649$ ft^2
18. $s = 0.1011$ ft, $A = 0.00152$ ft^2
20. $\theta = 2.830$ rad $= 162°\,09'$, $A = 39.75$ ft^2
22. $\theta = 4.413$ rad $= 252°\,51'$, $A = 1001$ cm^2
24. $\theta = 0.2564$ rad $= 14°\,41'$, $A = 34.90$ in^2
26. $\theta = 0.3213$ rad $= 18°\,25'$, $A = 2591$ in^2
28. $\theta = 1.895$ rad $= 108°\,35'$, $A = 5.012$ ft^2
30. $\theta = 1.024$ rad $= 58°\,40'$, $A = 12.8$ m^2 32. 314.2 ft/sec
34. 807 ft/sec 36. 42 mph, 9.2 sec 38. 0.64 mi/sec 40. $R = 3961$ mi

Exercise Group 5–2

2. 0.9122 4. 0.4928 6. 0.9950 8. 0.3246 10. 0.9906
12. 1.063 14. −0.8360 16. −1.007 18. −1.489 20. −0.9396

22. 1.352　24. 1.672　26. 50° 23′　28. 77° 34′　30. 6° 05′
32. 13° 18′　34. 23° 38′　36. 138° 55′　38. 39° 03′　40. 62° 05′
42. 131° 44′　44. 82° 51′　46. 79° 07′　48. 22° 06′

Exercise Group 5–3

2. $A = 16° 19'$, $b = 79.25$, $c = 82.59$
4. $B = 32° 47'$, $a = 53.03$, $b = 34.15$
6. $A = 61° 26'$, $a = 0.1126$, $c = 0.1282$
8. $B = 45° 03'$, $a = 715.0$, $c = 1012$
10. $A = 70° 34'$, $a = 218.9$, $b = 77.22$
12. $B = 10° 12'$, $A = 79° 48'$, $a = 1.188$
14. $A = 67° 16'$, $B = 22° 44'$, $b = 895.5$
16. $A = 84° 13'$, $B = 5° 47'$, $c = 0.07048$
18. $B = 21° 56'$, $a = 81.32$, $c = 87.67$
20. $B = 50° 26'$, $b = 117.9$, $c = 153.0$
22. $A = 40° 10'$, $B = 49° 50'$, $a = 227.3$
24. $A = 30° 48'$, $B = 59° 12'$, $b = 2.900$
26. $A = 55° 19'$, $B = 34° 41'$, $c = 7.681$
28. $B = 65° 39'$, $a = 26.47$, $b = 58.48$
30. $A = 24° 39'$, $B = 65° 21'$, $b = 6.802$
32. $h = (a\sqrt{4\pi\theta - \theta^2})/(2\pi)$

Exercise Group 5–4

2. 0.03422, 0.0342　4. 2.173, 2.17　6. 7132, 7130
8. 0.08976, 0.0898　10. 304800, 305000　12. 0.01324, 0.0132
14. ± 0.0005 in.　16. ± 0.00005 mi　18. ± 5 in^2
20. ± 0.5 cm^2　22. 6.3　24. 5.04
26. $1.93 \cdot 10^3$　28. 0.54　30. 0.00019
32. 0.01383　34. 7.9428×10^{-6}　36. 41°　38. 54°　40. 25° 15′
42. 4° 40′　44. 29°　46. 41°　48. $A = 41°$, $B = 49°$, $a = 2.6$
50. $A = 39°$, $B = 51°$, $b = 2.8$　52. $A = 73° 10'$, $B = 16° 50'$, $c = 24.8$
54. $B = 24°$, $a = 59$, $b = 26$　56. $A = 55°$, $B = 35°$, $a = 6.9$

Exercise Group 5–5

2. 1610 ft　4. 1010 ft　6. 123 mi, 140°　8. 1910 ft
10. 477 ft　12. 12,900 ft　14. 8700 ft　16. 20.78 in.
18. 130 in.　20. 2894 mi, 50.51 mi

Exercise Group 5–6

2. $H = 139.3$, $V = 105.9$　4. $H = 3.177$, $V = 43.05$
6. $H = K \cos \alpha$, $V = K \sin \alpha$　8. $H = 215.7$, $V = 43.16$
10. $H = K/r$, $V = K\sqrt{r^2 - 1}/r$　12. Direction 255°, $R = 51.75$
14. Direction 209° 26′, $R = 155.9$　16. $\theta = 261°$, $M = 338.8$
18. Course 148° 21′, groundspeed 532 mph
20. Airspeed 630 mph, time 1 hr 29 min　22. $T = 526$ lb, $\theta = 48° 20'$

24. $T_1 = \dfrac{W\cos\beta}{\sin\alpha\cos\beta + \cos\alpha\sin\beta}$, $T_2 = \dfrac{W\cos\alpha}{\sin\alpha\cos\beta + \cos\alpha\sin\beta}$
26. $T = C = 100$ lb
28. $T = 76.53$ lb, $C = 100$ lb
30. $T = 120.2$ lb, $C = 66.67$ lb

Supplementary Exercises for Chapter 5

2. $B = 54°$, $b = 1.1$, $a = 0.76$
4. $A = 72° \, 40'$, $B = 17° \, 20'$, $c = 4.13$
6. 66° with current, 8.7 mi/hr
8. 13°, 23 ft/sec
10. $\frac{1}{16}\left[9\sqrt{3} - \frac{\pi}{2}\right] \text{in}^3 = 0.88 \text{ in}^3$
12. $\sqrt{[F_3 - (F_1\sin\theta_1 + F_2\sin\theta_2)]^2 + (F_1\cos\theta_1 - F_2\cos\theta_2)^2}$
14. 235°

Exercise Group 6–1

2. (a) $x < -2$, (b) $x \geqq -2$
4. (a) $x > -6$, (b) $x \leqq -6$
6. (a) $3 < x < 10$, (b) $x \leqq 3$ or $x \geqq 10$
8. (a) $x < -\frac{2}{3}$, (b) $x \geqq -\frac{2}{3}$
10. (a) $x > 5$, (b) $x \leqq 5$
12. (a) No value of x, (b) All real values of x
14. (a) $0 < x < 3$, (b) $x \leqq 0$ or $x \geqq 3$
16. $x < 5$
18. $x < -\frac{9}{7}$
20. $x > -1$
22. $x < 2$
24. $x > 1$
26. $-5 < x < 5$
28. $x > a^2, x < -a^2$
30. $\frac{4}{3} < x < \frac{5}{3}$
32. $x < 3 - b, x > 3 + b$
34. $-1 < x < 0, 3 < x < 4$
36. $-\frac{3}{2} < x < \frac{1}{2}, \frac{1}{2} < x < \frac{5}{2}$

Exercise Group 6–2

2. $-3 < x < 2$
4. $2 < x < 3$
6. $-\frac{4}{3} < x < 2$
8. $-\frac{4}{3} < x < \frac{5}{2}$
10. $x < -9, x > 19$
12. $x < -33, x > 27$
14. $x < (7 - \sqrt{17})/4, x > (7 + \sqrt{17})/4$
16. $x < \frac{1}{2}, x > 1$
18. $x < (-1 - \sqrt{5})/2, x > (-1 + \sqrt{5})/2$
20. $x < \frac{2}{3}, x > \frac{3}{2}$
22. $-1 < x < 3$
24. $-2 < x < \frac{2}{3}$
26. $-5 < x < -\frac{1}{5}$
28. $x < -\frac{1}{2}, x > \frac{1}{2}$
30. $\frac{3}{5} < x < \frac{5}{3}$
32. $0 < x < \frac{5}{2}$
34. $x < -\frac{1}{2}, x > 2$
36. $-1 < x < 2$

Exercise Group 6–3

2. $-\frac{2}{3} < x < \frac{5}{2}$
4. $x < -2, x > \frac{1}{2}$
6. $1 < x < 3$
8. $x < -3, -2 < x < 1$
10. $-\frac{1}{2} < x < 0, x > \frac{5}{2}$
12. $-2 < x < 2, x > 3$
14. $x > 5$
16. $x < -\frac{3}{2}, -\frac{3}{2} < x < 1$
18. $x < -1, -\frac{1}{3} < x < 1, x > 1$
20. $-2 < x < \frac{4}{3}, \frac{3}{2} < x < 5$
22. $x < -4, \frac{3}{2} < x < 2$
24. $-\frac{1}{4} < x < 0, x > 3$
26. $0 < x < \frac{3}{2}, x > 3$
28. $x < -\frac{1}{2}, 0 < x < 1, x > 3$
30. $-4 < x < \frac{1}{3}, \frac{1}{3} < x < \frac{1}{2}$

Exercise Group 7–1

2. $0 < \theta < \pi$ 4. $\pi < \theta < \frac{3\pi}{2}, \frac{3\pi}{2} < \theta < 2\pi$ 6. None

8. $0 \leqq \theta < \frac{\pi}{2}, \frac{3\pi}{2} < \theta \leqq 2\pi$ 10. $0 \leqq \theta \leqq \frac{\pi}{6}, \frac{5\pi}{6} \leqq \theta \leqq 2\pi$

12. $0 \leqq \theta \leqq \frac{\pi}{4}, \pi \leqq \theta \leqq \frac{5\pi}{4}$ 14. $\pi \leqq \theta \leqq 2\pi$

16. $\frac{2\pi}{3} \leqq \theta \leqq \frac{4\pi}{3}$

18. $0 < \theta \leqq \frac{\pi}{4}, \frac{\pi}{2} < \theta \leqq \frac{3\pi}{4}, \pi < \theta \leqq \frac{5\pi}{4}, \frac{3\pi}{2} < \theta \leqq \frac{7\pi}{4}$

20. $-82°$ 22. $-\pi/2, \pi/2$ 24. $73°$ 26. $-153°, 27°$ 28. $-\pi/3$

30. $-\pi/5$ 32. $2\pi/3, -\pi/3$ 34. $-46°$ 36. $137°$

38. $0.6, \sqrt{0.91}, \sqrt{0.19}, \sqrt{0.19}$ 40. $0.91, 0.36, 0.91, 0.84$

Exercise Group 7–2

2. $A = 1$ 8. $A = 1$ 10. $A = \frac{1}{2}$ 14. $A = \frac{3}{5}$ 16. $A = 1$ 18. $A = 1$

Exercise Group 7–3

2. $(-5, 8)$ 4. $(1, 2)$ 6. $(\frac{5}{3}, -12)$ 8. $(5, 3)$

10. (a) $y = x^2 + 8x + 18$, (b) $y = x^2 + 6$ 12. $y = 1 + \sin(x - \pi)$

14. $y = 1 + \tan(x + \pi/2)$ 16. $y = 9x$ 18. $y = \cos 6x$

20. (a) $y = -x^2 - 2x$, (b) $y = -x^2 + 2x$

22. (a) $y = -4 \sin x$, (b) $y = 4 \sin(-x)$ 24. Odd; $\sin(-x) = -\sin x$

26. Odd; $\tan(-x) = -\tan x$ 28. Even; $\sec(-x) = \sec x$

30. $y = \frac{x + 4}{x + 3}$ 32. $y = 2 \sin\left(x - \frac{\pi}{2}\right)$

34. A translation of 4 units to the left.

36. Contraction in the x-direction in the ratio $1:\frac{1}{3}$, followed by a translation of 2 units to the left, followed by a reflection in the x-axis.

38. A translation of $\frac{3\pi}{2}$ units to the left, followed by a contraction in the y-direction in the ratio $1:\frac{1}{2}$, followed by a reflection in the x-axis.

40. Contraction in y-direction in the ratio $1:\frac{1}{2}$ and in the x-direction in the ratio $1:5$, followed by a reflection in the x-axis, and translations of $\frac{2\pi}{5}$ units to the right and 3 units up.

42. $P = \frac{2\pi}{3}, A = 2$ 44. $P = \frac{\pi}{3}$ 46. $P = \frac{\pi}{3}$

48. $P = 2\pi, A = 1$ 50. $P = \frac{2\pi}{3}, A = 4$

Supplementary Exercises for Chapter 7

2. $P = \pi, A = 3$ 4. $P = 2\pi$ 6. $P = 4\pi, A = \frac{1}{3}$
8. $P = 6\pi, A = 2$ 10. $P = \dfrac{2\pi}{3}$ 12. $P = 3\pi, A = 1$
14. $P = 2\pi, A = 2$ 16. $P = \dfrac{2\pi}{3}, A = \dfrac{1}{2}$ 18. $P = \dfrac{2\pi}{3}, A = 1$
20. $P = 2\pi$ 22. $P = 4\pi$ 28. $xy = -2$ 30. $x^2y = y - 1$
32. $y = \sec(x - 3\pi/2) + \tan(x - 3\pi/2)$ 34. $y \sec(-x) - x \tan y + 2 = 0$

Exercise Group 8–1

2. 5 4. -47 6. 87 8. 22 10. 506 12. -230 14. $34a^4$
16. $-\frac{137}{81}$ 18. $\frac{151}{9}$ 20. Yes 22. Yes 24. No 26. Yes 28. Yes
30. Yes 32. Yes 34. No

Exercise Group 8–2

2. $3x^3 + 10x^2 + 3x + 20, 65$ 4. $x^3 - 3x^2 + 2x - 10, 1$
6. $2x^3 + 4x^2 + 8x + 29, 52$ 8. $-2x^4 + 10x^3 - 50x^2 + 3, 0$
10. $-6x^2 + 2x + 1, 8$ 12. $4x^4 - x^3 + x^2 + 2x + 3, -9$
14. $3x^3 + 5ax^2 + 3a^2x + a^3, -2a^4$
16. $3x^3/2 + 5x^2/4 + 13x/8 + 153/16, 605/16$
18. $-2, -\frac{23}{4}, 33$ 20. $27, 88, -568$
22. $-8, 76, 8$ 24. 4.694, 8.174, 5.882

Exercise Group 8–3

2. $-3, -\frac{3}{2}, \frac{5}{2}$ 4. $-\frac{3}{7}, \frac{2}{3}, 4$ 6. No rational roots
8. $\frac{5}{3}, (1 \pm i\sqrt{7})/2$ 10. $-1, 2, (3 \pm i\sqrt{47})/4$ 12. $-1, 1$
14. No rational roots 16. $-\frac{3}{2}, \frac{1}{2}, \frac{6}{5}, \frac{5}{4}, \frac{4}{3}$ 18. $-2, \frac{1}{3}$
20. No rational roots

Exercise Group 8–4

12. $-4.5, -1, 1.5$ 14. $-1.7, 0.5, 1.7$ 16. $-2.5, -1.4, 0.7, 1.4$
18. $-3.7, -0.3, 0.3, 3.7$ 20. $-3, -1.8, 3, 3.8$

Exercise Group 8–5

2. 2.21 4. 0.67 6. -1.58 8. 0.62 10. -2.30
12. $-0.84, 1.75, 3.42$ 14. 2, 1.15 16. 8.65
18. $-2.193, 3.193$ 20. $-3.646, -1.193, 1.646, 4.193$
22. $-2.791, 1.791$ 24. $-2.303, -1.828, -\frac{1}{2}, 1.303, 3.828$

Supplementary Exercises for Chapter 8

2. $\pm i\sqrt{5}, (-1 \pm \sqrt{29})/2$ 4. (a) 3, (b) -4 6. (a) 4, (b) -2
8. $-2.79, -1.30, 1, 1.79, 2.30$ 10. $-4, -2.45, 2.45, 4$

Exercise Group 9–1

2. $\frac{\pi}{4} + n\pi$ 4. $\frac{\pi}{6} + n\pi$ 6. $\frac{\pi}{2} + 2n\pi$ 8. $\frac{2\pi}{3} + 2n\pi, \frac{4\pi}{3} + 2n\pi$
10. $\frac{3\pi}{4} + n\pi$ 12. $(2n + 1)\pi$ 14. $\frac{\pi}{2} + n\pi$ 16. $x = \arcsin \frac{y}{3}$
18. $x = 4 \operatorname{arcsec} \frac{y}{2}$ 20. $x = \frac{1}{2} \arcsin (y + 3)$ 22. $x = \tan \frac{y}{2}$
24. $x = \frac{1}{2} \cos 3y$ 26. $x = 2 \tan 3(y - 1)$
38. Inverse period $= \pi$, no inverse amplitude
40. Inverse period $= \pi$, inverse amplitude $= \frac{1}{3}$
42. Inverse period $= 4\pi$, inverse amplitude $= 3$
44. Inverse period $= 2\pi/3$, inverse amplitude $= \frac{1}{2}$
46. Inverse period $= 4\pi$, inverse amplitude $= \frac{1}{3}$

Exercise Group 9–2

2. 45° 4. 30° 6. 60° 8. 60° 47′ 10. 5° 22′
12. −60° 14. −21° 08′ 16. 173° 53′ 18. −35° 04′ 20. $-\frac{\pi}{4}$
22. $\frac{2\pi}{3}$ 24. $-\frac{\pi}{3}$ 26. 0 28. 0 30. $\frac{\pi}{2}$
32. $\frac{5\pi}{6}$ 34. −1.0361 36. −0.4276 38. $\frac{2\sqrt{3}}{3}$ 40. $\sqrt{5}$
42. $\frac{3}{2}$ 44. $\frac{4}{3}$ 46. $-\frac{2\sqrt{5}}{5}$ 48. $\frac{2\sqrt{13}}{13}$ 50. $-\frac{\sqrt{3}}{2}$

Exercise Group 9–3

2. $10^{1.1461}$ 4. $10^{2.1875}$ 6. $10^{0.1761}$ 8. $10^{-0.1963}$
10. $10^{3.5986}$ 12. $10^{4.8144}$ 14. $10^{2.6717}$ 16. $10^{0.4241}$
18. $10^{1.8195}$ 20. $10^{2.1673}$ 22. $10^{0.1717}$ 24. $10^{3.2966}$
26. $10^{0.1724}$ 28. $10^{0.5818}$ 30. $10^{0.9432}$ 32. $10^{1.0123}$
34. $10^{0.9180}$ 36. $10^{0.8774}$

Exercise Group 9–4

2. $\log_3 27 = 3$ 4. $\log_{49} 7 = \frac{1}{2}$ 6. $\log_{0.4} \frac{125}{8} = -3$
8. $\log_{27} 9 = \frac{2}{3}$ 10. $\log_{243} 81 = \frac{4}{5}$ 12. $\log_{128} 8 = \frac{3}{7}$
14. $(64)^{1/3} = 4$ 16. $(2.5)^3 = 15.625$ 18. $(16)^{0.75} = 8$
20. $(0.5)^{-5} = 32$ 22. $(0.1)^{-5} = 10^5$ 24. $a^0 = 1$
26. $y = 5$ 28. $y = a$ 30. $y = -\frac{3}{2}$ 32. $y = \frac{4}{3}$
34. $x = 625$ 36. $x = 10^{0.75}$ 38. $x = \frac{1}{1024}$ 40. $x = 243$
42. $x = \frac{1}{81}$ 44. $b = \frac{1}{125}$ 46. $b = a$ 48. $b = \frac{1}{343}$
50. $b = 0.01$ 52. $y = \frac{2}{3}$ 54. $x = a^{c/3}$

Exercise Group 9–6

2. 1.7782 4. 0.3590 6. 2.4671 8. 6.3284 10. 0.3775
12. 9.8650 − 10 14. 7.6149 − 10 16. 8.2293 − 10 18. 7.8410

20. 1.2532 22. 0.1063 24. 0.0117 26. 7.55 28. 492,000
30. 0.000244 32. 6260 34. 0.00574 36. 7850 38. 27.8 40. 722,000
42. 0.0887 50. $y = 7x^2$ 52. $y = 5(10^{3x})$
54. $y = 10^{mx+1}$ 56. $y = 2x\sqrt[3]{4x}$

Exercise Group 9–7

2. 0.6411 4. 3.9715 6. 8.8110 − 10 8. 5.5042 10. 7.2819 − 10
12. 3.9208 − 10 14. 4567 16. 95.38 18. 0.00004525 20. 0.000001985
22. 2.486×10^{-6} 24. 5.829×10^{-5} 26. 0.4857 28. 0.0001641
30. 0.0002248 32. 0.02015 34. 0.4252 36. 0.6003

Exercise Group 9–8

2. 112.8 4. 349.8 6. 717.0 8. 2.910×10^{-11}
10. 7.395×10^{-5} 12. 271,100 14. 4.621×10^{-5} 16. 17.08
18. 12.55 20. 23.13 22. 5.691×10^{-7} 24. 0.002140
26. 1.148×10^{-8} 28. 6.446×10^{-16} 30. 1,633,000

Exercise Group 9–9

2. 9.8238 − 10 4. 0.0560 6. 0.5535 8. 0.1145 10. 0.1459
12. 9.9949 − 10 14. 30° 17′ 16. 20° 42′ 18. 32° 34′ 20. 25° 27′
22. 23° 25′ 24. 42° 04′ 26. $A = 30° 48'$, $a = 0.1211$, $b = 0.2031$
28. $A = 29° 54'$, $B = 60° 06'$, $b = 636500$
30. $A = 83° 16'$, $B = 6° 44'$, $a = 0.3499$
32. $A = 79° 14'$, $B = 10° 46'$, $c = 98.48$
34. $B = 76° 44'$, $a = 0.3045$, $b = 1.292$ 36. Wind velocity 31 mph
38. $T_1 = 2155$ lb, $T_2 = 2001$ lb 40. 11 mi 42. 870.8 lb

Exercise Group 9–11

2. 1.447 4. 0.4531 6. 20.79 8. 1.771 10. 0.9349 12. 0.4402
14. 29.67 16. 0.067 18. 30.05 20. $5116 22. 17.5 yr 24. 4.4%

Exercise Group 9–12

2. 0.6999 4. 11.62 6. −0.3111 8. 4.346 10. 8.948 12. 1.112 14. 3.685

Supplementary Exercises for Chapter 9

2. $b = 4$ 4. $y = -3$ 6. $x = 27$ 16. $y = 3x^2$
18. $y = 4^{5/3}x^{2/3}$ 20. 28,840 22. 20.37 24. 7.867
26. 4.974 28. 3.573 30. 2.553 32. 1.76
34. 1.12 36. 23.5 38. $x = \frac{1}{2} \arcsin \frac{y}{3}$ 40. $x = \frac{1}{3} \tan y$
42. $x = 2 \cos \frac{y}{3}$ 44. $-\frac{\pi}{6}$ 46. $\frac{2\pi}{3}$ 48. −0.5764
50. $\frac{4}{5}$ 52. $\frac{13}{12}$ 54. $-2\sqrt{2}$

Exercise Group 10–1

52. $\sec\theta$
54. $3\cos\theta$
56. $a\sin^3\theta$
58. $4\cos\theta$
60. $x = \arcsin 0$, $x = \arcsin \sqrt{2}/2$
62. $x = \arccos(-\frac{1}{2})$, $x = \arccos 1$
64. $x = \arctan 0$, $x = \arctan\sqrt{3}$
66. $x = \arctan 1$
68. $x = \arctan \dfrac{\sqrt{3}}{3}$, $x = \arctan(-1)$

Exercise Group 10–2

2. (a) and (b) $-\cot 31°$, (c) $-\tan 59°$
4. (a) $\cos 59°$, (b) and (c) $\sin 31°$
6. (a) $-\tan 82°$, (b) and (c) $-\cot 8°$
8. (a) $-\cos 86°$, (b) and (c) $-\sin 4°$
10. (a) $\tan 53°$, (b) and (c) $\cot 37°$
12. (a) $\csc 80°$, (b) and (c) $\sec 10°$
14. (a) $-\sin 45°\,40'$, (b) and (c) $-\cos 44°\,20'$
16. (a) and (b) $-\tan 36°\,37'$, (c) $-\cot 53°\,23'$
18. (a) $\cot 56°\,47'$, (b) and (c) $\tan 33°\,13'$
20. (a) $-\cos 88°\,48'$, (b) and (c) $-\sin 1°\,12'$
40. $\sin\theta$
42. $\csc\theta$
44. $\sec\theta$
46. $-\tan\theta$
48. $\sin\theta$

Exercise Group 10–3

In Exercises 2, 4, and 6 the answers are given in the order $\sin(A + B)$, $\sin(A - B)$, $\cos(A + B)$, $\cos(A - B)$, $\tan(A + B)$, and $\tan(A - B)$.

2. $-\frac{33}{65}, -\frac{63}{65}, -\frac{56}{65}, -\frac{16}{65}, \frac{33}{56}, \frac{63}{16}$
4. $\frac{36}{325}, -\frac{204}{325}, \frac{323}{325}, -\frac{253}{325}, \frac{36}{323}, \frac{204}{253}$
6. $\frac{204}{325}, -\frac{36}{325}, \frac{253}{325}, -\frac{323}{325}, \frac{204}{253}, \frac{36}{323}$
8. $\dfrac{\sqrt{3}}{2}$
10. $\frac{1}{2}$
12. $\dfrac{3 - \sqrt{3}}{3 + \sqrt{3}} = 2 - \sqrt{3}$
14. $\frac{1}{2}$
16. 1
18. $\frac{1}{2}$
40. $\dfrac{1}{k}$

Exercise Group 10–4

2. $\tan 15°$
4. $\frac{1}{2}\sin 2\theta$
6. $\frac{1}{4}\sin^2 2\theta$
8. $\cos^2(3\theta/2)$
10. $\sin^2(3\theta/2)$
12. $\tan(3\theta/2)$
14. $-\frac{120}{169}, -\frac{119}{169}, \frac{120}{119}$
16. $-\frac{120}{169}, -\frac{119}{169}, \frac{120}{119}$
18. $\frac{24}{25}, \frac{7}{25}, \frac{24}{7}$
20. $\frac{12}{13}, \frac{5}{13}, \frac{12}{5}$
22. $-3\sqrt{7}/8, -\frac{1}{8}, 3\sqrt{7}$
24. 1, 0, —
26. $2\sqrt{5}/5, -\sqrt{5}/5, -2$
28. $2\sqrt{13}/13, -3\sqrt{13}/13, -\frac{2}{3}$
30. $3\sqrt{10}/10, -\sqrt{10}/10, -3$
32. $-\sqrt{3}/2, \frac{1}{2}, -\sqrt{3}$
34. $\frac{24}{25}$
36. $\frac{1}{3}$
38. $1 - 2x^2$
40. $(\sqrt{1 + x^2} - 1)/x$
64. $x = 2y^2 - 1$

Exercise Group 10–5

2. $2\cos 31°\cos 19°$
4. $2\sin 200°\cos 100°$
6. $2\sin 30°\cos 65°$
8. $2\cos 3\theta\cos\theta$
10. $2\sin 2\theta\cos(\theta/2)$
12. $\frac{1}{2}(\cos 20° - \cos 80°)$
14. $\frac{1}{2}(\sin 98° - \sin 22°)$
16. $\frac{1}{2}(\sin 3\theta + \sin\theta)$
18. $\frac{1}{2}(\sin 5\theta + \sin 3\theta)$
20. $\frac{1}{2}(\cos 2B - \cos 20B)$
22. $\frac{1}{2}(\sin 30\theta + \sin 14\theta)$

Exercise Group 10–6

2. $\theta = 3\pi/4, 7\pi/4$ 4. $\theta = \pi/3, 2\pi/3, 4\pi/3, 5\pi/3$ 6. $\theta = \pi/6, 5\pi/6, 3\pi/2$
8. $\theta = 0, 4\pi/3$ 10. $\theta = \pi/3, \pi, 5\pi/3$ 12. $\theta = 7\pi/6, 11\pi/6$ 14. $\theta = \pi$
16. $\theta = 0, \pi/2, \pi, 3\pi/2$ 18. $\theta = \pi/6, 5\pi/6, 7\pi/6, 11\pi/6$
20. $\theta = \pi/12, 5\pi/12, 7\pi/12, 11\pi/12, 13\pi/12, 17\pi/12, 19\pi/12, 23\pi/12$
22. $\theta = \pi/2, 3\pi/2$ 24. $\theta = 0, 2\pi/3, 4\pi/3$ 26. $\theta = \pi/4, 5\pi/4$
28. $\theta = 0, \pi/3, 2\pi/3, \pi, 4\pi/3, 5\pi/3$ 30. $\theta = \pi/8, 5\pi/8, 9\pi/8, 13\pi/8$
32. $\theta = 0, \pi/2$ 34. $\theta = 0$ 36. $\theta = \pi/2, 7\pi/6, 11\pi/6$
38. $\theta = 2\pi/3, 4\pi/3$ 40. $\theta = 0.9274$ rad
42. $\theta = 1.1990$ rad, 2.8699 rad 44. $\theta = 0.2839$ rad 46. $\theta = 2.8577$ rad
48. $\theta = 0, \pi/14, 3\pi/14, \pi/4, 5\pi/14, \pi/2, 9\pi/14, 3\pi/4, 11\pi/14, 13\pi/14, \pi, 15\pi/14, 17\pi/14, 5\pi/4, 19\pi/14, 3\pi/2, 23\pi/14, 7\pi/4, 25\pi/14, 27\pi/14$
50. $\theta = \pi/4, \pi/2, 3\pi/4, 5\pi/4, 3\pi/2, 7\pi/4$

Supplementary Exercises for Chapter 10

34. (a) $\sin 33°\,12'$, (b) $\sin 33°\,12'$ 36. (a) $\cot 6°\,48'$, (b) $\cot 6°\,48'$
38. (a) $\cos 14°$, (b) $\cos 14°$ 40. (a) $\cos \pi/3$, (b) $\sin \pi/6$
42. (a) $-\cot \pi/4$, (b) $-\cot \pi/4$ 44. (a) $\sin \pi/3$, (b) $\cos \pi/6$
46. (a) $-\cot \pi/3$, (b) $-\tan \pi/6$ 48. $\theta = 3\pi/4, 7\pi/4$
50. $\theta = \pi/8, 5\pi/8, 9\pi/8, 13\pi/8$ 52. $\theta = 0.9274$ rad, π
54. $\theta = 0, \pi/2, \pi, 3\pi/2$ 56. $\theta = 1.2310$ rad, π, 5.0521 rad
58. $\theta = \pi/9, 4\pi/9, 7\pi/9, 10\pi/9, 13\pi/9, 16\pi/9$
60. $\theta = 1.1286$ rad, 3.8676 rad 62. $\theta = \pi/2, 2\pi/3, 4\pi/3$

Exercise Group 11–2

2. 1, 17, 136, 680, 2380 4. 1, 29, 406, 3654, 23751
6. 1, 41, 820, 10660, 101270 8. 1, 47, 1081, 16215, 178365
10. $x^7 + 7x^6y + 21x^5y^2 + 35x^4y^3 + 35x^3y^4 + 21x^2y^5 + 7xy^6 + y^7$
12. $a^6 + 6a^5b + 15a^4b^2 + 20a^3b^3 + 15a^2b^4 + 6ab^5 + b^6$
14. $b^7x^7 + 7b^6x^6y + 21b^5x^5y^2 + 35b^4x^4y^3 + 35b^3x^3y^4 + 21b^2x^2y^5 + 7bxy^6 + y^7$
16. $81x^4 - 108x^3y + 54x^2y^2 - 12xy^3 + y^4$
18. $16x^4 - \frac{32}{3}x^3y + \frac{8}{3}x^2y^2 - \frac{8}{27}xy^3 + \frac{1}{81}y^4$
20. $\frac{1}{16}x^4 - \frac{3}{2}x^3y^2 + \frac{27}{2}x^2y^4 - 54xy^6 + 81y^8$
22. $-x^{10} + 10x^8y - 40x^6y^2 + 80x^4y^3 - 80x^2y^4 + 32y^5$
24. $16x^{-4} + 32x^{-3}y + 24x^{-2}y^2 + 8x^{-1}y^3 + y^4$
26. $a^6x^{-6} - 6a^5bx^{-5} + 15a^4b^2x^{-4} - 20a^3b^3x^{-3} + 15a^2b^4x^{-2} - 6ab^5x^{-1} + b^6$
28. $16 - 96i - 216 + 216i + 81 = -119 + 120i$
30. $1 - 6y^{1-x} + 15y^{2-2x} - 20y^{3-3x} + 15y^{4-4x} - 6y^{5-5x} + y^{6-6x}$
32. $u^{5-5x} - 5u^{4-4x}v^{1-x} + 10u^{3-3x}v^{2-2x} - 10u^{2-2x}v^{3-3x} + 5u^{1-x}v^{4-4x} - v^{5-5x}$
34. $1 + 18(0.025) + 153(0.025)^2$
36. $(a - b)^k + k(a - b)^{k-1}c + \dfrac{k(k-1)}{2}(a - b)^{k-2}c^2$
38. 1.601 40. 1.249

Exercise Group 11–3

2. $-792u^7v^5$ 4. $-2002x^{27}y^{10}$ 6. $\dfrac{1001 \times 3^{10}}{16}x^8y^{10}$

8. $-\dfrac{6188 \times 2^5}{3^{12}}x^{24}y^{15}$ 10. 0.007722 12. $59136x^3y^2$

14. $-3432u^7v^7$ 16. $210u^{6x+6y}v^{4x-4y}$ 18. 180 20. $24x^2y^5$

Exercise Group 11–4

2. $1 - 2v + 3v^2 - 4v^3$ 4. $1 + \frac{3}{2}v + \frac{15}{8}v^2 + \frac{35}{16}v^3$ 6. $1 - 3x^2 + \frac{3}{2}x^4 + \frac{1}{2}x^6$

8. $1 - 9x^2 + 54x^4 - 270x^6$ 10. $1 + 1 + \dfrac{1-x}{2} + \dfrac{(1-x)(1-2x)}{6}$

12. $x^{5/2} + \frac{5}{2}x^{1/2} + \frac{15}{8}x^{-3/2} + \frac{5}{16}x^{-7/2}$ 14. $\frac{315}{128}x^4$ 16. $-\dfrac{7480}{3^9}x^{7/2}$

18. Fifth 20. Seventh and eighth 22. Third and fourth
24. $1 + 0.30 + 0.0390$ 26. $1 - 0.90 + 0.4275$
28. $1 + 0.1575 + 0.01004$ 30. $x^{-1} - x^{-2} + x^{-3} - x^{-4}$

Exercise Group 11–5

2. 11.23 4. 0.633 6. 307.5 8. 0.7992 10. 8.318
12. 3091 14. 2.685 16. 35.32 18. −4.947 20. 347 yr
22. Increase is 63 times original amount. 24. 53.0 gm 26. 81.20 min
28. 8.546 min, 37.79% remains after 12 min. 30. 4.1% 32. 5.895%

Supplementary Exercises for Chapter 11

2. $462a^6b^5x^{12}y^5$ 4. $90720x^4y^8$ 6. $6435b^8x^7y^8$
8. $1 - \frac{4}{3}x - \frac{4}{9}x^2 - \frac{32}{81}x^3$
10. $x^x - x^{x-1} + \frac{1}{2}(x-1)x^{x-3} - \frac{1}{6}(x-1)(x-2)x^{x-5}$

12. $1 - 3ax + 6a^2x^2 - 10a^3x^3$ 14. $2 + \dfrac{1}{192} - \dfrac{5}{147{,}456} + \dfrac{55}{169{,}869{,}312}$

16. $1 - 0.54 + 0.1539 - 0.03078$ 18. $1 + 0.7 + 0.23275 + 0.0488775$
24. Increase is 1023 times original amount. 26. 4.93%

Exercise Group 12–1

2. $(\frac{14}{31}, \frac{44}{31})$ 4. $(\frac{10}{3}, \frac{1}{3})$ 6. (3, 5) 8. $(\frac{52}{57}, -\frac{17}{38})$
10. (2, 3) 12. $(\frac{26}{5}, \frac{26}{37})$ 14. (0.2, −0.3) 16. (−0.3, −0.7)
18. $(2ab/5, -3ab/7)$ 20. (b, a) 22. $(1.7a, -2.1b)$ 24. $(-\frac{77}{36}, \frac{169}{108})$

26. $(-\frac{11}{8}, \frac{3}{2})$ 28. $\left[\dfrac{q \sin A - p \sin B}{\sin (A - B)}, \dfrac{p \cos B - q \cos A}{\sin (A - B)}\right]$

30. $(\sin A + 3 \cos A, 3 \sin A - \cos A)$ 32. $\frac{3}{5}, \frac{4}{7}$
34. 5.5 oz of A, 3.5 oz of B, 6 oz of C 36. 7 hr 38. 4%, 4.5%
40. 200 ft, 100 ft 42. $\frac{2}{5}x + \frac{44}{5}$ 44. $A = 4, B = -1$

Exercise Group 12–2

2. $(3, -2, 1)$ 4. $(3, -3, 0)$ 6. $(2, \frac{1}{2}, 1)$ 8. $(\frac{2}{3}, \frac{3}{4}, \frac{4}{5})$
10. (a, b, c) 12. (a, ab, b) 14. $(u, 2u, 3u)$ 16. $(\frac{1}{3}, \frac{1}{2}, 1)$
18. $-2x^2 + 3x - 4$ 20. $A = 3, B = -6, C = 4$ 22. \$5000, \$1000, \$4000
24. 120 min, 180 min, 360 min

Exercise Group 12–4

2. $(0, 3), (4, 0)$ 4. $(1.5, 4), (-2, -3)$ 6. $(1, -2), (\frac{7}{4}, \frac{1}{4})$
8. $(-1, 5), (-\frac{4}{3}, \frac{13}{3})$ 10. $(1, 1), (\frac{3}{2}, \frac{2}{3})$ 12. $(-6, 5), (\frac{10}{3}, \frac{1}{3})$
14. $(7, -8), (8, -7)$ 16. $(2, 1), (\frac{28}{9}, \frac{4}{9})$ 18. $(0, -3), (4, 0)$
20. Inconsistent 22. $(2, \frac{3}{2}), (\frac{3}{2}, 2)$
24. (1) $k \leqq -\frac{\sqrt{39}}{4}, k \geqq \frac{\sqrt{39}}{4}$; (2) $-\frac{\sqrt{39}}{4} < k < \frac{\sqrt{39}}{4}$
26. (1) $-|b| < k < 0, 0 < k < |b|$; (2) $k < -|b|, k > |b|$ 28. 12, 4
30. 9, 12, 15 32. 7, 24, 25 34. 73 in., 55 in. 36. $k = \pm\sqrt{7}$

Exercise Group 12–5

2. $(\pm 4, \pm 4)$ 4. $(\pm 2, \pm 3)$ 6. $(\pm\sqrt{6}/3, \pm\sqrt{15}/5)$ 8. $(\pm a, \pm bc)$
10. $(\pm 3, \pm i\sqrt{5})$ 12. $(\pm\sqrt{5}, \pm\sqrt{6}/2)$ 14. $(\pm i\sqrt{237}/3, \pm\sqrt{21})$
16. $(\pm 2a\sqrt{10}/5, \pm b\sqrt{15}/5)$ 18. $(\pm 20\sqrt{36121}/881, \pm 60\sqrt{881}/881)$
20. $(\pm 2i\sqrt{10}, \pm\sqrt{2})$ 22. $(\pm 2, \pm 3i)$
24. $(\frac{13}{2}, \frac{1}{2}), (-\frac{13}{2}, -\frac{1}{2}), (\frac{1}{2}, \frac{13}{2}), (-\frac{1}{2}, -\frac{13}{2})$ 26. $(\pm\frac{1}{2}, \pm\frac{1}{5})$

Exercise Group 12–6

2. $(2, -1), (-2, 1), (1, 3), (-1, -3)$ 4. $(1, 2), (-1, -2), (2, -3), (-2, 3)$
6. $(1, 2), (-11, -22), (1, -3), (-\frac{11}{6}, \frac{11}{2})$
8. $(6, 4), (-6, -4), (4i, -6i), (-4i, 6i)$
10. $(1, 3), (-1, -3), (2\sqrt{7}, \sqrt{7}), (-2\sqrt{7}, -\sqrt{7})$
12. $(1, 1), (-1, -1), (2, -\frac{1}{3}), (-2, \frac{1}{3})$
14. $(i\sqrt{6}/12, -5i\sqrt{6}/12), (-i\sqrt{6}/12, 5i\sqrt{6}/12), (\frac{5}{4}, \frac{3}{4}), (-\frac{5}{4}, -\frac{3}{4})$
16. $[(-15 + i\sqrt{1455})/12, (-15 + i\sqrt{1455})/28]$,
$[(-15 - i\sqrt{1455})/12, (-15 - i\sqrt{1455})/28], (\frac{5}{2}, -1), (-5, 2)$
18. $(-2, -2), (\frac{1}{2}, \frac{1}{2}), [(9 + 3\sqrt{89})/20, (-3 - \sqrt{89})/20]$,
$[(9 - 3\sqrt{89})/20, (-3 + \sqrt{89})/20]$

Exercise Group 12–7

2. $(1, 2), (-1, -2), (2\sqrt{6}/3, -2\sqrt{6}/3), (-2\sqrt{6}/3, 2\sqrt{6}/3)$
4. $(2\sqrt{30}/3, \sqrt{30}/3), (-2\sqrt{30}/3, -\sqrt{30}/3), (3i\sqrt{5}, -2i\sqrt{5}), (-3i\sqrt{5}, 2i\sqrt{5})$
6. $(i\sqrt{10}/2, -i\sqrt{10}), (-i\sqrt{10}/2, i\sqrt{10}), (i\sqrt{10}/2, -3i\sqrt{10}/4), (-i\sqrt{10}/2, 3i\sqrt{10}/4)$
8. $(\sqrt{5}, -\sqrt{5}), (-\sqrt{5}, \sqrt{5}), (2\sqrt{3}, -\sqrt{3}), (-2\sqrt{3}, \sqrt{3})$
10. $(-\frac{3}{2}, 2), (-\frac{2}{3}, -\frac{1}{2})$
12. $[(1 + \sqrt{33})/4, (-1 + \sqrt{33})/2], [(1 - \sqrt{33})/4, (-1 - \sqrt{33})/2]$,
$[(-1 + \sqrt{33})/4, (1 + \sqrt{33})/2], [(-1 - \sqrt{33})/4, (1 - \sqrt{33})/2]$

14. $[1+\sqrt{10}, (-1+\sqrt{10}/3], [1-\sqrt{10}, (-1-\sqrt{10})/3],$
$[-1+\sqrt{10}, (1+\sqrt{10})/3], [-1-\sqrt{10}), (1-\sqrt{10})/3]$
16. $(1, -2), (-1, 2), (3\sqrt{21}/7, -2\sqrt{21}/7), (-3\sqrt{21}/7, 2\sqrt{21}/7)$
18. $(3, -1), (-3, 1), (4\sqrt{6}/3, -\sqrt{6}/6), (-4\sqrt{6}/3, \sqrt{6}/6)$
20. 7 ft, 24 ft
22. $\frac{1}{6}, -15/(-10), 15/(-15)$

Exercise Group 12–8

2. $r = \pm\sqrt{b^2 - a^2}, \theta = \arcsin \frac{a}{b}$
4. $x = A + 2k\pi, y = 2k'\pi; x = 2n\pi, y = A + 2n'\pi$
6. $x = \arctan\left(\frac{a}{b}\tan A\right) + \frac{1}{2}\arccos(2a^2\sin^2 A + 2b^2\cos^2 A - 1),$
$y = \arctan\left(\frac{a}{b}\tan A\right) - \frac{1}{2}\arccos(2a^2\sin^2 A + 2b^2\cos^2 A - 1)$
8. $x = \frac{1}{2}\arccos(1 - a + b), y = \frac{1}{2}\arccos(1 - a - b)$
10. $x = \arccos\left(\pm\sqrt[4]{\frac{b^2}{a(b-a)}}\right), y = \arccos\left(\pm\sqrt[4]{\frac{a}{b-a}}\right)$
12. $r = \frac{a+b-1}{2}, \theta = \frac{1}{2}\arccos(b-a)$
14. $x = \frac{\pi}{3}, y = \frac{5\pi}{3}; x = \frac{5\pi}{3}, y = \frac{\pi}{3}$

Supplementary Exercises for Chapter 12

2. $(-2, 3)$
4. $(\frac{7}{115}, \frac{11}{230})$
6. $(a, -b)$
8. $(-2, 2, 1)$
10. $\left(a, -\frac{b}{2}, \frac{b}{2}\right)$
12. $(-2, 2, 1)$
14. (a, b, c)
16. $(5, 3), (-5, 3), (5, -3), (-5, -3)$
18. $(5\sqrt{2}, 10), (5\sqrt{2}, -10), (-5\sqrt{2}, 10), (-5\sqrt{2}, -10)$
20. $\left(\frac{2+\sqrt{46}}{2}, \frac{-2+\sqrt{46}}{3}\right), \left(\frac{2-\sqrt{46}}{2}, \frac{-2-\sqrt{46}}{3}\right)$
22. $(0, 0), (-\frac{1}{11}, -\frac{2}{33}), (-\frac{20}{11}, \frac{12}{11})$
24. $(0, 0), (\frac{2}{3}, \frac{1}{3}), (-\frac{2}{7}, -\frac{6}{7})$
26. $\left(\frac{3\sqrt{10}}{5}, \frac{\sqrt{10}}{5}\right), \left(-\frac{3\sqrt{10}}{5}, -\frac{\sqrt{10}}{5}\right), \left(\frac{i\sqrt{10}}{5}, \frac{2i\sqrt{10}}{5}\right),$
$\left(-\frac{i\sqrt{10}}{5}, -\frac{2i\sqrt{10}}{5}\right)$
28. $(1, -2), (-1, 2), \left(\frac{7\sqrt{19}}{19}, \frac{\sqrt{19}}{19}\right), \left(-\frac{7\sqrt{19}}{19}, -\frac{\sqrt{19}}{19}\right)$
30. 60% from the 40% solution and 40% from the 65% solution

Exercise Group 13–1

2. 2, 7, 12, 17; 377
4. $\frac{1}{4}, \frac{1}{7}, \frac{1}{10}, \frac{1}{13}; \frac{1}{115}$
6. $\frac{3}{5}, \frac{6}{7}, 1, \frac{12}{11}; \frac{96}{65}$
8. $\frac{1}{2}, \frac{2}{5}, \frac{3}{10}, \frac{4}{17}; \frac{48}{2305}$

10. $1, \frac{1}{2}, \frac{4}{13}, \frac{1}{5}; \frac{64}{1093}$

12. $\frac{1}{\sqrt{2}}, -\frac{1}{\sqrt{2}}, -\frac{1}{\sqrt{2}}, \frac{1}{\sqrt{2}}; -\frac{1}{\sqrt{2}}$

14. $a_n = 3n - 1$

16. $a_n = \frac{1}{4n - 1}$

18. $a_n = \frac{n + 1}{n + 2}$

20. $a_n = 2^n$

22. $a_n = \frac{1 \cdot 2 \cdot 3 \cdots n}{3n - 1}$

Exercise Group 13–2

2. $13, \frac{29}{2}, 16$
4. $-11, -\frac{31}{3}, -\frac{29}{3}$
6. $b, b + c, b + 2c$
8. $a_{19} = -56, S_{19} = -551$
10. $a_{48} = -128, S_{48} = -2760$
12. $a_n = b + (n - 1)d, S_n = \frac{n}{2}[2b + (n - 1)d]$
14. $\frac{57}{2}$
16. $\frac{7}{15}$
18. $\frac{21}{2}, 16, \frac{43}{2}$
20. $-1, -4, -7, -10, -13, -16, -19, -22$
22. $a_{19} = 67, S_{19} = 760$
24. $d = -2, S_{27} = -513$
26. $a_1 = -17, S_{23} = -897$
28. $n = 53, S_{53} = 5035$
30. $n = 22, S_{22} = -33$
32. $n = 25, a_{25} = -45$
34. $a_{17} = 58, S_{17} = 442$
36. $n = 17, a_1 = -3; n = 19, a_1 = 1$
38. 1020
40. $a_1 = 3, d = 2$
42. 2,006,442
44. \$12.50, \$102
46. 2, 4, 6, 8, and the reverse of this A.P.; $5 - \sqrt{241}$, $5 - \frac{1}{3}\sqrt{241}$, $5 + \frac{1}{3}\sqrt{241}$, $5 + \sqrt{241}$, and the reverse of this A.P.
48. 434.7 ft, $16.1t^2$ ft
50. $n = 1{,}111$

Exercise Group 13–3

2. $-5, -10, -20$
4. $3, -\frac{9}{2}, \frac{27}{4}$
6. b, bc, bc^2
8. $a_{11} = -2(3)^{10}, S_{11} = 1 - 3^{11}$
10. $a_{15} = \frac{2}{3^{12}}, S_{15} = \frac{3^{15} + 1}{2(3^{12})}$
12. $a_n = \sin^{n-1}\theta, S_n = \frac{1 - \sin^n\theta}{1 - \sin\theta}$
14. $a_n = \cos^{n-1}\theta, S_n = \frac{1 - \cos^n\theta}{1 - \cos\theta}$
16. $a_n = \tan^{2n-6}\theta, S_n = \frac{1 - \tan^{2n}\theta}{\tan^4\theta - \tan^6\theta}$
18. $a_n = \sin^{n-2}\theta, S_n = (\csc^n\theta - \sin^n\theta)\sec^2\theta$
20. 27, 18, 12, 8
22. $\frac{81}{2}, \frac{27}{4}, \frac{9}{8}, \frac{3}{16}$
24. $\pm\csc\theta, 1, \pm\sin\theta, \sin^2\theta, \pm\sin^3\theta, \sin^4\theta, \pm\sin^5\theta$
26. $\pm\cot\theta\csc\theta, \csc^2\theta, \pm\csc^2\theta\sec\theta$
28. $a_6 = 160, S_6 = 315$
30. $r = 2, n = 8$
32. $r = -2, n = 7$
34. $a_8 = \frac{8}{729}, S_8 = 935(3\sqrt{2} + 2)/1458$
36. $a_1 = \sin^6\theta, n = 7$
38. $r = \csc\theta, n = 10$
40. $a_4 = \frac{1}{36}$
42. $a_3 = \pm\tan^3\frac{\theta}{2}\sec^3\frac{\theta}{2}$
44. $15{,}617/256$
46. 13 yr
48. $\frac{6778}{243} = 27.89$ (ft)

Exercise Group 13–4

2. $\frac{32}{9}$ 4. $10a/11$ 6. 13.527 8. $\frac{12}{35}$ 10. $3 + 2\sqrt{3}$
12. $1/(1 - x^2), |x| < 1$ 14. $(2\sqrt{x} - x)/(4 - x), 0 \leqq x < 4$
16. $(10x^2 - 20)/(x^2 + 8), |x| < 2\sqrt{3}$ 18. $1, x > -0.5$

Exercise Group 13–5

2. $\frac{400}{11}$ 4. $\frac{34}{333}$ 6. $\frac{67}{111}$ 8. $\frac{9}{11}$
10. $\frac{83}{11}$ 12. $\frac{79}{111}$ 14. $\frac{710}{303}$ 16. $\frac{2}{13}$

Supplementary Exercises for Chapter 13

4. $-(m + n)$ 18. 2 24. $\frac{5}{2}$ 26. $r = \frac{1}{3}$ 28. 30 ft

Exercise Group 14–2

2. $C = 59° 56', a = 152.0, b = 91.78$ 4. $A = 79° 34', b = 38.31, c = 19.48$
6. $C = 3° 51', a = 0.4310, b = 0.4173$ 8. $B = 31° 50', a = 634.1, c = 1747$
10. $A = 132° 52', b = 0.2203, c = 0.4604$
12. $C = 18° 19', a = 0.1108, b = 0.07960$
14. $A = 35° 20', a = 3767, c = 2162$ 16. $C = 64° 15', b = 0.1349, c = 0.1232$
18. $B = 70° 44', a = 36.26, b = 43.08$ 20. $A = 87° 11', a = 1.685, c = 1.652$
22. 66 ft 24. Groundspeed 445 mph, velocity of wind 24.3 mph
26. $F_2 = 1105$ lb, $R = 1141$ lb 28. 7 hr 9 min 30. 29 mi

Exercise Group 14–3

2. $A = 52° 52', C = 30° 53', a = 5.078$ 4. $A = 45° 34', C = 6° 55', c = 2.889$
6. $B = 35° 57', C = 10° 26', b = 0.6399$
8. $A = 71° 14', B = 61° 23', a = 0.09668; A' = 14° 00', B' = 118° 37', a' = 0.02470$
10. No solution
12. $A = 29° 49', B = 132° 18', b = 0.5726; A' = 150° 11', B' = 11° 56', b' = 0.1601$
14. $B = 39° 51', C = 5° 33', b = 0.1561$
16. $A = 58° 02', C = 90° 50', c = 380.5; A' = 121° 58', C' = 26° 54', c' = 172.2$
18. $B = 36° 12', A = 46° 20', a = 195.7$ 20. No solution
22. $A = 34° 49', C = 60° 24', c = 33.45$ 24. Heading 46° 41′ groundspeed 310 mph
26. 240.7 ft, 82° 00′ or 98° 00′
28. Magnitude of $F_3 = 257.5$, direction of $F_1 = 38° 42'$
30. 1.764 Astronomical Units

Exercise Group 14–4

2. $B = 49° 10', C = 70° 50', a = 4.6$ 4. $A = 17° 40', B = 27° 20', c = 464$
6. $A = 94° 50', C = 15° 10', b = 7.54$ 8. $B = 20° 10', C = 119° 40', a = 222$
10. $A = 109° 50', B = 31° 50', c = 0.165$ 12. $A = 29°, B = 47°, C = 104°$
14. $A = 29° 20', B = 49° 30', C = 101° 10'$
16. $A = 18° 10', B = 33° 10', C = 128° 40'$
18. $A = 20° 40', B = 32° 10', C = 127° 10'$
20. $A = 41° 40', B = 94° 20', C = 44°$ 22. Groundspeed 111 mph, course 220°
24. 76° between F_1 and F_2, 47° between F_1 and F_3 26. 23 in.

Exercise Group 14–5

2. $A = 29° 01', B = 37° 35', c = 815.8$
4. $A = 13° 14', B = 144° 32', c = 544.8$
6. $A = 34° 29', C = 23° 57', b = 0.9520$
8. $B = 23° 22', C = 21° 46', a = 164.8$

10. $B = 27° 49', C = 86° 51', a = 318400$
12. $A = 14° 52', C = 79° 14', b = 0.03194$
14. $B = 78° 05', C = 63° 39', a = 52.61$
16. $A = 59° 51', B = 56° 17', c = 507.9$
18. $A = 5° 16', C = 109° 38', b = 0.3101$
20. $B = 134° 57', C = 1° 35', a = 0.3088$
22. $F_3 = 384.1$ lb, $13° 35'$ with F_1
24. 633 naut mi, 166° 04′
26. 1127 mi, 124° 26′

Exercise Group 14–6

2. $A = 21° 48', B = 112° 18', C = 45° 54'$
4. $A = 32° 40', B = 51° 54', C = 95° 26'$
6. $A = 34° 28', B = 121° 56', C = 23° 36'$
8. $A = 47° 48', B = 109° 38', C = 22° 34'$
10. $A = 62° 54', B = 66° 58', C = 50° 10'$
12. $A = 79° 16', B = 49° 04', C = 51° 40'$
14. $A = 49° 30', B = 101° 46', C = 28° 44'$
16. $A = 22° 28', B = 144° 16', C = 13° 14'$
18. $A = 28° 30', B = 87° 02', C = 64° 28'$
20. $A = 103° 38', B = 31° 04', C = 45° 20'$
22. 53°, 82° 20′, 44° 30′
24. A to C, 60° 20′; B to C, 305° 50′
26. First plane 42° 38′, second plane 326° 32′

Exercise Group 14–7

2. 0.0006249
4. 0.05946
6. 284,500 or 102,100
8. 197,700
10. 0.1118
12. 34.11
14. 8.702
16. 3658
18. 6360 ft^2
20. 3220 ft^2
22. 1193 in^2
24. 9885 ft^2

Exercise Group 15–1

18. $\sqrt{2}, \frac{\pi}{4}; \sqrt{2}, -\frac{\pi}{4}$
20. $2, -\frac{2\pi}{3}; 2, \frac{2\pi}{3}$
22. 5, 0; 5, 0
24. $7, -\frac{\pi}{2}; 7, \frac{\pi}{2}$
26. $2\sqrt{3}, \frac{2\pi}{3}; 2\sqrt{3}, -\frac{2\pi}{3}$
28. 6, 123° 33′; 6, −123° 33′
30. 8, 28° 57′; 8, −28° 57′
32. 1.3, 67° 23′; 1.3, −67° 23′
34. $\frac{3\sqrt{2}}{2}, \frac{\pi}{4}; \frac{3\sqrt{2}}{2}, -\frac{\pi}{4}$
36. 5, −17°; 5, 17°
38. $x = 3, y = -2$
40. $x = -\frac{3}{2a}, y = -4b$
42. $x = \frac{3d}{b}, y = -\frac{5a}{b}$
44. $x = \frac{4a}{3}, y = \frac{5b}{4}$
46. $x = \frac{1}{a}, y = \frac{1 - ab}{a}$

Exercise Group 15–2

2. $i, 10 - 15i$
4. $-2 - 9i, -28 + 9i$
6. $-7 + 2i, -3 - 8i$
8. $1 - 9i, 9 + i$
10. $-1, 17 + 4i$
12. $5, -5 + 8i$
14. $4 - 17i, 2 + 9i$
16. $-1 - 2i, 9 + 8i$
18. $-6 + i\sqrt{3}, 1 - 6i\sqrt{3}$
20. $(r_1 \cos \theta_1 + r_2 \cos \theta_2) + i(r_1 \sin \theta_1 + r_2 \sin \theta_2)$, $(r_1 \cos \theta_1 - r_2 \cos \theta_2) + i(r_1 \sin \theta_1 - r_2 \sin \theta_2)$

Exercise Group 15–3

2. $2\left(\cos \frac{\pi}{3} + i \sin \frac{\pi}{3}\right)$
4. $2\left(\cos \frac{11\pi}{6} + i \sin \frac{11\pi}{6}\right)$
6. $2\sqrt{3}\left(\cos \frac{5\pi}{6} + i \sin \frac{5\pi}{6}\right)$
8. $2\left(\cos \frac{5\pi}{6} + i \sin \frac{5\pi}{6}\right)$
10. $5\left(\cos \frac{3\pi}{2} + i \sin \frac{3\pi}{2}\right)$
12. $5(\cos 53^\circ\, 08' + i \sin 53^\circ\, 08')$
14. $(10, 66^\circ\, 20')$
16. $(2.5, 286^\circ\, 16')$
18. $(13, 292^\circ\, 37')$
20. $(8, 208^\circ\, 57')$

Exercise Group 15–4

2. $-10 - 4i$
4. $8 + 6i$
6. $119 + 120i$
8. $\frac{101}{130} - \frac{37}{130}i$
10. $\frac{258}{533} - \frac{231}{533}i$
12. $\left(2\sqrt{2}, \frac{7\pi}{12}\right)$
14. $\left(6\sqrt{6}, -\frac{5\pi}{12}\right)$
16. $\left(\frac{2\sqrt{6}}{3}, \frac{\pi}{12}\right)$
18. $\left(\frac{2\sqrt{6}}{7}, -\frac{5\pi}{12}\right)$
20. $\left(\frac{3\sqrt{2}}{20}, \frac{7\pi}{12}\right)$
22. $\left(\frac{7\sqrt{3}}{30}, 140^\circ\, 16'\right)$
24. $(\frac{12}{7}, -84^\circ\, 24')$
26. $(1, -10^\circ)$
28. $(1, 216^\circ)$

Exercise Group 15–5

2. $128(1 + i)$
4. $512(-1 + i\sqrt{3})$
6. 1
8. $-i$
10. $\frac{\sqrt{3}}{2} + \frac{1}{2}i$
12. $\left(\frac{5^5 \cdot 13^4}{6^7}, 211^\circ\, 17'\right)$
14. $\left(\frac{17^7}{5^8 \cdot 2^{18} \cdot 3^3}, 221^\circ\, 31'\right)$
16. $\frac{1}{2} + i\frac{\sqrt{3}}{2}$
18. $2, -2, 2i, -2i$
20. $\sqrt{2}(1 + i), \sqrt{2}(-1 + i), \sqrt{2}(-1 - i), \sqrt{2}(1 - i)$
22. $(1, 54^\circ), (1, 126^\circ), (1, 198^\circ), -i, (1, 342^\circ)$
24. $(\sqrt[12]{2}, 52^\circ\, 30'), (\sqrt[12]{2}, 112^\circ\, 30'), (\sqrt[12]{2}, 172^\circ\, 30'), (\sqrt[12]{2}, 232^\circ\, 30'), (\sqrt[12]{2}, 292^\circ\, 30'), (\sqrt[12]{2}, 352^\circ\, 30')$
26. $(\sqrt[3]{5}, 17^\circ\, 43'), (\sqrt[3]{5}, 137^\circ\, 43'), (\sqrt[3]{5}, 257^\circ\, 43')$
28. $(\sqrt[4]{13}, 61^\circ\, 51'), (\sqrt[4]{13}, 151^\circ\, 51'), (\sqrt[4]{13}, 241^\circ\, 51'), (\sqrt[4]{13}, 331^\circ\, 51')$
30. $(\frac{1}{2}, 36^\circ), (\frac{1}{2}, 108^\circ), -\frac{1}{2}, (\frac{1}{2}, 252^\circ), (\frac{1}{2}, 324^\circ)$
32. $0, 0, 3, (3, 72^\circ), (3, 144^\circ), (3, 216^\circ), (3, 288^\circ)$
34. $(1, 5^\circ), (1 + i)/\sqrt{2}, (1, 85^\circ), (1, 125^\circ), (1, 165^\circ), (1, 205^\circ), (1, 245^\circ), (1, 285^\circ), (1, 325^\circ)$

Supplementary Exercises for Chapter 15

2. $47 + 13i$
4. $10 - 4i$
6. $-\frac{17}{61} + \frac{57}{61}i$

8. $-\frac{19}{58} - \frac{33}{58}i$ 10. $\sqrt{2}\,(\cos 60^\circ\, 45' + i \sin 60^\circ\, 45')$

12. $\frac{\sqrt{2}}{2}\,(\cos 285^\circ\, 40' + i \sin 285^\circ\, 40')$

14. $\frac{1}{10}(\cos 126^\circ\, 53' + i \sin 126^\circ\, 53')$

16. $2(\cos 60^\circ + i \sin 60^\circ) = 1 + \sqrt{3}i$, $2(\cos 180^\circ + i \sin 180^\circ) = -2$, $2(\cos 300^\circ + i \sin 300^\circ) = 1 - \sqrt{3}\,i$

18. $\sqrt[8]{32}(\cos 22^\circ\, 30' + i \sin 22^\circ\, 30')$, $\sqrt[8]{32}(\cos 67^\circ\, 30' + i \sin 67^\circ\, 30')$, $\sqrt[8]{32}(\cos 112^\circ\, 30' + i \sin 112^\circ\, 30')$, $\sqrt[8]{32}(\cos 157^\circ\, 30' + i \sin 157^\circ\, 30')$, $\sqrt[8]{32}(\cos 202^\circ\, 30' + i \sin 202^\circ\, 30')$, $\sqrt[8]{32}(\cos 247^\circ\, 30' + i \sin 247^\circ\, 30')$, $\sqrt[8]{32}(\cos 292^\circ\, 30' + i \sin 292^\circ\, 30')$, $\sqrt[8]{32}(\cos 337^\circ\, 30' + i \sin 337^\circ\, 30')$

20. $8^{1/8}(\cos 11^\circ\, 15' + i \sin 11^\circ\, 15')$, $8^{1/8}(\cos 101^\circ\, 15' + i \sin 101^\circ\, 15')$, $8^{1/8}(\cos 191^\circ\, 15' + i \sin 191^\circ\, 15')$, $8^{1/8}(\cos 281^\circ\, 15' + i \sin 281^\circ\, 15')$

Exercise Group 16–1

2. $(-2, 3)$ 4. $(\frac{1}{2}, \frac{5}{4})$ 6. $\left(\frac{a}{2} + 1, a - 2\right)$

8. $\left(\frac{u}{3}, 2u\right)$ 10. $(\frac{29}{54}, -\frac{8}{27}, -\frac{77}{54})$ 12. $(-3, 2, 3)$

14. $(\frac{2}{3}, -\frac{7}{3}, \frac{5}{3})$ 16. $(\frac{1}{5}, \frac{2}{5}, -\frac{3}{5})$ 18. $(7u, 9u, -5u)$

Exercise Group 16–2

2. 21 4. -6 6. 398 8. 9

10. $-6x - 4y - 2$ 12. 0 14. -1 20. 4900

22. 81 24. 16 26. 1

Exercise Group 16–3

2. 9 4. 0 16. $(7u, 9u, -5u)$

18. $(-1, 2, -3, 4)$ 20. $(-\frac{1}{5}, -\frac{11}{5}, \frac{6}{5}, \frac{11}{5})$

Exercise Group 17–1

2. 604,800; 19,656; 120 4. 70, 2520 6. $n = 10$

8. $n = 7$ 10. (a) 156, (b) 36, (c) 78

12. 1152 14. 35 16. 210

18. 11,880 20. 120 22. 120

Exercise Group 17–2

2. 8, 126 4. (a) 126, (b) 9 10. 1024

12. (a) 35, (b) 945, (c) 700 14. (a) 16, (b) 4, (c) 3

16. 525 18. 15 20. 126

Exercise Group 17–3

2. (a) 90, (b) 60, (c) 30 4. 35 6. 150 8. 630,630

10. $(1, a)$, $(2, a)$, $(3, a)$, $(4, b)$; $(1, a)$, $(2, a)$, $(3, b)$, $(4, a)$; $(1, a)$, $(2, b)$, $(3, a)$, $(4, a)$; $(1, b)$, $(2, a)$, $(3, a)$, $(4, a)$

Exercise Group 17–4

2. 35; -48 4. 21; 40 6. 28; -120 8. 21; 40 10. 165; 560
12. 35 14. 35 16. 715 18. 210 20. 153

Exercise Group 17–5

2. (a) $\frac{6}{5525}$, (b) $\frac{11}{850}$ 4. $\frac{3}{7}$ 6. $\frac{1}{6}$ 8. $\frac{5}{108}$ 10. $\frac{2}{9}$
12. $\dfrac{25 \cdot 99}{37 \cdot 149}$ 14. $\frac{1}{945}$ 16. $\frac{15}{64}$

Exercise Group 17–6

2. (a) $\frac{5}{11}$, (b) $\frac{7}{33}$ 4. (a) $\frac{3}{8}$, (b) $\frac{1}{4}$ 6. $\frac{13}{16}$ 8. $\dfrac{4}{C(52,13)}$
10. $\frac{23}{36}$ 12. $\frac{11}{15}$
14. (a) $\frac{21}{32}$, (b) $\frac{21}{32}$ 16. (a) $\frac{5}{216}$, (b) $\frac{5}{108}$, (c) $\frac{35}{324}$

Exercise Group 17–7

2. (a) $\frac{3}{8}$, (b) $\frac{1}{8}$, (c) $\frac{7}{8}$, (d) $\frac{1}{2}$ 4. (a) $\frac{3}{7}$, (b) $\frac{3}{17}$
6. (a) $\frac{34}{455}$, (b) $\frac{1}{5}$ 8. $\frac{1}{5}$

Exercise Group 17–8

2. (a) 4:1, (b) 2:1, (c) 57:43, (d) $(1 - a):a$
4. 1:17 6. 25:191 8. 1:1
10. (a) 1:34, (b) 1:13, (c) 3:4 12. (a) 2:3, (b) 3:2 14. 48

Exercise Group 17–9

2. $\frac{11605}{955942}$ 4. $\frac{577882}{955942} \cdot \frac{233018}{810900}$ 6. $\frac{400112}{924609} \cdot \frac{400112}{930788}$
8. Approximately 13:1 10. 50,990 boys

Supplementary Exercises for Chapter 17

2. (a) 1344, (b) 588 4. 1680 6. (a) $\dfrac{360}{7^5}$, (b) $\dfrac{391}{7^5}$
8. 5832 10. $\frac{5}{33}$ 12. 255 14. 49
16. $\frac{3}{32}$ 18. $\frac{1}{35}$ 20. 5040 22. (a) 45, (b) 220
24. $\frac{27}{6188}$ 26. $\frac{75}{154}$ 28. $\frac{2304}{3125}$

Exercise Group A–1

2. 64 4. 243 6. 10^{13} 8. 1000 10. $2^{15} \cdot 7^6$ 12. $2^{11} \cdot 3^2 \cdot 5^7$
14. $2^4 \cdot 3^6 \cdot a^6b^{12}$ 16. $-2^5 \cdot 5^4a^{17}b^{10}$ 18. $a^{3k}b^{3k}$
20. $3^{2d}a^{2bd}c^{2xd}$ 22. $6x^2 - 15x$ 24. $6y^2 - 3ay$
26. $6a^6 - 3a^3b - 6a^2b^4$ 28. $6x - 9x^2 + 12x^3$
30. $4x^2 - 20x + 25$ 32. $x^3 + 125$ 34. $x^3 - 8y^3$ 36. $4x^2 - 9y^2$

38. $x^5 - 10x^4 + 17x^3 + 33x^2 - 32x - 21$ 40. $a^{16} - 1$
42. $x^{3n} + y^{3k}$ 44. $2^5 = 32$ 46. $\frac{16}{243}$
48. $\dfrac{1}{3^5 \cdot 10^5}$ 50. $\dfrac{x^7}{27}$ 52. $\dfrac{2y^6z^6}{3x^4}$ 54. $\dfrac{8y^4}{9x^5}$
56. $\dfrac{a^{y-x}b^{z-y}}{2^{z-x}}$ 58. $\dfrac{a^5b^{z-x}}{2^{y-x}3^{z-y}}$ 60. $\dfrac{a^{y-x}b^{z-y}}{10^{z-x}}$
62. $x - 3, 0$ 64. $3a + 4b, 0$ 66. $2x^2 - x - 6, -11$
68. $4a^2 - a + 3, -a$ 70. $2x^{2n} + 3x^n - 4, 0$

Exercise Group A–2

6. $14x^3y^2z + 4xy^2z^3 - 6x^3yz^2$ 8. $4a^2 - 9b^2$ 10. $x^{2m} - y^{2m}$
12. $16\,d^4e^4 + 24\,d^2e^2f^2 + 9f^4$ 14. $6x^2 + 31xy + 35y^2$
16. $a^2 + 2ab + b^2 + ac + bc - 2c^2$ 18. $x^2 + 4xy + 6xz + 4y^2 + 12yz + 9z^2$
20. $0.008x^3 - 0.027y^3$ 22. $a^2 + 2ab + b^2 - 6a - 6b + 9$
24. $4a^2 - 12ab + 9b^2 + 16ac - 24bc - 20ad + 30bd + 16c^2 - 40cd + 25d^2$
26. $9x^2 - 30xy + 25y^2 - 42xu + 70uy + 54xv - 90vy + 49u^2 - 126uv + 81v^2$
28. $a^2 + 4ab + 4b^2 - 9c^2 + 6cd - d^2$

Exercise Group A–3

2. $x(x^2 - 5)$ 4. $9x^2y^2(z + 1)(z - 1)$ 6. $(2 - 3x)(3 + x)$
8. $2(1 - 6k)(1 + 6k)$ 10. $(x - y)(a + b + 2)$
12. $4xy(3 - 2x)(4 + x)$ 14. $(x - 3)(x - 2)(x + 2)$
16. $(x - 5)(x + 2)(x - 2)(x - 1)$ 18. $-x^n(x^n - 1)(2x^n - 1)$
20. $(a + 1)(a - 1)(a^2 - a + 1)(a^2 + a + 1)$
22. $(a + x)(a^2 - ax + x^2)(a^6 - a^3x^3 + x^6)$
24. $2x^2y^2(7x - 2y)^2$ 26. $(x - 6)(11x + 6)$
28. $x^ky^3(2x^2 - 5y^2)(3x^2 + 7y^2)$ 30. $(a + 3b)(a - b)(a + b)^2$

Exercise Group A–4

2. $(a - b)(x + y)$ 4. $(b + 2h)(u + v)$ 6. $-a(2 + b)(x + h)$
8. $(u + 2)(u^2 + 1)$ 10. $(x + y)(m + n)$ 12. $(x + my)(x - 4y)$
14. $(x - y)(x + y - 1)$ 16. $(x + y - 4z)(x + y + 4z)$
18. $(a + 3)(1 + a^2)$ 20. $(2x - 3y)(2x - 3y - 1)$
22. $(a^2 - b^2 + 5x^2 + 4y^2)(a^2 - b^2 - 5x^2 - 4y^2)$
24. $(x - 3y - 3)(x - 3y - 4)$ 26. $(3x + 2)(x + 1)(3x - 1)(x + 2)$
28. $(a + 2b - 3)(2a - 11b + 1)$ 30. $(x - 6)(x + 1)(x - 3)(x + 2)$

Exercise Group A–5

2. $\dfrac{3x^2}{5y}$ 4. $\dfrac{a + 2}{3}$ 6. $\dfrac{x - y}{a}$ 8. $\dfrac{x + 2}{x + 4}$ 10. $\dfrac{2x - 3}{3x - 2}$ 12. $x - y$

14. $\dfrac{(x+y)(a^2+x)}{a-b}$ 16. $\dfrac{(x+y)^2}{x^2+y^2}$ 18. $\dfrac{y-x}{y}$

20. $\dfrac{x^2-3x-3}{x^2+5x+3}$ 22. $\dfrac{(x-2)(x-1)}{(x+2)(x-3)}$

Exercise Group A–6

2. $-\frac{62}{35}$ 4. $\dfrac{3a^2-ab-2b^2}{ab}$ 6. $\dfrac{2x+1}{x-1}$

8. $\dfrac{10a}{4a^2-9}$ 10. $\dfrac{4}{1-a}$ 12. $-2a$

14. $\dfrac{x+3}{(x+1)(x-3)}$ 16. $\dfrac{2-x}{(x+2)(x+6)}$

18. $\dfrac{2(a-5)}{2a-7}$ 20. $\dfrac{29(x+1)}{(x-1)(x-3)}$

Exercise Group A–7

2. 1 4. $\dfrac{y^2(x-y)}{x^2(x-2y)}$ 6. $\dfrac{1}{x}$

8. $\dfrac{y}{2(1-y)}$ 10. $\dfrac{15}{2(a-1)}$ 12. $\dfrac{2a-3}{3a-2}$

14. $\dfrac{2x+3}{2x+1}$ 16. a 18. $\dfrac{a(3b+a)}{b+a}$ 20. $\dfrac{(x-12)(x^2-9)}{(x+2)(x-4)(x+9)}$

Exercise Group A–8

2. $\frac{117}{44}$ 4. $\frac{44}{53}$ 6. $\dfrac{a-2}{a+2}$ 8. $\dfrac{(x^2+1)^2}{x^2(x+1)^2}$ 10. $\dfrac{x+2}{x}$

12. $a-1$ 14. $\dfrac{a-b}{a+b}$ 16. $\dfrac{-1}{x^2-5x+7}$

18. $\dfrac{(x+1)(y-1)}{x(x-1)}$ 20. $\dfrac{4y-x}{y}$ 22. $\dfrac{(m+n)^2}{(m-r)^2}$

24. $\dfrac{2x^2-50x+62}{29-22x}$ 26. 1 28. $\dfrac{8(x+1)}{(x-1)(x+3)^3}$

30. $\dfrac{50-16x}{5-4x}$ 32. $\dfrac{abx-acx+acd}{abx-acx-bx+acd}$

Exercise Group A–9

2. x^{11} 4. b^{5a} 6. d^{6x} 8. y^{a-b}
10. b^{2-3x} 12. 3^{10} 14. $9x^{3+y}$ 16. y^{21}
18. b^{35} 20. 5^{6x} 22. $x^{14}y^{21}$ 24. $c^{21}z^{35}$

26. $3^{4x}5^{3x}$ 28. $a^{3xz}b^{4yz}$ 30. $3^{5a}b^{15}5^{5c}c^{10}$ 32. $\dfrac{x^5}{y^5}$

34. $\frac{16a^4}{81y^4}$ 36. $\frac{x^{21}}{y^{14}}$ 38. $\frac{2^{21}a^{28}}{3^{14}b^{21}}$ 40. $\frac{3^6x^{12}}{5^6y^{6a}}$

42. $\frac{(-1)^b a^{3b}}{b^{2b}c^{7b}}$ 44. $\frac{y^5}{x^3}$ 46. 5^4x^6 48. $2 \cdot 10^{11}$

50. $2^3 \cdot 3^3 \cdot 10^{31}$ 52. $\frac{2^7a^{27}}{3^7 5^3 b^{26}}$ 54. $-\frac{3^5}{2^7 5^3 x^2 y}$ 56. $\frac{x^{4a}y^{7b}}{a^{7x}b^{4y}}$

58. $\frac{4x^4 + 2x^3 - 8x^2 - 3x + 3}{x}$ 60. $\frac{a^{5m} - a^{4m} - 2a^{2m} - 1}{a^{3m}}$

62. $\frac{y^2(y - 2x^2)^2}{x^2(2y^2 - x)^2}$ 64. $\frac{y^{10}(2 - xy)^2}{9x^4}$

66. $\frac{9}{1 - 3^{3n-2}}$, if $3n - 2$ is positive 68. $\frac{8z^{k-2}}{27x^{k-7}y^k}$, if $k - 7$ is positive

70. x^{ac-ab}, if $ac - ab$ is positive 72. $\frac{x^2(2x^2 + 3x - 4)}{5x + 6}$

74. $\frac{3}{2xy^2}$ 76. $\frac{2b^2}{a^3}$ 78. $\frac{4x^4}{y^2}$ 80. $\frac{64a^2}{729b}$

82. $\frac{2a^2b^2}{5}$ 84. x^3 86. $\frac{4b^4}{3c^5}$ 88. $\frac{27b^{15}}{125a^9}$

90. $\frac{3^{4/3}a}{2^{4/3}b^{7/3}}$ 92. $a^{2/5}b^{2/7} - a^{4/5}b^{6/7}$ 94. $a^{1/3} + b^{1/3}$ 96. $a^{17/12}$

98. $16^{2/3}$ 100. $x^{17/12}$ 102. a^5b^2 104. $1/a^2$

106. $\frac{21}{4}$ 108. -415 110. $\frac{a^2}{(a^2 - x^2)^{\frac{1}{2}}}$ 112. $\frac{a^3 + x^3}{2x^{\frac{1}{2}}(a^3 - x^3)^{\frac{4}{3}}}$

Exercise Group A–10

2. $\frac{\sqrt{3}}{2}$ 4. $\frac{\sqrt[3]{6}}{2}$ 6. $\frac{3x^2\sqrt[3]{10xy^2z^2}}{5yz^2}$ 8. $\frac{x^2\sqrt[n]{xy}}{y^2}$

10. $\frac{\sqrt{v^2 + u^2}}{uv}$ 12. $\frac{\sqrt[4]{216x^2y^2(2x^2 - 3y^2)^2}}{6xy}$ 14. $\sqrt[3]{4x^2}$

16. $\sqrt[12]{2x^2y^3}$ 18. $(a + b)\sqrt[3]{a^2 - ab + b^2}$ 20. $\frac{(x^2 + y)\sqrt{x}}{x^2}$

22. $\sqrt{(a + b)(x - y)}$ 24. $\frac{4a}{3bc}\sqrt{6bc(ac - 6b^2)}$ 26. $5\sqrt{2}$

28. $6\sqrt{3}$ 30. $-5\sqrt[3]{2}$ 32. $(7x - 4a)\sqrt{ax}$ 34. $3a\sqrt[3]{2b} - 2b\sqrt[3]{2ab}$

36. $(7a - 4a^2)\sqrt[4]{a}$ 38. $\frac{2y\sqrt{x^2 - y^2}}{x^2 - y^2}$ 40. $\frac{-5 - \sqrt{10}}{5}$

42. $-\frac{q}{r}$ 44. $5\sqrt{3}$ 46. 6 48. $4\sqrt[3]{9}$ 50. $2ab^2\sqrt[3]{3a}$ 52. $24x^5$

54. $3\sqrt{2} - 3\sqrt{10}$ 56. 2 58. 2 60. $\frac{2}{3}$

62. $\sqrt{x - y} + (2y - x)\sqrt[3]{x - y}$ 64. $\sqrt[6]{72}$ 66. 0

68. 0 70. $-9 - 28\sqrt{3}$ 72. $\dfrac{3\sqrt{14}}{2}$ 74. $\dfrac{2}{x}$

76. $\dfrac{3}{2x}\sqrt{10}$ 78. $\dfrac{x}{3}\sqrt{2}$ 80. $\frac{1}{2}(2\sqrt{6} + 3\sqrt{2})$ 82. $\dfrac{75 - 17\sqrt{21}}{74}$

84. $\dfrac{(ax + y^2)\sqrt{xy} - axy - xy^2}{a^2x - y^3}$ 86. $\sqrt[6]{32}$ 88. $\dfrac{\sqrt[6]{27xy^3}}{3y}$